Ric...
Linscott
100 N. Main St.
Orono, ME

Fundamentals
of
Chemical Reaction
Engineering

PRENTICE-HALL INTERNATIONAL SERIES
IN THE PHYSICAL AND CHEMICAL ENGINEERING SCIENCES

NEAL R. AMUNDSON, EDITOR, *University of Houston*

PRENTICE-HALL, INC.
PRENTICE-HALL INTERNATIONAL, INC.
UNITED KINGDOM AND EIRE
PRENTICE-HALL OF CANADA, LTD., CANADA

Fundamentals
of
Chemical Reaction
Engineering

CHARLES D. HOLLAND
RAYFORD G. ANTHONY

Department of Chemical Engineering
Texas A&M University

P R E N T I C E - H A L L , I N C.

Englewood Cliffs, New Jersey 07632

Library of Congress Cataloging in Publication Data

HOLLAND, CHARLES DONALD.
    Fundamentals of chemical reaction engineering.

    (Prentice-Hall international series in the
physical and chemical engineering sciences)
    Includes bibliographical references and index.
    1. Chemical engineering.   2. Chemical reactions.
I. Anthony, Rayford Gaines, joint
author.   II. Title.
TP145.H64   660.2′9′9   78-18372
ISBN   0-13-335596-9

© 1979 by Prentice-Hall, Inc., Englewood Cliffs, New Jersey 07632

10 9 8 7 6 5 4 3 2

Printed in the United States of America

PRENTICE-HALL INTERNATIONAL, INC., *London*
PRENTICE-HALL OF AUSTRALIA PTY. LIMITED, *Sydney*
PRENTICE-HALL OF CANADA, LTD., *Toronto*
PRENTICE-HALL OF INDIA PRIVATE LIMITED, *New Delhi*
PRENTICE-HALL OF JAPAN, INC., *Tokyo*
PRENTICE-HALL OF SOUTHEAST ASIA PTE. LTD., *Singapore*
WHITEHALL BOOKS LIMITED, *Wellington, New Zealand*

Dedicated to

JAMES DONALD LINDSAY
Professor Emeritus
*of Chemical Engineering
at Texas A&M University*

Contents

SECTION II.   DESIGN OF THERMAL AND
              CATALYTIC REACTORS

SECTION III. ADVANCED TOPICS

Preface

This book is written for the beginning student in chemical kinetics and chemical reaction engineering. All topics are initiated by commencing with first principles. Derivations are complete, rigorous, and easily followed. The chapters are ordered with respect to the increasing difficulty of the subject matter. For example, Chapter 12, "Theory of Reaction Rates," could have been included in Chapter 1 but was deferred because the level of that subject matter is higher than that needed by the student in order to master the material presented in subsequent chapters. Likewise, the thermodynamics of nonideal solutions and the energy balances for systems containing such solutions could have been covered in Chapters 5 and 6 but has been deferred until Chapter 11 in order that the student might first have the opportunity to apply some of the fundamentals presented in Chapters 5 and 6 in the design of reactors.

The book is divided into three sections. The fundamental principles of chemical kinetics and chemical reactor engineering are presented in Section I. The design of both thermal and catalytic reactors is treated in Section II, while the advanced topics of polymerization, nonideal solutions, and theory of reaction rates are treated in Section III. Chapters 1 through 7 and part of Chapter 8 are covered in an undergraduate course, and Chapters 8 through 12 serve as a basis for a graduate course at Texas A&M University.

Through their support to the Department of Chemical Engineering, the following companies and individuals helped make the writing of this book possible: Alcoa Foundation, Amoco Foundation, John W. Askins, Atlantic Richfield Foundation, Celanese Chemical Company, Diamond Shamrock Corporation, Dow Chemical U.S.A., E. I. DuPont de Nemours & Company, El Paso Natural Gas Company, Exxon U.S.A. Foundation, Louis Gross, Gulf Oil Foundation, John B. Hawley, Jr., Pullman-Kellogg Company, The Lubrizol Foundation, Mobil Chemical Company, Mobil Oil Company, Monsanto Company, Olin Corporation Charitable Trust, PPG Industries Foundation, Petro-Tex Chemical Corporation, Phillips Petroleum Company, Paul Sieke Fund, Shell Oil Company, South Texas Section– AIChE, Sun Oil Company, Tenneco Oil, Texaco Inc., Texas Eastman, Joseph I. Thompson, Union Carbide, and the UOP Foundation. The authors are appreciative of this support as well as of the pictures and diagrams of reactors provided by Cosden Oil and Chemical Company, Goodyear Tire and Rubber Company, and Pullman-Kellogg.

Helpful suggestions made by Professors P. T. Eubank, K. R. Hall, D. T. Hanson, A. V. Kudchadker, and A. I. Liapis of the Department of Chemical Engineering are appreciated. The authors also wish to thank D. L. Tanner of Dow Chemical Company for his assistance in the solution of examples in Chapter 7, and to thank Dr. K. S. McMahon of Monsanto for his contributions. The authors also wish to express their appreciation for the inspiration and encouragement provided by Dr. P. G. Murdoch (Retired-Dow Chemical Company) and Professors Emeriti B. C. Moore, E. C. Klipple, and H. A. Luther.

The atmosphere that made the writing of this book possible was due to the able administration of Dean Fred J. Benson, to whom the authors are grateful.

*Fundamentals
of
Chemical Reaction
Engineering*

Section I:
Fundamentals

Reaction Rates and
Batch Reactors

1

I. INTRODUCTION

Chemical kinetics is the branch of physical chemistry that is concerned with the rates and mechanisms of chemical reactions. The first quantitative data on rates of reaction were reported in 1777 by Wenzel [1], who investigated the effect of acid concentration on the rate of dissolution of copper and zinc metals in acid solutions. The law of mass action for homogeneous reactions was formulated by Guldberg and Waage in 1867, and Van't Hoff extended it for heterogeneous reactions in 1877. The concept of the reaction velocity constant and the classification of reactions according to molecularity were introduced in 1884 by Van't Hoff [2]. In 1889, Arrhenius [3] suggested that only those molecules having an energy equal to or greater than a given level had the potential for reaction.

Van Narum appears to have been among the first to recognize catalysis when he observed in 1796 the effect of the surface catalysis in the dehydrogenation of alcohol. In 1902, Ostwald [4] defined a catalyst as "any substance which alters the velocity of a chemical reaction without appearing in the end products."

The beginning of the use of reaction kinetics in the design of reactors is marked by a paper published in 1923 by Lewis and Ries [5] on the catalytic oxidation of sulfur dioxide. Hougen [6] has given major credit for the early development of the theory and applications of chemical kinetics to process design, particularly in catalytic processes, to Kenneth M. Watson. A text written by Hougen and Watson [7] led to the further development and acceptance of the subject of reactor design.

Reactions may be classified in a variety of useful ways. Some of the methods of classification are enumerated. Reactions may be classified according to the number of phases involved in the reactions:

1. Homogeneous
2. Heterogeneous

They may be classified according to the manner in which the reaction is carried out:

3. Thermal or uncatalyzed
4. Catalyzed

Sometimes reactions are classified according to the nature of the reaction such as:

5. Unidirectional or irreversible
6. Reversible
7. Isothermal or nonisothermal
8. Biological

Sometimes reactions are classified according to the type of equipment used to carry out the reactions:

9. Batch reactors
10. Flow reactors
    (a) tubular
    (b) continuous tank
11. Catalytic reactors with fixed or fluidized beds

Batch reactors were no doubt the first type of reactor to be devised. They consist of well-stirred pots or kettles in which the reactants are mixed by stirring and allowed to react over a period of time. Provisions are generally made for heating or cooling the reacting mixture. Batch reactors are still used in the modern petrochemical industry. Figure 1-1 shows a picture of a reactor that may be used in either a batch or a continuous process.

Figure 1-1. Reactor used in the production of synthetic rubber (Courtesy of Goodyear Tire and Rubber Company).

4

The use of batch reactors in the manufacture of soap has been known for centuries and was recorded by early historians. During the excavation of Pompeii, a soap factory was discovered, complete with boiling pans and a quantity of soap which had been buried under volcanic ash for nearly 2000 years [8]. Batch-type reactors are still in use in the manufacture of soap by the "kettle or full-boiled method." This method consists of the saponification of neutral fats and oils (triglycerides) with caustic soda as follows:

$$
\begin{array}{c}
H \\
| \\
H-C-OOC-R_1 \\
| \\
H-C-OOC-R_2 + 3\,NaOH \\
| \\
H-C-OOC-R_3 \\
| \\
H
\end{array}
\longrightarrow
\begin{array}{c}
H \\
| \\
H-C-OH \quad Na-OOC-R_1 \\
| \\
H-C-OH + Na-OOC-R_2 \\
| \\
H-C-OH \quad Na-OOC-R_3 \\
| \\
H
\end{array}
$$

Triglyceride   Caustic soda   Glycerol   Sodium soap

High-grade toilet soaps as well as low-grade industrial soaps with a high glycerol recovery efficiency may be made by this method [9].

The fundamental principles upon which the field of chemical reaction engineering is based are introduced in Parts II and III of this chapter. The rate of reaction, introduced in Part II, is shown to depend upon the manner in which the molecules participate in a chemical reaction. After the development of the material-balance equations for batch reactors has been presented in Part III, expressions are developed for the variation of the moles reacted as a function of time.

II. FUNDAMENTAL KINETIC AND THERMODYNAMIC RELATIONSHIPS

Rate expressions for various types of reactions are formulated in this section. The fundamental principles of the theory of reaction rates which are needed in these formulations are also presented. (A comprehensive treatment of the theory of reaction rates is presented for the benefit of the advanced student in Chapter 12.) Also presented in this section is the relationship between reaction kinetics and thermodynamics as well as other relationships which are needed in subsequent chapters.

A. Definition of the Rate of Reaction

The following definition for the rate of reaction leads to rate expressions, based on experimental results, which are valid over wide ranges of operating conditions. The net rate of disappearance of component A of a given reacting mixture is defined as follows:

$$r_A = \frac{\text{moles of } A \text{ disappearing}}{(\text{unit time})(\text{unit of reactor volume})} \tag{1-1}$$

Suppose that the reacting mixture consists of components A, B, C, and D at a given temperature and pressure. Then the rate of reaction may be expected to depend upon the temperature, pressure, and concentrations of the reacting species; that is,

$$r_A = f(T, P, C_A, C_B, C_C, C_D) \tag{1-2}$$

The precise form of this functional relationship must be determined experimentally. Hereafter, this functional relationship is referred to as simply the rate expression. The form of the rate expression depends upon *how* the molecules participate in the reaction, and it is independent of the type of reactor used to carry out the reaction.

B. Relationships of the Rates of Reaction of the Members of a Reacting Mixture

Suppose that the stoichiometry of a reaction is given by

$$aA + bB = cC + dD$$

In the definition of the rates of reaction, it is convenient to define the rates for the reactants in terms of disappearance and the rates for the products in terms of appearance. Let the rates of reaction r_A and r_B for A and B, respectively, be defined in terms of disappearance and the rates r_C and r_D for C and D, respectively, be defined in terms of appearance. The stoichiometric equation asserts that b moles of B react every time a moles of A react. Then B disappears b/a times as fast as A, or

$$r_B = \frac{b}{a} r_A \tag{1-3}$$

For every a moles of A which react, c moles of C and d moles of D are formed. Thus

$$r_C = \frac{c}{a} r_A, \qquad r_D = \frac{d}{a} r_A \qquad (1\text{-}4)$$

EXAMPLE 1-1

Phosphine decomposes by the following stoichiometric equation:

$$4\,PH_3 \longrightarrow P_4 + 6\,H_2$$

At a given instant, phosphine decomposes at the rate of 10×10^{-5} g mole per second per liter. Let the rate of reaction for phosphine be defined in terms of disappearance; that is,

$$r_{PH_3} = \frac{\text{g moles of } PH_3 \text{ disappearing}}{\text{sec liter}} = 10 \times 10^{-5}$$

(a) Compute the rates of appearance of phosphorus and hydrogen.
(b) Compute the rates of disappearance of phosphorus and hydrogen, and the rate of appearance of phosphine.

SOLUTION

(a) Let the rates of reaction for phosphorus and hydrogen be defined in terms of appearance.

$$\frac{\text{g moles of } P_4 \text{ appearing}}{\text{sec liter}} = r_{P_4} = \frac{1}{4} r_{PH_3} = 2.5 \times 10^{-5}$$

$$\frac{\text{g moles of } H_2 \text{ appearing}}{\text{sec liter}} = r_{H_2} = \frac{6}{4} r_{PH_3} = 15 \times 10^{-5}$$

(b)
$$\frac{\text{g moles of } P_4 \text{ disappearing}}{\text{sec liter}} = -r_{P_4} = -2.5 \times 10^{-5}$$

$$\frac{\text{g moles of } H_2 \text{ disappearing}}{\text{sec liter}} = -r_{H_2} = -15 \times 10^{-5}$$

$$\frac{\text{g moles of } PH_3 \text{ appearing}}{\text{sec liter}} = -r_{PH_3} = -10 \times 10^{-5}$$

C. Order and Molecularity

In general, it is not possible to predict the mechanism from a knowledge of the stoichiometry. The mechanism and functional form of the rate expression [see Equation (1-2)] must be determined experimentally. If it is found by experiment that the expression for the rate of reaction is given by

$$r_A = k_c C_A^{n_1} C_B^{n_2} C_C^{n_3} \tag{1-5}$$

then the *order* N of the reaction is defined by

$$N = n_1 + n_2 + n_3 \tag{1-6}$$

The constant k_c is called the *rate constant* or the *specific reaction rate*. The order of a reaction is sometimes expressed relative to a participant. For example, the rate of reaction given by Equation (1-5) is of *order n_1* with respect to component A.

The molecularity of a single chemical reaction is defined as the minimum number of molecules which must combine or interact when the reaction goes one time in a given direction. The molecularity and the *law of mass action* are closely related. In 1867, Guldberg and Waage gave the first general statement of this law. The present accepted statement of this law is that the rate of reaction is proportional to the product of the concentrations of the reactants, where the concentration of each reactant is raised to the power given by the stoichiometric coefficient of that substance in the chemical equation that describes the process. The rate expressions for unimolecular, bimolecular, and trimolecular reactions are as follows:

Unimolecular: $A \longrightarrow$ *products*

$$r_A = k_c C_A \tag{1-7}$$

Bimolecular: $2A \longrightarrow$ *products*

$$r_A = k_c C_A^2 \tag{1-8}$$

Bimolecular: $A + B \longrightarrow$ *products*

$$r_A = k_c C_A C_B \tag{1-9}$$

Trimolecular: $3A \longrightarrow$ *products*

$$r_A = k_c C_A^3 \tag{1-10}$$

Trimolecular: $2A + B \longrightarrow$ *products*

$$r_A = k_c C_A^2 C_B \tag{1-11}$$

Trimolecular: $A + B + C \longrightarrow$ *products*

$$r_A = k_c C_A C_B C_C \tag{1-12}$$

Although the same symbol k_c is used in each of the preceding cases, it must be realized, of course, that it differs from reaction to reaction. Also, k_c in these rate expressions is defined with respect to component A. For example, for the reaction $2A + B \rightarrow$ products,

$$r_B = \frac{1}{2} r_A$$

and consequently, $$r_B = \frac{1}{2} k_c C_A^2 C_B \tag{1-13}$$

where k_c is the rate constant with respect to component A.

Molecularity as well as order is always stated for a single chemical reaction in a single direction. The molecularity of the reverse reaction of a reversible reaction may differ from that of the forward reaction. For example, in the reaction

$$A \underset{k_c'}{\overset{k_c}{\rightleftarrows}} R + S$$

the forward reaction is unimolecular and the reverse reaction is bimolecular. Therefore, the net rate of disappearance of A is given by

$$r_A = k_c C_A - k_c' C_R C_S \tag{1-14}$$

If component A reacts simultaneously by each of two reactions, then the net rate of reaction of A is given by the algebraic sum of the rates for each of the reactions. For example, consider the reactions,

$$A \xrightarrow{k_1} R, \qquad r_{A1} = k_1 C_A$$
$$A \xrightarrow{k_2} 2S, \qquad r_{A2} = k_2 C_A$$

Then

$$r_A = r_{A1} + r_{A2} = k_1 C_A + k_2 C_A \tag{1-15}$$

Also, first-order isomerization reactions of the following type may be encountered.

$$A \underset{k_1'}{\overset{k_1}{\rightleftarrows}} R \underset{k_2'}{\overset{k_2}{\rightleftarrows}} S \underset{k_3'}{\overset{k_3}{\rightleftarrows}} A$$

In this case, the net rate of reaction of A is given by

$$r_A = k_1 C_A - k_1' C_R + k_3' C_A - k_3 C_S \tag{1-16}$$

Multiple reactions are discussed in greater detail in Chapter 3.

If a reaction goes precisely as written, the order of the reaction is equal to the molecularity. However, the converse of this statement is not necessarily true; that is, a reaction may be first order but it is not necessarily unimolecular. The reaction may in fact have a complex reaction mechanism, whose rate may be represented by an empirical expression that depends upon the first power of the concentration.

The rate expressions presented previously apply regardless of whether the reaction occurs in the gas phase or the liquid phase.

GAS PHASE REACTIONS. The rate expressions for reactions which occur in the gas phase may be stated in terms of either concentrations or partial pressures. For example, the rate of reaction for the unimolecular reaction,

$$A \longrightarrow \text{products}$$

may be stated in terms of p_A, the partial pressure of A; namely,

$$r_A = k_p p_A \tag{1-17}$$

where k_p is the rate constant when partial pressures are used. Since the rate of reaction r_A is the same regardless of whether concentrations or partial pressures are used, it follows that

$$r_A = k_c C_A = k_p p_A \tag{1-18}$$

Similarly, for any of the previous reactions which occur in the gas phase, the rates may be expressed as a product of k_p and the appropriate partial pressures.

D. Dimensions of the Rate Constants k_c and k_p

Since r_A has the same units regardless of whether concentrations or partial pressures are used, it follows that k_c and k_p have precisely those dimensions required for the dimensions on the left-hand side of each equation to equal the dimensions on the right-hand side. For example, consider Equation (1-18),

$$r_A \left[\frac{\text{lb moles}}{\text{hr ft}^3} \right] = k_c \left[\frac{1}{\text{hr}} \right] C_A \left[\frac{\text{lb moles}}{\text{ft}^3} \right] = k_p \left[\frac{\text{lb moles}}{\text{hr ft}^3 \text{ atm}} \right] p_A \text{ (atm)} \tag{1-19}$$

Similarly, for the second-order reaction $2A \rightarrow$ products,

$$r_A \left[\frac{\text{lb moles}}{\text{hr ft}^3} \right] = k_c \left[\frac{\text{ft}^3}{\text{hr lb moles}} \right] C_A^2 \left[\frac{(\text{lb moles})^2}{(\text{ft}^3)^2} \right]$$

$$= k_p \left[\frac{\text{lb moles}}{\text{hr ft}^3 \text{ atm}^2} \right] p_A^2 \left[(\text{atm})^2 \right] \qquad (1\text{-}20)$$

E. Relationships of the Rate Constants

If the reacting mixture is a perfect gas mixture, then

$$p_A = C_A RT \qquad (1\text{-}21)$$

and it follows from Equation (1-20) that

$$k_c C_A^2 = k_p C_A^2 (RT)^2$$

or

$$k_c = k_p (RT)^2$$

Thus, in general, for an Nth-order reaction which occurs in the gas phase,

$$k_c = k_p (RT)^N \qquad (1\text{-}22)$$

where the volumetric behavior of the gas phase approximates that of a perfect gas.

EXAMPLE 1-2

The decomposition of nitrous oxide in glass or silica vessels is generally a homogeneous second-order reaction. In the presence of a gold wire at a high temperature, the decomposition of nitrous oxide was found by Hinshelwood and Prichard [10] to be first order. That is, the stoichiometry is given by

$$2 \, N_2O \longrightarrow 2 \, N_2 + O_2$$

and the rate of reaction is given by

$$r_{N_2O} = \left(\frac{\text{g moles of } N_2O \text{ disappearing}}{\text{sec cc}} \right) = k_c C_{N_2O}$$

At 900°C, Hinshelwood et al. found that

$$k_c = 0.013 \ \text{sec}^{-1}$$

Calculate the corresponding value of

$$k_p \left(\frac{\text{g moles}}{\text{sec cc atm}} \right)$$

SOLUTION

For a first-order reaction, Equation (1-22) becomes

$$k_p = k_c(RT)^{-1}$$

Thus

$$k_p = (0.013 \ \text{sec}^{-1}) \left[\left(82.05 \ \frac{\text{atm cc}}{\text{g mole °K}} \right)(1173.1°\text{K}) \right]^{-1}$$

$$= 1.3504 \times 10^{-7} \ \frac{\text{g mole}}{\text{sec cc atm}}$$

F. Reversible Reactions and Thermodynamic Equilibrium

The rate of reaction r_A as defined by Equation (1-1) is equal to the net rate of disappearance of A by all reactions that occur. When a single reversible reaction such as

$$2A \ \underset{k_c'}{\overset{k_c}{\rightleftharpoons}} \ R + S$$

occurs, the net rate of reaction is equal to the forward rate of reaction minus the reverse rate of reaction. That is, A disappears by the forward reaction at the rate r_{Af},

$$r_{Af} = k_c C_A^2 \tag{1-23}$$

and A appears by the reverse reaction

$$R + S \ \xrightarrow{k_c'} \ 2A$$

at the rate r_{Ar},

$$r_{Ar} = k_c' C_R C_S \tag{1-24}$$

Then r_A, the net rate of disappearance of A, is given by

$$r_A = r_{Af} - r_{Ar} = k_c C_A^2 - k_c' C_R C_S \tag{1-25}$$

At thermodynamic equilibrium,

$$r_A = 0 \tag{1-26}$$

and Equation (1-25) may be arranged in the well-known form

$$K_c = \frac{k_c}{k_c'} = \frac{C_R C_S}{C_A^2} \tag{1-27}$$

where K_c = equilibrium constant where concentrations are employed. For ideal solutions, the equilibrium constant K_c remains fixed (at a given temperature) for all possible combinations of the concentration of A, R, and S that satisfy the equality given by Equation (1-27). If the particular reaction also occurs in the gas phase, then in a manner similar to that described previously,

$$K_p = \frac{p_R p_S}{p_A^2} \tag{1-28}$$

where K_p = equilibrium constant where partial pressures are employed. If the mixture obeys the perfect gas law, the equilibrium constant K_p is independent of the total pressure as well as the partial pressure of A, R, and S at a given temperature.

In the literature, rate expressions can be found which are thermodynamically inconsistent. For example, for the reaction,

$$A + 3B \; \rightleftharpoons \; 2R$$

suppose that the experimental rate of formation of R is represented by $r_R = kC_A C_B^{1/2} - k'C_R^2$. At $r_R = 0$

$$\frac{k}{k'} = \frac{C_R^2}{C_A C_B^{1/2}}$$

The equilibrium constant K_c for the reaction as written is given by

$$K_c = \frac{C_R^2}{C_A C_B^3}$$

Comparison of the expressions for k/k' and K_c shows a disagreement in the power of C_B. Thus, the rate expression for r_R is said to be thermodynamically inconsistent. Since k/k' is unequal to K_c, one should guard against committing the fallacy of setting them equal in order to determine the reverse rate constant k'. Inconsistent thermodynamic rate expressions result from the fact that the reaction does not go as written. Instead of a single reaction being involved, a mechanism consisting of several reactions is needed to describe the experimental results that are discussed in subsequent chapters.

The use of thermodynamics in the analysis of reaction systems and in reactor design is presented in Chapters 5, 6, and 11.

EXAMPLE 1-3

One method for producing hydrogen is to treat water gas (carbon monoxide and hydrogen) with steam. Water gas is made by reacting the carbon in a fossil fuel such as coal or lignite with steam at temperatures in the neighborhood of 1500°K (11). The *water gas* reaction is

$$C + H_2O \longrightarrow CO + H_2$$
$$\text{(water gas)}$$

The water gas produced can be further reacted with steam at temperatures around 400°C in the presence of a catalyst to produce additional hydrogen by the *water-gas-shift* reaction (12).

$$CO + H_2O \longrightarrow CO_2 + H_2$$

At 400°C, $K_p = 11.772$ for the water-gas-shift reaction (13). Calculate the moles of hydrogen produced when an equimolar mixture of carbon monoxide and hydrogen is treated with 100% excess of steam at a pressure of 1 atm (absolute).

SOLUTION

As a basis, suppose that the feed consists of 1 mole of CO, 1 mole of H_2, and 2 moles of H_2O. Let x be the moles of CO reacted at equilibrium. Then the moles of CO, H_2O, CO_2, and H_2 at equilibrium may be stated in terms of x as follows:

$$\begin{array}{r} \text{moles of CO} = 1 - x \\ \text{moles of } H_2O = 2 - x \\ \text{moles of } CO_2 = x \\ \underline{\text{moles of } H_2 = 1 + x} \\ \text{total moles} = 4 \end{array}$$

$$p_{CO} = \left(\frac{1-x}{4}\right) P, \qquad p_{H_2O} = \left(\frac{2-x}{4}\right) P$$

$$p_{CO_2} = \left(\frac{x}{4}\right) P, \qquad p_{H_2} = \left(\frac{1+x}{4}\right) P$$

Then

$$K_p = \frac{p_{CO_2} p_{H_2}}{p_{CO} p_{H_2O}} = \frac{x(1+x)}{(1-x)(2-x)}$$

This equation can be solved for x in terms of K_p by use of the quadratic formula to give

$$x = \frac{(3K_p + 1) - \sqrt{(3K_p + 1)^2 - 8K_p(K_p - 1)}}{2(K_p - 1)}$$

After $K_p = 11.772$ has been substituted, one obtains

$$x = \frac{36.316 - \sqrt{(36.316)^2 - 8(11.772)(10.772)}}{21.544} = 0.876$$

which is equal to the moles of hydrogen produced.

G. Effect of Temperature on the Rate Constant, k_c

The rate constant normally varies in an exponential manner with temperature as proposed by Arrhenius [3].

$$k_c = A \exp\left(\frac{-E_A}{RT}\right) \tag{1-29}$$

where A = frequency factor or Arrhenius constant
$\qquad\quad\ E_A$ = the activation energy
$\qquad\quad\ R$ = gas law constant in consistent units

This general form of the expression for k_c is suggested by the kinetic theory of gases (see Chapter 12). By use of this theory, k_c is found to be proportional to

$$\sqrt{T} \exp\left(\frac{-E_A}{RT}\right)$$

By use of statistical mechanics (see Chapter 12), k_c is found to be proportional to

$$T \exp\left(\frac{-E_A}{RT}\right)$$

In most cases, the variation of k_c with temperature over limited temperature ranges may be represented by Equation (1-29), because the strong exponential function masks the effect of the weaker functions T and $\sqrt{T}$.

When evaluating the constants A and E_A in Equation (1-29), it is desirable from a statistical point of view [14] to put Equation (1-29) in the following form:

$$\log_e k_c = -\frac{E_A}{R}\left(\frac{1}{T} - \frac{1}{T_0}\right) + \log_e k_c^0 \tag{1-30}$$

where T_0 = mid-temperature for the temperature range considered and

$$k_c^0 = A \exp\left(\frac{-E_A}{RT_0}\right)$$

Thus E_A/R may be evaluated from the slope of a plot of $\log_e k_c$ versus $(1/T - 1/T_0)$. The intercept $\log_e k_c^0$ is evaluated at $(1/T - 1/T_0) = 0$, and A is calculated from the definition of k_c^0.

EXAMPLE 1-4

In a study of the isomerization of n-propylidene-cyclopropylamine to 5-ethyl-1-pyroline, Cocks and Egger [15] found the rate to be first order. The rate constants were

$T(^\circ K)$	573	600	623.5	635
$k_c \times 10^3$ (min^{-1})	4.15	26.8	114	246

Evaluate the activation energy, E_A, and the Arrhenius constant A.

SOLUTION

First the quantity T_0 in Equation (1-30) is evaluated as follows:

$$T_0 = \frac{573 + 600 + 623.5 + 635}{4} \cong 608^\circ K$$

For each value of T, the corresponding values of the independent variable $(1/T - 1/T_0)$ are as follows:

$T(^\circ K)$	573	600	623.5	635
$\left(\dfrac{1}{T} - \dfrac{1}{T_0}\right)$	1.005×10^{-4}	2.20×10^{-5}	-4.09×0.0^{-5}	-6.99×10^{-5}

A plot of the values of the dependent variable k_c versus the corresponding values of the independent variable $(1/T - 1/T_0)$ is shown in Figure 1-2. From this graph, it is found that $k_c^0 = 0.043$ min^{-1}, and $E_A/R = 23,364^\circ K$. Thus

$$k_c \text{ (min}^{-1}) = 0.043 \exp\left[-23,364\left(\frac{1}{T} - \frac{1}{608}\right)\right]$$

This expression may be restated in the form of Equation (1-29) as follows:

$$k_c \text{ (min}^{-1}) = 2.1007 \times 10^{15} \exp\left(-\frac{46,429}{RT}\right)$$

Figure 1-2. Determination of the constants of the Arrhenius equation.

or
$$k_c\,(\sec^{-1}) = 3.50 \times 10^{13} \exp\left(-\frac{46{,}429}{RT}\right)$$

where $R = 1.9872$ cal/g mole °K.

Thus the frequency factor A is given by $A = 3.50 \times 10^{13}$ sec^{-1}.

III. BATCH REACTORS

In the analysis that follows, expressions are obtained which give the moles or concentration of each component in the reactor at any time during the reaction period. The use of these expressions in the analysis of data collected with batch reactors is then demonstrated.

A. Material Balances for Batch Reactors

A typical autoclave reactor is shown in Figure 1-3. At the time this picture was taken, this experimental reactor was in the service of hydrogenating lignite. For developmental purposes the sketch of the batch reactor shown in Figure 1-4 is used. Such a reactor is fixed in space, and the total feed is introduced at the outset, and no withdrawal is made until the reaction has reached the degree of completion desired. The volume V of the reactor is the space filled by the reacting mixture. The mixture in the volume V is commonly mixed throughout the course of the reaction by a stirrer. Thus such reactors are also called "well-stirred tank reactors." The volume of the reacting mixture may vary during the course of a liquid phase reaction because of either shrinkage or expansion of the liquid phase with reaction. In the case of a gas phase reaction, the volume V may either be held fixed or varied in any prescribed manner. For example, the volume may be

Figure 1-3. An experimental autoclave reactor in the service of the hydrogenation of lignite.

THE TOP OF THE REACTOR
IS GENERALLY FIXED. ITS
POSITION COULD BE VARIED,
HOWEVER, WITH TIME.

MOLES OF A = N_A

CONTENTS OF REACTOR
ARE PERFECTLY MIXED

VOLUME V
OCCUPIED BY
THE REACTING
MIXTURE

Figure 1-4. Sketch of a batch reactor.

varied as required to maintain the pressure constant. The variation of the temperature T of the reaction mixture with time is also permitted.

By the very nature of a batch reactor, it is an *unsteady state process*, which is defined as a process that has one or more variables which vary with time. On the other hand, a *steady state process* is one whose variables at all points throughout the process are independent of time.

A material balance on a reactor constitutes an application of the *law of conservation of mass.* For purposes of applications, a convenient statement of this law follows: *Except for the conversion of mass to energy and conversely, mass can neither be created nor destroyed.* Consequently, for a system in which the conversion of mass to energy and conversely is not involved, it follows that during the time period from $t = t_n$ to $t = t_n + \Delta t$,

$$\left\{\begin{array}{l}\text{Input of mass to the}\\ \text{system during the}\\ \text{time period } \Delta t\end{array}\right\} - \left\{\begin{array}{l}\text{output of mass from}\\ \text{the system during the}\\ \text{time period } \Delta t\end{array}\right\} = \left\{\begin{array}{l}\text{accumulation of mass}\\ \text{within the system}\\ \text{during the time period}\\ \Delta t\end{array}\right\} \qquad (1\text{-}31)$$

The accumulation term is defined as follows:

$$\left\{\begin{array}{l}\text{Accumulation of mass}\\ \text{within the system}\\ \text{during the time period } \Delta t\end{array}\right\} = \left\{\begin{array}{l}\text{amount of mass}\\ \text{in the system}\\ \text{at time } t_n + \Delta t\end{array}\right\} - \left\{\begin{array}{l}\text{amount of mass}\\ \text{in the system}\\ \text{at time } t_n\end{array}\right\} \qquad (1\text{-}32)$$

The particular part of the universe under consideration is called the *system.* A more convenient form of the law of conservation of mass for use in the description of industrial processes follows:

$$\int_{t_n}^{t_n + \Delta t} \left[\left\{\begin{array}{l}\text{Input of mass to the}\\ \text{system per unit time}\end{array}\right\} - \left\{\begin{array}{l}\text{output of mass from the}\\ \text{system per unit time}\end{array}\right\}\right] dt =$$
$$\left\{\begin{array}{l}\text{Mass within the system}\\ \text{at time } t_n + \Delta t\end{array}\right\} - \left\{\begin{array}{l}\text{mass within the}\\ \text{system at time } t_n\end{array}\right\} \qquad (1\text{-}33)$$

Suppose that the volume V of the reactor shown in Figure 1-4 is filled with reactant A and other reactants if needed. Let M_A denote the molecular weight of A. Then a mass balance on component A in the system (the volume V) over the time period from t_n to $t_n + \Delta t$ is given by

$$\int_{t_n}^{t_n + \Delta t} [\underbrace{0}_{\substack{\text{Input of } A\\ \text{per unit time}}} - \underbrace{M_A r_A V}_{\substack{\text{output of } A\\ \text{by reaction}\\ \text{per unit time}}}] \, dt = \underbrace{M_A N_A \Big|_{t_n + \Delta t}}_{\substack{\text{mass of } A\\ \text{within the system}\\ \text{at time } t_n + \Delta t}} - \underbrace{M_A N_A \Big|_{t_n}}_{\substack{\text{mass of } A\\ \text{within the system}\\ \text{at time } t_n}} \qquad (1\text{-}34)$$

where N_A is equal to the moles of A within the volume V at any time. (Throughout this book, the term "mole" is used in the presentation of the developments. It is to be understood that a particular choice such as gram moles, kilogram moles, or pound moles must be made in the solution of numerical problems. Also, it should be emphasized that t_n and Δt are arbitrarily selected fixed values which are nonzero, finite, and positive.) The appearance of the product $M_A r_A V$ in Equation (1-34) implies that the rate of reaction r_A is the same for every element of reactor volume throughout the volume V, regardless of how small the elements of volume are taken to be. When this condition is satisfied for every t in the time domain of interest, the reactor is said to be "perfectly mixed" or "micromixed."

Since the molecular weight of A is independent of time, Equation (1-34) reduces to

$$\int_{t_n}^{t_n+\Delta t} [-r_A V] \, dt = N_A \Big|_{t_n+\Delta t} - N_A \Big|_{t_n} \qquad (1\text{-}35)$$

Equation (1-35) may be converted to its corresponding differential equation by use of the mean value theorems of calculus in the following manner. Consider first the left-hand side of Equation (1-35). This integral may be reduced to algebraic form by use of the *mean value theorem of integral calculus* (see appendix at the end of this chapter, Theorem 1) as follows:

$$-\int_{t_n}^{t_n+\Delta t} [r_A V] \, dt = -\left[(r_A V) \Big|_{t_n+\alpha\Delta t} \right] \Delta t \qquad (1\text{-}36)$$

where $0 \le \alpha \le 1$. The quantity $(r_A V)|_{t_n+\alpha\Delta t}$ represents the mean value of the integrand; it is that particular value of $r_A V$ for which the rectangle of height $(r_A V)|_{t_n+\alpha\Delta t}$ and base Δt has an area equal to that represented by the integral on the left-hand side of Equation (1-36).

Application of the *mean value theorem of differential calculus* (Appendix, Theorem 2) to the right-hand side of Equation (1-35) gives

$$N_A \Big|_{t_n+\Delta t} - N_A \Big|_{t_n} = \left(\frac{dN_A}{dt} \Big|_{t_n+\beta\Delta t} \right) \Delta t \qquad (1\text{-}37)$$

where $0 < \beta < 1$. The time $t_n + \beta\Delta t$ is that particular value of t in the interval $t_n \le t \le t_n + \Delta t$ at which the slope of the tangent to the curve of N_A versus t is equal to the slope of the secant drawn from t_n to $t_n + \Delta t$.

From Equations (1-34), (1-36), and (1-37) it follows that

$$-(r_A V) \Big|_{t_n+\alpha\Delta t} = \frac{dN_A}{dt} \Big|_{t_n+\beta\Delta t} \qquad (1\text{-}38)$$

In the limit as Δt goes to zero, Equation (1-38) reduces to

$$-(r_A V) \Big|_{t_n} = \frac{dN_A}{dt} \Big|_{t_n} \qquad (1\text{-}39)$$

Since t_n was arbitrarily selected as any t in the time domain other than $t = 0$ (the time of the beginning of the reaction), Equation (1-39) holds for all $t > 0$, or

$$r_A = -\frac{1}{V} \frac{dN_A}{dt} \qquad (1\text{-}40)$$

This equation represents the limit of a material balance on compound A in the volume V as the time period over which the balance is made is allowed to go to zero. In the interest of simplicity, this equation is referred to hereafter as simply the "material balance on component A."

It should be remarked that if the rate of reaction is defined in terms of the appearance of A,

$$r_A = \frac{\text{moles of } A \text{ appearing}}{\text{(unit time)(unit volume)}} \tag{1-41}$$

then instead of Equation (1-40), the following equation is obtained for the material balance on A:

$$r_A = \frac{1}{V}\frac{dN_A}{dt} \tag{1-42}$$

Note that the sign appearing on the right-hand side of Equations (1-40) and (1-42) does not depend upon whether or not A is in fact disappearing or appearing by reaction, but upon the definition of the rate of reaction.

B. Variation of the Moles Reacted with Time
(Conditions: Isothermal Operation, Perfectly
Mixed, and Constant Volume)

By "isothermal operation of a batch reactor" is meant that the temperature of the reacting mixture is maintained constant throughout the course of the reaction. A batch reactor is said to be "perfectly mixed" if the composition of the reacting mixture is uniform throughout the reactor at any time t. That is, the concentration of each element of volume ΔV of the reactor volume V is the same at any time t, regardless of how small the element of volume is taken to be. The mixing is generally accomplished by use of a stirrer. By "constant volume" is meant that the volume of the reacting mixture within the reactor remains constant throughout the course of the reaction. In order for the volume of the reacting mixture to remain constant, it is of course necessary for the mass density to remain constant.

To demonstrate the manner in which the expressions relating the moles reacted to the reaction time are obtained, the steps involved in the development of the expressions for three types of unidirectional reactions are presented.

1. FIRST-ORDER UNIDIRECTIONAL REACTIONS: $A \rightarrow$ PRODUCTS. For the first-order reaction $A \rightarrow$ products, the rate expression for r_A (moles of A disappearing per unit time per unit volume) is given by

$$r_A = k_c C_A$$

and the material balance for component A for a batch reactor is given by

$$r_A = -\frac{1}{V}\frac{dN_A}{dt}$$

Elimination of r_A from these two equations yields

$$-\frac{1}{V}\frac{dN_A}{dt} = k_c C_A \qquad (1\text{-}43)$$

Since the concentration C_A is defined by

$$C_A = \frac{N_A}{V} \qquad (1\text{-}44)$$

for a batch reactor (see Figure 1-4), then Equation (1-43) may be stated in terms of N_A and t to give

$$-\frac{1}{V}\frac{dN_A}{dt} = k_c \frac{N_A}{V} \qquad (1\text{-}45)$$

[Since the volume V cancels out, the final expression, Equation (1-48), is independent of whether or not the volume remains constant throughout the course of the first-order reaction.] Separation of variables in Equation (1-45) yields

$$-\int_{N_A^0}^{N_A}\frac{dN_A}{N_A} = \int_0^t k_c\, dt \qquad (1\text{-}46)$$

where $N_A^0 = $ total moles of A in the reactor at time $t = 0$

Since the reaction is carried out isothermally, the rate constant k_c is constant. If it is further supposed that the reaction remains first order over the entire range of concentration, Equation (1-46) may be integrated and rearranged.

$$\log_e N_A = -k_c t + \log_e N_A^0 \qquad (1\text{-}47)$$

For a first-order reaction, the plot of $\log_e N_A$ versus t is a straight line with the intercept of $\log_e N_A^0$ as illustrated in Figure 1-5. Equation (1-47) may be stated in exponential form as follows:

$$N_A = N_A^0 \exp\left(-k_c t\right) \qquad (1\text{-}48)$$

If it is supposed that the volume V remains constant throughout the course of the reaction, then division of both sides of Equation (1-48) by V yields

$$C_A = C_A^0 \exp\left(-k_c t\right) \qquad (1\text{-}49)$$

Figure 1-5. Determination of the order and rate constant for a reaction from experimental data taken with a batch reactor.

2. SECOND-ORDER UNIDIRECTIONAL REACTIONS: $2A \rightarrow$ PRODUCTS. Elimination of r_A from the rate expression for a second-order reaction [Equation (1-8)] and the material balance [Equation (1-40)] gives

$$-\frac{1}{V}\frac{dN_A}{dt} = k_c C_A^2 \tag{1-50}$$

If it is now supposed that the volume of the reacting mixture remains constant throughout the course of the reaction, then Equation (1-50) may be restated as follows:

$$-\frac{dC_A}{dt} = k_c C_A^2 \tag{1-51}$$

Separation of variables followed by integration and rearrangement yields

$$\frac{1}{C_A} = k_c t + \frac{1}{C_A^0} \tag{1-52}$$

Since $C_A = N_A/V$, it follows that

$$\frac{1}{N_A} = \frac{k_c t}{V} + \frac{1}{N_A^0} \tag{1-53}$$

As illustrated in Figure 1-5, the plot of $1/N_A$ versus t is a straight line for second-order reactions.

3. SECOND-ORDER UNIDIRECTIONAL REACTIONS: $A + B \rightarrow$ PRODUCTS. If $N_A^0 \neq N_B^0$, then one equation in the three variables N_A, N_B, and t is obtained by eliminating r_A from Equations (1-9) and (1-40).

$$-\frac{1}{V}\frac{dN_A}{dt} = k_c C_A C_B = \frac{k_c}{V^2} N_A N_B \tag{1-54}$$

If $N_A^0 = N_B^0$, then $N_A = N_B$ for all t and Equation (1-54) reduces to Equation (1-50). Equation (1-54) may be reduced to one equation in two variables by expressing N_A and N_B in terms of a single variable, conversion, which is defined herein as follows:

$$X = \frac{N_A^0 - N_A}{N_A^0} \tag{1-55}$$

Rearrangement gives

$$N_A = N_A^0 - N_A^0 X \tag{1-56}$$

Thus $N_A^0 X$ is seen to be the moles of A that have reacted since the initiation of the reaction. Since one mole of B disappears for each mole of A which disappears, the following stoichiometric relationship is obtained:

$$N_B = N_B^0 - N_A^0 X \tag{1-57}$$

From Equation (1-56), it follows that

$$\frac{dN_A}{dt} = -N_A^0 \frac{dX}{dt} \tag{1-58}$$

Thus Equation (1-54) may be restated in terms of the variables X and t to give

$$N_A^0 \frac{dX}{dt} = \frac{k_c}{V}(N_A^0 - N_A^0 X)(N_B^0 - N_A^0 X) \tag{1-59}$$

Separation of the variables followed by integration and rearrangement gives

$$t = \left(\frac{V}{k_c(N_A^0 - N_B^0)}\right) \log_e \left(\frac{N_B^0(N_A^0 - N_A^0 X)}{N_A^0(N_B^0 - N_A^0 X)}\right) \tag{1-60}$$

where it has been assumed that k_c and V remain constant. By use of the relationships given by Equations (1-56) and (1-57), the result given by Equation (1-60) may be stated in the form

$$t = \frac{V}{k_c(N_A^0 - N_B^0)} \log_e \left(\frac{N_B^0 N_A}{N_A^0 N_B}\right) \tag{1-61}$$

If the reaction is second order, a plot of $\log_e N_A/N_B$ versus t gives a straight line with the slope $k_c(N_A^0 - N_B^0)/V$.

4. THIRD-ORDER UNIDIRECTIONAL REACTIONS: $3A \rightarrow$ PRODUCTS. In the same manner demonstrated for second-order reactions with respect to A, the following equation is obtained for reactions which are third order with respect to A.

$$-\frac{1}{V}\frac{dN_A}{dt} = k_c C_A^3 \tag{1-62}$$

Separation of the variables followed by integration and rearrangement yields

$$\frac{1}{C_A^2} = 2k_c t + \frac{1}{(C_A^0)^2} \tag{1-63}$$

where it has been supposed that k_c and V are constant. When this result is expressed in terms of the moles of A, one obtains

$$\frac{1}{N_A^2} = \left(\frac{2k_c}{V^2}\right) t + \frac{1}{(N_A^0)^2} \qquad (1\text{-}64)$$

As illustrated in Figure 1-5, the plot of $1/N_A^2$ versus t is a straight line if the reaction is third order. Third-order reactions are, however, relatively rare. Additional design equations for batch reactors are presented in Table 1-1.

TABLE 1-1

DESIGN EQUATIONS FOR CARRYING OUT UNIDIRECTIONAL REACTIONS
IN A BATCH REACTOR

(Conditions: isothermal operation, perfectly mixed, and constant volume)

Reaction	Design Equation
1. $A \longrightarrow$ products	$t = \dfrac{1}{k_c} \log_e \dfrac{N_A^0}{N_A}$
2. $2A \longrightarrow$ products	$t = \dfrac{V}{k_c}\left[\dfrac{1}{N_A} - \dfrac{1}{N_A^0}\right]$
3. $A + B \longrightarrow$ products $N_A^0 \neq N_B^0$	$t = \dfrac{V}{k_c(N_A^0 - N_B^0)} \log_e \dfrac{N_B^0 N_A}{N_A^0 N_B}$
4. $3A \longrightarrow$ products	$t = \dfrac{V^2}{2k_c}\left[\left(\dfrac{1}{N_A}\right)^2 - \left(\dfrac{1}{N_A^0}\right)^2\right]$
5. $A + B + C \longrightarrow$ products $(N_A^0 \neq N_B^0 \neq N_C^0)$	$t = \dfrac{V^2}{k_c}\left[\dfrac{\log_e N_A^0/N_A}{(N_B^0 - N_A^0)(N_C^0 - N_A^0)} + \dfrac{\log_e N_B^0/N_B}{(N_A^0 - N_B^0)(N_C^0 - N_B^0)}\right.$ $\left. + \dfrac{\log_e N_C^0/N_C}{(N_A^0 - N_C^0)(N_B^0 - N_C^0)}\right]$
6. $2A + B \longrightarrow$ products $(N_A^0 \neq 2N_B^0)$	$t = \dfrac{V^2}{k_c}\left[\dfrac{2}{2N_B^0 - N_A^0}\left(\dfrac{1}{N_A} - \dfrac{1}{N_A^0}\right)\right.$ $\left. + \dfrac{2}{(2N_B^0 - N_A^0)^2}\log_e \dfrac{N_B^0 N_A}{N_A^0 N_B}\right]$
7. $NA \longrightarrow$ products $(N \neq 1)$	$t = \dfrac{1}{k_c(N-1)}(C_A^{1-N} - (C_A^0)^{1-N})$

EXAMPLE 1-5

A saponification reaction which is easily carried out in the laboratory is the reaction of ethyl acetate in an aqueous solution of sodium hydroxide,

$$CH_3COOC_2H_5 + NaOH \longrightarrow CH_3COONa + C_2H_5OH$$

In 1906, Walker [16] investigated this reaction at 25°C by commencing with equal concentrations (0.01 g mole/liter) of ethyl acetate and sodium hydroxide and following the course of the reaction by the electrical conductance method. Some of his results follow:

t (min)	5	9	13	20
g moles of NaOH per liter	0.00755	0.00633	0.00541	0.00434
t (min)	25	33	37	
g moles of NaOH per liter	0.00385	0.00320	0.00296	

On the basis of these data, determine the order of the reaction and evaluate the rate constant.

SOLUTION

The saponification reaction may be represented by

$$A + B \longrightarrow C + D$$

Since the initial concentrations of ethyl acetate and sodium hydroxide are equal, it follows from the stoichiometry of the saponification reaction that their concentrations remain equal for all time; that is, $C_A = C_B$. Assume the reaction is second order. Then

$$r_A = k_c C_A C_B = k_c C_A^2$$

For a second-order reaction which is carried out isothermally and at constant volume in a batch reactor, Equation (1-52) is applicable.

$$\frac{1}{C_A} = k_c t + \frac{1}{C_A^0}$$

Figure 1-6. Determination of the order and rate constant for the saponification of ethyl acetate [16].

To test the assumption of second order, the original data are plotted as shown in Figure 1-6. Since a straight line is obtained, the rate of reaction may be represented by a second-order rate expression. The slope of the line shown in Figure 1-6 is equal to $k_c = 6.48$ [liter/(min g mole)].

C. Determination of the Order and the Rate Constant for a Unidirectional Reaction

Suppose that a given reaction is carried out isothermally in a batch reactor at constant volume and that the progress of the reaction is followed by analyzing samples of the reacting mixture at selected time intervals throughout the course of the reaction. Further, suppose that these results indicate that the stoichiometry of the reaction is satisfied by an equation of the form:

$$A \longrightarrow \text{products} \qquad (1\text{-}65)$$

If the stoichiometry is satisfied by Equation (1-65), it is also satisfied by the equation

$$NA \longrightarrow N \text{ products} \qquad (1\text{-}66)$$

for all $N > 0$. If, however, a plot of $\log_e N_A$ versus t is a straight line, then the reaction is first order ($N = 1$) (see Figure 1-5). If, however, a plot of $1/C_A$ or $1/N_A$ versus t yields a straight line, the reaction is said to be second order ($N = 2$). The reaction is said to be third order ($N = 3$) if a plot of $1/C_A^2$ or $1/N_A^2$ versus t yields a straight line. If none of these plots yields a straight line, the rate of reaction is probably fractional order. For this case, the order may be determined by the following graphical procedure.

1. GRAPHICAL DETERMINATION OF THE ORDER AND RATE CONSTANT. Consider the case where the experimental results suggest that the rate of reaction is proportional to the concentration of A raised to some power N; that is,

$$r_A = k_c C_A^N$$

Since the material-balance expression for r_A for a batch reactor in which the volume is constant is given by $r_A = -dC_A/dt$, it follows that

$$r_A = -\frac{dC_A}{dt} = k_c C_A^N \tag{1-67}$$

A graphical procedure for determining k_c and N follows. Let

$$C_A \Big|_{t_n} = \text{concentration of } A \text{ at time } t_n$$

$$C_A \Big|_{t_{n+1}} = \text{concentration of } A \text{ at time } t_{n+1}$$

Now let the average values of C_A and r_A be approximated as follows:

$$C_A \Big|_{t_n + \Delta t/2} \cong \frac{C_A \Big|_{t_n} + C_A \Big|_{t_{n+1}}}{2} \tag{1-68}$$

$$r_A \Big|_{t_n + \Delta t/2} \cong -\left[\frac{C_A \Big|_{t_{n+1}} - C_A \Big|_{t_n}}{\Delta t}\right] = \frac{C_A \Big|_{t_n} - C_A \Big|_{t_{n+1}}}{\Delta t} \tag{1-69}$$

Then

$$\log r_A \Big|_{t_n + \Delta t/2} = \log k_c + N \log C_A \Big|_{t_n + \Delta t/2} \tag{1-70}$$

A graph of this equation is shown in Figure 1-7. The slope gives the order N and the intercept gives the logarithm of k. For some reactions a constant

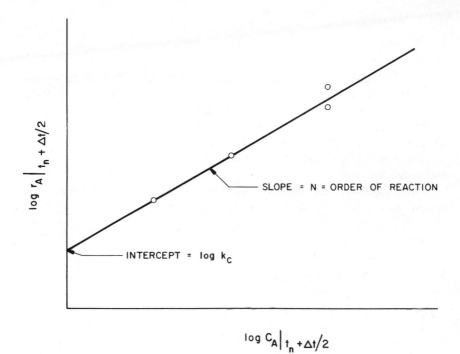

$$\log C_A \Big|_{t_n + \Delta t/2}$$

Figure 1-7. Determination of the order N and rate constant for a reaction from data taken with a batch reactor.

value of N cannot be obtained over the concentration range of interest. (The treatment of reactions for which N does not remain constant is considered in Chapter 4.) For additional techniques for the treatment of rate data, the work of Churchill is recommended [17].

2. USE OF THE HALF-LIFE IN THE DETERMINATION OF THE ORDER AND RATE CONSTANT. The half-life, denoted by $t_{1/2}$, of a reaction is the time required for one-half of the initial amount of a specified reactant to be consumed by the reaction. Consider the first-order reaction: $A \rightarrow$ products. At

$$t = t_{1/2}, \qquad N_A = \frac{N_A^0}{2} \tag{1-71}$$

Thus the expression given by Equation (1-47) for a first-order reaction reduces to

$$\log_e \frac{N_A^0}{N_A^0/2} = k_c t_{1/2}$$

or
$$t_{1/2} = \frac{\log_e 2}{k_c} \cong \frac{0.693}{k_c} \tag{1-72}$$

Thus, if the rate of reaction is first order, then the half-life time $t_{1/2}$ is independent of the amount of reactant A present initially, and the value for the rate constant is found by solving Equation (1-72) for k_c.

Many reactions involving radioactive decay are first order, and the speeds of such reactions are commonly compared by use of half-life times. From Equation (1-72), it is seen that a short half-life time corresponds to a large rate constant.

For a second-order reaction of the type $2A \rightarrow$ products, Equation (1-52) reduces to

$$t_{1/2} = \frac{1}{k_c C_A^0} \tag{1-73}$$

at $t = t_{1/2}$. Thus, for second-order reactions of the type stated, the half-life time is inversely proportional to the amount of A present initially, and k_c is readily computed by use of Equation (1-73).

The formula for the half-life time for a third-order reaction of the type $3A \rightarrow$ products may be obtained from Equation (1-64); namely,

$$t_{1/2} = \frac{1}{\frac{2}{3}k_c(C_A^0)^2} \tag{1-74}$$

Thus the half-life time is inversely proportional to the square of the initial concentration of A, and the value of the rate constant k_c is readily computed by use of Equation (1-74).

A second-order reaction of the form $A + B \rightarrow$ products has a half-life both with respect to A and B (see Problem 1-9).

D. Variable-Volume Batch Reactors

Reactors of this type are used to take advantage of the fact that, for certain reactions, the number of moles in the reacting mixture either increase or decrease as the reaction proceeds. For example, suppose the second-order gas phase reaction

$$2A \longrightarrow R$$

is carried out at constant pressure and temperature. Thus, as indicated in Figure 1-4, the volume V must be decreased as the reaction proceeds in order to maintain the pressure of the reacting mixture at a specified value. To treat this type of reactor, it is necessary to state the volume V that appears in Equation (1-50) in terms of a variable related to the amount of A present at any time t. Since C_A at any time t is equal to N_A/V, Equation (1-50) may be restated as follows:

$$-\frac{dN_A}{dt} = \frac{k_c}{V} N_A^2 \qquad (1\text{-}75)$$

This equation, which contains three variables, N_A, t, and V, may be solved by first expressing N_A and V in terms of the conversion X. Consider the case where the pressure-volume behavior of the gas mixture may be approximated by the perfect gas law,

$$PV = N_T RT \qquad , \qquad (1\text{-}76)$$

This equation makes it possible to state V in terms of conversion since N_T may be expressed in terms of conversion by use of the stoichiometric relationships. For the reaction $2A \rightarrow R$ and for the case where the feed contains only A and R, the following stoichiometric relationships are obtained:

$$\begin{aligned} N_A &= N_A^0 - N_A^0 X \\ N_R &= N_R^0 + \tfrac{1}{2}N_A^0 X \\ \hline N_T &= N_T^0 - \tfrac{1}{2}N_A^0 X \end{aligned} \qquad (1\text{-}77)$$

where N_T = total number of moles in the reacting mixture at any time t

N_T^0 = value of N_T at $t = 0$

Then, by substituting this expression for N_T into Equation (1-76), one obtains

$$V = \left[N_T^0 - \frac{N_A^0 X}{2} \right] \frac{RT}{P} \qquad (1\text{-}78)$$

for the case where it is assumed that the mixture obeys the perfect gas law. At $t = 0$, $V = V^0$, and $V^0 = N_T^0 RT/P$. Thus

$$\frac{V}{V^0} = 1 - \frac{y_A^0 X}{2} \qquad (1\text{-}79)$$

where $y_A^0 = N_A^0/N_T^0$, the mole fraction of A in the reactor at time $t = 0$.

By use of the previous relationships, it is possible to reduce Equation (1-75) to the following form:

$$\frac{dX}{dt} = \left(\frac{k_c N_A^0}{V^0}\right) \frac{(1 - X)^2}{[1 - (y_A^0 X/2)]} \tag{1-80}$$

Separation of variables followed by integration over the time interval from 0 to t yields

$$t = \frac{V^0}{k_c N_A^0}\left[\left(1 - \frac{y_A^0}{2}\right)\left(\frac{X}{1 - X}\right) + \frac{y_A^0}{2}\log_e\frac{1}{1 - X}\right] \tag{1-81}$$

where it has been assumed that k_c remains constant throughout the course of the reaction. Alternately, the time t may be expressed as a function of the reactor volume V (see Problem 1-10).

E. Use of Total Pressure to Follow the Progress of a Reaction

For gas reactions involving a change in the number of moles, say

$$A \longrightarrow 2R$$

the progress of the reaction may be followed by measuring the total pressure as a function of time at constant volume and temperature.

Consider the case where the gas mixture obeys the perfect gas law, Equation (1-76), and the initial mixture contains only A and R. The stoichiometric relationships for A and R are

$$\begin{aligned} N_A &= N_A^0 - N_A^0 X \\ N_R &= N_R^0 + 2N_A^0 X \\ \overline{N_T} &= N_T^0 + N_A^0 X \end{aligned} \tag{1-82}$$

Thus

$$\frac{P}{P^0} = \frac{N_T}{N_T^0} = 1 + y_A^0 X \tag{1-83}$$

Since

$$\frac{N_A^0}{N_A} = \frac{1}{1 - X}$$

and since Equation (1-47) holds, it follows that

$$t = \frac{1}{k_c}\log_e\frac{y_A^0}{1 + y_A^0 - P/P^0} \tag{1-84}$$

F. Reversible Reactions

Consider the reversible reaction

$$A \; \underset{k_c'}{\overset{k_c}{\rightleftarrows}} \; R \qquad (1\text{-}85)$$

which is first order in both directions. The net rate of disappearance of A is given by

$$r_A = r_{Af} - r_{Ar}$$

or the rate expression for r_A is given by

$$r_A = k_c C_A - k_c' C_R \qquad (1\text{-}86)$$

Thus

$$-\frac{dN_A}{dt} = k_c N_A - k_c' N_R \qquad (1\text{-}87)$$

This equation, which contains the three variables N_A, N_R, and t, may be reduced to one equation in two variables by expressing the moles of A and R at any time t in terms of X through the use of the stoichiometric relationships.

$$N_A = N_A^0 - N_A^0 X$$
$$N_R = N_R^0 + N_A^0 X \qquad (1\text{-}88)$$

Thus Equation (1-87) may be restated as follows:

$$N_A^0 \frac{dX}{dt} = k_c(N_A^0 - N_A^0 X) - k_c'(N_R^0 + N_A^0 X) \qquad (1\text{-}89)$$

Now suppose that k_c and k_c' remain constant throughout the course of the reaction. Separation of the variables of Equation (1-89) followed by integration and rearrangement gives

$$t = \frac{1}{k_c + k_c'} \log_e \frac{k_c - k_c'\beta}{(k_c - k_c'\beta) - (k_c + k_c')X} \qquad (1\text{-}90)$$

where

$$\beta = \frac{N_R^0}{N_A^0}$$

Integral expressions for other first and second-order reactions are given in Table 1-2.

TABLE 1-2
Design Equations for Carrying Out a Reversible Reaction in a Batch Reactor

(Conditions: isothermal operation, perfectly mixed, and constant volume)

$$t = \frac{1}{k_c} \int_0^X \frac{dX}{aX^2 + bX + c}$$

Reaction	Constants		
	a	b	c
1. $A \underset{k_c'}{\overset{k_c}{\rightleftharpoons}} 2R$ $\quad$ $N_T^0 = N_A^0 + N_R^0$	$-4\frac{C_A^0}{K_c}$	$-\left(1 + 4\beta\frac{C_A^0}{K_c}\right)$	$\left(1 - \frac{C_A^0\beta^2}{K_c}\right)$
2. $2A \underset{k_c'}{\overset{k_c}{\rightleftharpoons}} R$ $\quad$ $N_T^0 = N_A^0 + N_R^0$	C_A^0	$-\left(2C_A^0 + \frac{1}{2K_c}\right)$	$C_A^0 - \frac{\beta}{K_c}$
3. $A + B \underset{k_c'}{\overset{k_c}{\rightleftharpoons}} R$ $\quad$ $N_A^0 \neq N_B^0$ $\quad$ $N_T^0 = N_A^0 + N_B^0 + N_R^0$	C_A^0	$-\left(C_A^0(1 + \gamma) + \frac{1}{K_c}\right)$	$C_A^0\gamma - \frac{\beta}{K_c}$

4. $A + B \underset{k_c'}{\overset{k_c}{\rightleftharpoons}} R + S$ $C_A^0\left(1 - \dfrac{1}{K_c}\right)$ $-C_A^0\left(1 + \gamma + \dfrac{1}{K_c}(\beta + \alpha)\right)$ $C_A^0\left(\gamma - \dfrac{\beta\alpha}{K_c}\right)$

$N_A^0 \neq N_B^0, N_R^0 \neq N_S^0$
$N_T^0 = N_A^0 + N_B^0 + N_R^0 + N_S^0$

5. $2A \underset{k_c'}{\overset{k_c}{\rightleftharpoons}} R + S$ $C_A^0\left(1 - \dfrac{1}{K_c}\right)$ $-C_A^0\left(2 + \dfrac{1}{K_c}(\beta + \alpha)\right)$ $C_A^0\left(1 - \dfrac{\beta\alpha}{K_c}\right)$

$N_R^0 \neq N_S^0, \quad N_T^0 = N_A^0 + N_R^0 + N_S^0$

6. $2A \underset{k_c'}{\overset{k_c}{\rightleftharpoons}} 2R$ $C_A^0\left(1 - \dfrac{1}{K_c}\right)$ $-2C_A^0\left(1 + \dfrac{\beta}{K_c}\right)$ $C_A^0\left(1 - \dfrac{\beta^2}{K_c}\right)$

$N_T^0 = N_A^0 + N_R^0$

where

$$\gamma = \frac{N_B^0}{N_A^0}, \qquad \beta = \frac{N_R^0}{N_A^0}, \qquad \alpha = \frac{N_S^0}{N_A^0}, \qquad K_c = \frac{k_c}{k_c'}$$

The integrated forms of the above equations are:

$$t = \frac{1}{k_c}\int_0^X \frac{dX}{aX^2 + bX + c} = \frac{1}{k_c\sqrt{b^2 - 4ac}}\log_e\frac{(2aX + b - \sqrt{b^2 - 4ac})(b + \sqrt{b^2 - 4ac})}{(2aX + b + \sqrt{b^2 - 4ac})(b - \sqrt{b^2 - 4ac})}, \qquad \text{if } b^2 > 4ac$$

$$t = \frac{1}{k_c}\int_0^X \frac{dX}{aX^2 + bX + c} = \frac{2}{k_c\sqrt{4ac - b^2}}\left[\tan^{-1}\frac{2aX + b}{\sqrt{4ac - b^2}} - \tan^{-1}\frac{b}{\sqrt{4ac - b^2}}\right], \qquad \text{if } b^2 < 4ac$$

$$t = \frac{1}{k_c}\left[\frac{4aX}{(2aX + b)b}\right], \qquad \text{if } b^2 = 4ac$$

G. Cycle Time

When batch reactors are used commercially, the times required to charge and to empty the reactor become significant operating variables as well as the reaction time. The time required to complete one sequence of events is called the cycle time t_c; that is,

$$t_c = t_{charge} + t_{discharge} + t_{reaction}$$

EXAMPLE 1-6

For the reaction of $A \rightarrow R$, $k_c = 0.02$ min^{-1}. It is desired to produce 4752 g moles of R per 10-hr day, and 99% of A entering the reactor is to be converted. To charge the reactor and to heat it to reaction temperature requires 0.26 hr. To discharge the reactor and to prepare it for the next run takes 0.9 hr. Calculate the volume of the reactor required. Pure A with a molar density of 8 g moles per liter is charged to the reactor.

SOLUTION

From Equations (1-47) and (1-56) the reaction time is calculated:

$$t_{reaction} = \frac{-1}{0.02} \log_e (1 - 0.99) = \frac{1}{0.02} \log_e 100 = \frac{4.606}{0.02} = 230.2 \text{ min}$$

or

$$t_{reaction} = 3.84 \text{ hr}$$

Thus the total cycle time is

$$t_c = 0.26 + 0.9 + 3.84 = 5.0 \text{ hr}$$

To produce 4752 g moles in a 10-hr day, two cycles can be completed, and in each cycle 2376 g moles of R must be produced.

$$N_A^0 = \frac{N_R}{0.99} = \frac{2376}{0.99} = 2400 \text{ g moles}$$

Since $C_A^0 = N_A^0/V$, the reactor volume V is given by

$$V = \frac{2400 \text{ g moles}}{8 \text{ g moles/liter}} = 300 \text{ liters}$$

or

$$V = 79.3 \text{ gal}$$

Most mixing vessels are available in standard sizes. If it is supposed that the preceding reaction occurs in the liquid phase, then the next largest standard-size reactor should be specified. (A batch reactor should *never be charged completely full of a reacting liquid.*)

PROBLEMS

1-1. Begin with a material balance on reactant A and obtain the result given by Equation (1-42).

1-2. For the reaction

$$2A + 3B \; \rightleftharpoons \; C + 4D + 2F$$

the rate of loss of A is 5 moles per unit time per unit volume.
(a) What is the rate of disappearance of B, $r_B = $?
Answer: $r_B = 7.5$
(b) What is the rate of appearance of C, D, and F, respectively?
Answer: $r_C = 2.5, r_D = 10, r_F = 5.$

1-3. The following reactions,

$$2A \; \xrightarrow{k_{c1}} \; R + 2S$$
$$A \; \xrightarrow{k_{c2}} \; 2C + R$$

occur simultaneously as written. The rate constants k_{c1} and k_{c2} are defined with respect to component A. That is, the rate of disappearance of A by the first reaction is denoted by r_{A1} and is given by

$$r_{A1} = k_{c1} C_A^2$$

and the rate of disappearance of A by the second reaction is given by

$$r_{A2} = k_{c2} C_A$$

On the basis of these definitions of k_{c1} and k_{c2}, formulate the rate expressions for the following rates.
(a) r_A, where r_A denotes the net rate of disappearance of A
(b) r_A, where r_A denotes the net rate of appearance of A
(c) r_R, where r_R denotes the net rate of appearance of R
(d) r_C, where r_C denotes the net rate of appearance of C
(e) r_S, where r_S denotes the net rate of appearance of S

1-4. The following second-order rate constants were reported by Abraham and Benenati [18] for the epoxidation of oleic acid with perbenzoic acid.

T (°C)	11.3	23.4	30.8	37.8
k_c (liters/g mole min)	0.542	1.28	2.06	3.30

Evaluate the energy of activation E_A and the frequency factor A for the Arrhenius equation.

Answer: $E_A = 11,554$ cal/g mole; $A = 4.18 \times 10^8$ liters/g mole min

1-5. Bodenstein [19] found that the decomposition of nitrogen dioxide was a second-order reaction with rate constants as follows:

T (°K)	592	603.2	627	651.2	656
k_c (cc/g mole sec)	522	755	1700	4020	5030

Calculate the activation energy E_A and the frequency factor A for the Arrhenius equation.

Answer: $E_A = 14,640.2$ cal/g mole; $A = 2.793 \times 10^9$ (liters g mole)$^{1/2}$ min^{-1}

1-6. The following data were obtained by Worsfold and Bywater [20] in a study of the polymerization of styrene in the solvent benzene by use of a butyllithium initiator.

k_c (liter/g mole)$^{1/2}$ min^{-1}	T (°C)
0.929	30.3
0.563	25.0
0.387	20.0
0.265	15.0
0.155	10.0

Use these data to evaluate the activation energy E_A and the frequency factor A of the Arrhenius equation.

Answer: $E_A = 14,640.2$ cal/g mole, $A = 2.793 \times 10^{10}$ (liters g mole)$^{1/2}$ min^{-1}

1-7. Hairston and O'Brien [21] studied the reaction

$$(CH_3)_3\!-\!Si\!-\!\overset{\displaystyle CH_3}{\underset{\displaystyle CH_3}{C}}\!-\!Cl + SbF_5 \xrightarrow{\ k_1\ }$$

$$
\begin{array}{c}
F \\
|
\end{array}
$$

$$
\begin{array}{ccc}
CH_3 & & \\
| & \xrightarrow{k_2} & (CH_3)_6Si\!-\!C(CH_3)_3 + SbX_5 \\
(CH_3)_3Si\!-\!C^{(+)} + SbX_6^{(-)} & & \\
| & \xrightarrow{k_3} & \\
CH_3 & & (CH_3)_3Si\!-\!F + SbX_5
\end{array}
$$

at 40°C in nitromethane by use of nuclear magnetic resonance. From the following data, determine the order of the first reaction and evaluate the rate constant k_1.

Time (min)	2-Trimethylsilyl-2-Chloropropane (g mole/liter)	SbF$_5$ (g mole/liter)
2	0.1259	0.0900
4.25	0.1225	0.0866
9.25	0.1150	0.0791
16.75	0.1010	0.0696
25.75	0.0968	0.0609
36.25	0.0882	0.0523

Answer: $k_1 = 0.1486$ liter/min g mole

1-8. A second-order reaction may be made to appear first order with respect to A by taking $N_B^0 \gg N_A^0$. (Such reactions are sometimes called "pseudo first order.") Show how the rate constant k_c may be determined, where $r_A = k_c C_A C_B$.

1-9. (a) For the second-order reaction $A + B \rightarrow$ products, show that the half-life time with respect to A is given by

$$
(t_{1/2})_A = \frac{1}{k_c(C_A^0 - C_B^0)} \log_e \left[\frac{C_B^0}{2(C_B^0 - \frac{1}{2}C_A^0)} \right]
$$

Hint: At time $(t_{1/2})_A$, show that the concentration of B is given by

$$
C_B = C_B^0 - \frac{1}{2}C_A^0
$$

(b) Show that a necessary condition for the reaction in Part (a) to proceed to the point where $\frac{1}{2}$ of A has been reacted in finite time is that

$$
N_B^0 > \frac{1}{2}N_A^0
$$

1-10. By use of Equation (1-79), state t as given by Equation (1-81) in terms of V.

1-11. Show how a variable volume batch reactor may be used to follow the first-order gas phase reaction: $A \rightarrow 2B$.

1-12. Gordon [22] studied the pyrolysis of 4,4-bisperfluoromethylbutene-1,4-01 in the gas phase.

$$(CF_3)_2C(OH)CH_2CH{=}CH_2 \rightleftharpoons C_3H_6 + F_3COCF_3$$

The temperature range for the study was chosen such that the rate constant for the reverse reaction was small relative to the rate constant for the forward reaction. From the data presented, evaluate the order, the frequency factor, and the activation energy for this reaction. The reaction was carried out isothermally at each of several temperatures in a batch reactor which had a volume of 45.7 cc. At the beginning of each run, the reactor was filled with the pure reactant.

Pyrolysis Data

Initial Pressure (torr)	Temperature (°C)	Time (sec)	C_3H_6 Produced (microgram moles)
25	325	60	1.67
25	325	60	1.68
20	300	120	0.628
20	300	120	0.566
20	300	180	0.797
38	300	120	1.30
20	300	120	0.621
20	300	120	0.597
20	250	900	0.198
20	250	300	0.0723
20	250	300	0.0739
20	200	3600	0.0143
20	200	7200	0.0236
20	200	7200	0.0244
20	200	7200	0.0242
20	200	3600	0.0121

1-13. Swain [23] investigated the reaction of triphenyl methyl chloride with methanol in a dry benzene solution in a batch reactor.

$$\begin{array}{ccccccc} (C_6H_5)_3CCl & + & CH_3OH & \longrightarrow & (C_6H_5)_3COCH_3 & + & HCl \\ A & + & B & \longrightarrow & C & + & D \end{array}$$

HCl was removed by reaction with pyridine with subsequent precipitation of pyridine hydrochloride in order to prevent the reverse reaction from occurring. From the data in the following table, show that this reaction is second order with respect to methanol and first order with respect to triphenyl methyl chloride, and evaluate the rate constant. The initial concentrations of $(C_6H_5)_3COCH_3$ and HCl are zero.

Data: Initial conditions. 0.106 molar chloride and 0.054 molar methanol in dry benzene solution in the presence of pyridine at 25°C.

Time (min)	Triphenyl Methyl Chloride Reacted (g moles/liter)
168	0.0091
174	0.0110
418	0.0181
426	0.0189
444	0.0207
1150	0.0318
1440	0.0334
1510	0.0345
1660	0.0354
2890	0.0418
2900	0.0414
3120	0.0416
193,000	0.0514

Answer: $k_c = 0.2687$ liter^2/min (g mole)^2

1-14. Kistiakowsky and Lacher [24] investigated the condensation of acrolein and butadiene at 291.2°C. This reaction was found to be second order, and at this reaction temperature (291.2°C), the following rate constant was reported: $k_p = 2.71 \times 10^{-11}$ g moles/sec mm^2 liter. Find the value of k_c at these conditions.
Answer: $k_c = 0.03356$ liter/sec g mole

1-15. In the rate equations

$$r_A = k_c C_A^2, \qquad k_c = 0.004 \quad \text{at} \quad 700°K$$
$$r_A = k_c C_A, \qquad k_c = 0.05 \quad \text{at} \quad 400°K$$

where r_A is expressed in lb moles/hr ft^3 and C_A in lb moles/ft^3. Calculate the values of k_p for these same reactions when r_A is stated in terms of partial pressures as follows:

$$r_A = k_p p_A^2$$
$$r_A = k_p p_A$$

Again r_A is expressed in lb moles/hr ft^3. The partial pressure of p_A is in atmospheres.
Answer: $k_p = 4.726 \times 10^{-9}$ lb moles/hr ft^3 atm^2, and $k_p = 9.511 \times 10^5$ lb moles/hr ft^3 atm

1-16. A third-order reaction in a perfect gas system has a reaction velocity constant $k_c = 300$ (ft^3)^2/(hr)(lb mole)^2 at 700°R. Calculate the value of k_p and express it in the units of hr, atm, ft^3, and lb moles.
Answer: $k_p = 2.2468 \times 10^{-6}$ lb moles/hr ft^3 atm^3

1-17. Cain and Nicoll [25] obtained the following data for the decomposition of diazobenzene chloride in aqueous solution at 50°C.

$$C_6H_5N_2Cl \longrightarrow C_6H_5Cl + N_2$$

Time (min)	6	9	12	14	18	20	22	24	26	30
Gas liberated (cc)	19.3	26.0	32.6	36.0	41.3	43.3	45.0	46.5	48.5	50.35

After a very long period of time ($t \to \infty$), a sample with an initial concentration of 10 g per liter liberated 58.3 cc of nitrogen. Determine the reaction velocity constant k_c.   *Answer:* $k_c = 0.0675$ min^{-1}

1-18. Determine the rate constant for the thermal decomposition of dimethyl ether in the gas phase by use of measurements reported by Hinshelwood and Askey [26]. The reaction is carried out isothermally at 504°C in a constant volume reactor. At time $t = 0$, the reactor is filled to a pressure of 312 mm with pure dimethyl ether.

Time (sec)	390	777	1195	3155	∞
Pressure increase (mm)	96	176	250	476	619

$$(CH_3)_2O \longrightarrow CH_4 + H_2 + CO$$

Answer: $k_c = 4.13 \times 10^{-4}$ sec^{-1}

1-19. Consider the decomposition of di-t-butyl peroxide to acetone and ethane. Use the data obtained by Raley et al. [27] to determine whether the reaction rate is first or second order, and evaluate the rate constant k_c. These data were collected at 154.6°C.

$$(CH_3)_3COOC(CH_3)_3 \longrightarrow 2(CH_3)_2CO + C_2H_6$$

Time (min)	Total Pressure (mm Hg)	Time (min)	Total Pressure (mm Hg)
0	173.5	11	239.8
2	187.3	12	244.4
3	193.4	14	254.5
5	205.3	15	259.2
6	211.3	17	268.7
8	222.9	18	273.9
9	228.6	20	282.0
		21	286.8
		∞	491.8

Answer: $k_c = 2.095 \times 10^{-2}$ min^{-1}

1-20. Begin with the rate expressions for r_A and the material balance for A and develop the design equations presented in Tables 1-1 and 1-2.

1-21. In an investigation of the isomerization of n-propylidene-cyclopropylamine to 5-ethyl-1-pyroline by Cocks and Egger [15] the following data were obtained in a batch reactor which was operated isothermally and at constant volume.

n-propylidene-cyclopropylamine   5-ethyl-pyroline

Temperature (°K)	Time (min)	Pressure (torr)	Conversion (percent)
572.9	30	15.4	11.13
572.9	100	18.3	33.13
573.0	20	55.2	7.83
573.1	60	18.1	21.04
573.3	210	17.5	57.84
599.9	20	5.9	39.04
600.1	6	2.5	14.70
600.3	40	6.6	65.79
600.5	60	4.4	81.02
622.9	4	13.6	38.17
623.0	5	15.1	43.37
624.4	6	6.8	50.55
623.5	10	8.0	67.99
635.4	3	9.0	70.32
635.4	6	7.8	77.07
635.5	2	13.8	40.00
635.5	3	14.9	52.89
635.5	4	13.8	63.20

Determine whether the reaction is first or second order. Evaluate the rate constant k_c, the activation energy, and the Arrhenius constant.

Answer: $A = 10.421 \times 10^{14}$, $E_A = 45,581$ cal/g mole °K

1-22. (a) For a reaction having a rate which is nth order with respect to A

$$r_A = k_c C_A^n$$

where $n \neq 1$, show that the half-life time is given by

$$t_{1/2} = \frac{(2^{n-1} - 1)}{(n-1)k_c(C_A^0)^{n-1}}$$

(b) Suppose that two experiments are conducted for the reaction of $A \rightarrow$ products and that the following data are obtained.

Experiment 1 $t_{1/2} = \frac{1}{8}$ hr, $C_A^0 = 2$ g moles/liter
Experiment 2 $t_{1/2} = \frac{1}{2}$ hr, $C_A^0 = 1$ g mole/liter

On the basis of these data, predict the order of the reaction.

1-23. Hairston and O'Brien [21, 28] studied the reaction of 2-trimethylsilyl-2 chloro-prane with antimony pentafluoride by use of nuclear magnetic resonance. In order to determine the first step of a proposed mechanism, the following data were obtained at a temperature of 40°C. The initial concentration of A [(CH$_3$)$_3$Si-C(CH$_3$)$_2$Cl], was 0.1841 g mole per liter, and the initial concentration of B [SbF$_5$] was 0.1846 g mole per liter.

t (min)	C_A (g mole/liter)
0	0.1841
8	0.1501
10	0.1429
21	0.112
44	0.0812
76	0.0579
114	0.0433
151	0.0344
153	0.0341

The following mechanism was proposed.

$$(CH_3)_3Si\!-\!C(CH_3)_2Cl + SbF_5 \xrightarrow[40°C]{k_1} [(CH_3)_3Si\!-\!C(CH_3)_2]^+$$

$$\begin{array}{c}
\text{F}\\
|\\
k_2 \longrightarrow (CH_3)_2SiC(CH_3)_3 + SbF_4Cl\\
+ [SbF_5Cl]^-\\
CH_2\\
||\\
k_3 \longrightarrow (CH_3)_3SiF + CH \;\; + SbF_4Cl\\
|\\
CH_3
\end{array}$$

Determine the order of the first step of the proposed mechanism for this reaction and evaluate the rate constant k_1.

1-24. The gas phase reaction of acrolein with cyclopentadiene to produce endomethylenetetrahydrobenzaldehyde was also studied by Kistiakowsky and Lacher [24]. The reaction may be represented symbolically by

$$A + B \; \rightleftarrows \; C$$

with the rate of reaction being given by

$$r_A = k_c C_A C_B - k'_c C_C$$

On the basis of an initial pressure of 1 atm and $C_A^0 = C_B^0, C_C^0 = 0$, calculate the time required to obtain a conversion X equal to 90% of the equilibrium conversion at 200°C. The rate constants are given by

$$k_c = 1.5 \times 10^9 \exp \frac{-15,200}{RT}, \text{ cc/(g mole sec)}$$

$$k'_c = 2.2 \times 10^{12} \exp \frac{-33,600}{RT}, \text{ sec}^{-1}$$

where T is in °K.
Answer: $t = 14.3$ min,
          $R = 1.9872$ cal/mole °K

NOTATION

C_A = concentration of component A, moles/unit volume.

E_A = activation energy [see Equation (1-29)].

k_c, k_p = rate constants where concentrations and partial pressures are used in the rate expressions, respectively. In the case of multiple reactions, the subscripts c and p are sometimes dropped and the rate constants denoted by $k_1, k_2, \ldots$.

k'_c, k'_p = rate constants for the reverse reaction as distinguished from the rate constants for the forward reactions.

M_A = molecular weight of A.

N = order of a reaction.

N_A^0, N_A = total number of moles of component A in the reactor at time $t = 0$ and the total number of moles of A in the reactor at any time t.

N_T = total number of moles at any time t.

p_A = partial pressure of component A, force/unit area.

P = total pressure, force/unit area.

r_A = net rate of reaction of component A; defined by Equation (1-1).

r_{Af} = forward rate of reaction of component A.

r_{Ar} = reverse rate of reaction of component A.

R = constant in the perfect gas law; defined by Equation (1-21).

t = time.

$t_{1/2}$ = half-life.

T = temperature, °R or °K.

V = reactor volume or more precisely that portion of the reactor volume occupied by the reacting mixture.

X = moles of the base component A converted per mole of A in the feed.

y_A° = mole fraction of component A in the feed.

REFERENCES

1. Wenzel, K. F., *Lehre von der Chemischen Affinitat der Korper* (1777).

2. Van't Hoff, J. H., *Etudes de Dynamique Chimique*, F. Muller & Co., Amsterdam (1884).

3. Arrhenius, Svante, *Z. Physikal Chem.*, *4*:226 (1889).

4. Ostwald, W., *Z. Physikal Chem.*, *15*:704 (1894).

5. Lewis, W. K., and E. D. Ries, *Ind. Eng. Chem.*, *19*:830 (1923).

6. Hougen, O. A., *Reaction Kinetics in Chemical Engineering*, Chemical Engineering Progress Monograph Series, *No. 1*, Vol. 47 (1951).

7. Hougen, O. A., and K. M. Watson, *Chem. Progress Principles*, Part III, *Kinetics and Catalysis*, John Wiley & Sons, Inc., New York (1947).

8. Busby, G. W., "Soap," *Encyclopedia of Chemical Technology*, *12*:573, Wiley/Interscience, New York (1954).

9. Godfrey, T. M., *Glycerol*, Edited by C. S. Miner and N. N. Dalton, Reinhold Publishing Corporation, New York (1953).

10. Hinshelwood, C. N., and C. R. Prichard, *Proc. Roy. Soc. A108*:211 (1925).

11. Groggins, P. H., Editor-in-Chief, *Unit Processes in Organic Synthesis*, 5th Ed., McGraw-Hill Book Company, New York (1958).

12. Seestrom, H. E., J. P. Hughes, and W. H. Shearon, Jr., *Modern Chemical Processes*, Vol. II, W. J. Murphy, Editor, *Ind. Eng. Chem.*, Reinhold Publishing Corporation, New York (1954).

13. Gumz, Wilhelm, *Gas Producers and Blast Furnaces*, Theory and Methods of Calculation, John Wiley & Sons, Inc., New York (1950).

14. Himmelblau, D. M., *Process Analysis by Statistical Methods*, John Wiley & Sons, Inc., New York (1970).

15. Cocks, A. T., and K. W. Egger, *Int. J. of Chem. Kin.*, *4*:169 (1972).

16. Walker, J., *Proc. Roy. Soc. A78*:157 (1906).

17. Churchill, S. W., The *Determination and Use of Rate Data: The Rate Concept.*, McGraw-Hill Book Company, New York (1974).

18. Abraham, M. E., and R. F. Benenati, *AIChE J.*, *18*:807 (1972).

19. Bodenstein, M., *Z. Physikal Chem.*, *100*:106 (1922).

20. Worsfold, S., and S. Bywater, *Canadian J. of Chem.*, *38*:1891 (1960).

21. Hairston, T. J., and D. H. O'Brien, *J. Organometallic Chem.*, *29*:79 (1971).

22. Gordon, A. S., *Int. J. of Chem. Kin.*, *4*:541 (1972).

23. Swain, C. G., *J. Am. Chem. Soc.*, *70*:1119 (1948).

24. Kistiakowsky, G. B., and J. R. Lacher, *J. Am. Chem. Soc.*, *58*:123 (1936).

25. Cain, J. C., and F. Nicoll, *Proc. Chem. Soc.*, *24*:282 (1909).

26. Hinshelwood, C. H., and P. S. Askey, *Proc. Roy. Soc.*, *A115*:215 (1927).

27. Raley, J. H., R. R. Rust, and W. E. Vaughan, *J. Am. Chem. Soc.*, *70*:98 (1948).

28. O'Brien, D. H., *Personal Communication*, Texas A&M University (1972).

APPENDIX

THEOREM 1. *Mean Value Theorem of Integral Calculus*

If the function $f(x)$ is continuous in the interval $a \leq x \leq b$, then

$$\int_a^b f(x)\,dx = f(\varepsilon)(b - a)$$

where $\varepsilon = a + \alpha(b - a)$ and $0 \leq \alpha \leq 1$.

Figure A-1 is useful in the geometrical interpretation of this theorem. The theorem asserts that there exists a number ε lying in the closed interval

$a \leq \varepsilon \leq b$ such that the area of the rectangle of height $f(\varepsilon)$ and base $(b - a)$ is equal to the area bounded by curve C and the x-axis from $x = a$ to $x = b$.

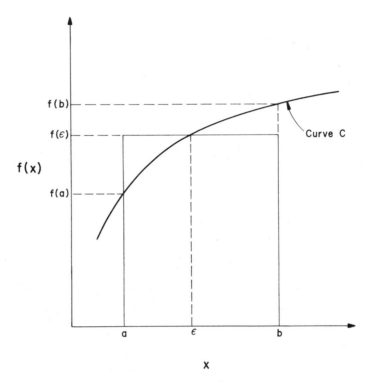

Figure A-1. Geometrical interpretation of the mean value theorem of integral calculus.

THEOREM 2. *Mean Value Theorem of Differential Calculus*

If the function $f(x)$ is continuous in the interval $a \leq x \leq b$, and differentiable at every point in the interval $a < x < b$, then there exists at least one value of β such that

$$\left.\frac{df(x)}{dx}\right|_{\varepsilon} = \frac{f(b) - f(a)}{b - a}$$

where $\varepsilon = a + \beta(b - a)$ and $0 < \beta < 1$.

Figure A-2 is useful in the geometrical interpretation of this theorem. This theorem asserts that there exists a number ε lying in the open interval $a < \varepsilon < b$ at which the slope of the tangent line to curve C is equal to the slope of the secant line drawn through the points $(a, f(a))$ and $(b, f(b))$. The slope of the secant is equal to $[f(b) - f(a)]/[b - a]$. At the point $(\varepsilon, f(\varepsilon))$ the slope of the tangent line is equal to $df(x)/dx$ evaluated at ε.

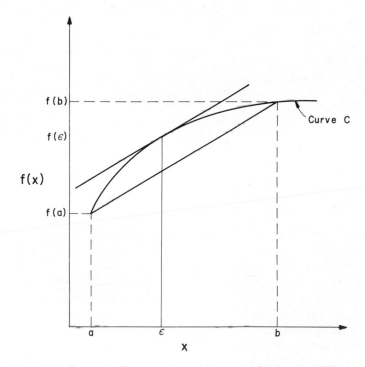

Figure A-2. Geometrical interpretation of the mean value theorem of differential calculus.

Flow Reactors at Isothermal Operation

2

The modern chemical industry is characterized by the almost exclusive use of continuous processes. This type of operation calls for continuous, or flow, reactors. The chemical reactions occur while the reacting stream is flowing through the reactor. Provisions are commonly made to heat the reactants to the reacting temperature just before they enter the reactor and to terminate the reaction by cooling the mixture as it leaves the reactor. Unless it is desired to operate the reactor *adiabatically*, provisions are made to maintain some control over the temperature of the reacting mixture by adding or removing heat from the reacting mixture as it passes through the reactor. The reacting mixture is customarily passed through the reactor at an appreciable velocity in order to insure good mixing and heat transfer.

The conversion per pass of the reacting stream through the reactor is proportional to the length of time the reacting mixture resides in the reactor, which is in turn proportional to the reactor volume. Thus, to achieve a significant conversion per pass, the reactor must be operated at conditions such that the rate constant for the desired reaction is appreciable. Many commercial reactors are operated, however, at relatively low conversions per pass, and yet relatively high overall conversions are achieved by recycling a portion of the effluent stream. In many reactors, the selectivity of one particular reaction over other possible reactions becomes a more important consideration than does the conversion per pass. In fact, many industrial processes are based on producing a valuable intermediate product rather than the final products which would be obtained at thermodynamic equilib-

52

rium. For example, in the dehydrogenation of ethane, the desirable product is the intermediate ethylene rather than carbon, hydrogen, and methane, which are more thermodynamically favorable.

The analysis and design of flow reactors are introduced in this chapter by the consideration of isothermally operated reactors in which single reactions occur. The resulting simplification of the chemical kinetics makes it relatively easy to predict the behavior which can be expected for various types of flow patterns and mixing mechanisms. The methods developed in this chapter in the treatment of the relatively simple systems are useful in the preliminary analysis of commercial reactors in which any number of reactions may occur at nonisothermal conditions.

The steady state operation of flow reactors is considered in Part I and unsteady state operation is considered in Part II.

I. STEADY STATE OPERATION OF FLOW REACTORS

Steady state operation means that the variables at each point within the system do not vary with time. Therefore, the total amount of component A within the system at time $t_n + \Delta t$ is equal to the amount at time t_n. Since the rates of input and output of mass to and from the system, respectively, are independent of time, Equation (1-33) reduces to

$$\left\{ \begin{array}{l} \text{Input of mass to the} \\ \text{system per unit time} \end{array} \right\} - \left\{ \begin{array}{l} \text{output of mass from the} \\ \text{system per unit time} \end{array} \right\} = 0 \tag{2-1}$$

or simply

$$\text{Input} - \text{output} = 0 \tag{2-2}$$

Equation (2-1) [or (2-2)] is used to make the material balances for the various types of reactors considered in Part I.

The application of Equation (2-1) in the making of a material balance on a given reactor depends upon the particular mixing model assumed for the fluid within the reactor. The development that follows is subdivided according to the classic mixing models: (1) plug-flow, (2) perfectly mixed, (3) partial axial mixing, (4) partial axial and radial mixing, and (5) laminar-flow reactors.

A. Plug-Flow Reactors

The first model used to describe the mixing in tubular reactors is the plug-flow model (see Figure 2-1). The reacting stream flowing through a reactor is said to be in plug flow if the contents of the reactor are perfectly mixed in the radial direction while no mixing occurs in the axial direction

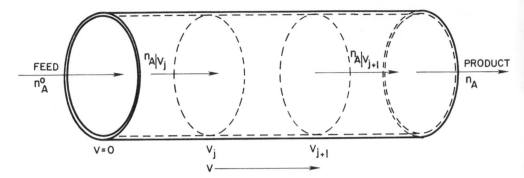

Figure 2-1. Sketch of a tubular reactor in which the mixing is described by the plug-flow model (perfect mixing in the radial direction, and no mixing in the horizontal direction).

(the direction of flow). These mixing assumptions are sometimes called the "plug-flow assumption" [1, 2].

Near perfect mixing in the radial direction may be achieved by passing the fluid through the reactor at relatively high flow rates where the Reynolds numbers are large. The mixing in the axial direction is generally small, provided that the length of the reactor is large relative to its diameter. Denbigh [3] has suggested that the mixing assumptions for plug-flow reactors are valid, provided that the length-to-diameter ratio is greater than 50 and that the Reynolds number of the flowing stream is greater than 10^4.

1. MATERIAL BALANCES FOR PLUG-FLOW REACTORS. Let n_A denote the flow rate of A in moles per unit time. Let V_j and $V_j + \Delta V$ be selected arbitrarily $(0 < V_j < V_j + \Delta V < V_T$ where V_T is the total volume of the reactor). Since r_A generally depends upon the temperature and concentration of the reactants, it will take on a different value at each V in the interval $V_j < V < V_j + \Delta V$. Then by Equation (2-1), it follows that a material balance for component A over the element of volume ΔV is given by

$$\underbrace{M_A n_A \Big|_{V_j}}_{\substack{\text{Input of } A \text{ per unit time by flow} \\ \text{to the element of volume } \Delta V}} - \underbrace{\left[M_A n_A \Big|_{V_j + \Delta V} + \int_{V_j}^{V_j + \Delta V} M_A r_A \, dV \right]}_{\substack{\text{output of } A \text{ per unit time from the element of} \\ \text{volume by flow and by reaction}}} = 0 \quad (2\text{-}3)$$

Since the molecular weight M_A of a pure component does not vary, Equation (2-3) reduces to

$$\left[n_A \Big|_{V_j} - n_A \Big|_{V_j + \Delta V} \right] - \int_{V_j}^{V_j + \Delta V} r_A \, dV = 0 \quad (2\text{-}4)$$

The difference in the flow rate of A at V_j and $V_j + \Delta V$ may be replaced by its equivalent as given by the *mean value theorem of differential calculus*. (See

Theorem 2 in the Appendix of Chapter 1.)

$$\left[n_A \Big|_{V_j} - n_A \Big|_{V_j + \Delta V} \right] = -\Delta V \frac{dn_A}{dV} \Big|_{V_j + \alpha \Delta V} \tag{2-5}$$

where $0 < \alpha < 1$. (That is, at the point $V_j + \alpha \Delta V$, the slope of the tangent line to the curve of n_A versus V is equal to the slope of the straight line connecting $n_A|_{V_j}$ and $n_A|_{V_j + \Delta V}$.) Next the *mean value theorem of integral calculus* may be used to replace the integral of r_A over the element of volume from V_j to $V_j + \Delta V$ by a rectangle having the same area.

$$\int_{V_j}^{V_j + \Delta V} (-r_A)\, dV = \left(-r_A \Big|_{V_j + \beta \Delta V} \right) \Delta V \tag{2-6}$$

where $0 \le \beta \le 1$. Substitution of the results given by Equations (2-5) and (2-6) into Equation (2-4) yields

$$-\frac{dn_A}{dV} \Big|_{V_j} - r_A \Big|_{V_j} = 0 \tag{2-7}$$

Since V_j was arbitrarily selected in the open interval $(0 < V < V_T)$, it follows that the material-balance expression for r_A is given by

$$r_A = -\frac{dn_A}{dV} \tag{2-8}$$

For the case where the rate of reaction is defined in terms of the appearance of A [see Equation (1-41)], the expression corresponding to Equation (2-8) is

$$r_A = \frac{dn_A}{dV} \tag{2-9}$$

2. VARIATION OF CONVERSION WITH REACTOR VOLUME FOR LIQUID-PHASE REACTIONS. (Other conditions: isothermal and steady state operation, constant mass density). Consider first the case where the first-order reaction

$$A \longrightarrow \text{products}$$

is carried out in the liquid phase in a plug-flow reactor. If it is further supposed that the mass density of the reacting stream is constant throughout the reactor, then the volumetric flow rate v_T (volume/time) of the reacting mixture throughout the reactor is also constant. (Note: The volumetric flow rate is equal to the mass-flow rate divided by the mass density and the mass-flow rate is constant at steady state operation.)

Elimination of r_A from the material balance [Equation (2-8)] by use of the rate expression

$$r_A = k_c C_A$$

for a first-order reaction gives

$$-\frac{dn_A}{dV} = k_c C_A \tag{2-10}$$

Since the mixing is assumed to be perfect in the radial direction, the concentration C_A may be expressed in terms of the flow rates

$$C_A = \frac{n_A}{v_T} \tag{2-11}$$

and this expression may be used to restate Equation (2-10) in terms of n_A

$$-\frac{dn_A}{dV} = k_c \frac{n_A}{v_T} \tag{2-12}$$

For a first-order reaction which is carried out isothermally, the rate constant k_c is independent of n_A and V. Since v_T is also constant throughout the reactor, Equation (2-12) may be solved by separation of the variables. Thus

$$-\int_{n_A^0}^{n_A} \frac{dn_A}{n_A} = \frac{k_c}{v_T} \int_0^V dV$$

and upon carrying out the integrations indicated, it is found that

$$V = \frac{v_T}{k_c} \log_e \frac{n_A^0}{n_A} \tag{2-13}$$

or

$$n_A = n_A^0 \exp(-N_R) \tag{2-14}$$

where $\quad N_R = \dfrac{k_c V}{v_T}, \quad$ the reaction number for a first-order liquid-phase reaction.

Since the volumetric flow rate is constant, it follows that $n_A/v_T = C_A$ (the concentration of A at a given volume V) and $n_A^0/v_T = C_A^0$ (the concentration of A at the inlet of the reactor). Thus, at any given V or N_R, Equation (2-14) may be stated in terms of concentrations as follows:

$$C_A = C_A^0 \exp(-N_R) \tag{2-15}$$

For the case where v_T remains constant throughout the reactor, C_A may be expressed in terms of the *true residence time*, which is equal to the actual time (V/v_T) that a unit of mass remains in the volume V. (The quantity V/v_T is also equal to the time required to sweep out the volume V one time.)

Let the *true residence time* be denoted by θ; that is,

$$\theta = \frac{V}{v_T} \tag{2-16}$$

Thus, $N_R = k_c\theta$, and for the case under consideration C_A at any V may be expressed in terms of the true residence time θ; namely,

$$C_A = C_A^0 \exp\left(-k_c\theta\right) \tag{2-17}$$

This equation is identically the same as Equation (1-49), the material-balance equation for a batch reactor. This identity leads immediately to the interpretation that the amount of A reacted in each element of fluid that resides in the plug-flow reactor an amount of time θ is exactly equal to the amount of A which would have reacted in an isothermal batch reactor in the same amount of time. This one-to-one correspondence between batch and plug-flow reactors holds for all reactions which are carried out isothermally and at constant mass density. Expressions for the variation of the reactor volume with conversion (or molar flow rate of A) for first-, second-, and third-order reactions are presented in Table 2-1.

TABLE 2-1

DESIGN EQUATIONS FOR CARRYING OUT UNIDIRECTIONAL REACTIONS
IN A PLUG-FLOW REACTOR

(Conditions: isothermal and steady state operation, plug flow,
and constant mass density)

Reaction	Design Equation
1. $A \longrightarrow$ products	$V = \dfrac{v_T}{k_c} \log_e \dfrac{n_A^0}{n_A}$
2. $A + B \longrightarrow$ products	$V = \dfrac{v_T^2}{k_c}\left[\dfrac{1}{n_A^0 - n_B^0} \log_e \dfrac{n_B^0 n_A}{n_A^0 n_B}\right]$
3. $2A \longrightarrow$ products	$V = \dfrac{v_T^2}{k_c}\left[\dfrac{1}{n_A} - \dfrac{1}{n_A^0}\right]$
4. $3A \longrightarrow$ products	$V = \dfrac{v_T^3}{2k_c}\left[\left(\dfrac{1}{n_A}\right)^2 - \left(\dfrac{1}{n_A^0}\right)^2\right]$
5. $NA \longrightarrow$ products	$V = \dfrac{v_T^N}{(N-1)k_c}\left[\left(\dfrac{1}{n_A}\right)^{N-1} - \left(\dfrac{1}{n_A^0}\right)^{N-1}\right]$

By comparing Tables 1-1 and 2-1 one notes that if the concentration $C_i = N_i/V$ of component i in Table 1-1 is replaced by n_i/v_T, and t is replaced by V/v_T, then the two tables are equivalent. These substitutions are not permissible unless the mass density remains constant.

EXAMPLE 2-1

When bromine cyanide is reacted with methylamine

$$CNBr + CH_3NH_2 \longrightarrow CNNH_2 + CH_3Br$$

in the liquid phase with water as a solvent, the rate of disappearance of bromide cyanide was found to be second order by Griffith et al [4] and Reference [5].

$$r_{CNBr} = k_c C_{CNBr} C_{CH_3NH_2}$$

At 10°C, Griffith et al. found that

$$k_c = 2.22 \text{ liters/(sec)(g mole)}$$

For a residence time of 4 sec and the initial concentration $C_{CNBr}^0 = C_{CH_3NH_2}^0 = 0.1$ g mole/liter, calculate the concentration of bromine cyanide in the effluent stream from the reactor as well as the corresponding percentage conversion of bromine cyanide which can be expected when the reaction is carried out in a plug-flow reactor operated isothermally at 10°C.

SOLUTION

For convenience, let the compounds participating in the above reaction be denoted by A, B, C, and D to give

$$A + B \longrightarrow C + D$$

Since the initial concentration of the reactants are equal, their concentrations remain equal throughout the reactor, and thus

$$r_A = k_c C_A^2 = k_c \frac{n_A^2}{v_T^2}$$

When the second-order reaction is carried out in a plug-flow reactor, the concentration of A in the outlet stream may be found by rearranging Equation (3) of Table 2-1 as follows:

$$\theta = \frac{V}{v_T} = \frac{1}{k_c}\left[\frac{1}{n_A/v_T} - \frac{1}{n_A^0/v_T}\right] = \frac{1}{k_c}\left[\frac{1}{C_A} - \frac{1}{C_A^0}\right]$$

$$C_A = \frac{C_A^0}{1 + k_c C_A^0 \theta} = \frac{0.1}{1 + (2.22)(0.1)(4)} = 0.05297$$

$$\text{Percentage conversion} = \frac{C_A^0 - C_A}{C_A^0} \times 100 = \left(\frac{0.1 - 0.05297}{0.1}\right)100 = 47.03$$

3. VOLUME VERSUS CONVERSION FOR GAS PHASE REACTIONS. (Other conditions: isothermal and steady state operation, negligible pressure drop

across the reactor, and perfect gas behavior) For reactions in which there is no change in the total number of moles, such as

$$A \longrightarrow R, \quad 2A \longrightarrow 2R, \quad A + B \longrightarrow C + D$$

the total molar flow rate, n_T, is independent of conversion, and consequently it remains constant throughout the reactor. Thus, for isothermal and isobaric operation of a plug-flow reactor, it follows from the perfect gas law that the volumetric flow rate v_T is constant throughout the reactor,

$$v_T = n_T \frac{RT}{P}$$

Thus, for reactions which do not produce a change in the total number of moles, the expressions for volume versus conversion (or flow rate of A) are the same as those for liquid phase reactions in Table 2-1.

EXAMPLE 2-2

Fisher and Smith [6] studied the thermal reaction of methane with sulfur,

$$CH_4 + 2S_2 \longrightarrow CS_2 + 2H_2S$$

in the gas phase and found that at 600°C, the rate of disappearance of sulfur is given by

$$r_{S_2} = k_c C_{CH_4} C_{S_2}$$

where $k_c = 11.98 \times 10^6$ ml/(hr)(g mole)

Suppose that this reaction is to be carried out in a plug-flow reactor which is to be operated isothermally at 600°C and at a pressure of 1 atm. The molar flow rate of sulfur in the feed is to be twice that of methane, whose flow rate is 23.8 g moles/hr. Calculate the residence time required to convert 18% of the methane.

SOLUTION

For convenience, let the chemical compounds in the above reaction be represented by the letters A = methane, B = sulfur, C = carbon disulfide, and D = hydrogen sulfide,

$$A + 2B \longrightarrow C + 2D$$

Since the reaction does not produce a change in the number of moles, the volumetric flow rate v_T remains constant throughout the reactor. Furthermore, since 2 moles of B react for each mole of A that reacts and the amount of B in the feed is twice that of A, it follows that $C_B = 2C_A$ throughout the reactor. Also, the stoichiometry of the reaction requires that r_A (the rate of disappearance of A) be equal to one-half of r_B (the rate of disappearance of B). Thus, since k_c is defined with respect to S_2 in the statement of the problem,

$$r_A = \frac{1}{2} r_B = \frac{k_c}{2} C_A C_B = \frac{k_c}{2} C_A (2C_A) = k_c C_A^2$$

The following relationship between residence time and the outlet flow rate of A is given by Equation (3) of Table 2-1.

$$\theta = \frac{V}{v_T} = \frac{v_T}{k_c} \left(\frac{1}{n_A} - \frac{1}{n_A^0} \right)$$

Let x denote the fraction of A converted,

$$x = \frac{n_A^0 - n_A}{n_A^0} \quad \text{or} \quad n_A = n_A^0 - n_A^0 x$$

Use of this expression to eliminate n_A from the above formula for θ gives

$$\theta = \frac{v_T}{k_c n_A^0} \left(\frac{x}{1 - x} \right)$$

The volumetric flow rate v_T is computed by use of the perfect gas law as follows:

$$v_T = \frac{n_T RT}{P} = \frac{(3)(23.8)(82.05)(873.15)}{1} = 5.115 \times 10^6 \text{ ml/hr}$$

Then

$$\theta = \frac{5.115 \times 10^6}{(11.98 \times 10^6)(23.8)} \left(\frac{0.18}{1 - 0.18} \right) = 0.003938 \text{ hr}$$

If the reaction produces a change in the total number of moles, then the volumetric flow rate v_T varies with the conversion x, For example, consider the first-order unidirectional reaction

$$A \longrightarrow 2R$$

The rate expression is given by

$$r_A = k_c C_A = \frac{k_c n_A}{v_T}$$

and the material balance on A is given by

$$r_A = -\frac{dn_A}{dV}$$

Thus

$$-\frac{dn_A}{dV} = \frac{k_c n_A}{v_T} \tag{2-18}$$

which constitutes one equation in the three unknowns, V, n_A, and v_T. The conversion of A in a flow system is defined in a manner analogous to that for batch systems,

$$x = \frac{n_A^0 - n_A}{n_A^0} \tag{2-19}$$

The flow rates n_A and v_T are expressed in terms of conversion by use of the following stoichiometric relationships:

$$\begin{aligned} n_A &= n_A^0 - n_A^0 x \\ n_R &= n_R^0 + 2n_A^0 x \\ n_T &= n_T^0 + n_A^0 x \end{aligned} \tag{2-20}$$

Since the gaseous mixture is assumed to obey the perfect gas law, it follows that

$$Pv_T = n_T RT, \quad \text{and} \quad v_T = n_T \frac{RT}{P} = (n_T^0 + n_A^0 x) \frac{RT}{P}$$

Then Equation (2-18) may be expressed in terms of x and V as follows:

$$n_A^0 \frac{dx}{dV} = \frac{k_c}{RT} \left[\frac{(n_A^0 - n_A^0 x)P}{n_T^0 + n_A^0 x} \right] = k_p \left[\frac{(n_A^0 - n_A^0 x)P}{n_T^0 + n_A^0 x} \right] \tag{2-21}$$

where k_c/RT has been replaced by its equivalent k_p as given by Equation (1-22). Separation of variables followed by integration and rearrangement yields

$$V = \left(\frac{n_T^0}{k_p P} \right) \left[\left\{ (1 + y_A^0) \log_e \frac{1}{1-x} \right\} - y_A^0 x \right] \tag{2-22}$$

where it has been assumed that k_p is constant. This result suggests that one could start with the rate expressed in terms of k_p and partial pressures rather than k_c and concentrations. In fact, this alternate approach is the one most commonly employed in the analysis of gas phase reactions.

To demonstrate this approach, the previous example is solved again. Since $r_A = k_c C_A = k_p p_A$, it follows that

$$-\frac{dn_A}{dV} = k_p p_A \tag{2-23}$$

For perfect gas mixtures.

$$p_A = \frac{n_A}{n_T} P = \left(\frac{n_A^0 - n_A^0 x}{n_T^0 + n_A^0 x} \right) P \tag{2-24}$$

Thus Equation (2-23) reduces to

$$n_A^0 \frac{dx}{dV} = k_p \left(\frac{n_A^0 - n_A^0 x}{n_T^0 + n_A^0 x} \right) P \tag{2-25}$$

which upon integration yields the final result given by Equation (2-22).

Expressions for reactor volume as a function of conversion for other gas phase reactions are given in Table 2-2.

TABLE 2-2
DESIGN EQUATIONS FOR CARRYING OUT UNIDIRECTIONAL REACTIONS
IN THE GAS PHASE IN PLUG-FLOW REACTORS
(Conditions: isothermal and steady state operation, negligible pressure drop,
and perfect gas behavior)

Reactions	Design Equation
1. $A \longrightarrow R$ $n_T^0 = n_A^0 + n_R^0 + n_I^0$	$V = \dfrac{n_T^0}{k_p P} \log_e \dfrac{1}{1 - x}$
2. $2A \longrightarrow 2R$ $n_T^0 = n_A^0 + n_R^0 + n_I^0$	$V = \dfrac{n_T^0}{k_p P^2 y_A^0} \left[\dfrac{x}{1 - x} \right]$
3. $3A \longrightarrow 3R$ $n_T^0 = n_A^0 + n_R^0 + n_I^0$	$V = \dfrac{n_T^0}{2k_p P^3 (y_A^0)^2} \left[\dfrac{2x - x^2}{(1 - x)^2} \right]$
4. $A + B \longrightarrow R$ $n_A^0 \neq n_B^0$ $n_T^0 = n_A^0 + n_B^0 + n_I^0 + n_R^0$	$V = \dfrac{n_A^0}{k_p (y_A^0 P)^2} \left[(y_A^0)^2 x + \dfrac{(1 - \alpha y_A^0)^2}{\alpha - 1} \log_e \left(\dfrac{\alpha - x}{\alpha} \right) \right.$ $\left. - \dfrac{(1 - y_A^0)^2}{\alpha - 1} \log_e (1 - x) \right]$ $\alpha = \dfrac{n_B^0}{n_A^0}$
5. $A + B \longrightarrow R + S$ $n_A^0 \neq n_B^0$ $n_T^0 = n_A^0 + n_B^0 + n_R^0 + n_S^0 + n_I^0$	$V = \dfrac{n_A^0}{k_p (\alpha - 1)(y_A^0 P)^2} \log_e \dfrac{\alpha - x}{(1 - x)\alpha}$ $\alpha = \dfrac{n_B^0}{n_A^0}$

EXAMPLE 2-3

Marek and McCluer [7] investigated the thermal decomposition of ethane and found that the stoichiometry of the decomposition could be represented by

$$C_2H_6 \longrightarrow C_2H_4 + H_2$$

The rate of decomposition of ethane was found to be first order with respect to ethane, and the following expression for the rate constant was given:

$$\log_{10} k_c = 15.12 - \frac{15,970}{T}$$

where T is in °K and k_c has the units of reciprocal seconds. Calculate the conversion of ethane which can be achieved in a plug-flow reactor which is operated isothermally at 650°C and 1 atm pressure with $V/v_T^0 = 4$ sec, where V is the total volume of the reactor and v_T^0 is the volumetric flow rate of the feed at the reactor conditions, 650°C and 1 atm. The feed consists of pure ethane.

SOLUTION

Let the above reaction be represented by

$$A \longrightarrow B + C$$

Then

$$
\begin{array}{rl}
n_A = & n_A^0 - n_A^0 x \\
n_B = & n_A^0 x \\
n_C = & n_A^0 x \\
\hline
n_T = & n_A^0 (1 + x)
\end{array}
$$

$$r_A = n_A^0 \frac{dx}{dV} = k_c C_A = k_c \frac{n_A}{v_T}$$

For a perfect gas mixture,

$$\frac{v_T}{v_T^0} = \frac{n_T}{n_T^0} = \frac{n_A^0(1 + x)}{n_A^0} = 1 + x$$

or

$$v_T = v_T^0(1 + x)$$

Thus

$$n_A^0 \frac{dx}{dV} = \frac{k_c n_A^0 (1 - x)}{v_T^0 (1 + x)}$$

Separation of variables followed by integration over the volume V gives

$$-2 \log_e (1 - x) - x = k_c \frac{V}{v_T^0} \qquad (A)$$

63

At 650°C,

$$\log_{10} k_c = 15.12 - \frac{15,970}{923.15}$$

$$k_c = 0.0066 \ \text{sec}^{-1}$$

Since V/v_T^0 is given, Equation (A) becomes

$$-2 \log_e (1 - x) - x = (0.0066)(4) = 0.0264$$

Since this equation cannot be solved explicitly for x, it must be solved by a trial and error process. Newton's method [8] will be used. In the application of Newton's method, it is convenient to restate the problem. Let

$$f(x) = 0.0264 + x + 2 \log_e (1 - x)$$

Then it is desired to find that x $(0 < x < 1)$ such that $f(x) = 0$. Newton's method [8] consists of the repeated use of the equation

$$x_{n+1} = x_n - \frac{f(x_n)}{f'(x_n)}$$

where x_n is the assumed value of x, and

$$f'(x) = 1 - \frac{2}{1 - x}$$

A good approximation of the solution value of x may be found by neglecting the increase in the number of moles (or the change in v_T). Instead of Equation (A), one obtains

$$-\log_e (1 - x) = k_c \frac{V}{v_T^0}$$

Thus

$$x = 1 - \exp(-k_c\theta) = 1 - \exp[(-0.0066)(4)]$$

$$x = 0.0261$$

When this starting value of x is used, the following results are obtained by application of Newton's method.

x_n	$f(x_n)$	$f'(x_n)$	$f(x_n)/f'(x_n)$	x_{n+1}
0.0261	-3.933×10^{-4}	-1.0536	3.7329×10^{-4}	0.02573
0.02573	-3.612×10^{-6}	-1.0528	3.4309×10^{-6}	0.02573

Thus the solution is $x = 0.02573$. It should be pointed out that the pyrolysis of ethane has received considerable attention in recent years, and models of the pyrolysis which are more complete than the one used for this example have been proposed as noted in References [9] and [10].

4. VOLUME VERSUS CONVERSION FOR REVERSIBLE REACTIONS CARRIED OUT IN THE GAS PHASE. (Other conditions: isothermal and steady state operation, negligible pressure drop, and perfect gas behavior.) As an example, consider the following reaction, which has a first-order rate in each direction.

$$A \;\rightleftharpoons\; R$$

For illustrative purposes, suppose that the feed contains components A, R, and chemically inert components in the gas phase. The flow rate (moles/unit time) of these inert components is denoted by n_I. Also, suppose that the gaseous mixture obeys the perfect gas law. The stoichiometric relationships are as follows:

$$\begin{aligned}
n_A &= n_A^0 - n_A^0 x \\
n_R &= n_R^0 + n_A^0 x \\
n_I &= n_I \\
\hline
n_T &= n_T^0
\end{aligned} \tag{2-26}$$

Thus

$$n_A^0 \frac{dx}{dV} = \frac{k_p(n_A^0 - n_A^0 x)P}{n_T^0} - \frac{k_p'(n_R^0 + n_A^0 x)P}{n_T^0} \tag{2-27}$$

or

$$\frac{dx}{dV} = \frac{k_p'P}{n_T^0}\left[K_p(1 - x) - (\beta + x)\right] \tag{2-28}$$

where

$$\beta = \frac{n_R^0}{n_A^0}$$

Separation of variables followed by integration and rearrangement yields

$$V = \left[\frac{n_T^0}{Pk_p'(K_p + 1)}\right]\log_e \frac{K_p - \beta}{(K_p - \beta) - (K_p + 1)x} \tag{2-29}$$

An alternate form of this expression may be obtained by introducing the conversion at thermodynamic equilibrium (see Problem 2-5). Expressions for reactor volume as a function of conversion for other reactions are given in Table 2-3.

TABLE 2-3

Design Equations for Carrying Out Reversible Reactions in the Gas Phase in Plug-Flow Reactors
(Conditions: isothermal and steady state operation, negligible pressure drop, and perfect gas behavior)

Reaction	Design Equation
1. $A \xrightleftharpoons[k_p']{k_p} 2R$	$\dfrac{k_p PV}{K_p n_T^0} = \dfrac{(y_A^0)^2 x}{a} + \left[2y_A^0 - \dfrac{(y_A^0)^2 b}{a} \right] \displaystyle\int_0^x \dfrac{x\, dx}{ax^2 + bx + c} + \left[1 - \dfrac{(y_A^0)^2 c}{a} \right] \displaystyle\int_0^x \dfrac{dx}{ax^2 + bx + c}$
	where $= -y_A^0(4P + K_p), \quad b = K_p(y_A^0 - 1) - 4y_A^0 \beta P$
	$\qquad c = K_p - y_A^0 P \beta^2, \qquad y_A^0 = \dfrac{n_A^0}{n_T^0}, \qquad \beta = \dfrac{n_R^0}{n_A^0}$
2. $2A \xrightleftharpoons[k_p']{k_p} 2R$	$\dfrac{k_p (y_A^0 P)^2 V}{n_A^0} = \displaystyle\int_0^x \dfrac{dx}{ax^2 + bx + c}$
	where $a = 1 - \dfrac{1}{K_p}, \quad b = -\left(\dfrac{2\beta}{K_p} + 2 \right), \quad c = 1 - \dfrac{\beta^2}{K_p}, \quad \beta = \dfrac{n_R^0}{n_A^0}$
3. $A + B \xrightleftharpoons[k_p']{k_p} 2R$ $\quad n_A^0 \neq n_B^0$	$\dfrac{k_p (y_A^0 P)^2 V}{n_A^0} = \displaystyle\int_0^x \dfrac{dx}{ax^2 + bx + c}$
	where $a = 1 - \dfrac{4}{K_p}, \quad b = -(1 + \gamma) - \dfrac{4\beta}{K_p}$
	$\qquad c = \gamma - \dfrac{\beta^2}{K_p}, \qquad \gamma = \dfrac{n_B^0}{n_A^0}, \qquad \beta = \dfrac{n_R^0}{n_A^0}$

4. $A + B \rightleftharpoons R$
$n_B^0 \neq n_A^0$
$n_T^0 = n_A^0 + n_B^0 + n_R^0 + n_I^0$

$$\frac{k_p y_A^0 PV}{K_p n_A^0} = \int_0^x \frac{(1 - y_A^0 x)^2 \, dx}{ax^2 + bx + c}$$

where $a = y_A^0(PK_p + 1)$, $\quad b = -PK_p y_A^0(\gamma + 1) - (1 - \beta y_A^0)$, $\quad c = y_A^0 K_p P\gamma - \beta$

$$\beta = \frac{n_R^0}{n_A^0}, \quad \gamma = \frac{n_B^0}{n_A^0}, \quad K_p = \frac{k_p}{k_p'}$$

The integrated forms of the above integrals are:

$$\int_0^x \frac{x \, dx}{ax^2 + bx + c} = \frac{1}{2c} \log_e\left(\frac{ax^2 + bx + c}{c}\right) - \frac{b}{2a}\int_0^x \frac{dx}{ax^2 + bx + c}$$

$$\int_0^x \frac{x^2 \, dx}{ax^2 + bx + c} = \frac{x}{a} - \frac{b}{2a^2}\log_e\left(\frac{ax^2 + bx + c}{c}\right) + \frac{b^2 - 4ac}{2a^2}\int_0^x \frac{dx}{ax^2 + bx + c}$$

where the integrated forms of the integral

$$\int_0^x \frac{dx}{ax^2 + bx + c}$$

are given in Table 1-2.

5. DETERMINATION OF THE ORDER AND RATE CONSTANT FOR A REACTION. The use of plug-flow reactors for the determination of the order and rate constant for a unidirectional reaction is similar to that described for batch reactors. For example, suppose the stoichiometry is satisfied by

$$NA \longrightarrow NR$$

where $N > 0$. The problem is to find the N that satisfies the rate expression

$$r_A = k_p p_A^N$$

For $N = 1$, 2, and 3, the corresponding integral expressions are given in Table 2-2. The plots of these expressions are presented in Figure 2-2. Note, however, for any one sequence of runs, P and y_A^0 must be held fixed; otherwise a family of curves may be obtained since both P and y_A^0 are parameters.

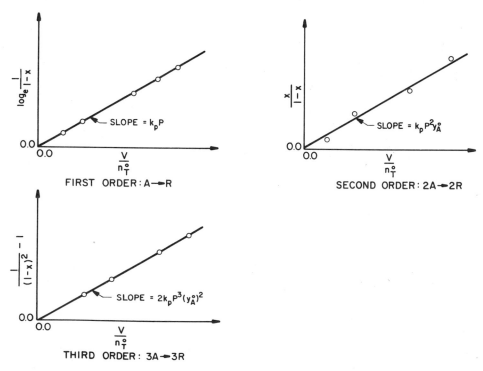

Figure 2-2. Determination of the order and rate constant for gas phase reactions from data taken with a plug-flow reactor.

Furthermore, the ratio V/n_T^0, which is plotted on the abscissa in Figure 2-2, may be varied experimentally by varying either the reactor volume V or the feed rate n_T^0 to the reactor.

The reaction rate is said to be first order if the experimental data fall on a straight line when plotted as indicated for a first-order reaction in Figure 2-2. If instead of being first order, the reaction rate is second or third order, then a straight line is obtained when the data are plotted as indicated for second- and third-order reactions in Figure 2-2. Fractional order and complex reactions are considered in a subsequent chapter.

EXAMPLE 2-4

Fisher and Smith [6] investigated the formation of carbon disulfide from methane and sulfur by the reaction,

$$CH_4 + 2S_2 \longrightarrow CS_2 + 2H_2S$$

in a flow reactor that consisted of a stainless steel pipe 1 in. in diameter and 6 in. long. The reactor was packed with varying amounts of rock salt in order to promote heat transfer and to insure homogeneity of the reacting mixture. The following data were obtained at 600°C and 1 atm pressure.

Void Volume of Reactor (ml)	g moles of Methane fed per hr	Conversion of Methane
67	0.238	0.105
67	0.417	0.075
67	0.119	0.180
35.2	0.0595	0.133
35.2	0.02975	0.269
35.2	0.119	0.058
35.2	0.0298	0.268
35.2	0.238	0.025
35.2	0.119	0.066
35.2	0.0595	0.144
35.2	0.119	0.060

In all runs, the feed consisted of methane and sulfur alone in the stoichiometric ratio of one to two. Evaluate the rate constant in the following rate expression for the disappearance of sulfur:

$$r_{S_2} = k_c C_{CH_4} C_{S_2}$$

Assume that the reactor is described by the plug-flow model.

SOLUTION

For convenience, let the participants in the reaction be denoted by A, B, C, and D to give

$$A + 2B \longrightarrow C + 2D$$

Then

$$r_B = k_c C_A C_B = 2r_A$$

and the stoichiometric relationships are

$$
\begin{aligned}
n_A &= n_A^0 - n_A^0 x \\
n_B &= n_B^0 - 2n_A^0 x \\
n_C &= n_A^0 x \\
n_D &= 2n_A^0 x \\
\hline
n_T &= n_T^0
\end{aligned}
$$

Since $n_B^0 = 2n_A^0$ for all runs, the flow rate of B is twice that of A throughout the reactor, and

$$r_A = \frac{1}{2} r_B = \frac{1}{2} k_c C_A (2C_A) = k_c C_A^2 = k_c \frac{n_A^2}{v_T^2}$$

The expression for the outlet flow rate of A versus the reactor volume V given by Item 2 of Table 2-2 also applies for the above reaction, since they are both second order and no change in the number of moles occurs with reaction. Thus

$$\frac{V}{n_T^0} = \left(\frac{1}{k_p P^2 y_A^0} \right) \left(\frac{x}{1 - x} \right)$$

Since $n_T^0 = 3n_A^0$, this expression may be rearranged to form

$$\frac{x}{1 - x} = \left(\frac{k_p P^2 y_A^0}{3} \right) \frac{V}{n_A^0}$$

A plot of $x/(1 - x)$ versus V/n_A^0 is shown in Figure 2-3. The straight line shown was found by the method of least squares (see Reference [11]). The slope of this line is equal to 2.96×10^{-4}. Thus

$$\frac{k_p P^2 y_A^0}{3} = 2.96 \times 10^{-4}$$

Figure 2-3. Evaluation of the rate constant for Example 2-4.

Since $P = 1$ atm, $y_A^0 = \frac{1}{3}$, it follows that

$$k_p = 26.64 \times 10^{-4} \text{ g mole/(ml hr atm}^2)$$

and from Equation (1-22),

$$k_c = k_p(RT)^2 = (26.64 \times 10^{-4})[(82.05)(873.15)]^2 = 13.67 \times 10^6 \left(\frac{\text{ml}}{\text{g mole hr}}\right)$$

Instead of using the ratio V/n_T^0 (or V/n_A^0 as was done in the above example) as an independent variable, it has become increasingly popular to use the variable called "space velocity."

The *gas space velocity* S_V is defined as follows:

$$S_V = \frac{\text{volumetric flow rate of feed as a gas at } P_s \text{ and } T_s}{\text{reactor volume}} \qquad (2\text{-}30)$$

where P_s, T_s = standard conditions, which may be selected arbitrarily. Suppose that P_s and T_s are selected such that the feed mixture obeys the perfect gas law. Then

$$S_V = \frac{n_T^0(RT_s/P_s)}{V} \tag{2-31}$$

and

$$\frac{V}{n_T^0} = \left(\frac{RT_s}{P_s}\right)\left(\frac{1}{S_V}\right) \tag{2-32}$$

Thus the integral expressions given in Table 2-2 may be stated in terms of $1/S_V$, which is frequently referred to as the *space time*. For example, for the first-order reaction $A \to R$, the integral expression is given by

$$\frac{1}{S_V} = \frac{P_s/RT_s}{k_p P} \log_e \frac{1}{1 - x} \tag{2-33}$$

FIRST ORDER: A → R

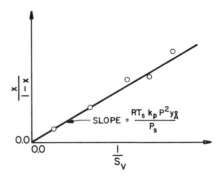

SECOND ORDER: 2A → 2R

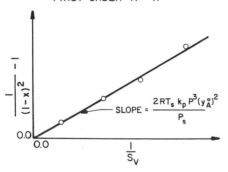

THIRD ORDER: 3A → 3R

Figure 2-4. Use of the gas space velocity and data taken with a plug-flow reactor in the determination of the order and rate constant for a gas phase reaction.

When gas space velocities are used, the plots for first-, second-, and third-order reactions are as shown in Figure 2-4.

Alternately, one may choose P_s and T_s such that the feed is all liquid even though the reaction occurs in the gas phase. The *liquid space velocity* S_L is defined in the following manner.

$$S_L = \frac{\text{volumetric flow rate of the feed in the liquid state at } P_s \text{ and } T_s}{\text{reactor volume}} \qquad (2\text{-}34)$$

Then

$$S_L = \frac{n_T^0}{CV} \qquad (2\text{-}35)$$

where C = molar density of the feed in the liquid state at P_s and T_s, moles per unit volume

When the liquid space velocity is employed, the integral expression for the first-order gas phase reaction $A \rightarrow R$ becomes

$$\frac{1}{S_L} = \left(\frac{C}{k_p P}\right) \log_e \frac{1}{1-x} \qquad (2\text{-}36)$$

EXAMPLE 2-5

Kunzru et al. [12] investigated the thermal cracking of 2-pentene over the temperature range of 670 to 725°C. At 670°C, the following data were obtained:

	Set I	Set II
Temperature, °C	670	670
$1/S_V$, sec	0.26	0.87
Conversion, percent	8.8	22.0

Moles of product per 100 moles of reactant consumed

H_2	20.6	27.1
CH_4	61.2	69.1
C_2H_4	15.6	20.6
C_2H_6	6.1	6.5
C_3H_6	12.4	13.2
2-C_4H_8	30.5	32.9
1,3-C_4H_6	10.8	15.9
C_5^+	14.0	9.1
Total	171.2	194.5

The data were obtained by use of a plug-flow reactor, and $1/S_V$ was based on a P_s and T_s equal to those used in the experiments. Determine the order of reaction and the corresponding value of the rate constant.

SOLUTION

Assume that the reaction rate is first order with respect to A,

$$A \longrightarrow bB$$

where B represents the products and is referred to as a lumped product. Then for plug flow, the following equation (for the case where the feed is pure A) is obtained in a manner analogous to that demonstrated for Equation (2-22).

$$-b \log_e (1 - x) - (b - 1)x = k_c \left(\frac{1}{S_V}\right)$$

The lumped stoichiometric coefficient b is equal to the moles of products produced per mole of A reacted. Thus, for the first set of data,

$$b = \frac{171.2}{100} = 1.712$$

and for the second set,

$$b = \frac{194.5}{100} = 1.945$$

Then for the first set of data, the left-hand side of the above equation has the value

$$-1.712 \log_e (1 - 0.088) - (0.712)(0.088) = 0.0950$$

and for the second set, the value

$$-1.945 \log_e (1 - 0.22) - (0.945)(0.22) = 0.2754$$

These data points are plotted in Figure 2-5. The fact that the two experimental points and the origin all fall on the same straight line suggests that the rate of reaction is first order with respect to A. Although Kunzru et al. present a minimum of four data points for each isotherm studied, only the two sets of data given above were reported in tabular form. The additional points were included, however, on a graph. Since several reactions

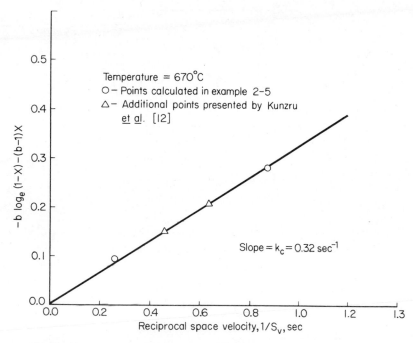

Figure 2-5. Use of the experimental results from a tubular reactor and the plug-flow model in the determination of the order and rate constant for the reactor in Example 2-5.

occurred in the system investigated by Kunzru et al., the lumped stoichiometry coefficient b varied from run to run. In particular, for their sets of experiments, b varied between 1.71 to 2.21.

B. Perfectly Mixed Flow Reactors

A flow reactor of volume V is said to be perfectly mixed if the composition, temperature, and pressure are the same throughout each element of the volume V regardless of how small the element is taken to be.

Because of end effects which may produce appreciable backmixing, many tubular reactors closely approach the limiting condition of perfect mixing. Backmixing is quite pronounced where the length and diameter of a reactor are of the same order of magnitude. Also, if the diameters of the inlet and outlet are considerably smaller than the diameter of the reactor, considerable backmixing can be expected. A sketch of a perfectly mixed tubular reactor is shown in Figure 2-6.

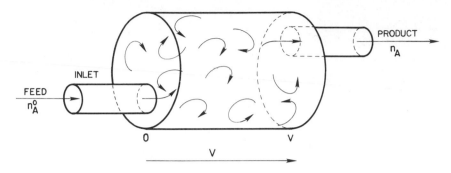

Figure 2-6. Perfectly mixed tubular reactor.

Reactors having the geometry illustrated in Figure 2-7 are called *continuous stirred tank reactors*. If the mixing is perfect in all directions, then the reactor is called a *perfectly mixed flow reactor*. Again, the definition of a perfectly mixed reactor is the same as the one given above. Continuous

Figure 2-7. A perfectly mixed tank reactor.

Figure 2-8. An experimental glass reactor used in the study of the kinetics of the polymerization of styrene (operated as batch or flow reactor).

stirred tank reactors are used primarily for the purpose of controlling the reaction temperature. A continuous stirred-tank reactor in the service of polymerization of styrene is shown in Figure 2-8.

1. MATERIAL BALANCES FOR PERFECTLY MIXED FLOW REACTORS. For a flow reactor whose mixing effects are described by the perfectly mixed model, the composition, temperature, and pressure are uniform throughout the total volume V. Thus the rate of reaction r_A is also the same at every point throughout the volume V. The material balance on component A over the

volume V (see Figures 2-6 and 2-7) at steady state operation is given by

$$\underbrace{n_A^0}_{\substack{\text{Input of} \\ A \text{ to the} \\ \text{reactor} \\ \text{per unit} \\ \text{time}}} - \underbrace{[n_A + r_A V]}_{\substack{\text{output of } A \text{ by} \\ \text{flow and by} \\ \text{reaction}}} = 0 \qquad (2\text{-}37)$$

where $n_A^0 =$ flow rate of A into the reactor, moles/time.

This material balance on A may be restated in the following form, which is more convenient for subsequent use:

$$r_A = \frac{n_A^0 - n_A}{V} \qquad (2\text{-}38)$$

2. VOLUME VERSUS CONVERSION FOR PERFECTLY MIXED FLOW REACTORS. For reactors of this type which are perfectly mixed in all directions, the determination of the reactor volume as a function of conversion is simplified by the fact that at steady state the component-material balance [Equation (2-38)] for reactant A is an algebraic equation.

Consider again the first-order reaction

$$A \longrightarrow \text{products}$$

which is carried out in the liquid phase. Furthermore, suppose that the mass density is constant. Then the rate of reaction at every point within the reactor is given by

$$r_A = k_c C_A = k_c \frac{n_A}{v_T} \qquad (2\text{-}39)$$

Elimination of r_A from Equations (2-38) and (2-39) followed by rearrangement yields

$$V = \left(\frac{v_T}{k_c}\right)\left(\frac{n_A^0 - n_A}{n_A}\right) \qquad (2\text{-}40)$$

or $\qquad n_A = \dfrac{n_A^0}{1 + N_R} \quad$ and $\quad x = \dfrac{N_R}{1 + N_R} \qquad (2\text{-}41)$

where, again, $N_R = k_c V/v_T$. Expressions for the volumes required to achieve a given conversion are presented in Table 2-4. These relationships are valid for reactions which are carried out in either the vapor or liquid phase.

TABLE 2-4

DESIGN EQUATIONS FOR CARRYING OUT UNIDIRECTIONAL AND REVERSIBLE REACTIONS
IN THE LIQUID OR VAPOR PHASE IN A PERFECTLY MIXED FLOW REACTOR
AT STEADY STATE OPERATION

Reactions	Design Equation
1. $2A \longrightarrow R$ $n_T^0 = n_A^0 + n_R^0 + n_I^0$	$\dfrac{V}{v_T} = \left[\dfrac{v_T}{n_A^0 k_c}\right]\left[\dfrac{x}{(1-x)^2}\right]$
2. $A + B \longrightarrow R$ $n_T^0 = n_A^0 + n_B^0 + n_R^0 + n_I^0$ $n_A^0 \neq n_B^0$	$\dfrac{V}{v_T} = \left[\dfrac{v_T}{n_A^0 k_c}\right]\left[\dfrac{x}{(1-x)(\beta - x)}\right], \quad \beta = \dfrac{n_B^0}{n_A^0}$
3. $3A \longrightarrow R + S$ $n_T^0 = n_A^0 + n_R^0 + n_S^0$	$\dfrac{V}{v_T} = \dfrac{v_T^2}{(n_A^0)^2 k_c}\left[\dfrac{x}{(1-x)^3}\right]$
4. $A \underset{k_c'}{\overset{k_c}{\rightleftharpoons}} R$ $n_T^0 = n_A^0 + n_R^0 + n_I^0$	$\dfrac{V}{v_T} = \dfrac{x}{k_c\{[1 - \beta/K_c] - [1 + 1/K_c]x\}}, \quad K_c = \dfrac{k_c}{k_c'}$
5. $A \longrightarrow 3R$	$\dfrac{V}{v_T} = \dfrac{1}{k_c}\left[\dfrac{x}{1-x}\right]$

where v_T is the flow rate at the outlet of the reactor.

For gas phase reactions, expressions relating reactor volume and conversion are developed as demonstrated by the following example. Consider the unidirectional gas phase reaction,

$$A \longrightarrow 2R$$

whose rate is given by

$$r_A = k_p p_A$$

Again the component-material balance on A is given by

$$r_A = \frac{n_A^0 - n_A}{V} = \frac{n_A^0 x}{V}$$

Elimination of r_A from these two expressions followed by rearrangement gives

$$\frac{V}{n_T^0} = \frac{y_A^0 x}{k_p p_A} \tag{2-42}$$

TABLE 2-5
DESIGN EQUATIONS FOR CARRYING OUT UNIDIRECTIONAL AND REVERSIBLE REACTIONS IN THE GAS PHASE IN A PERFECTLY MIXED FLOW REACTOR AT STEADY STATE OPERATION

Reaction	Design Equation
1. $2A \longrightarrow R$ $n_T^0 = n_A^0 + n_R^0 + n_I^0$	$\dfrac{k_p(y_A^0 P)^2 V}{n_A^0} = \dfrac{x[1 - (1/2)y_A^0 x]^2}{(1-x)^2}, \quad y_A^0 = \dfrac{n_A^0}{n_T^0}$
2. $A + B \longrightarrow R$	$\dfrac{k_p(y_A^0 P)^2 V}{n_A^0} = \dfrac{x(1 - y_A^0 x)^2}{(1-x)(\beta - x)}, \quad \beta = \dfrac{n_B^0}{n_A^0}$
3. $3A \longrightarrow R + S$	$\dfrac{k_p(y_A^0 P)^3 V}{n_A^0} = \dfrac{x(1 - (1/3)/y_A^0 x)^3}{(1-x)^3}$
4. $A \rightleftharpoons R$	$\dfrac{k_p(y_A^0 P)V}{n_A^0} = \dfrac{x}{[(1 - \beta/K_p) - (1 + 1/K_p)x]}, \quad \gamma = \dfrac{n_R^0}{n_A^0}$
5. $2A \underset{k_p'}{\overset{k_p}{\rightleftharpoons}} R$	$\dfrac{V(y_A^0 P)^2 k_p}{n_A^0} = \dfrac{x(1 - (1/2)y_A^0 x)^2}{x^2[1 + (1/4K_p P)] - x[2 - (1/2PK_p)(\gamma - (1/2y_A^0)] + \left(1 - \dfrac{\gamma}{y_A^0 PK_p}\right)}$ $K_p = \dfrac{k_p}{k_p'}, \quad \gamma = \dfrac{n_R^0}{n_A^0}$

By use of the stoichiometric relationship

$$n_A = n_A^0 - n_A^0 x$$
$$n_R = n_R^0 + 2n_A^0 x$$
$$\overline{n_T = n_T^0 + n_A^0 x}$$

the partial pressure p_A may be stated in terms of conversion,

$$p_A = \frac{n_A}{n_T} P = \frac{y_A^0(1 - x)P}{(1 + y_A^0 x)} \qquad (2\text{-}43)$$

for a perfect gas mixture. Elimination of p_A from Equations (2-42) and (2-43) followed by rearrangement gives

$$\frac{V k_p P}{n_T^0} = \frac{x(1 + y_A^0 x)}{1 - x} \qquad (2\text{-}44)$$

The expressions for V as a function of conversion for other gas phase reactions are presented in Table 2-5.

EXAMPLE 2-6

Hinshelwood and Askey [13] studied the thermal decomposition of dimethyl ether in a batch reactor. For pressures above 400 mm Hg, the decomposition was first order and proceeded as follows:

$$(CH_3)_2O \longrightarrow [CH_4 + CH_2O] \longrightarrow CH_4 + CO + H_2$$

The presence of formaldehyde was transitory in that it decomposed to carbon monoxide and hydrogen as soon as it was formed. The expression found for the rate constant for the first-order decomposition of dimethyl ether was

$$\log_e k_c = 30.36 - \frac{58,500}{RT}$$

where k_c has the units of $\sec^{-1}$, T is in $^\circ K$, and $R = 1.9872$ cal/(g mole $^\circ K$).

It is proposed to carry this same reaction out in a perfectly mixed flow reactor operated at 550°C and 1 atm pressure. Calculate the respective space velocities (evaluated at the temperature and pressure of the reactor) which are required to achieve conversions of 20, 50, and 80% of dimethyl ether in the perfectly mixed flow reactor. Assume that the mixture behaves as a perfect gas.

SOLUTION

Let the reactant dimethyl ether be denoted by A, and the products methane, carbon monoxide, and hydrogen by B, C, and D, respectively, to give

$$A \longrightarrow B + C + D$$

The stoichiometric relationships are

$$
\begin{aligned}
n_A &= n_A^0 - n_A^0 x \\
n_B &= n_A^0 x \\
n_C &= n_A^0 x \\
n_D &= n_A^0 x \\
\hline
n_T &= n_A^0 + 2n_A^0 x
\end{aligned}
$$

For a perfectly mixed flow reactor in which the above first-order reaction is carried out,

$$r_A = \frac{n_A^0 x}{V} = k_c C_A = k_c \frac{n_A}{v_T} = \frac{k_c n_A^0 (1 - x)}{v_T}$$

For a perfect gas mixture,

$$\frac{n_T}{n_T^0} = \frac{v_T}{v_T^0}; \qquad v_T = v_T^0 \frac{n_T}{n_T^0} = v_T^0 (1 + 2x)$$

Thus

$$\frac{v_T^0}{V} = S_V = \frac{k_c(1 - x)}{x(1 + 2x)}$$

At 550°C,

$$\log_e k_c = 30.36 - \frac{58,500}{(1.9872)(823.15)}$$

$$k_c = 4.50 \times 10^{-3} \; \text{sec}^{-1}$$

Thus, for $x = 0.2$, 0.5, and 0.8, the space velocities are computed as follows:

x	$\dfrac{1 - x}{x(1 + 2x)}$	$S_V = \dfrac{k_c(1 - x)}{x(1 + 2x)}$ (sec^{-1})	$\dfrac{1}{S_V}$ (sec)
0.2	2.857	12.857×10^{-3}	77.78
0.5	0.5	2.250×10^{-3}	444.4
0.8	0.09615	0.433×10^{-3}	2309

A perfectly mixed flow reactor may be used to determine the order and the rate constant for a reaction. For example, if the reaction $A \rightarrow 2R$ (considered above) is first order, the mixing is perfect, and the perfect gas law is obeyed, a plot of V/n_T^0 versus the right-hand side of Equation (2-44) should give a straight line with the slope $1/k_p P$. The experimental points may be determined by varying either the reactor volume or the total flow rate of the feed, n_T^0, with the composition of the feed held fixed for all runs.

C. Comparison of the Plug-Flow and the Perfectly Mixed Flow Reactor Models

The difference between the plug-flow and the perfectly mixed models is perhaps best illustrated by use of Figure 2-9, which shows the concentration profiles predicted by each of these models for a first-order reaction in a tubular reactor. More precisely, the curves were computed for the case where the first-order reaction

$$A \longrightarrow \text{products}$$

is carried out isothermally in the liquid phase at constant mass density with the parameter k_c/v_T fixed such that at $V = V_T$ (the total volume of the reactor), the reaction number $N_R = 2$.

Figure 2-9. Concentration profiles predicted by the plug-flow and perfectly mixed models for a first-order liquid phase reaction carried out in a tubular reactor of volume V_T and at a reaction number, $N_R = k_c V_T/v_T = 2$.

For the plug-flow model, values of the ratio C_A/C_A^0 were obtained by use of Equation (2-17) over the range of values of N_R from 0 to 2. (Note: $N_R = k_c\theta = k_c V/v_T$.) At $N_R = 2$, the outlet concentration for the plug-flow model is computed by use of Equation (2-17); namely,

$$C_A = C_A^0 \exp\left(-N_R\right) = 0.1353 C_A^0$$

For the perfectly mixed reactor, the concentration of A at each point within the reactor is equal to the concentration of A in the stream leaving the reactor. The exit concentration is found by first restating Equation (2-41) in the form

$$C_A = \frac{C_A^0}{1 + N_R}$$

and then for $N_R = 2$,

$$C_A = \frac{C_A^0}{3}$$

Now suppose that the reaction considered above is carried out in two perfectly mixed reactors in series with reactor volumes equal to one-half the volume of the tubular reactor. The reaction number for each of the perfectly mixed reactors is then equal to one-half of the N_R at $V = V_T$ for the tubular reactor. Then the terminal composition, C_{A1}, of the first perfectly mixed reactor is given by

$$C_{A1} = \frac{C_A^0}{1 + N_{R1}} = \frac{C_A^0}{1 + N_R/2} = \frac{C_A^0}{2}$$

For the second perfectly mixed reactor, the outlet concentration, C_{A2}, is given by

$$C_{A2} = \frac{C_{A1}}{1 + N_{R2}} = \frac{C_{A1}}{1 + N_R/2} = \frac{C_A^0}{(1 + N_R/2)^2} = \frac{C_A^0}{4}$$

A comparison of the concentration profiles given by the two perfectly mixed reactors with the concentration profile for the plug-flow reactor is

Figure 2-10. Comparison of the concentration profile for two perfectly mixed reactors with the concentration profile for a single plug-flow reactor.

depicted in Figure 2-10. Comparison of Figures 2-9 and 2-10 suggests that as the number of perfectly mixed reactors is increased, the terminal concentration from the last reactor of the series tends to approach the outlet concentration of a plug-flow reactor having a total volume equal to the sum of the volumes of the perfectly mixed reactors.

An expression for the concentration of A in the effluent stream from the last reactor in a series of N reactors is developed as follows. By use of the procedure above to compute C_{A1} and C_{A2}, it follows that for N perfectly mixed reactors connected in series in which the same first-order reaction considered above occurs,

$$C_{A1} = \frac{C_A^0}{1 + N_R/N}$$

$$C_{A2} = \frac{C_{A1}}{1 + N_R/N} = \frac{C_A^0}{(1 + N_R/N)^2}$$

$$\vdots$$

$$C_{A,N-1} = \frac{C_{A,N-2}}{1 + N_R/N} = \frac{C_{A,N-3}}{(1 + N_R/N)^2} = \cdots = \frac{C_A^0}{(1 + N_R/N)^{N-1}}$$

$$C_{A,N} = \frac{C_{A,N-1}}{1 + N_R/N} = \frac{C_{A,N-2}}{(1 + N_R/N)^2} = \cdots = \frac{C_A^0}{(1 + N_R/N)^N}$$

$$(2\text{-}45)$$

where N_R is based on the total volume of the N reactors.

To find the limit of $C_{A,N}$ as the number of reactors N is increased without bound while the total volume of the reactor is held fixed, it is convenient to restate Equation (2-45) in the following form:

$$\log_e \frac{C_{A,N}}{C_A^0} = \frac{-\log_e (1 + N_R/N)}{1/N} \tag{2-46}$$

As N is increased without bound, the term on the right-hand side becomes indeterminate. Application of l'Hôpital's rule gives

$$\lim_{N \to \infty} \log_e \frac{C_{A,N}}{C_A^0} = \lim_{N \to \infty} \left[\frac{-\log_e (1 + N_R/N)}{1/N} \right] = -N_R \tag{2-47}$$

Upon comparison of Equation (2-15) and (2-47), it is evident that the concentration $C_{A,N}$ of A in the stream leaving the Nth-perfectly mixed reactor is equal to the concentration of A in the terminal stream leaving a plug-flow reactor as the number of perfectly mixed reactors is increased without bound.

D. Plug-Flow Reactors with Recycle

In order to maintain adequate control of the reaction temperature, it may be necessary to operate at a small conversion per pass of the reacting stream through the reactor. Yet from an economic point of view a relatively high conversion of the feed may be desirable. By recycling of a portion of the product stream back through the reactor, both of these objectives (a small conversion per pass with a relatively large conversion of the feed) may be achieved.

Commercial reactors with recycle are also used to increase reactivity and shorten reaction time by efficiently removing the heat of reaction and improving mass transfer when more than one phase is involved as described by Leuteritz et al. [14]. Also, the yield of the desired products may be improved in certain cases where complex reactions are involved as demonstrated by Carberry [15].

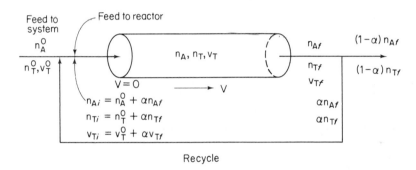

Figure 2-11. Sketch of a tubular reactor with recycle.

A sketch of a tubular reactor with a recycle stream is shown in Figure 2-11. Most of the notation to be used in the analysis of reactors with recycle streams is also shown in Figure 2-11. The fraction of the product stream which is recycled to the inlet of the reactor is denoted by α, and the fraction of the product stream which leaves the system is denoted by $1 - \alpha$. The symbols are perhaps best described by following component A through the system. The molar flow rates n_A^0, n_{Ai}, and n_{Af} denote the rates at which component A enters the system, enters the reactor, and leaves the reactor, respectively. The molar flow rate of A at any point in the reactor is denoted by n_A.

1. CONVERSION PER PASS. The equations developed above for conversion versus volume for plug-flow reactors (see Tables 2-1, 2-2, and 2-3) are applicable to reactors with recycle provided that the superscript zero on all

symbols is replaced by the subscript i and the subscript i is added to the symbol for the volumetric flow rate to give v_{Ti}. Also, in the interest of clarity, for reactors with recycle all values of the variable at the outlet of the reactor are identified by the symbol f.

To illustrate the treatment of plug-flow reactors in recycle systems, the equations are developed for two relatively simple cases. Consider again the first-order reaction

$$A \longrightarrow \text{products}$$

which is carried out in the liquid phase at constant mass density. Again the limit of a material balance on A over the element of volume ΔV in the reactor shown in Figure 2-11 takes the form

$$r_A = -\frac{dn_A}{dV}$$

as the element over which the balance is made is allowed to go to zero. Elimination of r_A from this material-balance equation by use of the rate expression $r_A = k_c C_A$ gives

$$-\frac{dn_A}{dV} = k_c C_A = k_c \frac{n_A}{v_T}$$

Since the mass density is constant, $v_{Ti} = v_{Tf} = v_T$, the variables may be separated, and the resulting equation integrated.

$$-\int_{n_A = n_{Ai}}^{n_A = n_{Af}} \frac{dn_A}{n_A} = \frac{k_c}{v_{Ti}} \int_{V=0}^{V=V_T} dV$$

The subscript T has been added to the volume to emphasize that the upper limit is equal to the total volume of the reactor. After the indicated integration has been performed, the result so obtained may be rearranged to the form given by Equation (2-14) or the first expression of Table 2-1; namely,

$$n_{Af} = n_{Ai} \exp\left(\frac{-k_c V_T}{v_{Ti}}\right) \tag{2-48}$$

or

$$V_T = \frac{v_{Ti}}{k_c} \log_e \frac{n_{Ai}}{n_{Af}} \tag{2-49}$$

Consider next the case where the reaction

$$A \longrightarrow R$$

is carried out in the gas phase in a plug-flow reactor with recycle as shown in Figure 2-11. Let the conversion at any V of the reactor be defined in the usual way as the moles of A reacted per mole of A fed to the reactor; that is,

$$x = \frac{n_{Ai} - n_A}{n_{Ai}} \tag{2-50}$$

Then the stoichiometric relationships follow:

$$\begin{aligned} n_A &= n_{Ai} - n_{Ai}x \\ n_R &= n_{Ri} + n_{Ai}x \\ \hline n_T &= n_{Ti} \end{aligned} \tag{2-51}$$

By use of Equation (2-50), the material balance on A may be stated in terms of x,

$$n_{Ai}\frac{dx}{dV} = r_A \tag{2-52}$$

Elimination of r_A by use of the rate expression, $r_A = k_p p_A$, gives

$$n_{Ai}\frac{dx}{dV} = k_p p_A = k_p \frac{(n_{Ai} - n_{Ai}x)P}{n_{Ti}} \tag{2-53}$$

where it is assumed that the mixture obeys the perfect gas law. Then

$$\int_{x=0}^{x=x_f} \frac{dx}{(1-x)} = \frac{k_p P}{n_{Ti}} \int_0^{V_T} dV \tag{2-54}$$

and integration followed by rearrangement gives

$$V_T = \frac{n_{Ti}}{k_p P}\log_e \frac{1}{1-x_f} \tag{2-55}$$

which is seen to be the same form as the first expression of Table 2-2.

In conclusion then, the equations given in Tables 2-1, 2-2, and 2-3 for reactors without recycle also apply to reactors with recycle provided that the appropriate changes are made in the subscripts and superscripts.

2. TOTAL CONVERSION FOR THE SYSTEM. Let the total conversion χ for the system be defined as the moles of the the base component A reacted in

the system per mole of A that enters the system. Component A enters the system at the rate n_A^0 and leaves at the rate $(1 - \alpha)n_{Af}$. Then

$$\chi = \frac{n_A^0 - (1 - \alpha)n_{Af}}{n_A^0} \tag{2-56}$$

Since $n_A^0\chi$ is equal to the moles of A reacted in the system per unit time, the following stoichiometric relationships for the system are readily deduced:

$$\begin{aligned}
(1 - \alpha)n_{Af} &= n_A^0 - n_A^0\chi \\
(1 - \alpha)n_{Rf} &= n_R^0 + n_A^0\chi \\
\overline{(1 - \alpha)n_{Tf}} &= n_T^0
\end{aligned} \tag{2-57}$$

The conversion per pass and the total conversion for the system may be related by commencing with Equation (2-50) and Equation (2-56), and the fact that $n_{Ai} = n_A^0 + \alpha n_{Af}$

$$x_f = \frac{(1 - \alpha)\chi}{1 - \alpha\chi} \tag{2-58}$$

or

$$\chi = \frac{x_f}{1 - \alpha(1 - x_f)} \tag{2-59}$$

3. VARIATION OF THE CONVERSION PER PASS AND THE TOTAL CONVERSION WITH THE FRACTION OF THE PRODUCT STREAM RECYCLED. Equation (2-55) may be restated in terms of the total conversion and n_T^0 by use of Equation (2-58) and the fact that

$$n_{Ti} = n_T^0 + \alpha n_{Tf} = n_T^0 + \left(\frac{\alpha}{1 - \alpha}\right)n_T^0 = \frac{n_T^0}{1 - \alpha} \tag{2-60}$$

The result so obtained may be solved for the total conversion to give

$$\chi = \frac{1 - \exp\left[-N_R(1 - \alpha)\right]}{1 - \alpha \exp\left[-N_R(1 - \alpha)\right]} \tag{2-61}$$

In this case

$$N_R = \frac{V_T k_p P}{n_T^0} \tag{2-62}$$

At $\alpha = 0$, Equation (2-61) reduces to

$$\chi = 1 - \exp(-N_R) \tag{2-63}$$

which is the equation for a plug-flow reactor without recycle.

As $\alpha \to 1$, the right-hand side of Equation (2-61) becomes indeterminate. This indeterminate form may be evaluated by use of l'Hôpital's rule

$$\lim_{\alpha \to 1} \chi = \lim_{\alpha \to 1} \frac{1 - \exp\left[-N_R(1 - \alpha)\right]}{1 - \alpha \exp\left[-N_R(1 - \alpha)\right]} = \frac{N_R}{1 + N_R} \tag{2-64}$$

Comparison of this result with Equation (2-41) shows that as $\alpha \to 1$, the system conversion χ approaches that which could be obtained by operating a perfectly mixed reactor with the same total volume V_T and total feed rate n_T^0 as those used for the plug-flow reactor of the system.

The results obtained above are summarized by the graphs of χ and x_f versus α which are shown in Figure 2-12.

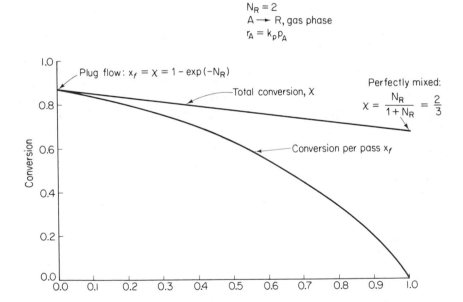

Figure 2-12. Variation of the total conversion of the system and the conversion per pass with the fraction of the product stream recycled.

E. Laminar-Flow Reactors

When the fluid passes through the reactor in laminar flow, there is no mixing in either the radial or the horizontal directions. As indicated in Figure 2-13, laminar flow may be visualized as consisting of a set of concentric cylinder walls of the incremental thickness Δr which pass through the reactor at successively greater velocities as the radii of the cylinders decrease. In the

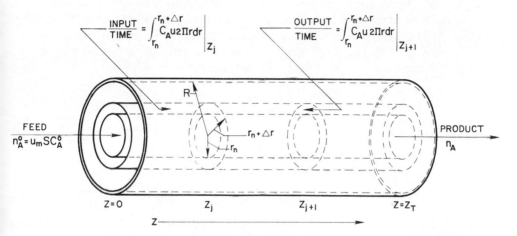

Figure 2-13. Laminar flow of the reacting stream through a tubular reactor.

limit as Δr goes to zero, the linear velocity u at which a shell of fluid of radius r passes through the reactor is given by the following relationship, which may be found in standard texts on fluid dynamics:

$$u = u_{\max}\left[1 - \left(\frac{r}{R}\right)^2\right] \tag{2-65}$$

where r = radius of the reactor; measured from center, as in Figure 2-13,
$$0 \le r \le R$$

$u_{\max}$ = maximum velocity

The maximum velocity occurs at $r = 0$ and is given by the following form of the Poiseuille equation:

$$u_{\max} = \left(\frac{P_1 - P_2}{4\mu z_T}\right)R^2 \tag{2-66}$$

91

where P_1 is the pressure at the inlet of the reactor, P_2 is the pressure at the outlet of the reactor, and μ is the viscosity where all quantities are expressed in appropriate units. The average velocity u_m is related to the volumetric flow rate v_T and the maximum velocity $u_{\max}$ as follows:

$$u_m = \frac{v_T}{S} = \frac{u_{\max}}{2} \qquad (2\text{-}67)$$

1. Material Balances for Laminar-Flow Reactors. Now consider the element of volume $2\pi r_n \,\Delta r\, \Delta z$ shown in Figure 2-13, where z_j, Δz, r_n, and Δr are arbitrarily selected in the domains $[0 < z_j < (z_j + \Delta z) < z_T;$ $0 < r_n < (r_n + \Delta r) < R]$ of interest. A material balance on component A over this element of volume at steady state operation is given by

$$\underbrace{\int_{r_n}^{r_n+\Delta r} C_A u 2\pi r\, dr \Big|_{z_j}}_{\text{Input by flow}} - \underbrace{\int_{r_n}^{r_n+\Delta r} C_A u 2\pi r\, dr \Big|_{z_j+\Delta z}}_{\text{output by flow}} - \underbrace{\int_{z_j}^{z_j+\Delta z}\int_{r_n}^{r_n+\Delta r} r_A 2\pi r\, dr\, dz}_{\text{output by reaction}} = 0$$

$$(2\text{-}68)$$

The first two integrals may be written as a single integral and the *mean value theorem of differential calculus* applied to give

$$2\pi \int_{r_n}^{r_n+\Delta r} \left[(ruC_A)\Big|_{z_j,r} - (ruC_A)\Big|_{z_j+\Delta z,r} \right] dr$$

$$= -2\pi\, \Delta z \int_{r_n}^{r_n+\Delta r} \frac{\partial(ruC_A)}{\partial z}\bigg|_{z_j+\alpha(r)\cdot \Delta z, r}\, dr \qquad (2\text{-}69)$$

where $\alpha(r)$ depends upon r and $0 < \alpha(r) < 1$. Application of the *mean value theorem of integral calculus* to the integral on the right-hand side of Equation (2-69) follows:

$$-2\pi\, \Delta z \int_{r_n}^{r_n+\Delta r} \frac{\partial(ruC_A)}{\partial z}\bigg|_{z_j+\alpha(r)\cdot \Delta z, r}\, dr = -2\pi\, \Delta z\, \Delta r\, \frac{\partial(ruC_A)}{\partial z}\bigg|_{z_j+\alpha(r_p)\cdot \Delta z, r_p}$$

$$(2\text{-}70)$$

where $\qquad r_p = r_n + \gamma_1\, \Delta r, \qquad 0 \le \gamma_1 \le 1$

Application of the *mean value theorem of integral calculus* first with respect to r and then with respect to z to the double integral appearing in Equation (2-68) gives

$$\Bigg|^{+\Delta r}\int_{z_j}^{z_j+\Delta z}\int_{r_n}^{r_n+\Delta r} r_A 2\pi r\, dr\, dz = 2\pi\, \Delta r\, \Delta z (r_A r)\Big|_{r_n+\beta(z_p)\,\Delta r, z_p} \qquad (2\text{-}71)$$

where $0 \leq \beta(z_p) \leq 1$, $z_p = z_j + \gamma_2 \, \Delta z$, and $0 \leq \gamma_2 \leq 1$. When the results given by Equations (2-70) and (2-71) are substituted into Equation (2-68), the following result is obtained:

$$-\left[\frac{\partial(ruC_A)}{\partial z}\right]\Bigg|_{z_j + \alpha(r_p) \cdot \Delta z, r_p} - (r_A r)\Big|_{r_n + \beta(z_p) \cdot \Delta r, z_p} = 0 \qquad (2\text{-}72)$$

If Δz and Δr are allowed to go to zero in any order whatsoever, one obtains

$$\left[\frac{\partial(ruC_A)}{\partial z}\right]\Bigg|_{z_j, r_n} + (r_A r)\Big|_{r_n, z_j} = 0 \qquad (2\text{-}73)$$

Since z_j and r_n were arbitrarily selected in the domains of interest, Equation (2-73) holds for all such choices of z_j and r_n in these domains. Thus the subscript z_j and r_n may be removed and Equation (2-73) restated to give the following form of the material-balance expression for r_A.

$$r_A = -\frac{1}{r}\frac{\partial(ruC_A)}{\partial z} = -\frac{\partial(uC_A)}{\partial z} \qquad \begin{array}{l}(0 < r < R)\\(0 < z < z_T)\end{array} \qquad (2\text{-}74)$$

2. VARIATION OF CONVERSION WITH REACTOR VOLUME FOR FIRST-ORDER LIQUID PHASE REACTIONS IN LAMINAR FLOW. (Other Conditions: isothermal and steady state operation, constant mass density, and constant viscosity) At any given radius r, the linear velocity u in Equation (2-74) is the same for all z. Thus, at a fixed r, Equation (2-74) reduces to

$$r_A = -u\frac{dC_A}{dz} \qquad (2\text{-}75)$$

where u at this fixed value of r is given by Equation (2-65) for all z. For the first-order reaction, $r_A = k_c C_A$, Equation (2-75) may be solved to give

$$C_A = C_A^0 \exp\left(-\frac{k_c z}{u}\right) \qquad (2\text{-}76)$$

The rate at which A enters the reactor (see Figure 2-13) is given by

$$n_A^0 = u_m \pi R^2 C_A^0 \qquad (2\text{-}77)$$

where $\qquad u_m = \dfrac{v_T}{S} = \dfrac{u_{max}}{2} \qquad$ [see Equation (2-67]

The molar flow rate n_A at which A leaves the reactor shown in Figure 2-13 may be computed as follows:

$$n_A = \int_0^R C_A u(2\pi r \; dr) = 2\pi C_A^0 \int_0^R \left[\exp\left(\frac{-k_c z_T}{u} \right) \right] ur \; dr \qquad (2\text{-}78)$$

where u as a function of r is given by Equation (2-65). The integral appearing in Equation (2-78) may be restated in the following form (see Problem 2-8):

$$n_A = n_A^0 \left[\left(\frac{1 - N_R}{2} \right) \exp\left(\frac{-N_R}{2} \right) + \left(\frac{N_R}{2} \right)^2 E\left(\frac{N_R}{2} \right) \right] \qquad (2\text{-}79)$$

where $\qquad N_R = \dfrac{2 \, k_c z_T}{u_{\max}} = \dfrac{k_c z_T}{u_m} = \dfrac{k_c V}{v_T} = k_c \theta$

the reaction number for a first-order reaction.

The function $E(y)$ is defined by

$$E(y) = \int_y^\infty \frac{\exp\left(-\phi \right) d\phi}{\phi} \qquad (2\text{-}80)$$

The function $E(y)$ is commonly tabulated in standard sets of tables as $-Ei(-x)$ (see, for example, Reference [16]).

This general approach used to relate conversion and reaction number for the particular reaction considered may be used for other types of reactors, but it may be necessary to evaluate the integral in Equation (2-78) numerically.

As shown in a subsequent section, the conversion which can be obtained per pass by the laminar-flow model is less than that which can be obtained by use of a plug-flow model and more than that which can be obtained by use of the perfectly mixed model.

EXAMPLE 2-7

Styrene in the solvent dioxane is to be polymerized in a tubular reactor at 25°C by use of sodium naphthalene as the initiator. Laminar flow through the reactor may be assumed. The concentration of styrene in the feed is 1.0 g mole per liter. The polymerization reaction of styrene (denoted by A) in the presence of the initiator (denoted by I) may be represented by

$$A \xrightarrow{\;(I)\;} \text{polymer}$$

In the presence of 0.0005 g mole per liter of sodium naphthalene, the rate of reaction of styrene [17] is given by

$$r_A = kC_A$$

where
$$k = 1.7 \times 10^{-3} \text{ sec}^{-1}$$

The mass density may be assumed to remain constant throughout the reactor. For a residence time of 20 min, calculate the conversion of styrene which can be expected in a laminar-flow reactor at the conditions outlined above.

SOLUTION

First calculate the reaction number N_R as follows:

$$N_R = k\theta = (1.7 \times 10^{-3})(20)(60) = 2.04$$

Next the conversion is calculated by use of Equation (2-79) as follows:

$$\frac{n_A}{n_A^0} = 1 - x = \left[\left(1 - \frac{2.04}{2}\right)\exp\left(\frac{-2.04}{2}\right) + \left(\frac{2.04}{2}\right)^2 E\left(\frac{2.04}{2}\right)\right]$$

$$x = 1 - [-0.007212 + (1.0404)E(1.02)] = 0.7859$$

F. Partial Axial Mixing Model

A stream in turbulent flow is characterized by point velocities which deviate about a mean velocity just as the velocities of the molecules of a body of fluid deviate about a mean velocity. Experience has shown that the molecules of, say, type A of such a system tend to have a net movement in the direction in which molecules of type A are least abundant. *Fick's first law* is a quantification of this experience for molecular diffusion. To account for the mass transfer resulting from molecular motion and turbulent motion, the following form of Fick's first law is commonly used:

$$\mathscr{J}_A = -\mathscr{D}A\frac{dC_A}{dz} \tag{2-81}$$

where A = area perpendicular to the direction of mass transfer
   C_A = concentration of A, moles per unit volume
   $\mathscr{D}$ = effective diffusivity due to both molecular motion and turbulent motion, consistent units of (length)^2 per unit time
   $\mathscr{J}_A$ = rate of transfer of component A in the positive direction z, moles per unit time

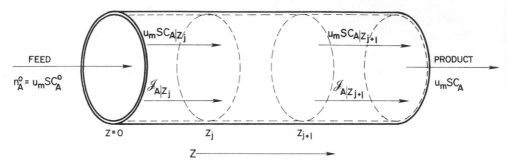

Figure 2-14. Partial axial mixing model: perfect mixing in the radial direction and partial mixing in the axial direction are assumed.

1. MATERIAL BALANCES. A sketch of a tubular reactor in which axial diffusion is considered is shown in Figure 2-14. The component-material balance for component A over the element of volume $S \Delta z$ is given by

$$u_m S C_A \Big|_{z_j} + \mathscr{J}_A \Big|_{z_j} - \left[u_m S C_A \Big|_{z_{j+1}} + \mathscr{J}_A \Big|_{z_{j+1}} + \int_{z_j}^{z_{j+1}} r_A S \, dz \right] = 0 \quad (2\text{-}82)$$

where $u_m = v_T/S$, the average linear velocity. Application of the mean value theorems to Equation (2-82) followed by the limiting process, wherein Δz is allowed to go to zero, yields

$$S \frac{d(u_m C_A)}{dz} + \frac{d\mathscr{J}_A}{dz} + r_A S = 0 \quad (2\text{-}83)$$

Evaluation of $d\mathscr{J}_A/dz$ by use of Equation (2-81) followed by rearrangement gives the material balance for component A.

$$\frac{d(u_m C_A)}{dz} - \mathscr{D} \frac{d^2 C_A}{dz^2} + r_A = 0 \quad (2\text{-}84)$$

(Note that in this particular example the area A in Equation (2-81) is equal to the cross-sectional area S.)

2. VARIATION OF CONVERSION WITH REACTOR VOLUME FOR A FIRST-ORDER REACTION. (Other Conditions: isothermal operation, constant mass density, and diffusivity) In order to compare the behavior of the model for partial axial mixing with that exhibited by other mixing models, an expression for conversion versus reactor volume is developed for the case where the first-order reaction $A \rightarrow R$ is carried out in the liquid phase at constant mass density.

At constant mass density, the mean velocity u_m in the material balance for A, Equation (2-84), becomes independent of z. Then upon elimination of r_A from Equation (2-84) by use of the rate expression $r_A = k_c C_A$, the following result is obtained:

$$\frac{d^2 C_A}{dz^2} - \left(\frac{u_m}{\mathscr{D}}\right)\frac{dC_A}{dz} - \left(\frac{k_c}{\mathscr{D}}\right)C_A = 0 \tag{2-85}$$

This equation is recognized as a second-order, linear differential equation with constant coefficients. The general solution of equations of this type are obtained in the following manner. Let

$$C_A = C e^{mz} \tag{2-86}$$

where C and m are finite and nonzero constants. After the first and second derivatives of C_A with respect to z have been found by use of Equation (2-86) and substituted into Equation (2-85), the following result is obtained upon rearrangement:

$$\left[m^2 - \left(\frac{u_m}{\mathscr{D}}\right)m - \left(\frac{k_c}{\mathscr{D}}\right)\right] = 0 \tag{2-87}$$

The two values of m that make the left-hand side equal to zero are the roots of the quadratic equation

$$m_1 = \frac{u_m}{2\mathscr{D}}(1 - \sqrt{1 + 4\alpha})$$

$$m_2 = \frac{u_m}{2\mathscr{D}}(1 + \sqrt{1 + 4\alpha})$$

where
$$\alpha = \frac{k_c \mathscr{D}}{u_m^2}$$

$$u_m = \frac{v_T}{S}$$

Since $C_1 e^{m_1 z}$ and $C_2 e^{m_2 z}$ are both linearly independent solutions of Equation (2-85), their sum is also a solution, a fact which is readily shown by direct substitution. Thus the general solution of Equation (2-85) is given by

$$C_A = C_1 e^{m_1 z} + C_2 e^{m_2 z} \tag{2-88}$$

The values of C_1 and C_2 are to be selected such that the boundary conditions are satisfied. Reactant A enters the reactor at the boundary $z = 0$ at the rate $n_A^0 = Su_m C_A^0$ and leaves this boundary at the rate $[Su_m C_A(0+) + \mathscr{I}_A(0+)]$, where $C_A(0+)$ and $\mathscr{I}_A(0+)$ are the values of C_A and $\mathscr{I}_A$, respectively, at $z = 0+$. Thus the boundary condition at the inlet consists of the material balance on A at the inlet; namely,

$$Su_m C_A^0 - [Su_m C_A(0+) + \mathscr{I}_A(0+)] = 0 \qquad (2\text{-}89)$$

A second boundary condition may be deduced by commencing with a material balance on A at $z = z_T$.

$$Su_m C_A(z_T-) + \mathscr{I}_A(z_T-) - Su_m C_A(z_T+) = 0 \qquad (2\text{-}90)$$

This balance is based on the supposition that the mechanism of axial diffusion is not involved for all $z > z_T$. This condition is satisfied if, for example, the reactor empties into a large tank. If it is further supposed that the concentration of A at $z = z_T-$ is approximately equal to the concentration at $z = z_T+$, then, by Equation (2-90),

$$\mathscr{I}_A(z_T-) \cong 0$$

or
$$\frac{dC_A}{dz} = 0 \quad \text{at} \quad z = z_T- \qquad (2\text{-}91)$$

This boundary condition is commonly referred to as the "closed system" or "closed-end" boundary condition because axial diffusion across the boundary at $z = z_T$ has been ruled out. Thus the end of the reactor is closed with respect to axial diffusion.

When the arbitrary constants C_1 and C_2 are evaluated by use of these two boundary conditions [Equations (2-89) and (2-91)], the following solution to the differential equation [Equation (2-85)] is obtained [18]:

$$C_A = \frac{4\beta C_A^0}{(1+\beta)^2 \exp{[(-N_{Pe}/2)(1-\beta)]} - (1-\beta)^2 \exp{[(-N_{Pe}/2)(1+\beta)]}} \qquad (2\text{-}92)$$

where $N_{Pe} = \dfrac{u_m z_T}{\mathscr{D}}$, the Peclet number; $\beta = \sqrt{1 + 4\alpha}$

To obtain expressions for the outlet concentration versus the reactor volume for other types of reactions, it will be necessary, generally, to solve

Equation (2-84) by use of an appropriate numerical method. A comparison of the results predicted by the partial axial mixing model with other models is presented below.

G. Comparison of the Plug-Flow, Perfectly Mixed, Laminar-Flow, and Partial Axial Mixing Models

The effect of mixing on the behavior of a tubular reactor is perhaps best visualized by use of a numerical example in which it is supposed that the first-order reaction

$$A \longrightarrow R$$

is carried out in the liquid phase in each of four reactors. Further suppose that the mixing in each of the reactors may be represented by

1. Plug flow:

$$x = 1 - \exp(-N_R)$$

$$N_R = k_c\theta = \frac{k_cV}{v_T} = \frac{k_cz_T}{u_m}, \quad \begin{array}{l} \text{the reaction number for} \\ \text{a first-order reaction.} \end{array}$$

(2-93)

2. Partially mixed:

$$x = 1 - \frac{4\beta}{(1 + \beta)^2 \exp\left[(-N_{Pe}/2)(1 - \beta)\right] - (1 - \beta)^2 \exp\left[(-N_{Pe}/2)(1 + \beta)\right]}$$

(2-94)

3. Laminar flow:

$$x = 1 - \left[(1 - N_R/2) \exp(-N_R/2) + (N_R/2)^2 E(N_R/2)\right]$$

(2-95)

4. Perfectly mixed:

$$x = \frac{N_R}{1 + N_R}$$

(2-96)

Graphs of the above equations for the plug-flow, laminar-flow, and the perfectly mixed models for tubular reactors are presented in Figure 2-15.

Figure 2-15. Comparison of the plug-flow, laminar-flow, and perfectly mixed models for tubular reactors.

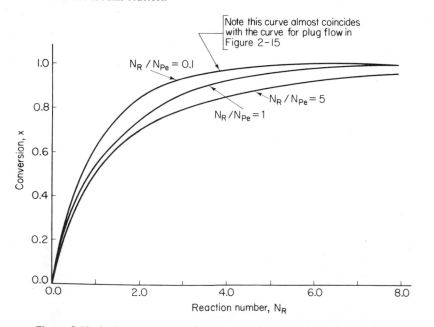

Figure 2-16. As the Peclet number is increased relative to the reaction number, the conversion given by the partial axial mixing model approaches that given by a plug-flow model.

100

These graphs show that for a given value of N_R or θ, the plug-flow model gives the largest conversion, followed by the laminar-flow model and then the perfectly mixed model. The behavior of the partially mixed model is depicted in Figure 2-16. As the ratio of N_R to N_{Pe} is decreased, the conversion at a given N_R is increased. For example, the curve for $N_R/N_{Pe} = 0.1$ in Figure 2-16 closely approximates the plug-flow model shown in Figure 2-15.

Also, at relatively small and at relatively large conversions, all of the mixing models are seen to predict very nearly the same conversions. In fact, in these regions of conversion, the differences in conversions predicted by the respective models are, in many cases, the same order of magnitude as the inaccuracies of the experimental data, and one mixing model will be found to fit the data about as well as another as illustrated by the following example.

EXAMPLE 2-8

On the basis of the two data points given in Example 2-5 and the two interior data points given in Figure 2-5, repeat Example 2-5 for the case where it is assumed that the behavior of the tubular reactor may be represented by the perfectly mixed model. For the two interior points shown in Figure 2-5, the values of b and x were not given by Kunzru [12]. On the basis of the assumption of a linear variation of b between the two values found in Example 2-5, the values of b and the conversions for each of the two interior points shown in Figure 2-5 were estimated. A summary of the data given in Example 2-5 plus the estimated values of b and x follows.

$\dfrac{1}{S_V}$	b	x
0.26	1.712	0.088
0.47	1.787	0.133
0.64	1.86	0.177
0.87	1.945	0.22

SOLUTION

Assume the reaction $A \rightarrow bB$ is first order. On the basis of this assumption, the following expression may be obtained in a manner similar to that demonstrated above in the development of Equation (2-44).

$$\frac{VPk_p}{n_T^0} = \frac{x[1 + (b - 1)x]}{1 - x}$$

When the space velocity is based on the temperature and pressure of the system, the left-hand side of the above expression reduces to k_c/S_V. Thus, if the reaction is first order and the reactor is perfectly mixed, a straight line should be obtained when the data are plotted as shown in Figure 2-17.

Figure 2-17. Use of the experimental results from a tubular reactor and the perfectly mixed model in the determination of the order and rate constant for the reaction in Example 2-5.

A comparison of Figures 2-5 and 2-17 shows that the data are fit by each model about equally well. That equally good fits should be obtained at values of $x \leq 0.22$ is suggested by the curves shown in Figure 2-15.

H. The Partial Axial and Partial Radial Mixing Models and Other Mixing Models

For the sake of completeness, the material-balance equation is developed for the case where a reactor is partially mixed in the axial and radial directions.

1. THE PARTIAL AXIAL AND PARTIAL RADIAL MIXING MODEL. In this generalized mixing model depicted in Figure 2-18, mixing in both the radial and axial directions is assumed to occur. It is further supposed that this mixing can be described by the forms of Fick's first law for the diffusion of A by mixing in the positive directions of r and z. For the rate of diffusion of A by mixing in the radial direction, the following form of Fick's first law is used.

$$\mathcal{J}_r \left[\frac{\text{moles of } A \text{ transferred}}{(\text{unit time})(\text{unit area})} \right] = -\mathscr{D}_r \frac{\partial C_A}{\partial r} \tag{2-97}$$

Figure 2-18. Partial mixing in the radial direction and partial mixing in the axial direction of a tubular reactor.

The rate of diffusion of A by mixing in the positive direction of z is given by

$$\mathscr{J}_z \left[\frac{\text{moles of } A \text{ transferred}}{\text{(unit time)(unit area)}} \right] = -\mathscr{D}_z \cdot \frac{\partial C_A}{\partial z} \qquad (2\text{-}98)$$

The symbols $\mathscr{D}_r$ and $\mathscr{D}_z$ are used in order to emphasize that different effective diffusivities are permitted in the r and z directions. Let $u(r, z)$ denote the velocity of the fluid at any point (r, z) inside the boundaries $(0 < r < R;$ $0 < z < z_T)$ of the reactor. At steady state operation, a material balance on A must take into account the amount of component A entering and leaving the element of volume $2\pi r\,\Delta r\,\Delta z$ in Figure 2-18 by flow and by diffusion as well as the amount of A reacted within the element of volume as follows:

$$\int_{r_n}^{r_n + \Delta r} \left[(C_A u 2\pi r + \mathscr{J}_z 2\pi r) \Big|_{z_j, r} - (C_A u 2\pi r + \mathscr{J}_z 2\pi r) \Big|_{z_j + \Delta z, r} \right] dr$$

Input by flow plus diffusion at z_j − output by flow plus diffusion at $z_j + \Delta z$

$$+ \int_{z_j}^{z_j + \Delta z} \left[\mathscr{J}_r 2\pi r \Big|_{r_n, z} - \mathscr{J}_r 2\pi r \Big|_{r_n + \Delta r, z} \right] dz$$

Input by diffusion at r_n − output by diffusion at $r_n + \Delta r$

$$- \int_{r_n}^{r_n + \Delta r} \int_{z_j}^{z_j + \Delta z} r_A 2\pi r \, dr \, dz = 0 \qquad (2\text{-}99)$$

Output by reaction

To reduce Equation (2-99) to its corresponding partial differential equation, the *mean value theorem of differential calculus* is first applied to each difference appearing in the integrals. Then the *mean value theorem of integral calculus* is applied once to the single integrals and twice to the double integral to give

$$+ 2\pi \, \Delta r \, \Delta z \left[\frac{\partial (C_A u r + \mathcal{J}_z r)}{\partial z} \Bigg|_{①} + \frac{\partial (\mathcal{J}_r r)}{\partial r} \Bigg|_{②} + (r_A r) \Bigg|_{③} \right] = 0 \quad (2\text{-}100)$$

where

$$① = [(z_j + \alpha_1(r_p) \cdot \Delta z), r_p], \quad 0 < \alpha_1(r_p) < 1, \quad r_p = r_n + \gamma_1 \, \Delta r, \quad 0 \le \gamma_1 \le 1$$

$$② = [(r_n + \alpha_2(z_p) \cdot \Delta r), z_p], \quad 0 < \alpha_2(z_p) < 1, \quad z_p = z_j + \gamma_2 \, \Delta z, \quad 0 \le \gamma_2 \le 1$$

$$③ = [(r_n + \alpha_3(z_k) \cdot \Delta r), z_k], \quad 0 < \alpha_3(z_k) < 1, \quad z_k = z_j + \gamma_3 \, \Delta z, \quad 0 \le \gamma_3 \le 1$$

Division of each member of Equation (2-100) by $(-2\pi \, \Delta r \, \Delta z)$ followed by the limiting process wherein Δz and Δr are allowed to go to zero gives the following result upon recognition of the fact that r_n and z_j were arbitrarily selected within the domains $(0 < r < R; 0 < z < z_T)$ of interest.

$$\frac{\partial (C_A u r + \mathcal{J}_z r)}{\partial z} + \frac{\partial (\mathcal{J}_r r)}{\partial r} + r_A r = 0 \quad (2\text{-}101)$$

After $\mathcal{J}_z$ and $\mathcal{J}_r$ have been replaced by their equivalents as given by Equations (2-97) and (2-98), respectively, and the partial differentiation implied by Equation (2-101) has been performed, the following result is obtained upon rearrangement:

$$\mathcal{D}_z \frac{\partial^2 C_A}{\partial z^2} + \mathcal{D}_r \frac{\partial^2 C_A}{\partial r^2} + \frac{\mathcal{D}_r}{r} \frac{\partial C_A}{\partial r} - \frac{\partial (C_A u)}{\partial z} - r_A = 0 \quad (2\text{-}102)$$

A comparison of Equations (2-8), (2-74), and (2-84) with Equation (2-102) shows that the plug-flow model, the laminar-flow model, and the partial axial mixed model are all special cases of the generalized model represented by Equation (2-102).*

---

* The boundary conditions are deduced in the following manner. Since A does not pass through the wall, the radial flux is zero for all z at the wall; that is,

$$\mathcal{J}_r(R) = 0 \qquad (0 + \le z \le z_T -)$$

The condition of symmetry requires

$$\frac{\partial C_A}{\partial r} \Bigg|_{r=0} \qquad (0 + \le z \le z_T -)$$

The boundary conditions with respect to z are given by Equations (2-89) and (2-90). For a first-order reaction, an analytical solution can be obtained, but development of this is beyond the scope of this book.

2. OTHER MIXING MODELS. Beginning with the work of Danckwerts [19] and Zwietering [20], the degree of mixing in chemical reactors has received considerable attention. Extensive work has been done on the residence time distributions for stirred tank reactors. These models recognize the fact that the mixing is not perfect, with the result that all of the molecules do not reside in the reactor the same amount of time. The analysis of these models is beyond the scope of this text. Summaries of recent work in this area are presented by Himmelblau et al. [21] and by Wen et al. [22].

II. UNSTEADY STATE OPERATION

The behavior of continuous reactors at unsteady state operation becomes of importance in the continuous control and in the start up of reactors. The purpose of the treatment presented below is to introduce this important subject by developing the material-balance equations for the plug-flow and perfectly mixed reactor models at unsteady state operation and to demonstrate the use of these equations in the prediction of the dynamic behavior of these respective reactor models.

A. Plug-Flow Reactors

Suppose that the tubular reactor shown in Figure 2-1 is adequately represented by the plug-flow model. Further suppose that an upset in the operation of the reactor has just occurred, such as a change in the concentration of reactant A in the feed. The development of the equations needed to describe the behavior of this reactor is initiated by making a material balance on A in a given element of reactor volume over a given time period.

To make a material balance on A over the time period from t_n to t_{n+1}, Equation (1-33) is applied. Let the volume from V_j to $V_j + \Delta V$ (see Figure 2-1) be selected as the system. Then the material balance on component A over the element of volume from V_j to V_{j+1} and over the time period from t_n to t_{n+1} is given by

$$\int_{t_n}^{t_{n+1}} \left[n_A \Big|_{V_j,t} - n_A \Big|_{V_{j+1},t} - \int_{V_j}^{V_{j+1}} r_A \, dV \right] dt = \int_{V_j}^{V_{j+1}} \left[C_A \Big|_{t_{n+1},V} - C_A \Big|_{t_n,V} \right] dV$$

$$(2\text{-}103)$$

where
$$t_{n+1} = t_n + \Delta t$$
$$V_{j+1} = V_j + \Delta V$$

By application of the mean value theorems followed by the limiting process wherein ΔV and Δt are allowed to go to zero, the following form of the material-balance equation is obtained:

$$-\frac{\partial n_A}{\partial V} - r_A = \frac{\partial C_A}{\partial t}, \qquad (0 < V < V_T) \qquad (2\text{-}104)$$

The material-balance equation is used to find the variation of C_A or n_A with time and position in the reactor. The concentration of A in the reactor at a given position at any time t depends upon the initial conditions and the nature of the chemical reaction. For purposes of illustration, consider the relatively simple situation wherein the first-order reaction

$$A \longrightarrow R, r_A = kC_A$$

is being carried out in the liquid phase at constant mass density. Suppose that at time $t = 0$ the concentration of A at each point in the reactor and in the feed is C_A^0. (This condition implies that the reaction is not occurring at time $t = 0$.) Now suppose that at time $t = 0 +$ the reactor is heated instantaneously to the reaction temperature and held constant at this temperature for all $t > 0+$.

For convenience, let the following changes of variables be made:

$$n_A = C_A v_T, \qquad x = \frac{V}{v_T}, \qquad Y(x, t) = \frac{(C_A - C_A^0)}{C_A^0}$$

to give

$$\frac{\partial Y}{\partial x} + \frac{\partial Y}{\partial t} = -k(1 + Y) \qquad \left(\begin{matrix} t > 0+ \\ 0 < x < x_f \end{matrix}\right) \qquad (2\text{-}105)$$

where

$$x_f = \frac{V_T}{v_T}$$

The initial and boundary conditions are

$$Y(x, 0) = 0, \qquad Y(0, t) = 0 \qquad (2\text{-}106)$$

The first of these follows immediately from the above definition of $Y(x, t)$. The boundary condition is obtained by first observing that as V approaches zero, the concentration C_A approaches the inlet value C_A^0.

Let the Laplace transform of $Y(x, t)$ with respect to t be denoted by $y(x, s)$; that is,

$$L\{Y(x, t)\} = \int_0^\infty e^{-st} Y(x, t)\, dt = y(x, s) \qquad (2\text{-}107)$$

After the Laplace transform of each term of Equation (2-105) has been taken by use of the procedures described in standard texts on Laplace transforms (see, for example, [23]), the following ordinary differential equation with constant coefficients is obtained.

$$\frac{dy}{dx} + sy = -k\left(\frac{1}{s} + y\right) \tag{2-108}$$

The conditions given by Equation (2-106) may be transformed to give

$$y(x, 0) = 0, \qquad y(0, s) = 0 \tag{2-109}$$

Equation (2-108) may be solved by separation of the variables followed by integration.

$$\int_0^y \frac{dy}{k/s + (k + s)y} = -\int_0^x dx \tag{2-110}$$

After the integrals have been evaluated, the result so obtained may be rearranged to give

$$y(x, s) = -\frac{1}{s} + \frac{e^{-xs}}{s} e^{-kx} + \frac{1}{s + k} - \frac{e^{-(s+k)x}}{s + k} \tag{2-111}$$

To obtain $Y(x, t)$, the inverse Laplace transform of each term of Equation (2-111) is taken as described by Churchill [23].

$$Y(x, t) = -1 + (e^{-kx} - e^{-kt})S_x(t) + e^{-kt} \tag{2-112}$$

where $S_x(t)$ is the step function defined by

$$S_x(t) = \begin{cases} 0 & \text{when} \quad 0 < t < x \\ 1 & \text{when} \quad t > x \end{cases}$$

Restatement of Equation (2-112) in terms of concentration gives

$$C_A = C_A^0[e^{-kx} - e^{-kt}]S_X(t) + C_A^0 e^{-kt} \tag{2-113}$$

The equation may be restated as two cases.

1. For $0 < t < x$, $S_x(t) = 0$, and Equation (2-113) reduces to

$$C_A = C_A^0 e^{-kt} \qquad (0 < t < x) \tag{2-114}$$

2. For $t > x$, $S_x(t) = 1$, and Equation (2-113) reduces to

$$C_A = C_A^0 \exp\left(-k\frac{V}{v_T}\right) = C_A^0 e^{-k\theta} \qquad (t > x) \tag{2-115}$$

where $\theta = V/v_T$, the true residence time. Comparison of Equations (2-115) and (2-15) leads to the conclusion that steady state operation is achieved after the reactor has been swept out one time. This characteristic results from the fact that in the case of plug flow at constant mass density and isothermal operation, each element of fluid passes through the volume V independently of the elements of fluid ahead and behind it. As a consequence of this fact, it is possible to deduce from intuitive reasoning the solutions given above by Equations (2-114) and (2-115) as well as the solutions for other sets of boundary conditions and other reactions.

B. Perfectly Mixed Reactors

Suppose that the tank reactor in Figure 2-6 may be represented by the perfectly mixed model. Further suppose that an upset in the operation of the reactor has just occurred.

The component material balance on A in the volume V over the time period Δt is given by

$$\int_{t_n}^{t_n + \Delta t} [n_A^0 - n_A - r_A V] \, dt = N_A \big|_{t_n + \Delta t} - N_A \big|_{t_n} \qquad (2\text{-}116)$$

In this expression, n_A^0 and n_A represent the inlet and outlet flow rates, respectively, to the reactor at any time t. The total moles of A in the reactor at any time t is denoted by N_A, and the volume occupied by the reacting mixture at any time t is V. Application of the mean value theorems, followed by the limiting process wherein Δt is allowed to go to zero, gives the following form of the material-balance equation

$$n_A^0 - n_A - r_A V = \frac{dN_A}{dt} \qquad (2\text{-}117)$$

1. VARIATION OF THE OUTLET CONCENTRATION WITH TIME. To illustrate the use of the material-balance equation in predicting the variation of the outlet flow rate of A with respect to time, one simple example is solved. Suppose that the first-order reaction $A \rightarrow R$ is being carried out in a perfectly mixed tank reactor. Further suppose that at time $t = 0$ a step change in the concentration of A in the feed occurs, and, for $t = 0+$, the flow rate at which A enters the reactor is n_A^0 while the total volumetric flow rate remains constant. Let the moles of A in the reactor at time $t = 0$ be denoted by N_A^0. Further suppose that the volume V of the reactor which is filled by the reacting mixture remains constant.

Elimination of r_A from Equation (2-117) by use of the rate expression yields

$$\frac{n_A^0 - n_A}{V} - \frac{1}{V} \frac{dN_A}{dt} = k_c C_A \qquad (2\text{-}118)$$

Since the reactor is perfectly mixed,

$$C_A = \frac{n_A}{v_T} = \frac{N_A}{V} \tag{2-119}$$

When C_A and n_A are expressed in terms of N_A by use of this relationship, Equation (2-118) reduces to

$$\left[\frac{n_A^0 - (v_T/V)N_A}{V}\right] - \frac{1}{V}\frac{dN_A}{dt} = k_c\left(\frac{N_A}{V}\right) \tag{2-120}$$

Separation of variables followed by integration and rearrangement yields

$$N_A = \frac{n_A^0}{\beta}\left[1 - \left(1 - \frac{N_A^0\beta}{n_A^0}\right)\exp\left(-\beta t\right)\right] \tag{2-121}$$

where $N_A^0 = $ moles of A in the reactor at time $t = 0$

$$\beta = \frac{v_T}{V} + k_c$$

Equation (2-121) may be rearranged to the following form.

$$n_A = \frac{n_A^0}{\theta\beta}\left[1 - \left\{\left(1 - \frac{N_A^0\beta}{n_A^0}\right)\exp\left(-k_c t\right)\right\}\exp\left(\frac{-t}{\theta}\right)\right] \tag{2-122}$$

where $\theta = V/v_T$, the residence time. The correct steady state value of n_A is given by taking the limit of both sides of Equation (2-122) as the process time t is allowed to increase without bound.

$$\lim_{t \to \infty} n_A = \frac{n_A^0}{\theta\beta} = \frac{n_A^0}{1 + k_c\theta} \tag{2-123}$$

This steady state value of n_A is closely approached after the reactor has been in operation for a period of time equal to three to five times the residence time. That is, for $t = 3\theta$,

$$e^{-t/\theta} = e^{-3\theta/\theta} = 0.05$$

and for $t = 5\theta$,

$$e^{-t/\theta} = e^{-5\theta/\theta} = 0.007$$

For $t = 3\theta$, Equation (2-122) gives a value of n_A which is slightly greater than 95% of the steady state value, and for $t = 5\theta$, a value of n_A slightly greater than 99.3% of the steady state value is given by Equation (2-122). In this particular case, the term $\exp(-k_c t)$ improves the steady state approximation since k_c is always positive.

Aris [1] has shown that after a process time t equal to 3θ to 5θ has elapsed, the steady state is closely approximated for reactions of all orders.

PROBLEMS

2-1. Let r_A be defined in terms of the appearance of A; that is, r_A is equal to the moles of A appearing per unit time per unit volume. On the basis of this definition of r_A, make a material balance on A over the element ΔV of a plug-flow reactor. Apply the mean value theorems and take the limit of the result so obtained as $\Delta V \rightarrow 0$, and show that the resulting expression for the component material balance is given by Equation (2-9).

2-2. For the case where the following liquid phase reactions
(a) $2A \rightarrow$ products
(b) $A + B \rightarrow$ products
(c) $3A \rightarrow$ products
are carried out isothermally at constant mass density in a plug-flow reactor at steady state operation, show that the flow rate n_A at which A leaves the reactor is related to the reactor volume V as follows:

(a) $\dfrac{k_c V}{v_T^2} = \dfrac{1}{n_A} - \dfrac{1}{n_A^0}$

(b) $\dfrac{k_c V}{v_T^2} = \dfrac{1}{n_A^0 - n_B^0} \log_e \dfrac{n_A n_B^0}{n_B n_A^0}$

(c) $\dfrac{2k_c V}{v_T^3} = \dfrac{1}{n_A^2} - \dfrac{1}{(n_A^0)^2}$

2-3. Suppose that the following data are obtained for the gas phase reaction $2A \rightarrow R$ in a perfectly mixed batch reactor which is operated isothermally at $100°C$ and at constant volume. Initially the reactor is filled with pure A with a concentration of 3 g moles/liter.

Data:

Time (min)	Conversion X
10	0.310
30	0.674
60	0.894
80	0.950

(a) Determine whether the reaction is first or second order, and evaluate the rate constant.
(b) Calculate the space velocity required to obtain a 95% conversion of A in a plug-flow reactor. The reactor is to be operated at 50 atm pressure and

100°C, and pure A is fed to the reactor. In the evaluation of the space velocities, take $T_s = 273.15°K$ and $P_s = 1$ atm.
Answer: **(b)** $1/S_V = 1.4412$ min

2-4. Over most metal catalysts, the rate of hydrogenation of ethylene is

$$C_2H_4 + H_2 \longrightarrow C_2H_6$$

zero order with respect to ethylene and first order with respect to hydrogen [24, 25]; that is, the rate of disappearance of ethylene is given by

$$r_{C_2H_4} = k_p p_{H_2}$$

If $k_p = 0.17$ g mole/(sec liter atm) at 100°C and if a reactor pressure of 10 atm and a feed rate of 100 g moles/sec are used, calculate the reactor volume required to obtain 90% conversion at a reaction temperature of 100°C. The feed is equi-molar and plug flow prevails throughout the reactor.
Answer: $V = 94.2$ liters

2-5. For the case where the reversible reaction $A \rightleftarrows R$ is carried out in the gas phase in a plug-flow reactor, the reactor volume V required to obtain a conversion x may be expressed in terms of x and the equilibrium conversion x^*. At equilibrium,

$$K_p = \frac{p_R^*}{p_A^*} = \frac{n_R^*}{n_A^*} = \frac{n_R^0 + n_A^0 x^*}{n_A^0 - n_A^0 x^*}$$

for a perfect gas mixture.
(a) Show that this same expression for K_p may be obtained by imposing the condition on Equation (2-28) that at equilibrium

$$\frac{dx}{dV} = 0$$

What does this condition imply about the reactor volume?
(b) For the above reversible reaction show that

$$\frac{dx}{dV} = \bar{k}(x^* - x)$$

where

$$\bar{k} = \left(\frac{k_p' P}{n_T^0}\right)(K_p + 1)$$

What other rate process is sometimes described by an equation of this type?
(c) Show that when the above reaction is carried out as described

$$V = \frac{1}{\bar{k}} \log_e \frac{x^*}{x^* - x}$$

2-6. For the second-order reaction, $2A \rightarrow$ products, which occurs in the liquid phase in a tubular reactor, show that for the case of plug flow and constant mass density

$$\theta = \frac{V}{v_T} = \left(\frac{1}{k_c C_A^0}\right)\left(\frac{x}{1-x}\right)$$

For an $x = 0.6$, what will be the ratio of the volume for the plug-flow reactor to that of a perfectly mixed flow reactor? The feed rate and concentration to each reactor are the same.

Answer: 0.4

2-7. Suppose that the following half-life data are available from an investigation of the isothermal decomposition of reactant A at constant mass density in the liquid phase in a plug-flow reactor.

Half-life (min)	C_A^0 (g moles/liter)
0.030	5
0.0468	4
0.1880	2

(a) Determine the order of the reaction and evaluate the rate constant.

(b) Calculate the residence time θ required to reduce the concentration of A ($C_A^0 = 3.0$ g moles/liter) to one-half of its initial value in a perfectly mixed flow reactor and in a plug-flow tubular reactor.

Answer: **(b)** perfectly mixed: 0.2222 min; plug flow: 0.08333 min

2-8. Begin with Equation (2-78) and obtain the result given by Equation (2-79).

Hints:

(a) By use of Equation (2-65), show that

$$\left(\frac{R^2}{-2u_{max}}\right) u\, du = ur\, dr$$

(b) First make the change in variable,

$$\psi = \frac{1}{(u/u_{max})}$$

and then make the change in variable,

$$\phi = y\psi \quad \text{where} \quad y = \frac{k_c^z{}_T}{u_{max}}$$

and integrate two times by parts.

2-9. Suppose that it is desired to convert 50% of reactant A to R by the reaction $A \rightarrow R$ in the liquid phase. The reaction is first order, $r_A = k_c C_A$.

(a) Show that if this reaction is carried out isothermally at constant mass density in a perfectly mixed flow reactor,

$$\frac{V}{v_T} = \frac{1}{k_c}$$

(b) Show that if the same reaction is carried isothermally in a plug-flow reactor,

$$\frac{V}{v_T} = \frac{0.693}{k_c}$$

2-10. Begin with Equation (2-103) and apply the mean values theorems and a limiting process in a manner analogous to that demonstrated in the text for partial mixing in the axial and radial mixing and show that the material balance expression given by Equation (2-104) is obtained.

2-11. Begin with Equation (2-116) and show that the material balance expression given by Equation (2-117) may be obtained by following the procedure described below Equation (2-116).

2-12. Show that in the limit as the diffusivity $\mathscr{D}$ goes to zero, the material balance for reactors with partial axial mixing [Equation (2-84)] reduces to the material balance for a plug-flow reactor [Equation (2-8)].

2-13. Show that in the limit as the diffusivities $\mathscr{D}_r$ and $\mathscr{D}_z$ go to zero, the material balance expressions for reactors with partial axial and radial mixing [Equation (2-102)] reduces to the material balance for a laminar-flow reactor [Equation (2-74)].

2-14. Cyclopropane is to be isomerized to form propylene in a tubular reactor by the reaction

Davis and Scott [26] carried this reaction out in a borosilicate glass reactor and found the reaction to be first order at 1 atm with the following rate constant.

$$\log_e k_c = 36.1923 - \frac{66,950}{RT}$$

where k_c has the units of reciprocal seconds, T is in $^\circ K$ and $R = 1.9872$ (cal/g mole $^\circ K$).

Calculate the space velocity required to achieve a conversion of 60% at a reaction temperature of 570°C and a reaction pressure of 1 atm (absolute). Evaluate the space velocity on the basis of $T_s = 273.15^\circ K$ and $P_s = 1$ atm. Assume that plug-flow conditions prevail and that none of the propylene pyrolyzes to other products at this temperature.

Answer: $S_V = 29.466$ hr^{-1}

2-15. The decomposition of cyclohexane over a platinum-alumina-mordenite catalyst was studied by Allan and Voorhies [27]. The principal reactions which were found to occur were

$$C_6H_9 \rightleftharpoons \underset{\text{Benzene}}{C_6H_6} + 3\,H_2$$

$$C_6H_9 \rightleftharpoons \underset{\text{Methyl cyclopentane}}{C_6H_9}$$

At the reaction conditions investigated, isomerization was $\frac{1}{5}$ the rate of dehydrogenation. Let the first reaction be denoted by

$$A \rightleftharpoons B + 3C$$

For this reaction Allan and Voorhies give the following expression for the rate of appearance of benzene.

$$\frac{1}{\rho}\frac{dn_B}{dV} = \left(\frac{k_1}{\rho}\right)p_A - \left(\frac{k_1'}{\rho}\right)p_B p_C^3$$

where ρ is equal to the bulk density (grams catalyst per cubic centimeter of catalyst bed) of the catalyst bed through which the reacting stream passes.

For a reaction temperature of 775°R, a reactor pressure of 85 psia, and a feed composition of 20 moles of hydrogen per mole of cyclohexane, calculate the value of the parameter $\rho V/n_T^0$ required to achieve an 80% conversion of cyclohexane per pass. In this calculation, neglect the isomerization reaction and the variation of the partial pressure of hydrogen at these conditions

$$K_p = \frac{k_1}{k_1'} = \frac{(k_1/\rho)}{(k_1'/\rho)} = 8301 \text{ atm}^3$$

$$\frac{k_1}{\rho} = 0.045 \text{ g mole/(min-g catalyst-atm)}$$

Answer: $\rho V/n_T^0 = 6.385$ g/(g mole/min)

2-16. Anthracene was oxidized over a cobalt molybdate catalyst at 300°C and 760 mm Hg by Subramanian and Murthy [28],

$$\underset{\text{Anthracene}}{C_{14}H_{10}} + 1.5O_2 \longrightarrow C_{14}H_8O_2 + H_2O$$

For a feed mixture which was 10% (by volume) anthracene and 90% O_2, the reaction was found to be first order with respect to oxygen and zero order with respect to anthracene; that is, the above reaction is represented by

$$A + 1.5B \longrightarrow C + D$$

$$-\frac{1}{\rho}\frac{dn_A}{dV} = \left(\frac{k_1}{\rho}\right)p_B$$

where ρ is the bulk density of the catalyst bed (grams of catalyst per liter of catalyst bed).

Calculate the value of the parameter $\rho V/n_T^0$ required to achieve a conversion of 90% of the anthracene in a plug-flow reactor at the operating conditions enumerated above. Subramanian and Murthy [28] give the following value for the rate constant

$$\frac{k_1}{\rho} = 2.61 \times 10^{-7} \text{ g moles/(min-g catalyst-mm Hg)}$$

Answer: $\rho V/n_T^0 = 533.6$ g/(g mole min)

NOTATION

$A =$ area perpendicular to the direction of mass transfer, ft^2.

$C_A =$ concentration of component A, moles/unit volume.

$\mathscr{D} =$ eddy diffusivity due to both molecular motion and turbulent motion, (length)^2/unit time; defined by Equation (2-81).

$\mathscr{J}_A =$ rate of dispersion of component A as a consequence of molecular diffusion and turbulent motion [see Equation (2-81)].

$n_A^0, n_A =$ molar flow rate of component A at the inlet to the reactor and at any point in the reactor, respectively, moles/unit time.

$n_T^0 =$ molar flow rate of the feed to the reactor.

$n_T =$ total molar flow rate at any point in the reactor.

$n_A^0 =$ (for reactors with recycle) n_A^0 is the molar flow rate of A in the feed to the system (see Figure 2-11).

$n_{Ai} =$ (for reactors with recycle) n_{Ai} is the molar flow rate of A at the inlet of the reactor.

$n_{Af} =$ (for reactors with recycle) n_{Af} is the molar flow rate of A at the outlet of the reactor $V = V_T$.

$n_T^0 =$ (for reactors with recycle) n_T^0 is the total molar flow rate of A in the feed to the system (see Figure 2-11).

$n_{Ti} =$ (for reactors with recycle) n_{Ti} is the total molar flow rate at the inlet to the reactor.

$n_T =$ (for reactors with recycle) n_T is the total molar flow rate at any point in the reactor.

$n_{Tf} =$ (for reactors with recycle) n_{Tf} is the total molar flow rate at the outlet of the reactor $V = V_T$.

$N =$ order of a reaction.

$N_A^0, N_A =$ total moles of component A in the reactor at time $t = 0$ and the total moles of A in the reactor at any time t, moles.

$N_R =$ reaction number; for a first-order reaction $N_R = k_c \theta = k_c V/v_T = k_c z_T/u_m$.

N_{Pe} = Peclet number, $u_m z_T / \mathscr{D}$.

p_A = partial pressure of component A, mass/unit area.

P = total pressure, mass/unit area.

r = radius of a tubular reactor (see Figure 2-13).

r_A = net rate of reaction of component A. Except where noted r_A is defined in terms of disappearance; that is, r_A is equal to the moles of A disappearing by reaction per unit time per unit volume.

R = constant in the perfect gas law; defined by Equation (2-18). Also used to denote the radius of a tubular reactor (see Figure 2-13).

S = cross-sectional area of a reactor.

S_V = gaseous space velocity; defined by Equation (2-30).

S_L = liquid space velocity; defined by Equation (2-34).

t = time.

u = linear velocity at any given radius r of a tubular reactor in which the contents are in laminar flow.

$u_{\max}$ = velocity at the center of the reactor (at $r = 0$).

u_m = average velocity; $u_m = v_T / S$.

v_T = total volumetric flow rate.

V = reactor volume or more precisely that portion of the reactor volume occupied by the reacting mixture, $0 \leq V \leq V_T$, where V_T is the total volume.

x = moles of the base converted per mole of the base component in the feed.

χ = moles of the base component converted in a system consisting of a reactor plus a recycle stream per mole of the base component in the feed to the system.

y_A^0 = mole fraction of component A in the feed.

z = reactor length; z_T = total length of the reactor.

REFERENCES

1. Aris, R., *Elementary Chemical Reactor Analysis*, Prentice-Hall, Inc., Englewood Cliffs, N.J. (1969).

2. Levenspiel, O., *Chemical Reaction Engineering*, John Wiley & Sons, Inc., New York (1972).

3. Denbigh, K. G., *Chemical Reactor Theory*, Cambridge Press, London (1965).

4. Griffith, R. O., R. S. Jobin, and A. McKeown, *Trans. Faraday Soc.*, *34*:316 (1938).

5. NBS Circular 510, *Tables of Chemical Kinetics-Homogeneous reactions*, United States Department of Commerce, National Bureau of Standards, Table 352. 475 (Sept. 28, 1951).

6. Fisher, R. A., and J. M. Smith, *Ind. Eng. Chem.*, *42*:704 (1950).

7. Marek, L. F., and W. B. McCluer, *Ind. Eng. Chem.*, *23*:878 (1931).

8. Carnahan, B., H. A. Luther, and J. O. Wilkes, *Applied Numerical Methods*, John Wiley & Sons, Inc., New York (1969).

9. Snow, R. H., *J. Phys. Chem.*, *70*:2780 (1966).

10. Snow, R. H., R. E. Peck, and C. G. Von Fredersdorff *AIChE J. 5*:304 (1959).

11. Himmelblau, D. M., *Process Analysis by Statistical Methods*, John Wiley & Sons, Inc., New York (1970).

12. Kunzru, D., Y. T. Shah, and E. B. Stuart, *I&EC Proc. Design and Develop.*, *2*, No. 3, 339 (1923).

13. Hinshelwood, C. H., and P. S. Askey, *Proc. Roy. Soc.*, *A115*:215 (1927).

14. Leuteritz, G. M., P. Reimann, and P. Vergeris, *Hydrocarbon Processing*, *55*: 99 (1976).

15. Carberry, J. J., *Applied Kinetics and Chemical Engineering*, American Chemical Society Publications, Washington, D.C. (1976).

16. *Handbook of Mathematical Tables*, Supplement to Handbook of Chemistry and Physics, The Chemical Rubber Company, Cleveland, Ohio (1964).

17. Bhattacharyya, D. N., J. Smid, and M. Szwarc *J. Phys. Chem. 69*:624 (1965).

18. Burghardt, A., and T. Zaleski *Chem. Eng. Sci. 23*:575 (1968).

19. Danckwerts, P. V., *Chemical Reaction Engineering, 12th Meeting, Eur. Fed. Chem. Eng.*, Amsterdam (1957).

20. Zwietering, Th. N., *Chem. Eng. Sci.*, *11*:1 (1959).

21. Himmelblau, D. M., and K. B. Bishoff, *Process Analysis and Simulation: Deterministic Systems*, John Wiley & Sons, Inc., New York (1968).

22. Wen, C. Y., and C. T. Fan, *Models for Flow Systems and Chemical Reactors*, Marcel Dekker, Inc., New York (1975).

23. Churchill, R. W., *Operational Mathematics*, 2d ed., McGraw-Hill Book Company, New York (1958).

24. Wynkoop, R., and R. Wilhelm, *CEP*, *46*:300 (1950).

25. Horiutu, J., and K. Miyahara, *Hydrogenation of Ethylene on Metallic Catalysts*. National Standard Reference Data Series, N.B.S., *13: Category 6, Chem. Kin.*

26. Davis, B. R., and D. S. Scott, *I&EC Fund.*, *3*:20 (1964).

27. Allan, D. E., and A. Voorhies, Jr., *I&EC Prod. Research and Develop.*, *11*:159 (1972).

28. Subramanian, P., and M. S. Murthy, *Chem. Eng. Sci.*, *29*:25 (1974).

Simultaneous and Consecutive Reactions

3

In the majority of industrial reactors, more than one chemical reaction occurs. In this chapter, expressions relating reactor volume or reactor time to the conversion of a base component or the extent to which the group of reactions has progressed is treated. Simultaneous reactions are treated in Part I and consecutive reactions are treated in Part II.

I. SIMULTANEOUS REACTIONS

Simultaneous reactions, as the name implies, includes those cases where two or more reactions involving some base component A occur simultaneously. These reactions are also referred to as *parallel reactions*. Expressions relating conversion and the appropriate independent variable, time or reactor volume, are developed for batch reactors, plug-flow reactors, and perfectly mixed flow reactors.

The system of notation used in the analysis of simultaneous reactions occurring in batch reactors is presented in Table 3-1. For flow reactors, the corresponding system of notation is given by replacing N_i, the moles of A reacted by the ith reaction, with the corresponding flow rate n_i, moles per unit time.

118

TABLE 3-1

DEFINITION OF THE MOLES OF COMPOUND A
REACTED BY EACH REACTION OF A SET OF
SIMULTANEOUS REACTIONS

Reactions	Moles of A Reacted	Moles of Product
(1) $A \longrightarrow R$	N_1	$N_R = N_R^0 + N_1$
(2) $A \longrightarrow 2D$	N_2	$N_D = N_D^0 + 2N_2$
(3) $2A \longrightarrow S$	N_3	$N_S = N_S^0 + \frac{1}{2}N_3$
(4) $2A \longrightarrow 2M$	N_4	$N_M = N_M^0 + N_4$
(5) $3A \longrightarrow U$	N_5	$N_U = N_U^0 + \dfrac{N_5}{3}$
(6) $3A \longrightarrow 2V$	N_6	$N_V = N_V^0 + \dfrac{2N_6}{3}$
(7) $3A \longrightarrow 3W$	N_7	$N_W = N_W^0 + N_7$

Expressions relating conversion or progress of the reactions versus time for batch reactors and versus reactor volume for flow reactors follow. The case where all reactions occur in the gas phase and the case where all reactions occur in the liquid phase are treated.

A. Simultaneous Reactions Carried Out Isothermally In Batch Reactors

The three types of simultaneous reactions are considered in the order listed below. Throughout the treatment that follows for batch reactors, it is supposed that the volume of the reactor filled by the reacting mixture remains constant throughout the course of the reaction. Perfect mixing of the contents of the reactor during the reaction period is also assumed. Under these conditions, the equations for gas and liquid phase reactions are identical.

1. FIRST ORDER REACTIONS. Consider first the case where the two simultaneous reactions of Table 3-2.

$$(1) \quad A \xrightarrow{k_1} R$$

$$(2) \quad A \xrightarrow{k_2} 2S$$

TABLE 3-2

Two Simultaneous Reactions and The Material Balances

Reaction and Definitions of Rate Constants		Moles of A Reacted	Moles of Product Formed
(1) $A \longrightarrow R,$	$r_{A1} = k_1 C_A$	N_1	$N_R = N_R^0 + N_1$
(2) $A \longrightarrow 2S,$	$r_{A2} = k_2 C_A$	N_2	$N_S = N_S^0 + 2N_2$

occur in a batch reactor. (Throughout this Chapter, the subscript c on the rate constant k_c has been dropped in the interest of simplicity.) The rate constant for each reaction is defined with respect to component A. Note that in general $k_1 \neq k_2$. For if k_1 did equal k_2, then 1 mole of R would be produced for each 2 moles of S produced, and it would appear that only the single reaction

$$2A \longrightarrow R + 2S$$

had occurred.

The net rate of disappearance of A is equal to the sum of the rates at which A disappears by Reactions (1) and (2); that is,

$$r_A = r_{A1} + r_{A2} \tag{3-1}$$

where
$$r_{A1} = k_1 C_A$$

$$r_{A2} = k_2 C_A$$

For a batch reactor, the material balance on component A is given by

$$r_A = -\frac{1}{V}\frac{dN_A}{dt} \tag{3-2}$$

Thus

$$-\frac{1}{V}\frac{dN_A}{dt} = k_1 C_A + k_2 C_A = (k_1 + k_2)\frac{N_A}{V} \tag{3-3}$$

Separation of variables followed by integration and rearrangement yields

$$N_A = N_A^0 \exp\left[-(k_1 + k_2)t\right] \tag{3-4}$$

To compute the moles of each of the products formed, the following procedure may be used. Let the rates of reaction of the products be stated in terms of appearance and the rate of reaction of the reactant A in terms of disappearance. Then for the two simultaneous reactions (1) $A \rightarrow R$ and

(2) $A \rightarrow 2S$, component-material balances give

$$r_A = -\frac{1}{V}\frac{dN_A}{dt}, \qquad r_R = \frac{1}{V}\frac{dN_R}{dt}, \qquad r_S = \frac{1}{V}\frac{dN_S}{dt} \tag{3-5}$$

The rates of disappearance of A by reactions (1) and (2) (r_{A1} and r_{A2}) are related to the rates of formation of R and S as follows:

$$r_{A1} = \boxed{r_R}, \qquad r_{A2} = \tfrac{1}{2}r_S \tag{3-6}$$

where the expressions for r_{A1} and r_{A2} are given below Equation (3-1). Thus, Equations (3-5) and (3-6) may be combined to give

$$\frac{1}{V}\frac{dN_R}{dt} = k_1 C_A \tag{3-7}$$

$$\frac{1}{2V}\left(\frac{dN_S}{dt}\right) = k_2 C_A \tag{3-8}$$

If N_R and N_S in these expressions are expressed in terms of N_1 and N_2, as defined in Table 3-2, the following result is obtained:

$$\frac{dN_1}{dt} = k_1 N_A \tag{3-9}$$

$$\frac{dN_2}{dt} = k_2 N_A \tag{3-10}$$

Division of the members of Equation (3-9) by the corresponding members of Equation (3-10) yields

$$\frac{dN_1}{dN_2} = \frac{k_1}{k_2} \tag{3-11}$$

Then by integration of this expression, it is found that

$$\frac{N_1}{N_2} = \frac{k_1}{k_2} \tag{3-12}$$

since $N_1 = N_2 = 0$ at $t = 0$.

To obtain N_1 as a function of time, first note that

$$N_A = N_A^0 - N_1 - N_2 \tag{3-13}$$

Then by use of Equation (3-12), it follows that

$$N_A = N_A^0 - N_1(1 + k_2/k_1)$$

or
$$N_1 = \frac{k_1(N_A^0 - N_A)}{k_1 + k_2} \tag{3-14}$$

where N_A is given by Equation (3-4). From Equations (3-12) and (3-14), one obtains

$$N_2 = \frac{k_2(N_A^0 - N_A)}{k_1 + k_2} \tag{3-15}$$

where N_A is again given by Equation (3-4). Since $N_R = N_R^0 + N_1$ and $N_S = N_S^0 + 2N_2$, Equations (3-4), (3-14), and (3-15) may be used to express N_R and N_S as functions of time.

The equations for the case where n simultaneous, irreversible first-order reactions are carried out isothermally in a perfectly mixed batch reactor at constant volume are given in Table 3-3. (The expressions given in this table for plug-flow and perfectly mixed reactors are discussed below in subsequent sections.)

2. SECOND-ORDER REACTIONS. Consider the case of two second-order simultaneous reactions,

$$\begin{aligned} 2A &\longrightarrow R, & r_{A1} &= k_1 C_A^2 \\ 2A &\longrightarrow 2S, & r_{A2} &= k_2 C_A^2 \end{aligned} \tag{3-16}$$

The moles of A, R, and S may be stated in terms of N_1 and N_2 (defined in Table 3-1) as follows:

$$\begin{aligned} N_A &= N_A^0 - N_1 - N_2 \\ N_R &= N_R^0 + \tfrac{1}{2}N_1 \\ N_S &= N_S^0 + N_2 \end{aligned} \tag{3-17}$$

Since r_A is equal to the net rate of disappearance of A, it is again related to r_{A1} and r_{A2} as indicated by Equation (3-1). The material balance on component A is given by

$$r_A = -\frac{1}{V}\frac{dN_A}{dt} \tag{3-18}$$

Thus

$$-\frac{1}{V}\frac{dN_A}{dt} = k_1 C_A^2 + k_2 C_A^2 = (k_1 + k_2)\left(\frac{N_A}{V}\right)^2 \tag{3-19}$$

TABLE 3-3
SIMULTANEOUS AND IRREVERSIBLE FIRST-ORDER REACTIONS

$$A \longrightarrow \alpha_1 R_1, \qquad r_{A1} = k_1 C_A$$

$$A \longrightarrow \alpha_2 R_2, \qquad r_{A2} = k_2 C_A$$

$$\vdots \qquad \qquad \vdots \qquad \qquad \vdots$$

$$A \longrightarrow \alpha_n R_n, \qquad r_{An} = k_n C_A$$

Batch Reactors
(Conditions: perfectly mixed, isothermal, and constant volume)

$$N_A = N_A^0 - N_1 - N_2 - \cdots - N_n \qquad N_A = N_A^0 e^{-at}$$

$$N_{R1} = N_{R1}^0 + \alpha_1 N_1$$

$$\vdots \qquad \vdots \qquad \vdots \qquad\qquad a = \sum_{i=1}^{n} k_i$$

$$N_{Rn} = N_{Rn}^0 + \alpha_n N_n$$

$$-\frac{1}{V}\frac{dN_A}{dt} = r_A = \sum_{i=1}^{n} r_{Ai} \qquad N_j = \frac{k_j}{a}(N_A^0 - N_A), \quad (j = 1, 2, \ldots, n)$$

$$r_{Ai} = \frac{1}{\alpha i} r_{Ri}, \quad (i = 1, 2, \ldots, n)$$

$$\frac{N_i}{N_1} = \frac{k_i}{k_1}, \quad (i = 1, 2, \ldots, n)$$

Plug-Flow Reactors
(Conditions: steady state, plug flow, isothermal operation, liquid phase, and constant mass density)

$$n_A = n_A^0 - n_1 - n_2 - \cdots - n_n \qquad n_A = n_A^0 e^{-a\theta}$$

$$n_{R1} = n_{R1}^0 + \alpha_1 n_1$$

$$\vdots \qquad \vdots \qquad \vdots \qquad\qquad a = \sum_{i=1}^{n} k_i$$

$$n_{Rn} = n_{Rn}^0 + \alpha_n n_n \qquad\qquad \theta = V/v_T$$

$$-\frac{dn_A}{dV} = r_A = \sum_{i=1}^{n} r_{Ai} \qquad n_j = \frac{k_j}{a}(n_A^0 - n_A), \quad (j = 1, 2, \ldots, n)$$

$$r_{Ai} = \frac{1}{\alpha_i} r_{Ri}, \quad (i = 1, 2, \ldots, n)$$

$$\frac{n_i}{n_1} = \frac{k_i}{k_1}, \quad (i = 1, 2, \ldots, n)$$

Perfectly Mixed Flow Reactors
(Conditions: steady state)

The expressions for perfectly mixed reactors are obtained by replacing

$$-\frac{dn_A}{dV} = r_A = \sum_{i=1}^{n} r_{Ai}, \text{ and } n_A = n_A^0 e^{-a\theta}$$

in the above expressions for plug-flow reactors by

$$\frac{n_A^0 - n_A}{V} = r_A = \sum_{i=1}^{n} r_{Ai}, \text{ and } n_A = \frac{n_A^0}{1 + a\theta}$$

For reactions which occur at constant volume, Equation (3-19) may be rearranged and integrated to give

$$\frac{1}{N_A} - \frac{1}{N_A^0} = (k_1 + k_2)\frac{t}{V}$$

or
$$N_A = \frac{1}{1/N_A^0 + (k_1 + k_2)(t/V)} \qquad (3\text{-}20)$$

The product distribution may be obtained by use of relationships which are developed as follows. Let r_R and r_S be defined as the net rates of appearance of R and S, respectively. Then

$$r_R = \tfrac{1}{2}r_{A1}, \qquad r_S = r_{A2} \qquad (3\text{-}21)$$

The component-material balances on R and S are given by

$$r_R = \frac{1}{V}\frac{dN_R}{dt}, \qquad r_S = \frac{1}{V}\frac{dN_S}{dt} \qquad (3\text{-}22)$$

From the stoichiometric relationships given by Equation (3-17), it is evident that

$$r_R = \frac{1}{V}\frac{dN_R}{dt} = \frac{1}{2V}\frac{dN_1}{dt} \qquad (3\text{-}23)$$

$$r_S = \frac{1}{V}\frac{dN_S}{dt} = \frac{1}{V}\frac{dN_2}{dt} \qquad (3\text{-}24)$$

The above relationships may be used to show that

$$\frac{1}{2V}\frac{dN_1}{dt} = \frac{1}{2}k_1 C_A^2 \qquad (3\text{-}25)$$

$$\frac{1}{V}\frac{dN_2}{dt} = k_2 C_A^2 \qquad (3\text{-}26)$$

When the members of Equation (3-25) are divided by the corresponding members of Equation (3-26), one obtains Equation (3-11), which may be integrated to give Equation (3-12). Since $N_A = N_A^0 - N_1 - N_2$, it follows by use of Equation (3-12) that

$$N_1 = \frac{k_1(N_A^0 - N_A)}{k_1 + k_2} \qquad (3\text{-}27)$$

where N_A is given by Equation (3-20). After a number value for N_1 has been found, the corresponding values of N_2, N_S, and N_R may now be calculated by use of Equations (3-12) and (3-17). The equations for the general case of n simultaneous, irreversible second-order reactions are presented in Table 3-4. (The equations given in this table for plug-flow and perfectly mixed reactors are discussed in subsequent sections.)

TABLE 3-4

SIMULTANEOUS AND IRREVERSIBLE SECOND-ORDER REACTIONS

$$2A \longrightarrow 2\alpha_1 R_1, \qquad r_{A1} = k_1 C_A^2$$

$$2A \longrightarrow 2\alpha_2 R_2, \qquad r_{A2} = k_2 C_A^2$$

$$\vdots \qquad\qquad \vdots \qquad\quad \vdots \qquad \vdots$$

$$2A \longrightarrow 2\alpha_n R_n, \qquad r_{An} = k_n C_A^2$$

Batch Reactors
(Conditions: perfectly mixed, isothermal, and constant volume)

The expressions for second-order irreversible reactions in batch reactors are obtained from those shown for batch reactors in Table 3-3 by replacing

$$N_A = N_A^0 e^{-at}$$

by

$$N_A = \frac{1}{1/N_A^0 + at/V}$$

Plug-flow Reactors
(Conditions: steady state, plug flow, isothermal operation, liquid phase, and constant mass density)

The expressions for second-order irreversible reactions in a plug-flow reaction are obtained from those shown for plug-flow reactors in Table 3-3 by replacing

$$n_A = n_A^0 e^{-a\theta}$$

by

$$n_A = \frac{1}{1/n_A^0 + (a/v_T)\theta}$$

Perfectly Mixed Flow Reactors
(Conditions: steady state)

The expressions for second-order irreversible reactions in perfectly mixed reactors are obtained from those shown for plug-flow reactors in Table 3-3 by replacing

$$-\frac{dn_A}{dV} = r_A = \sum_{i=1}^{n} r_{Ai}, \text{ and } n_A = n_A^0 e^{-a\theta}$$

by

$$\frac{n_A^0 - n_A}{V} = r_A = \sum_{i=1}^{n} r_{Ai}, \text{ and } \theta = \frac{v_T}{a}\left(\frac{n_A^0 - n_A}{n_A^2}\right)$$

3. THIRD-ORDER REACTIONS. The equations for carrying out third-order reactions in a batch reactor are developed in a manner analogous to that demonstrated above for second-order reactions. For the general case of n simultaneous irreversible third-order reactions, the equations are given in Table 3-5.

TABLE 3-5
SIMULTANEOUS AND IRREVERSIBLE THIRD-ORDER REACTIONS

$$3A \longrightarrow 3\alpha_1 R_1, \qquad r_{A1} = k_1 C_A^3$$

$$3A \longrightarrow 3\alpha_2 R_2, \qquad r_{A2} = k_2 C_A^3$$

$$\vdots$$

$$3A \longrightarrow 3\alpha_n R_n, \qquad r_{A3} = k_3 C_A^3$$

Batch Reactors
(Conditions: perfectly mixed, isothermal, and constant volume)

The expressions for third-order irreversible reactions in batch reactors are obtained from those shown for batch reactors in Table 3-3 by replacing

$$N_A = N_A^0 e^{-at}$$

by
$$n_A = \frac{1}{[(1/(N_A^0)^2) + (2at/V^2)]^{1/2}}$$

Plug-Flow Reactors
(Conditions: steady state, plug flow, isothermal operation, liquid phase, and constant mass density).

The expressions for third-order irreversible reactions in plug-flow reactors are obtained from those shown for plug-flow reactors in Table 3-3 by replacing

$$n_A = n_A^0 e^{-a\theta}$$

by
$$n_A = \frac{1}{[(1/(n_A^0)^2) + (2a\theta/v_T^2)]^{1/2}}$$

Perfectly Mixed Flow Reactors
(Conditions: steady state)

The expressions for third-order irreversible reactions in perfectly mixed flow reactors are obtained from those shown for plug-flow reactors in Table 3-3 by replacing

$$-\frac{dn_A}{dV} = r_A = \sum_{i=1}^{e} r_{Ai}, \text{ and } n_A = n_A^0 e^{-a\theta}$$

by
$$\frac{n_A^0 - n_A}{V} = r_A = \sum_{i=1}^{n} r_{Ai}, \text{ and } \theta = \frac{v_T^2}{a}\left(\frac{n_A^0 - n_A}{n_A^3}\right)$$

EXAMPLE 3-1

Let it be supposed that the two first-order reactions given in Table 3-2 are carried out isothermally in a batch reactor. After a reaction time of 50 min, 90% of reactant A has decomposed and the product is found to contain 9.1 moles of R per mole of S. Neither R nor S is present initially in the reaction vessel. Evaluate the rate constants k_1 and k_2.

SOLUTION

Equation (3-4) may be written in terms of conversion to give

$$-\log_e(1 - X) = (k_1 + k_2)t$$

$$k_1 + k_2 = \frac{-\log_e(1 - 0.90)}{50} = \frac{-\log_e 0.1}{50} = 0.04605 \text{ min}^{-1}$$

Now $N_R = 9.1 N_S$, and from Table 3-2, $N_R = N_1$. Thus $9.1 N_S = N_1$, and from Table 3-2, $N_S = 2N_2$. Therefore, $N_1/N_2 = 18.2$. From Equation (3-12) this ratio is also equal to k_1/k_2. Thus

$$k_1 + k_2 = 18.2 k_2 + k_2 = 0.04606$$

and

$$k_2 = \frac{0.04602}{19.2} = 2.4 \times 10^{-3} \text{ min}^{-1}$$

$$k_1 = 0.0437 \text{ min}^{-1}$$

It should be emphasized that the ratio of the moles of R produced to the moles of S produced is constant throughout the course of the reaction cycle. Generally, this ratio may be changed by altering the temperature of the reaction since the rate constants are usually different functions of temperature.

B. Simultaneous Reactions Carried Out Isothermally in Plug-Flow Reactors at Steady State Operation

To illustrate the treatment of reactors of this type, consider the case where the following first-order reactions occur in the liquid phase:

$$A \longrightarrow R$$

$$A \longrightarrow 2S$$

For flow reactors, the stoichiometric relationships are stated in terms of the flow rates of each component rather than the moles of the component in the reactor. Thus the stoichiometric relationships are as follows:

$$n_A = n_A^0 - n_1 - n_2$$
$$n_R = n_R^0 + n_1 \qquad (3\text{-}28)$$
$$n_S = n_S^0 + 2n_2$$

where n_1 is the flow rate of A that has reacted by the first reaction and n_2 is the flow rate of A that has reacted by the second reaction. Since r_{A1} and r_{A2} are the rates at which A reacts by the first and second reactions, respectively, it follows that the net rate of reaction r_A is given by

$$r_A = r_{A1} + r_{A2}$$

A component-material balance on A gives

$$r_A = -\frac{dn_A}{dV}$$

Thus

$$-\frac{dn_A}{dV} = k_1 C_A + k_2 C_A = (k_1 + k_2)\frac{n_A}{v_T}$$

Separation of the variables followed by integration yields

$$n_A = n_A^0 \exp\left[-(k_1 + k_2)\theta\right] \qquad (3\text{-}29)$$

where $n_A = n_A^0$ at $\theta = 0$, and $\theta = V/v_T$, the residence time. Again as in the case of the batch reactor, the rates of appearance of R and S are related to r_{A1} and r_{A2}, respectively, as follows:

$$r_R = r_{A1}, \qquad r_S = 2r_{A2} \qquad (3\text{-}30)$$

and from the above stoichiometric relationships,

$$\frac{dn_R}{dV} = \frac{dn_1}{dV}, \qquad \frac{dn_S}{dV} = \frac{2dn_2}{dV} \qquad (3\text{-}31)$$

Thus

$$\frac{dn_1}{dV} = k_1 C_A \qquad (3\text{-}32)$$

$$2\frac{dn_2}{dV} = 2k_2 C_A \qquad (3\text{-}33)$$

Division of the members of Equation (3-32) by the corresponding members of Equation (3-33) yields

$$\frac{dn_1}{dn_2} = \frac{k_1}{k_2} \qquad (3\text{-}34)$$

Separation of the variables followed by integration yields

$$\frac{n_1}{n_2} = \frac{k_1}{k_2} \qquad (3\text{-}35)$$

where $n_1 = n_2 = 0$ at $V = 0$.

To find moles of R and S produced in a given reactor of volume V and flow rate v_T, expressions for n_1 and n_2 as a function of V/v_T are first obtained. To obtain such an expression for n_1, consider first the stoichiometric relationship

$$n_A = n_A^0 - n_1 - n_2 = n_A^0 - n_1(1 + n_2/n_1) \qquad (3\text{-}36)$$

Elimination of n_2/n_1 from this expression by use of Equation (3-35) yields the following result upon rearrangement:

$$n_1 = \frac{k_1(n_A^0 - n_A)}{k_1 + k_2} \qquad (3\text{-}37)$$

where n_A is given by Equation (3-29). After n_1 has been determined, n_2 may be calculated by use of Equation (3-35), and then n_R and n_S may be evaluated since $n_R = n_R^0 + n_1$, and $n_S = n_S^0 + 2n_2$.

The equations for the case where n simultaneous, irreversible first-order reactions are carried out isothermally in a tubular reactor are given in Table 3-3. These equations are based on the additional assumptions of plug flow and constant mass density. The corresponding equations for second- and third-order reactions are shown in Tables 3-4 and 3-5. The equations obtained when gas phase reactions are carried out isothermally in plug-flow reactors are developed in a manner similar to that shown above (see Problems 3-2 and 3-3).

C. Simultaneous Reactions Carried Out Isothermally
in Perfectly Mixed Flow Reactors at Steady State Operation

A sketch of this type of reactor is shown in Figure 2-7. In order to demonstrate the development of the material-balance equations, consider the first-order reactions given in Table 3-2. Suppose that these reactions occur in the liquid phase at constant-mass density. The stoichiometric relationships given by Equation (3-28) are also valid for the perfectly mixed flow reactor. Again the net rate of disappearance of A is given by Equation (3-1). The material balance on A for a perfectly mixed flow reactor is given by

$$r_A = \frac{n_A^0 - n_A}{V} \qquad (3\text{-}38)$$

Thus

$$\frac{n_A^0 - n_A}{V} = (k_1 + k_2) \frac{n_A}{v_T} = a \frac{n_A}{v_T} \qquad (3\text{-}39)$$

where $a = k_1 + k_2$. The volumetric flow rate v_T is evaluated at the conditions within (and at the outlet of) the reactor.

Equation (3-39) may be solved for n_A to give

$$n_A = \frac{n_A^0}{1 + a\theta} \qquad (3\text{-}40)$$

Again let r_A and r_S be defined as the net rates of appearance of R and S, respectively. Then these rates are related to r_{A1} and r_{A2}, as given by Equation (3-6). Thus

$$\frac{n_R - n_R^0}{V} = k_1 \frac{n_A}{v_T} \qquad (3\text{-}41)$$

$$\frac{n_S - n_S^0}{V} = 2k_2 \frac{n_A}{v_T} \qquad (3\text{-}42)$$

After n_R and n_S in Equations (3-41) and (3-42) have been expressed in terms of n_1 and n_2 by use of the stoichiometric relationships given by Equation (3-28), and after the members of the first expression have been divided by the corresponding members of the second expression, the result given by Equation (3-35) is obtained.

To find the moles of R and S produced in a given reactor of volume V and flow rate v_T, n_A may be eliminated from Equations (3-41) and (3-42) by use of Equation (3-40) to give

$$n_R = n_R^0 + n_A^0 \left(\frac{k_1 \theta}{1 + a\theta} \right) \qquad (3\text{-}43)$$

$$n_S = n_S^0 + n_A^0 \left(\frac{2k_2 \theta}{1 + a\theta} \right) \qquad (3\text{-}44)$$

For the general case of n simultaneous first-order, second-order, and third-order reactions, the equations are presented in Tables 3-3, 3-4, and 3-5 (also see Problem 3-4). Gas phase reactions are treated in a manner similar to that shown above for liquid phase reactions.

D. Simultaneous Reactions of Mixed Orders

The special techniques used to solve the differential equations for simultaneous reactions of the same order are no longer applicable when the orders differ. For example, consider the case in which one reaction is first order and the other reaction is second order:

$$A \longrightarrow R, \qquad r_{A1} = k_1 C_A \qquad (3\text{-}45)$$

$$2A \longrightarrow 2S, \qquad r_{A2} = k_2 C_A^2 \qquad (3\text{-}46)$$

Consider first the case where these reactions are carried out isothermally in a batch reactor. The volume V of the reactor filled by the reacting mixture remains constant, and the density of the reacting mixture also remains fixed throughout the course of the reactions.

The net rate of disappearance of A is again given by Equation (3-1). A material balance on A is given by

$$r_A = -\frac{dC_A}{dt} \qquad (3\text{-}47)$$

where the variation of the volume of the reacting mixture is negligible. Thus

$$-\frac{dC_A}{dt} = k_1 C_A + k_2 C_A^2 \qquad (3\text{-}48)$$

where $C_A = C_A^0$ at $t = 0$. Separation of variables followed by integration yields

$$t = \frac{-1}{k_1} \log_e \frac{C_A(k_1 + k_2 C_A^0)}{C_A^0(k_1 + k_2 C_A)}$$

or

$$C_A = \frac{C}{f \exp (k_1 t) - 1} \qquad (3\text{-}49)$$

where

$$C = \frac{k_1}{k_2}$$

$$f = \frac{k_1/k_2}{C_A^0} + 1$$

The variation of C_R with time is obtained in the following manner. First note that

$$r_{A1} = r_R = \frac{dC_R}{dt} = k_1 C_A \qquad (3\text{-}50)$$

131

and that $C_R = C_R^0$ at $t = 0$. After C_A has been replaced by its equivalent as given by Equation (3-49) and the equation so obtained is integrated, the following expression is obtained for C_R:

$$C_R = C_R^0 + C\left[-k_1 t - \log_e \left(\frac{f-1}{f \exp(k_1 t) - 1} \right) \right] \qquad (3\text{-}51)$$

The corresponding integral expression for C_S is

$$C_S = C_S^0 + k_2 C^2 \int_0^t \frac{dt}{[f \exp(k_1 t) - 1]^2} \qquad (3\text{-}52)$$

The concentration of S may also be obtained from the stoichiometry $C_S = C_A^0 - C_R - C_A$, where C_R and C_A are given by Equations (3-49) and (3-51). The equations describing the use of plug-flow reactors and perfectly mixed flow reactors in carrying out mixed order reactions are presented in Problems 3-5 and 3-6.

E. General Observations on Simultaneous Reactions

For simultaneous reactions of equal order, it is to be observed that the ratio of the moles of A reacted by any reaction to the moles of A reacted by the reference reaction is equal to the ratio of rate constants. Since the rate constants are functions only of temperature, the rate of one reaction relative to another can be increased by altering the temperature. For example, suppose for the set of second-order reactions given by Equation (3-16), it is desired to increase the moles of R produced relative to the moles of S produced. To accomplish this, the rate of the first reaction must be increased. Examination of Equation (3-12) shows that the ratio of the moles of A reacted by each reaction is a function only of temperature. By combining Equation (3-35) with Equation (1-29), one obtains

$$\frac{n_1}{n_2} = \frac{k_1}{k_2} = \frac{A_1 \exp(-E_{A1}/RT)}{A_2 \exp(-E_{A2}/RT)}$$

or

$$\frac{n_1}{n_2} = \frac{A_1}{A_2} \exp\left[\frac{E_{A2} - E_{A1}}{RT} \right]$$

If $E_{A1} > E_{A2}$, an increase in temperature will increase the rate of the first reaction over the second. However, if $E_{A2} > E_{A1}$, then the temperature should be decreased in order to increase the production of R relative to S. This is a general conclusion which is independent of the type of reactor.

For simultaneous reactions which are of mixed order, the yield of one product over another can be increased by altering the temperature and the concentration of the reactants. Consider the reactions given by Equations (3-45) and (3-46). One can show that

$$\frac{n_2}{n_1} = \frac{k_2 C_A}{k_1}$$

Maintaining a high concentration of A in the reactor will favor the production of S over that of R. The effect of temperature on the ratio of the rate constants is the same as that described above.

II. CONSECUTIVE REACTIONS

Reactions that occur consecutively (one after another) are called *consecutive reactions*. As an example of reactions of this type, the following set of reactions is considered:

$$
\begin{aligned}
A &\longrightarrow R, & r_{R1} = r_A = k_1 C_A \\
R &\longrightarrow S, & r_{R2} = r_S = k_2 C_R
\end{aligned}
\tag{3-53}
$$

Each reaction rate is first order, and the stoichiometry is as indicated.

The development of the equations for computing the moles of A, R, and S at any time in a batch reactor follows.

A. Batch Reactors

Suppose the consecutive reactions given by Equation (3-53) are carried out isothermally in either the gas or liquid phase in a perfectly mixed batch reactor. Then for component A,

$$r_A = -\frac{1}{V}\frac{dN_A}{dt} = k_1 C_A = \frac{k_1 N_A}{V}$$

which may be integrated and rearranged to give

$$N_A = N_A^0 \exp(-k_1 t) \tag{1-48}$$

The net rate of disappearance of R is given by

$$r_R = r_{R2} - r_{R1} = k_2 C_R - k_1 C_A \tag{3-54}$$

and a material balance on R gives

$$r_R = -\frac{1}{V}\frac{dN_R}{dt} \tag{3-55}$$

Elimination of r_R and V from Equations (3-54) and (3-55) gives

$$\frac{dN_R}{dt} + k_2 N_R = k_1 N_A$$

When N_A is replaced by its equivalent as given by Equation (1-48), the following differential equation is obtained:

$$\frac{dN_R}{dt} + k_2 N_R = k_1 N_A^0 \exp(-k_1 t) \tag{3-56}$$

Equation (3-56) is a special case of the general class of linear, first-order differential equations with variable coefficients which are of the form

$$\frac{dy}{dx} + P(x)y = Q(x) \tag{3-57}$$

where $N_R = y$, $t = x$, $k_2 = P(x)$, and $k_1 N_A^0 \exp(-k_1 t) = Q(x)$. A general solution of the differential equation given by Equation (3-57) is

$$y = e^{-\int P(x)\,dx}\left[\int e^{\int P(x)\,dx} Q(x)\,dx + K\right] \tag{3-58}$$

where K is the constant of integration [1]. After the integrations indicated by Equation (3-58) have been carried out for the case where the functions and variables have the meanings given by Equation (3-57), the following result is obtained:

$$N_R = \left(\frac{k_1 N_A^0}{k_2 - k_1}\right)\exp(-k_1 t) + K\exp(-k_2 t) \tag{3-59}$$

Suppose that at $t = 0$, $N_R = N_S = 0$, and $N_A = N_A^0$. The value of K that satisfies this initial condition is

$$K = -\frac{k_1 N_A^0}{k_2 - k_1}$$

After this value of K has been substituted into Equation (3-59), the following expression for N_R is obtained:

$$N_R = \left[\frac{k_1 N_A^0}{k_2 - k_1}\right][\exp(-k_1 t) - \exp(-k_2 t)] \qquad (3\text{-}60)$$

The expression for N_S as a function of time may be obtained by noting that at any time t, the stoichiometry of the reactions requires that

$$N_A^0 = N_A + N_R + N_S \qquad (3\text{-}61)$$

When N_A and N_R are eliminated from Equation (3-61) by use of Equations (1-48) and (3-60), respectively, the following expression for N_S is obtained upon rearrangement:

$$N_S = N_A^0 \left[1 - \left(\frac{k_2}{k_2 - k_1}\right)\exp(-k_1 t) + \left(\frac{k_1}{k_2 - k_1}\right)\exp(-k_2 t)\right] \quad (3\text{-}62)$$

Sketches of N_A, N_R, and N_S versus time are shown in Figures 3-1 and 3-2. Formulas for the time at which N_R is a maximum, the time at which N_S passes

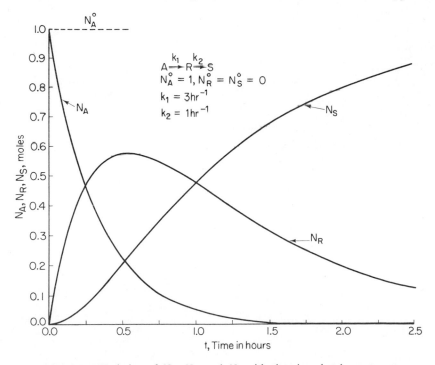

Figure 3-1. Variation of N_A, N_R, and N_S with time in a batch reactor at isothermal operation.

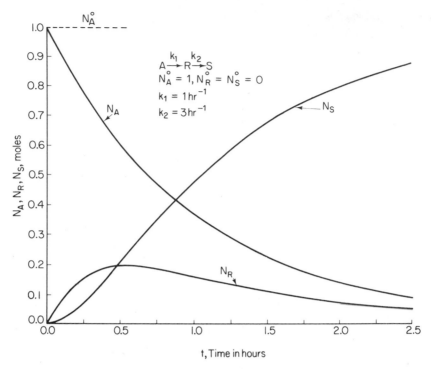

Figure 3-2. Comparison of the above values of k_1 and k_2 with those used for Figure 3-1 shows that the moles of R in the system at any time decreases as the ratio k_2/k_1 increases.

through its point of inflection, and the time at which N_R passes through its point of inflection are given in Problem 3-7.

B. Plug-Flow Reactors

Suppose that the reactions given by Equation (3-53) are carried out isothermally in the liquid phase in a plug-flow reactor at steady state operation. Plug flow of the reacting mixture throughout the reactor is assumed, and it is also supposed that the density of the reacting mixture is constant throughout the reactor. In this case,

$$n_A = n_A^0 \exp(-k_1\theta) \tag{3-63}$$

and

$$n_R = \left[\frac{k_1 n_A^0}{k_2 - k_1}\right] [\exp(-k_1\theta) - \exp(-k_2\theta)] \tag{3-64}$$

$$n_S = n_A^0 \left[1 - \left(\frac{k_2}{k_2 - k_1}\right)\exp(-k_1\theta) + \left(\frac{k_1}{k_2 - k_1}\right)\exp(-k_2\theta)\right] \tag{3-65}$$

These relationships also hold for gas phase reactions if the gaseous mixture behaves as a perfect gas and if the pressure drop across the reactor is negligible.

For a perfectly mixed flow reactor at steady state operation and isothermal conditions, the corresponding expressions for n_A, n_R, and n_S are as follows:

$$n_A = \frac{n_A^0}{1 + k_1 \theta} \tag{3-66}$$

$$n_R = n_A^0 \left[\frac{k_1 \theta}{(1 + k_1 \theta)(1 + k_2 \theta)} \right] \tag{3-67}$$

$$n_S = n_A^0 \left[1 - \left\{ \frac{1 + (k_1 + k_2)\theta}{(1 + k_1 \theta)(1 + k_2 \theta)} \right\} \right] \tag{3-68}$$

(Equations (3-63) through (3-68) apply for the case where $(n_R^0 = n_S^0 = 0.)$

There exists a residence time (called the optimum residence time) for which the production of R is maximized in a given reactor (see Problem 3-10).

EXAMPLE 3-2

The reactions involved in the cracking of gas oils to jet fuels and the subsequent cracking of the jet fuel over an Isomax catalyst were approximated by Strangeland et al. [2] by use of the following simplified kinetic model for operating pressures in the range of 2000 lb per sq in.,

$$A \xrightarrow{k_1} v_1 R \xrightarrow{k_2} v_2 S$$

where A represents the gas oil, R represents the jet fuel, and S represents secondary products.

$$r_A = k_1 C_A$$

$$r_R = v_1 r_A - k_2 C_R$$

$$k_1 = 1.81 \times 10^{16} \exp\left(\frac{-50,000}{RT}\right) \quad \text{in hr}^{-1}$$

$$R = 1.9872 \quad \text{and} \quad T \text{ is in } °K$$

$$k_2 = 1.93 \times 10^{16} \exp\left(\frac{-55,000}{RT}\right) \quad \text{in hr}^{-1}$$

$$R = 1.9872 \quad \text{and} \quad T \text{ is in } °K$$

$$v_1 = 0.90$$

(a) Calculate the conversion of A and the moles of R produced per mole of A fed for a reciprocal space velocity of 2 hr and a reaction temperature and pressure of 750°F and 2000 psi. The change in the total number of moles may be neglected, and the reciprocal space velocity $1/S_V$ may be taken equal to $V/v_T = \theta$.

(b) Determine the value of the reciprocal space velocity θ at which the moles of R produced per mole of A fed are at their maximum value. At this value of θ, evaluate n_R/n_A^0 and n_A/n_A^0.

SOLUTION

(a) At 750°F,
$$k_1 = 1.005 \text{ hr}^{-1}$$
$$k_2 = 0.02538 \text{ hr}^{-1}$$
For this case,
$$n_A = n_A^0 \exp(-k_1\theta) \tag{A}$$

and since $x = (n_A^0 - n_A)/n_A^0$, it follows that

$$x = 1 - \exp(-k_1\theta)$$

$$x = 1 - \exp(-1.005 \times 2) = 0.866$$

(b) The net rate of appearance of R as given by material balance is

$$r_R = \frac{dn_R}{dV}$$

Since $r_R = v_1 r_A - k_2 C_R$, it follows that

$$\frac{dn_R}{dV} = v_1 k_1 \frac{n_A}{v_T} - \frac{k_2 n_R}{v_T}$$

Then

$$\frac{dn_R}{d\theta} + k_2 n_R = v_1 k_1 n_A$$

After n_A has been expressed in terms of θ by use of Equation (A), the resulting differential equation may be solved in a manner analogous to that demonstrated for Equation (3-56) to give

$$\frac{n_R}{n_A^0} = \left[\frac{v_1 k_1}{k_2 - k_1}\right][\exp(-k_1\theta) - \exp(-k_2\theta)] \tag{B}$$

where it has been supposed that $n_R^0 = 0$. Thus

$$\frac{n_R}{n_A^0} = \frac{(0.9)(1.005)}{(0.02538 - 1.005)}[\exp(-1.005 \times 2) - \exp(-0.02538 \times 2)]$$

$$= 0.7539$$

(b) At the maximum value of n_R/n_A^0,

$$\frac{d(n_R/n_A^0)}{d\theta} = 0$$

By use of this condition and Equation (B), it is found that

$$\theta = \frac{\log_e k_2/k_1}{k_2 - k_1}$$

and
$$\theta = \frac{\log_e (0.02538/1.005)}{(0.02538 - 1.005)} = 3.755$$

At this value of θ,

$$x = 1 - \exp(-1.005 \times 3.755) = 0.977$$

and $$\frac{n_R}{n_A^0} = \frac{(0.9)(1.005)}{(0.02538 - 1.005)} [\exp(-1.005 \times 3.755) - \exp(-0.02581 \times 3.755)]$$

$$= 0.817 \text{ mole of jet fuel produced per mole of gas oil fed}$$

C. Solution of Kinetic Problems by Numerical Methods

For most systems involving either simultaneous or consecutive reactions or combination of these types of reactions, it is difficult if not impossible to obtain a solution of closed form. Such problems may be solved, however, by use of numerical methods. A variety of numerical methods which are suitable for solving problems of this type are to be found in books on numerical analysis. For the convenience of the reader, one of the Runge and Kutta methods, called Kutta's fourth-order method, is presented and demonstrated.

Consider first the differential equation

$$\frac{dy}{dt} = f(t, y) \tag{3-69}$$

for which a solution [sensed pairs (t, y) that satisfy both the initial condition $y = y_0$ when $t = t_0$ and the differential equation] is sought. Kutta's fourth-order method consists of the alternate use of the above differential equation and the following predictor.

$$y_{n+1} = y_n + \frac{(k_1 + 2k_2 + 2k_3 + k_4)}{6} \tag{3-70}$$

where
$$k_1 = hf(t_n, y_n)$$

$$k_2 = hf\left(t_n + \frac{h}{2}, y_n + \frac{k_1}{2}\right)$$

$$k_3 = hf\left(t_n + \frac{h}{2}, y_n + \frac{k_2}{2}\right)$$

$$k_4 = hf(t_n + h, y_n + k_3)$$

where h is equal to the time step used in the numerical solution of the differential equation.

The derivations of formulas for the fourth- and higher order predictors are readily available [3, 4]. A modified form of Kutta's fourth-order method that reduces the storage requirement has been presented by Gill [5] and is to be found in most of the recent books on numerical analysis.

To demonstrate the application of Kutta's fourth-order method, the following example is used.

EXAMPLE 3-3

The first-order reaction

$$A \longrightarrow R$$

is carried out isothermally in a batch reactor. At $t = 0$, $N_A = N_A^0 = 1$ g mole. The rate constant $k = 3$ hr^{-1}.

(a) Use a time step $h = 0.2$ hr to compute the moles of A present at the end of the first time step, $t = 0.2$ hr and at $t = 0.4$ hr.

(b) Compare the result found in (a) with that given by the exact solution of the differential equation.

SOLUTION

(a) The differential equation is

$$\frac{-dN_A}{dt} = 3N_A$$

When this equation is restated in terms of the notation of the Runge-Kutta method, it becomes

$$y' = -3y$$

Thus

$$f(t, y) = -3y$$

At $t = t_0 = 0$, $y = y_0 = 1$, and Equation (3-70) is applied as follows:

$$k_1 = 0.2[(-3)(1)] = -0.6$$

$$k_2 = 0.2\left[(-3)\left(1 - \frac{0.6}{2}\right)\right] = -0.42$$

$$k_3 = 0.2\left[(-3)\left(1 - \frac{0.42}{2}\right)\right] = -0.474$$

$$k_4 = 0.2[(-3)(1 - 0.474)] = -0.3156$$

Thus

$$y_1 = 1 + \frac{[(-0.6) + 2(-0.42) + 2(-0.474) + (-0.3156)]}{6}$$

$$y_1 = 0.5494 \quad \text{at} \quad t_1 = 0.2 \text{ hr}$$

At $t_1 = 0.2$ hr, $y_1 = 0.5494$, and y_2 at $t_2 = 0.4$ hr is computed by use of Equation (3-70) as follows:

$$k_1 = 0.2[(-3)(0.5494)] = -0.32964$$

$$k_2 = 0.2\left[(-3)\left(0.5494 - \frac{0.32964}{2}\right)\right] = -0.23075$$

$$k_3 = 0.2\left[(-3)\left(0.5494 - \frac{0.23075}{2}\right)\right] = -0.26042$$

$$k_4 = 0.2[(-3)(0.5494 - 0.26042)] = -0.17339$$

Thus

$$y_2 = 0.5494 + \frac{[(-0.32964) + 2(-0.23075) + 2(-0.264042) + (-0.17339)]}{6}$$

$$= 0.3018 \quad \text{at} \quad t_2 = 0.4 \text{ hr}$$

(b) At $t = 0.2$ hr,

$$N_A = N_A^0 e^{-kt} = (1)e^{-(3)(0.2)} = 0.5488$$

which is to be compared with the approximate value of 0.5494 found by the Runge-Kutta method. At $t = 0.4$ hr

$$N_A = N_A^0 e^{-kt} = (1)e^{-(3)(0.4)} = 0.3012$$

The value of 0.3018 found above compares well with the correct value of 0.3012.

SOLUTION OF SYSTEMS OF DIFFERENTIAL EQUATIONS BY THE RUNGE-KUTTA METHOD

A system of differential equations may be solved numerically by use of a generalization of the Runge-Kutta method; see for example Conte and de Boor [6]. For the case of two differential equations,

$$y' = f(t, y, z)$$

$$z' = g(t, y, z)$$

the predictor formulas corresponding to Equation (3-70) are

$$y_{n+1} = y_n + \frac{(k_1 + 2k_2 + 2k_3 + k_4)}{6}$$

$$z_{n+1} = z_n + \frac{(l_1 + 2l_2 + 2l_3 + l_4)}{6}$$

where

$$k_1 = hf(t_n, y_n, z_n)$$

$$l_1 = hg(t_n, y_n, z_n)$$

$$k_2 = hf\left(t_n + \frac{h}{2}, y_n + \frac{k_1}{2}, z_n + \frac{l_1}{2}\right)$$

$$l_2 = hg\left(t_n + \frac{h}{2}, y_n + \frac{k_1}{2}, z_n + \frac{l_1}{2}\right)$$

$$k_3 = hf\left(t_n + \frac{h}{2}, y_n + \frac{k_2}{2}, z_n + \frac{l_2}{2}\right)$$

$$l_3 = hg\left(t_n + \frac{h}{2}, y_n + \frac{k_2}{2}, z_n + \frac{l_2}{2}\right)$$

$$k_4 = hf(t_n + h, y_n + k_3, z_n + l_3)$$

$$l_4 = hg(t_n + h, y_n + k_3, z_n + l_3)$$

The ks and ls with the lower subscripts must be computed before proceeding to those having the next higher subscript. Extension of this method to a system of three or more differential equations is carried out in a manner analogous to that of going from one to two differential equations. The use

142

of the above predictor method is demonstrated by applying it to the reaction system shown in Figure 3-1.

EXAMPLE 3-4

The first-order consecutive reaction

$$A \xrightarrow{k_1} R \xrightarrow{k_2} S$$

is carried out isothermally in a batch reactor. At $t = 0$, $N_A = N_A^0 = 1$ g mole, and $N_R = N_R^0 = 0$. The rate constants are: $k_1 = 3$ hr^{-1} and $k_2 = 1$ hr^{-1}.

(a) Use a time step $h = 0.2$ hr to compute the moles of A and R present at the end of the first time step, $t = 0.2$ hr.

(b) Compare the results found in Part (a) with those given by the exact solution of the differential equations for this system.

SOLUTION

(a) The differential equations are

$$\frac{-dN_A}{dt} = 3N_A$$

$$\frac{dN_R}{dt} = 3N_A - N_R$$

Restatement of these equations in terms of the notation of the Runge-Kutta method gives

$$\frac{dy}{dt} = -3y$$

$$\frac{dz}{dt} = 3y - z$$

Thus

$$f(t, y, z) = -3y$$

$$g(t, y, z) = 3y - z$$

At $t = t_0 = 0$, $y = y_0 = 1$, and $z = z_0 = 0$. Equation (3-72) is applied as follows:

$$k_1 = 0.2[(-3)(1)] = -0.6$$

$$l_1 = 0.2[(3)(1) - 0] = 0.6$$

$$k_2 = 0.2\left[(-3)\left(1 - \frac{0.6}{2}\right)\right] = -0.42$$

$$l_2 = 0.2\left[(3)\left(1 - \frac{0.6}{2}\right) - \left(0 + \frac{0.6}{2}\right)\right] = 0.36$$

$$k_3 = 0.2\left[(-3)\left(1 - \frac{0.42}{2}\right)\right] = -0.474$$

$$l_3 = 0.2\left[(3)\left(1 - \frac{0.42}{2}\right) - \left(0 + \frac{0.36}{2}\right)\right] = 0.438$$

$$k_4 = 0.2[(-3)(1 - 0.474)] = -0.3156$$

$$l_4 = 0.2[(3)(1 - 0.474) - (0 + 0.438)] = 0.228$$

Thus

$$y_1 = 1 + \frac{[(-0.6) + 2(-0.42) + 2(-0.474) + (-0.3156)]}{6}$$

$$y_1 = 0.5494$$

$$z_1 = 0 + \frac{[(0.6) + 2(0.36) + 2(0.438) + 0.228]}{6}$$

$$z_1 = 0.404$$

(b) Again as in Example 3-3,

$$N_A = N_A^0 e^{-k_1 t} = (1)e^{-(3)(0.2)} = 0.5488$$

and N_R is found by use of Equation (3-60),

$$N_R = \frac{(3)(1)}{1 - 3}\left[e^{-(3)(0.2)} - e^{-(1)(0.2)}\right] = 0.4049$$

When the rate constant k_1 differs appreciably from k_2 (say $k_1/k_2 > 50$), the numerical techniques described above generally become unstable, and the corresponding equations are called "stiff or moderately stiff differential equations." Such equations may be solved by use of the simple one-point implicit method, the two-point trapezoidal rule, or multipoint methods such as those described by Gear (7) and Michelson (8).

PROBLEMS

3-1. Develop the equations presented in **(a)** Table 3-3, **(b)** Table 3-4, and **(c)** Table 3-5.

3-2. (a) Suppose that the following reactions are carried out isothermally in the gas phase in a plug-flow reactor:

$$A \longrightarrow 2R, \qquad r_{A1} = k_1 p_A$$

$$A \longrightarrow 3S, \qquad r_{A2} = k_2 p_A$$

(The subscript p on the rate constant k_p has been omitted in the interest of simplicity.) Suppose that the pressure drop across the reactor is negligible and that the reacting mixture obeys the perfect gas law. Show that

$$V = \frac{b}{aP}\left[\left(\frac{n_A^0}{a} + \frac{n_T^0}{b}\right)\log_e \frac{n_A^0}{n_A} - \left(\frac{n_A^0 - n_A}{a}\right)\right]$$

where

$$a = k_1 + k_2$$
$$b = k_1 + 2k_2$$

(b) For the general case where n simultaneous first-order reactions,

$$A = \alpha_1 R_1, \qquad r_{A1} = k_1 p_A$$

$$A = \alpha_2 R_2, \qquad r_{A2} = k_2 p_A$$

$$\vdots$$

$$A = \alpha_n R_n, \qquad r_{An} = k_n p_A$$

are carried out in the gas phase in a plug-flow reactor under the same conditions stated in Part (a), show that the above expression is again obtained for the reactor volume V, provided that a and b are given the following meanings:

$$a = \sum_{i=1}^{n} k_i$$

$$b = \sum_{i=1}^{n} (\alpha_i - 1)k_i$$

3-3. The following set of reactions is to be carried out in the gas phase in a plug-flow reactor.

$$2A \longrightarrow 2\alpha_1 R_1, \qquad r_{A1} = k_1 p_A^2$$

$$2A \longrightarrow 2\alpha_2 R_2, \qquad r_{A2} = k_2 p_A^2$$

$$\vdots \qquad \qquad \vdots \qquad \qquad \vdots \qquad \vdots$$

$$2A \longrightarrow 2\alpha_n R_n, \qquad r_{An} = k_n p_A^2$$

If the reactor is operated isothermally, the gas behaves as a perfect gas, and the pressure drop across the reactor is negligible. Show that

$$V = \frac{1}{aP^2}\left[\frac{2bc}{a}\log_e \frac{n_A}{n_A^0} + \left\{\left(\frac{b}{a}\right)^2 (n_A^0 - n_A)\right\} + c^2\left(\frac{1}{n_A} - \frac{1}{n_A^0}\right)\right]$$

where $c = n_T^0 + (bn_A^0/a)$ and a and b are defined in Problem 3-2(b)

3-4. (a) For the case where the n simultaneous first-order reactions listed in Table 3-3 are carried out in the gas phase in a perfectly mixed flow reactor at steady state operation, show that

$$V = \frac{n_1(n_T^0 + bn_1/k_1)}{k_1(n_A^0 - an_1/k_1)P}$$

where $a = \sum_{i=1}^{n} k_i$ (In this case the k_is represent the k_{pi}s.)

$$b = \sum_{i=1}^{n} (\alpha_i - 1)k_i$$

(b) Repeat (a) for the case of the n simultaneous second-order reactions listed in Table 3-4,

$$V = \frac{n_1(n_T^0 + bn_1/k_1)^2}{k_1(n_A^0 - an_1/k_1)^2 P^2}$$

(c) Repeat (b) for the case of the n simultaneous third-order reactions listed in Table 3-5,

$$V = \frac{n_1(n_T^0 + bn_1/k_1)^3}{k_1(n_A^0 - an_1/k_1)^3 P^3}$$

3-5. The mixed-order reactions given by Equations (3-45) and (3-46) are to be carried out isothermally in the liquid phase in a plug-flow reactor at steady state operation. Also suppose that the total volumetric flow rate v_T is constant throughout the reactor. Show that

$$\theta = \frac{1}{k_1} \log_e \frac{n_A^0[1 + k_2 n_A/(k_1 v_T)]}{n_A[1 + k_2 n_A^0/(k_1 v_T)]}$$

and that

$$n_R = n_R^0 + C\left[-k_1\theta - \log_e \frac{f - 1}{f \exp(k_1\theta) - 1}\right]$$

where

$$C = \frac{k_1 v_T}{k_2}$$

$$f = \frac{k_1 v_T/k_2}{n_A^0} + 1$$

3-6. (a) If the mixed-order reactions given by Equations (3-45) and (3-46) are carried out in the liquid phase in a perfectly mixed flow reactor at steady state operation, show that

$$\theta = \frac{n_A^0 - n_A}{k_1 n_A + (k_2/v_T)n_A^2}$$

(b) For the reactions and reactor of (a), show that

$$n_R = n_R^0 + k_1 \theta n_A$$

where $$n_A = \frac{-(k_1\theta + 1) + \sqrt{(k_1\theta + 1)^2 + 4(k_2\theta/v_T)n_A^0}}{(2k_2\theta/v_T)}$$

3-7. (a) When the reaction

$$A \xrightarrow{k_1} R \xrightarrow{k_2} S$$

is carried out isothermally in a perfectly mixed batch reactor, show that the maximum values of N_R occur at $t = t_m$,

$$t_m = \frac{\log_e k_1/k_2}{k_1 - k_2}$$

(b) Show that at $t = t_m$, N_S has a point of inflection.
(c) Show that N_R has a point of inflection at $t = 2t_m$.
(d) Obtain an expression for N_R/N_A^0 for $t = t_m$.

3-8. Develop the expressions given by Equations (3-64) and (3-65).

3-9. Develop the expressions given by Equations (3-66), (3-67), and (3-68).

3-10. When the reaction given by Equation (3-53) is carried out in a perfectly mixed flow reactor, show that n_R takes on its maximum value at

$$\theta_m = \frac{1}{\sqrt{k_1 k_2}}$$

3-11. The following liquid phase reactions are carried out isothermally at plug-flow conditions in a tubular reactor. The mass density of the mixture remains constant throughout the reactor.

$$A \xrightarrow{k_1} 2R, \qquad r_{A1} = k_1 C_A$$
$$A \xrightarrow{k_2} 3S, \qquad r_{A2} = k_2 C_A$$

For a conversion of A of 70% at $\theta = V/v_T = 15$ sec, the moles of R produced per mole of S produced are 3 to 1. The feed to the reactor consists of pure A. Calculate the value of k_1 and k_2.
Answer: $k_1 = 0.0657 \text{ sec}^{-1}, k_2 = 0.0146 \text{ sec}^{-1}$

3-12. The decomposition of cyclohexane over a platinum-aluminum-mordenite catalyst was investigated by Allan and Voorhies [9]. The principal reactions were the dehydrogenation and the isomerization of cyclohexane. The results could be explained by the following mechanism.

$$C_6H_{12} \rightleftharpoons C_6H_6 + 3H_2$$

Benzene

$$C_6H_{12} \rightleftharpoons C_6H_{12}$$

Methyl cyclopentane

At 775°F, $k_1/\rho = 0.045$ g mole/(min-g catalyst-atm) and $k_2/\rho = 0.0078$ g mole/(min-g catalyst-atm). The equilibrium constants at 775°F are as follows:

$$K_{p1} = 8301 \text{ atm}^3$$

$$K_{p2} = 8.58$$

These reactions are to be carried out in a plug-flow reactor at 775°F and 85 psia. The feed to the reactor consists of 20 moles of hydrogen per mole of cyclohexane. On the basis of these conditions, compute the value of $\rho V/n_T^0$ required to achieve a conversion of 80% of the cyclohexane. At these conditions, compute the moles of methyl cyclopentane produced per mole of cyclohexane in the feed. The change in the total number of moles as well as the change in the moles of hydrogen may be neglected.

Answer: $\rho V/n_T^0 = 5.409$ g/g mole/min

3-13. Adams et al. [10] used the following network of first-order reactions for the oxidation of propylene over a bismuth molybdate catalyst.

$$C_3H_6 \xrightarrow{k_1} C_3H_4O$$

with k_3 and k_2 branches to CO_2

The corresponding stoichiometric reactions are:

$$C_3H_6 + O_2 \xrightarrow{k_1} C_3H_4O + H_2O$$

$$C_3H_4O + 3.5O_2 \xrightarrow{k_2} 3CO_2 + 2 H_2O$$

$$C_3H_6 + 4.5O_2 \xrightarrow{k_3} 3CO_2 + 3 H_2O$$

The following ratios of the rate constants at 460°C were reported by Adams et al. [10]: $k_3/k_1 = 0.10$, $k_2/k_1 = 0.25$. Compute the moles of acrolein produced per mole of propylene reacted versus the fraction of propylene reacted for plug-flow and perfectly mixed flow reactors.

3-14. The following reaction network has been proposed by Adams et al. [10] for the oxidation of butene over a bismuth molybdate catalyst:

$$C_4H_8 \xrightarrow{k_1} C_4H_6 \xrightarrow{k_2} C_4H_4O$$

$$\searrow k_3 \qquad \downarrow k_4 \qquad \swarrow k_5$$

$$CO_2$$

at $460°C$, $k_3/k_1 = 0.05$ and $(k_2 + k_4)/k_1 = 0.05$. Determine the moles of buta-diene produced per mole of butene reacted when 10% of the butene is reacted in **(a)** a plug-flow reactor, and **(b)** in a perfectly mixed reactor.
Answer: **(a)** 0.94995 **(b)** 0.94737.

3-15. The intermediate R is to be produced in a flow reactor by the following reaction

$$A \xrightarrow{k_1} R \xrightarrow{k_2} S$$

For $k_1/k_2 = 3$ and $k_1 = 2 \text{ sec}^{-1}$, calculate the value of θ for a perfectly mixed flow and a plug-flow reactor for maximum production of R. On the basis of the optimum value of θ for each reactor, calculate the conversion of A and the values of n_R/n_A^0 and n_S/n_A^0 for each reactor.
Answer: Perfectly mixed: $x = 0.634$, $n_R/n_A^0 = 0.402$, $n_S/n_A^0 = 0.232$. Plugflow: $x = 0.808$, $n_R/n_A^0 = 0.5774$, $n_S/n_A^0 = 0.2306$.

3-16. For the reactions

$$A \xrightarrow{k_1} R$$

$$A \xrightarrow{k_2} S$$

$k_1 = 2 \text{ sec}^{-1}$ and $k_2 = 0.667 \text{ sec}^{-1}$
(a) Calculate the moles of R and the moles of S produced per mole of A fed for a plug-flow and a perfectly mixed flow reactor. The conversion of A is 95% for both reactors.
(b) Calculate the residence time θ required to achieve 95% conversion in each type of reactor.
Answer: **(a)** $n_R/n_A^0 = 0.7124$, $n_S/n_A^0 = 0.2376$ **(b)** Plug-flow: $\theta = 1.123$ sec; Perfectly mixed: $\theta = 7.124$ sec.

3-17. For the reactions,

$$2A \xrightarrow{k_1} R$$

$$2A \xrightarrow{k_2} S$$

$$k_1 = 10^{14} \exp\left(\frac{-20,000}{RT}\right)\left(\frac{\text{liters}}{\text{g mole sec}}\right)$$

$$k_2 = 10^{15} \exp\left(\frac{-10,000}{RT}\right)\left(\frac{\text{liters}}{\text{g mole sec}}\right)$$

where T is in $°K$

The reactions occur in the temperature range of 300°C to 500°C. At what temperature should the reactions be carried out in order to maximize the moles of R per mole of S produced for a plug-flow and a perfectly mixed flow reactor?

3-18. The reactions

$$A \xrightarrow{k_1} R$$

$$A \xrightarrow{k_2} 2S$$

are to be carried out isothermally in a plug-flow reactor. Because of market considerations, it is desired to make two moles of R per mole of S. If the rate constants for these two first order reactions are

$$k_1 = 6 \times 10^{14} \exp\left(-\frac{40,000}{RT}\right)$$

$$k_2 = 3.7 \times 10^{13} \exp\left(-\frac{37,000}{RT}\right)$$

find the temperature at which the reactor should be operated.
Answer: $T = 1078.5°K$

NOTATION
(See also Chapters 1 and 2)

N_i = moles of the reactant A reacted by reaction i, $(i = 1, 2, \ldots, n)$.

n_i = moles per unit time of the reactant A reacted by reaction i, $(i = 1, 2, \ldots, n)$.

n = total number of reactions.

$a = \sum\limits_{i=1}^{n} k_i$

$b = \sum\limits_{i=1}^{c} (\alpha_i - 1)k_i$

α_i = stoichiometric numbers in the reactions: $A \rightarrow \alpha_i R_i$, $2A \rightarrow 2\alpha_i R_i$, and $3A = 3\alpha_i R_i$.

$\theta = V/v_T$, residence time.

REFERENCES

1. Rainville, E. D., *Elementary Differential Equations*, 2d ed., The Macmillan Co., New York (1958).

2. Strangeland, B. E., and J. R. Kittrell, *I&EC Proc. Design and Develop.*, *11*:15 (1972).

3. Carnahan, B., H. A. Luther, and J. O. Wilkes, *Applied Numerical Methods*, John Wiley & Sons, Inc., New York (1964).

4. Stanton, R. G., *Numerical Methods for Science and Engineering*, Prentice-Hall, Inc., Englewood Cliffs, N.J. (1961).

5. Gill, S., *Proc. Cambridge Phil. Soc.*, *47*:96 (1951).

6. Conte, S. D., and C. de Boor, *Elementary Numerical Analysis*, McGraw-Hill Book Company, New York (1965).

7. Gear, C. W., *Numerical Initial Value Problems in Ordinary Differential Equations*, Prentice-Hall Inc., Englewood Cliffs, New Jersey, 1971.

8. Michelsen, M. L., *AIChE J.*, *22*, 594 (1976).

9. Allan, D. E., and A. Voorhies, *I&EC Prod. Research and Develop.*, *11*:15 (1972).

10. Adams, C. R., H. H. Voge, C. Z. Morgan, and W. E. Armstrong, *J. Catalysis*, 3:379 (1964).

Complex Reactions
and Interpretation
of Experimental Results

4

Reactions which cannot be classified as a unidirectional reaction, a reversible reaction, a set of simultaneous reactions, or a set of consecutive reactions are called complex reactions. Many reactions which are carried out commercially fall under the classification of complex reactions. In Part I of this chapter, reaction mechanisms involving a combination of simultaneous and consecutive reactions are presented. Simplifying assumptions commonly used in the treatment of complex reactions are presented and demonstrated in Part II. In Part III, some methods and techniques which are useful in the interpretation of experimental results are presented.

I. COMBINATIONS OF SIMULTANEOUS AND CONSECUTIVE REACTIONS

One of the simplest combinations of simultaneous and consecutive reactions is the set

$$A \; \underset{k_1'}{\overset{k_1}{\rightleftarrows}} \; R \; \underset{k_2'}{\overset{k_2}{\rightleftarrows}} \; S \tag{4-1}$$

where the rate constants are defined below as indicated by Equation (4-3). The reactions $A \rightarrow R \rightarrow S$ constitute consecutive reactions, and the reactions

$R \rightarrow A$ and $R \rightarrow S$ constitute simultaneous reactions. Equation (4-1) is representative of isomerization reactions. Again, throughout this chapter, the symbol k is used to represent all rate constants regardless of whether the rate expression is stated in terms of concentrations or pressures. It is supposed in each case, however, that the rate constants possess the appropriate dimensions and corresponding numerical values required for the rate expressions to be numerically and dimensionally consistent.

First suppose that the above set of reactions is carried out isothermally in a batch reactor. Further, suppose that initially the reactor is filled with pure A. Since the set of reactions given by Equation (4-1) does not result in any change in the total moles present at any time, it follows that

$$N_A^0 = N_A + N_R + N_S \qquad (4\text{-}2)$$

Let r_A be the net rate of disappearance of A, and r_R and r_S be the net rates of appearance of R and S, respectively. Then

$$r_A = k_1 C_A - k_1' C_R$$
$$r_R = k_1 C_A + k_2' C_S - k_2 C_R - k_1' C_R \qquad (4\text{-}3)$$

Component-material balances on A, R, and S give

$$r_A = -\frac{1}{V}\frac{dN_A}{dt}, \qquad r_R = \frac{1}{V}\frac{dN_R}{dt}, \qquad r_S = \frac{1}{V}\frac{dN_S}{dt} \qquad (4\text{-}4)$$

These two sets of equations may be combined to give

$$-\frac{dN_A}{dt} = k_1 N_A - k_1' N_R \qquad (4\text{-}5)$$

$$\frac{dN_R}{dt} = k_1 N_A + k_2' N_S - k_1' N_R - k_2 N_R \qquad (4\text{-}6)$$

$$\frac{dN_S}{dt} = k_2 N_R - k_2' N_S \qquad (4\text{-}7)$$

To obtain N_A as a function of time, the following procedure may be used. First N_S is eliminated from Equation (4-6) by use of Equation (4-2),

$$\frac{dN_R}{dt} = (k_1 - k_2')N_A - (k_1' + k_2' + k_2)N_R + k_2' N_A^0 \qquad (4\text{-}8)$$

An expression for dN_R/dt as a function of the derivatives of N_A is obtained by differentiating each member of Equation (4-5) with respect to t and rearranging to give

$$\frac{dN_R}{dt} = \frac{1}{k_1'}\frac{d^2N_A}{dt^2} + \frac{k_1}{k_1'}\frac{dN_A}{dt} \tag{4-9}$$

Use of this expression and Equation (4-5) to eliminate dN_R/dt and N_R, respectively, from Equation (4-8) yields upon rearrangement,

$$\frac{d^2N_A}{dt^2} + a\frac{dN_A}{dt} + bN_A - c = 0 \tag{4-10}$$

where
$$a = k_1 + k_1' + k_2 + k_2'$$

$$b = k_1k_2 + k_1k_2' + k_1'k_2'$$

$$c = k_1'k_2'N_A^0$$

Equation (4-10) may be transformed to a homogeneous differential equation by making the following change of variable. Let

$$y = bN_A - c \tag{4-11}$$

This change of variable reduces Equation (4-10) to

$$\frac{d^2y}{dt^2} + a\frac{dy}{dt} + by = 0 \tag{4-12}$$

This is an ordinary, linear, homogeneous differential equation with constant coefficients. Such equations may be solved in the following manner. Assume a solution of the form

$$y = C\exp(mt) \tag{4-13}$$

where m and C are nonzero constants. Since

$$\frac{dy}{dt} = Cm\exp(mt) \quad \text{and} \quad \frac{d^2y}{dt^2} = Cm^2\exp(mt)$$

Equation (4-12) reduces to

$$m^2 + am + b = 0 \tag{4-14}$$

The values of m that satisfy this equation are

$$m_1 = \frac{-a + \sqrt{a^2 - 4b}}{2}$$

$$m_2 = \frac{-a - \sqrt{a^2 - 4b}}{2} \tag{4-15}$$

For the case where m_1 and m_2 are real and unequal, the general solution of Equation (4-12) is as follows:

$$y = \bar{C}_1 \exp{(m_1 t)} + \bar{C}_2 \exp{(m_2 t)} \qquad (4\text{-}16)$$

where $\bar{C}_1$ and $\bar{C}_2$ are arbitrary constants. In view of Equation (4-11), the result given by Equation (4-16) may be restated in the form

$$N_A = C_1 \exp{(m_1 t)} + C_2 \exp{(m_2 t)} + \frac{c}{b} \qquad (4\text{-}17)$$

where C_1 and C_2 are arbitrary constants, which are determined by the following initial conditions:

(1)   At $t = 0$, $N_A = N_A^0$, $N_R = N_S = 0$

(2)   At $t = 0$, $-\dfrac{dN_A}{dt} = k_1 N_A^0$

The second initial condition follows from Equation (4-5), since $N_R = 0$ at $t = 0$. On the basis of these initial conditions, the following values are obtained for C_1 and C_2:

$$C_1 = \frac{-k_1 N_A^0 - (N_A^0 - c/b)m_2}{m_1 - m_2} \qquad (4\text{-}18)$$

$$C_2 = \frac{k_1 N_A^0 + (N_A^0 - c/b)m_1}{m_1 - m_2} \qquad (4\text{-}19)$$

The formula for N_R as a function of time is found by use of Equations (4-5) and (4-17).

$$N_R = \frac{1}{k_1'}\left[(m_1 + k_1)C_1 \exp{(m_1 t)} + (m_2 + k_1)C_2 \exp{(m_2 t)} + \frac{k_1 c}{b}\right] \qquad (4\text{-}20)$$

The formula for N_S as a function of time is readily found by eliminating N_A and N_R from the material balance [Equation (4-2)] by use of Equations (4-17) and (4-20).

If the complex reactions given by Equation (4-1) are carried out isothermally in the liquid phase in a plug-flow reactor at steady state operation and the total volumetric flow rate is constant, then the corresponding relationships for n_A and n_R are obtained by replacing t by V/v_T, N_A by n_A, N_A^0 by n_A^0, and N_R by n_R in Equations (4-17) through (4-20). These relationships also hold for the case where the complex reactions given by Equation (4-1) are carried out in the gas phase, provided, of course, that the pressure drop is negligible and the gaseous mixture obeys the perfect gas law. [Note that under these conditions, the total volumetric flow rate is independent of conversion since no change in the number of moles is involved in the reactions given by Equation (4-1).]

When the complex reactions given by Equation (4-1) are carried out isothermally in a perfectly mixed flow reactor at steady state operation, the expression for n_A as a function of V is obtained by the same general approach as demonstrated previously for these reactors (see Problem 4-3).

Another example of a complex reaction is the combination of simultaneous and consecutive reactions of the form

$$B + C \xrightarrow{k_1} M + H$$

$$M + C \xrightarrow{k_2} D + H \tag{4-21}$$

$$D + C \xrightarrow{k_3} T + H$$

These reactions are seen to be simultaneous with respect to C and consecutive with respect to B, M, D, and T.

An industrial example of reactions of the type given by Equation (4-21) is the chlorination of benzene,

$$C_6H_6 + Cl_2 \longrightarrow C_6H_5Cl + HCl$$

$$C_6H_5Cl + Cl_2 \longrightarrow C_6H_4Cl_2 + HCl$$

$$C_6H_4Cl_2 + Cl_2 \longrightarrow C_6H_3Cl_3 + HCl$$

where ferric chloride ($FeCl_3$) is used as a catalyst [1].

Suppose that the reactions under consideration are carried out isothermally in a batch reactor in which the reactions go as written; that is, they are unidirectional second-order reactions. Then

$$r_B = -\frac{1}{V}\frac{dN_B}{dt} = \frac{k_1}{V^2}N_B N_C \tag{4-22}$$

$$r_M = \frac{1}{V}\frac{dN_M}{dt} = \frac{k_1}{V^2}N_B N_C - \frac{k_2}{V^2}N_M N_C \tag{4-23}$$

$$r_D = \frac{1}{V}\frac{dN_D}{dt} = \frac{k_2}{V^2}N_M N_C - \frac{k_3}{V^2}N_D N_C \tag{4-24}$$

$$r_T = \frac{1}{V}\frac{dN_T}{dt} = \frac{k_3}{V^2}N_D N_C \tag{4-25}$$

Note that r_B is defined in terms of the disappearance of B, while r_M, r_D, and r_T are defined in terms of the appearance of M, D, and T, respectively. The relationships between N_B, N_C, N_M, N_D, and N_T at any time t are developed in the following manner. Suppose that the reactants consist of N_B^0 moles of benzene in the presence of chlorine. Since $N_M^0 = N_D^0 = N_T^0 = 0$.

$$N_B^0 = N_B + N_M + N_D + N_T \qquad (4\text{-}26)$$

$$\left.\begin{array}{l}\text{Moles of }C\\\text{consumed}\end{array}\right\} = N_M + 2N_D + 3N_T \qquad (4\text{-}27)$$

The method presented below for solving Equations (4-22) through (4-25) is similar to the one shown by Smith [2]. This problem was originally solved by MacMullin [1] in a somewhat different manner.

Division of the members of Equation (4-23) by the corresponding members of Equation (4-22) yields, upon rearrangement

$$\frac{dN_M}{dN_B} - \left(\frac{\alpha}{N_B}\right)N_M = -1 \qquad (4\text{-}28)$$

where
$$\alpha = \frac{k_2}{k_1}$$

The general solution to this linear differential equation with the variable coefficient (α/N_B) is given by Equation (3-58). The following result is obtained on the basis of the initial condition that when $N_B = N_B^0$, $N_M = N_M^0 = 0$.

$$\frac{N_M}{N_B} = \left(\frac{1}{\alpha - 1}\right)\left[1 - \left(\frac{N_B}{N_B^0}\right)^{\alpha - 1}\right] \qquad (4\text{-}29)$$

Next, division of the members of Equation (4-24) by the corresponding members of Equation (4-22) yields, upon rearrangement,

$$\frac{dN_D}{dN_B} - \left(\frac{\beta}{N_B}\right)N_D = -\alpha\frac{N_M}{N_B} \qquad (4\text{-}30)$$

where
$$\beta = \frac{k_3}{k_1}$$

When N_M/N_D is eliminated from Equation (4-30) by use of Equation (4-29), the resulting expression is again seen to be a member of the general class of differential equations given by Equation (3-57). After the integrations indicated by Equation (3-58) have been carried out and the constant of integration has been selected such that the initial condition, $N_D = 0$ when

$N_B = N_B^0$, is satisfied, the resulting expression found for N_D is

$$N_D = \left(\frac{\alpha N_B^0}{1 - \alpha}\right)\left[\frac{N_B/N_B^0}{1 - \beta} - \frac{(N_B/N_B^0)^{\alpha}}{\alpha - \beta}\right] + \frac{\alpha N_B^0 (N_B/N_B^0)^{\beta}}{(1 - \beta)(\alpha - \beta)} \qquad (4\text{-}31)$$

Next N_T may be stated in terms of N_B by use of Equations (4-26), (4-29), and (4-31).

For a given amount of B consumed, the corresponding amount of C consumed is given by use of Equations (4-26), (4-27), (4-29), and (4-31). If the concentration of C is maintained constant throughout the course of the reaction by supplying the batch reactor with C at the same rate at which it is consumed, then the expression given by Equation (4-22) may be solved to give

$$N_B = N_B^0 \exp\left[-\left(\frac{k_1 N_C}{V}\right)t\right] \qquad (4\text{-}32)$$

By substitution of this result into Equations (4-29) and (4-31), expressions for N_M and N_D as functions of time are obtained. By use of the expressions so obtained, the remaining quantities (N_T and the moles of C consumed) are readily obtained as functions of time.

EXAMPLE 4-1

Suppose that the reactions shown above for the chlorination of benzene go as written in the liquid phase; that is, benzene, monochlorobenzene, and dichlorobenzene react with absorbed chlorine in the liquid phase. The chlorination is to be carried out isothermally at 55°C in a perfectly mixed semibatch reactor. This semibatch reactor consists of a batch reactor (see Figure 1-4) into which chlorine gas is introduced continuously. Chlorine gas is to be introduced continuously in a manner such that its concentration in the liquid phase remains essentially constant throughout the chlorination. Also, it may be supposed that the volume of the reacting mixture does not vary during the chlorination.

MacMullin [1] has reported the following values for the ratio of the rate constants at 55°C:

$$\frac{k_1}{k_2} = 8, \qquad \frac{k_2}{k_3} = 30$$

For an initial feed of N_B^0 moles of pure benzene, find the moles of chlorine required to maximize the production of monochlorobenzene. Also, find the corresponding product distribution.

SOLUTION

Since monochlorobenze is produced by the first reaction and consumed by the second reaction of Equation (4-21), there exists the possibility for a maximum concentration of monochlorobenzene to occur. In particular, since $N_M^0 = 0$ and $k_1 > k_2$, N_M

increases initially as the moles of benzene reacted ($N_B^0 - N_B$) increases. This process continues until the concentration of monochlorobenzene builds up to a value such that $r_M = 0$ [Equation (4-23)]. At the point where $r_M = 0$, it can be shown by use of Equations (4-23) and (4-28) that

$$\frac{dN_M}{dN_B} = 0$$

When the expression given by Equation (4-29) for N_M is differentiated with respect to N_B and set equal to zero, the following formula is obtained. This formula gives the moles of benzene remaining when the number of moles of monochlorobenzene is maximized,

$$N_B = N_B^0 \left(\frac{1}{\alpha}\right)^{1/(\alpha - 1)}$$

Since $\alpha = \frac{1}{8}$, it follows that

$$N_B = N_B^0(8)^{-8/7} = 0.09287 N_B^0$$

This value of N_B may be used in Equation (4-29) to compute the maximum value of N_M; namely,

$$(N_M)_{\text{max}} = \frac{0.09287 N_B^0}{(-7/8)} [1 - (0.09287)^{-7/8}] = 0.743 N_B^0$$

The fraction of benzene converted when $N_M = (N_M)_{\text{max}}$ is given by

$$\frac{N_B^0 - N_B}{N_B^0} = 1 - 0.09287 = 0.90713$$

The moles of dichlorobenzene formed when $N_M = (N_M)_{\text{max}}$ may be found by use of Equation (4-31). First note that

$$\beta = \frac{k_3}{k_1} = \frac{k_2}{k_1} \cdot \frac{k_3}{k_2} = \left(\frac{1}{8}\right)\left(\frac{1}{30}\right) = \frac{1}{240}$$

Thus

$$N_D = \frac{N_B^0(1/8)}{(7/8)} \left[\frac{0.09287}{(1 - 1/240)} - \frac{(0.09287)^{1/8}}{(1/8 - 1/240)}\right] + \frac{N_B^0(1/8)(0.09287)^{1/240}}{(1 - 1/240)(1/8 - 1/240)}$$

$$= 0.1635 N_B^0$$

The corresponding moles of trichlorobenzene may be found by use of the total material balance [Equation (4-26)].

$$N_T = N_B^0 \left[1 - \frac{N_B}{N_B^0} - \frac{N_M}{N_B^0} - \frac{N_D}{N_B^0}\right] = N_B^0[1 - 0.09287 - 0.7430 - 0.1635]$$

$$= 0.0006 N_B^0$$

Then the moles of chlorine reacted when $N_M = (N_M)_{max}$ is given by

$$N_C = N_M + 2N_D + 3N_T = N_B^0[0.743 + 2(0.1635) + 3(0.0006)] = 1.0718N_B^0$$

Other examples of the combination of simultaneous and consecutive reactions are polymerization reactions. One type of polymerization reaction may be represented by the following set of reactions:

$$R_1 + M \xrightarrow{k_1} R_2$$

$$R_2 + M \xrightarrow{k_2} R_3$$

$$\vdots \qquad\qquad \vdots \qquad\qquad\qquad (4\text{-}33)$$

$$R_j + M \xrightarrow{k_3} R_{j+1}$$

where R_1 represents the monomer which has been activated instantaneously by an initiator, and R_j denotes the polymer molecule which is composed of j monomer units. The symbol M denotes the monomer involved, such as styrene, propylene, or ethylene. (Because of the commercial importance of polymerization reactions, Chapter 10 is devoted to this topic.)

Let $R_1, R_2, \ldots, R_{j+1}$ represent concentrations of the polymer molecule $R_1, R_2, \ldots, R_{j+1}$ and let M denote the concentration of the monomer. If the reactions given by Equation (4-33) are assumed to go as written and the propagation rate constants, k_j, are independent of chain length, then k_j is equal to a constant k for all j.

$$\frac{dR_1}{dt} = -kMR_1$$

$$\frac{dR_2}{dt} = kM(R_1 - R_2)$$

$$\vdots \qquad\qquad \vdots \qquad\qquad\qquad (4\text{-}34)$$

$$\frac{dR_j}{dt} = kM(R_{j-1} - R_j)$$

$$\vdots \qquad\qquad \vdots$$

Let the new variable τ be defined by

$$\tau = \int_0^t M \, d\xi \qquad\qquad\qquad (4\text{-}35)$$

where ξ is the dummy variable of integration. This definition implies that when $t = 0$, $\tau = 0$, and that

$$\frac{d\tau}{dt} = M \qquad (4\text{-}36)$$

With this change of variable, the expressions given by Equation (4-34) reduce to the following set:

$$\frac{dR_1}{d\tau} + kR_1 = 0$$

$$\frac{dR_j}{d\tau} + kR_j = kR_{j-1} \qquad (4\text{-}37)$$

$$\vdots \qquad \vdots \qquad \vdots$$

where $j \geq 2$. At $t = 0$,

$$R_1 = R_1^0 \quad \text{and} \quad R_j = 0 \quad \text{for all} \quad j > 1$$

The solution that satisfies both the set of differential equations and the initial conditions is:

$$R_1 = R_1^0 \exp(-k\tau)$$

$$R_2 = R_1^0(k\tau) \exp(-k\tau)$$

$$R_3 = R_1^0 \frac{(k\tau)^2}{2} \exp(-k\tau) \qquad (4\text{-}38)$$

$$\vdots \qquad \vdots$$

$$R_j = R_1^0 \frac{(k\tau)^{j-1}}{(j-1)!} \exp(-k\tau)$$

$$\vdots \qquad \vdots$$

The expressions given by Equation (4-38) are recognized as the Poisson distribution. A solution has been given by Aris [3] for the case where k depends upon the reaction number j.

An expression for the monomer concentration as a function of time is developed as follows. A material balance on the monomer gives

$$r_M = -\frac{dM}{dt}$$

The rate of disappearance r_M of the monomer M is given by

$$r_M = kMR_1 + kMR_2 + kMR_3 + \cdots$$

Thus

$$-\frac{dM}{dt} = kM \sum_{j=1}^{\infty} R_j \tag{4-39}$$

Since the polymers $R_2, R_3, \ldots, R_j \ldots$ present at any time t were formed from an activated monomer R_1, it follows by material balance that

$$R_1^0 = R_1 + R_2 + R_3 + \cdots + R_j + \cdots \tag{4-40}$$

The sum of the infinite series appearing in Equation (4-39) may be replaced by first replacing R_j by its equivalent as given by Equation (4-40). Consequently, Equation (4-39) reduces to

$$-\frac{dM}{dt} = kR_1^0 M \tag{4-41}$$

Separation of variables followed by integration and rearrangement gives

$$M = M^0 \exp(-kR_1^0 t) \tag{4-42}$$

where M^0 is the concentration of the monomer at $t = 0$.

By first replacing M in Equation (4-35) by its equivalent as given by Equation (4-42) and then integrating, the following expression for τ as a function of t is obtained:

$$\tau = \frac{M^0}{kR_1^0} [1 - \exp(-kR_1^0 t)] \tag{4-43}$$

It is of interest to note that the variable τ takes on a maximum value in the limit as t increases without bound. In particular,

$$\tau_{max} = \frac{M^0}{kR_1^0}$$

A numerical example which illustrates the use of the above expressions follows.

EXAMPLE 4-2

Styrene in the solvent dioxane is to be polymerized in a batch reactor at 25°C by use of sodium naphthalene as the initiator. The initial concentration of sodium naphthalene is 0.0005 g mole/liter. It may be assumed that the initiation reaction of styrene and sodium naphthalene is exceedingly fast and goes to completion; that is, it may be assumed that

$$R_1^0 = 0.0005 \text{ g mole/liter}$$

The following value of the rate constant has been reported [4, 5]

$$k = 3.4 \text{ liters/(g mole)(sec)}$$

(a) Find the time required to convert 99.9% of the monomer styrene. (b) For the time t found in Part (a), compute the corresponding value of τ. (c) Construct the distribution curve of R_j/R_1^0 versus j, where j ranges from $j = 0$ to $j = 10^6$.

SOLUTION

(a) The time required for 99.9% of the monomer to react may be found by use of Equation (4-42), which may be restated as follows:

$$t = \frac{1}{k_1 R_1^0} \log_e \frac{M^0}{M}$$

Since $M = (1 - 0.999)M^0$

$$t = \frac{1}{(3.4)(0.0005)} \log_e \frac{1}{(1 - 0.999)} = 4063.39 \text{ sec} = 67.72 \text{ min}$$

(b) By use of this value of t and the known values for $k_1 R_1^0$ and M^0, the value of τ may be found by use of Equation (4-43).

$$\tau = \frac{1}{(3.4)(0.0005)} \{1 - \exp[-(3.4)(0.0005)(4063.39)]\}$$

$$= 587.65 \text{ (g moles sec/liter)}$$

(c) On the basis of the value of τ found in Part (b), the values of R_j/R_1^0 used in the construction of the distribution curve in Figure 4-1 were found by use of Equation (4-38). For large values of j, the factorial in Equation (4-38) may be evaluated with good accuracy by use of Sterling's formula,

$$(j - 1)! \cong \sqrt{2\pi(j - 1)}(j - 1)^{j-1} \exp[-(j - 1)]$$

163

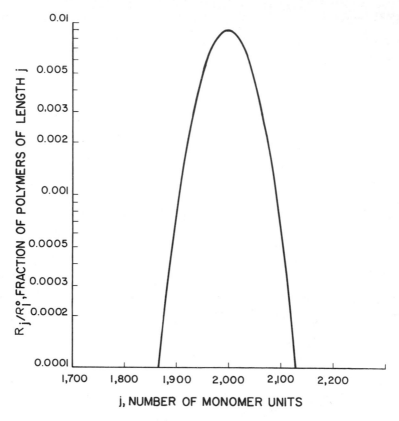

Figure 4-1. Distribution of polymer for Example 4- (2)

From the results presented in Figure 4-1, it is evident that most of the polymer molecules formed have chain lengths ranging from 1850 to 2150 monomer units; that is, each polymer molecule is composed of from 1850 to 2150 styrene molecules.

II. SIMPLIFICATIONS USED IN THE ANALYSIS OF COMPLEX REACTIONS

Many rate expressions for complex reactions may be formulated on the basis of one or more simplifying assumptions. Two of the most widely used assumptions are presented and their use is demonstrated below. The first of these is known by two names, the *pseudo steady state* assumption and the *stationary state* assumption. The second approximation is known as the *rate controlling step* assumption.

A. The Pseudo Steady State Assumption

Consider the two consecutive reactions given by Equation (3-53), namely,

$$A \longrightarrow R, \qquad r_A = k_1 C_A$$
$$R \longrightarrow S, \qquad r_S = k_2 C_R \tag{3-53}$$

where r_A is the rate of disappearance of A and r_S is the rate of formation of S. If $k_1 \ll k_2$, then the expressions for N_R and N_S given by Equations (3-60) and (3-62), respectively, reduce to the following expressions in the limit as k_1/k_2 approaches zero; namely,

$$\lim_{k_1/k_2 \to 0} N_R = 0 \tag{4-44}$$

$$\lim_{k_1/k_2 \to 0} N_S = N_A^0[1 - \exp(-k_1 t)] \tag{4-45}$$

This same expression for N_S may be obtained by use of the pseudo steady state assumption in which it is supposed that

$$k_1 \ll k_2 \tag{4-46}$$

and that R is consumed by reaction at approximately the same rate at which it is formed,

$$\frac{dN_R}{dt} \cong 0$$

Now consider the case where A reacts first to form R which then reacts to form S as indicated by Equation (3-53). For the case where the amount of A in the form of R at any time is negligible, then the stoichiometry which can be expected experimentally is given by

$$A \longrightarrow S \tag{4-47}$$

Suppose that the rate of reaction of A and the rate of formation of S are found by experiment to be of the form

$$r_S = r_A = kC_A \tag{4-48}$$

Now it will be shown that the stoichiometric relationship given by Equation (4-47) and the first-order rate expression given by Equation (4-48) may be explained on the basis of the mechanism given by Equation (3-53), the assumption $k_1 \ll k_2$, and the assumption $dN_R/dt \cong 0$.

Since $r_A = -dC_A/dt$ by material balance, and since $r_A = k_1 C_A$ by the first step of the mechanism [Equation (3-53)], the following well-known result is readily obtained as shown in Chapter 1:

$$N_A = N_A^0 \exp(-k_1 t) \tag{1-48}$$

Thus the proposed mechanism (Equation (3-53)) satisfies the observed first-order rate, Equation (4-48).

Next an approximate expression for the moles of R present at any time t is obtained. Since the net rate of appearance of R is assumed to be negligible, it follows that

$$\frac{dN_R}{dt} = k_1 N_A - k_2 N_R \cong 0 \tag{4-49}$$

or

$$N_R = \frac{k_1}{k_2} N_A = \frac{k_1}{k_2} N_A^0 \exp(-k_1 t) \tag{4-50}$$

A comparison of the pseudo steady state value of N_R and the correct value of N_R [given by Equation (3-60)] is presented in Figures 4-2 and 4-3. The maximum error in the pseudo steady state value of N_R is seen to occur at

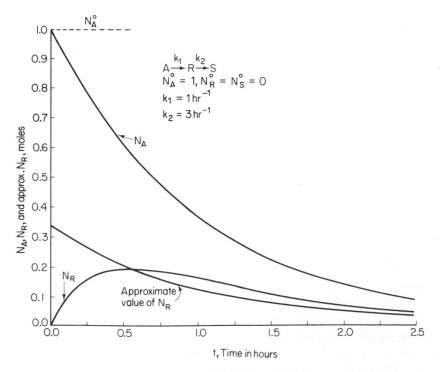

Figure 4-2. Comparison of the correct and approximate values of N_R ($k_2 = 3k_1 = 3$ hr^{-1}).

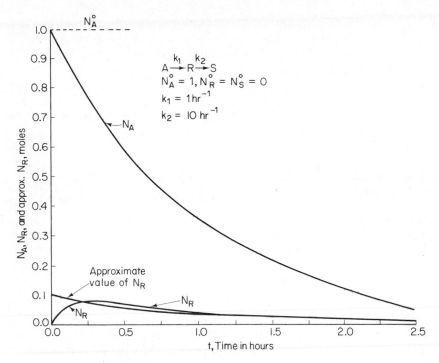

Figure 4-3. Comparison of the correct and approximate values of N_R ($k_2 = 10k_1 = 10 \text{ hr}^{-1}$).

$t = 0$. Also, Figures 4-2 and 4-3 show that the pseudo steady state value of N_R tends to approach the correct value of N_R for $t > 0$ as k_2/k_1 increases.

Next it will be shown that the expression given by Equation (4-45) is obtained for N_S by use of the pseudo steady state assumption. Since

$$\frac{dN_S}{dt} = k_2 N_R \qquad (4\text{-}51)$$

it follows from Equation (4-50) that

$$\frac{dN_S}{dt} = k_2 \left[\frac{k_1}{k_2} N_A^0 \exp\left(-k_1 t\right) \right] = k_1 N_A^0 \exp\left(-k_1 t\right) \qquad (4\text{-}52)$$

Again as in the development of Equation (3-62) it will be supposed that only A is present initially. Then after the variables in Equation (4-52) have been separated, the following expression is obtained for N_S upon integration and rearrangement.

$$N_S = N_A^0 [1 - \exp\left(-k_1 t\right)] \qquad (4\text{-}53)$$

$$= N_A^0 - N_A \qquad (4\text{-}54)$$

Thus the approximate value of N_S is seen to be equal to the limiting value given by Equation (4-45). The relationship given by Equation (4-54) implies that A is either in the form of A or S; that is, $N_R \cong 0$, which is precisely the implication of Equation (4-47).

The pseudo steady state concept may be used in the analysis of reactions having widely different stoichiometric relationships and mechanisms. For example, consider the case of a reaction whose stoichiometry is given by

$$A + B \longrightarrow D \tag{4-55}$$

and whose rate is given by the first-order expression

$$r_A = kC_A \tag{4-56}$$

To explain both the stoichiometry and first-order rate expression, the following mechanism is postulated:

$$A \xrightarrow{\ k_1\ } C \tag{4-57}$$

$$C + B \xrightarrow{\ k_2\ } D \tag{4-58}$$

where $k_1 \ll k_2$ and $dN_C/dt \cong 0$. The first step of the mechanism satisfies the observed rate expression, Equation (4-56). Thus the first step leads to

$$N_A = N_A^0 \exp\left(-k_1 t\right) \tag{1-48}$$

To show that the proposed mechanism satisfies the stoichiometry [Equation (4-55)], the pseudo steady state postulate may be used to obtain

$$-\frac{dN_C}{dt} = \frac{k_2}{V} N_C N_B - k_1 N_A \cong 0 \tag{4-59}$$

Thus

$$N_C = \left(\frac{k_1 V}{k_2}\right)\left(\frac{N_A}{N_B}\right) = \left(\frac{k_1 V N_A^0}{k_2 N_B}\right)\exp\left(-k_1 t\right) \tag{4-60}$$

As a consequence of the second reaction of the proposed mechanism, it follows that

$$\frac{dN_D}{dt} = \frac{k_2}{V} N_C N_B \tag{4-61}$$

Elimination of N_C by use of the relationship given by Equation (4-60) yields

$$\frac{dN_D}{dt} = k_1 N_A^0 \exp\left(-k_1 t\right) \tag{4-62}$$

Since $N_D = 0$ at $t = 0$, integration of Equation (4-62) yields

$$N_D = N_A^0 \left(1 - \exp\left(-k_1 t\right)\right) \tag{4-63}$$

which may be stated in the form

$$N_D = N_A^0 - N_A \tag{4-64}$$

Since Equation (4-64) implies that $N_C = 0$, it follows that all of A is either in the form of A or D, which is precisely the implication of Equation (4-55). Consequently, the proposed mechanism satisfies both the stoichiometry and first-order rate expression.

To account for the fact that certain reactions are second order at relatively low pressures and first order at high pressures, Lindermann [6] and Hinshel-wood [7] proposed the following example and mechanism. Suppose that the stoichiometry of a reaction is given by

$$A \longrightarrow B + C \tag{4-65}$$

At low pressures,

$$r_A = kC_A^2 \tag{4-66}$$

At high pressures,

$$r_A = \bar{k}C_A \tag{4-67}$$

The following mechanism was proposed:

$$A + A \underset{k_1'}{\overset{k_1}{\rightleftarrows}} A^* + A \tag{4-68}$$

$$A^* \xrightarrow{k_2} B + C \tag{4-69}$$

where the amount of A in the activated form of A^* at any time is negligible. (The forward reaction $A + A \xrightarrow{k_1} A^* + A$ represents the formation of an activated molecule A^* by means of a bimolecular collision. The reverse reaction $A^* + A \xrightarrow{k_1'} A + A$ represents the deactivation of A^* by means of a bimolecular collision.) In this case the pseudo steady state assumptions are taken to be

$$k_1 \ll k_2 \quad \text{and} \quad \frac{dC_A^*}{dt} \cong 0$$

The first assumption compliments the second assumption and also satisfies the condition that the amount of A in the form of A^* at any time is negligible. Note that it is not necessary to place any restriction on the size of k_1' relative to k_1 and k_2. Any value of k_1' supports the observation that A^* is negligible at any time by providing another path by which A^* may disappear.

On the basis of this mechanism, the stoichiometry and the rate expressions may be explained as shown by the following analysis. First

$$\frac{dC_A^*}{dt} = k_1 C_A^2 - k_1' C_A^* C_A - k_2 C_A^* \cong 0$$

Thus

$$C_A^* = \frac{k_1 C_A^2}{k_1' C_A + k_2} \tag{4-70}$$

The net rate of disappearance of A is given by

$$r_A = -\frac{dC_A}{dt} = k_1 C_A^2 - k_1' C_A^* C_A \tag{4-71}$$

Elimination of C_A^* from this expression by use of Equation (4-70) gives

$$r_A = -\frac{dC_A}{dt} = \frac{k_1 k_2 C_A^2}{k_1' C_A + k_2} \tag{4-72}$$

At high pressures $k_1' C_A \gg k_2$, and Equation (4-72) reduces to

$$r_A = -\frac{dC_A}{dt} = \frac{k_1 k_2}{k_1'} C_A$$

which is of the same form as Equation (4-67). At low pressures $k_1' C_A \ll k_2$, and Equation (4-72) reduces to

$$r_A = -\frac{dC_A}{dt} = k_1 C_A^2$$

which is of the same form as Equation (4-66). Since $k_1 \ll k_2$, essentially all of A^* must be in the form of either A or B and C at any time. Thus the stoichiometry [Equation (4-65)] is satisfied.

B. Concept of the Rate Controlling Step

Although the concepts of the *rate controlling step* and the *pseudo steady state* are fundamentally different, they do have some similarities and they frequently lead to the same results. In the application of the concept of the rate controlling step, it is supposed that one reaction of the mechanism is the rate controlling step and that the remaining reactions of the mechanism are in dynamic equilibrium.

To illustrate the concept of the rate controlling step, the reaction with the stoichiometry given by Equation (4-65) and rate expression given by Equation (4-67) are used. In particular, it is supposed that the second reaction [Equation (4-69)] of the mechanism is the rate controlling step while the first reaction [Equation (4-68)] is in dynamic equilibrium, and again the amount of A in the form of A^* is negligible. By dynamic equilibrium it is meant that even though the ratios of the concentrations remain fixed as required by the respective equilibrium constants, the individual concentrations are continually changing as required by the rate controlling step. Such a dynamic equilibrium is approached as k_1 and k_1' become very large relative to k_2. Then suppose $k_1 \gg k_2$ and $k_1' \gg k_2$. The fact that the amount of A in the form of A^* at any time is negligible implies that $K_1 \ll 1$. Since the first reaction is assumed to be in a state of dynamic equilibrium,

$$K_1 = \frac{C_A^* C_A}{C_A^2} = \frac{C_A^*}{C_A} \tag{4-73}$$

Since the second reaction is assumed to be the rate controlling step, it follows that

$$r_B = r_C = k_2 C_A^* \tag{4-74}$$

Elimination of C_A^* from Equations (4-73) and (4-74) gives

$$r_B = r_C = K_1 k_2 C_A \tag{4-75}$$

In order for the mechanism to satisfy the stoichiometry ($A \rightarrow B + C$), it is evident that A must be in the form of either A, B, or C, but not A^*. This result has been assured by taking $K_1 \ll 1$. Consequently, the stoichiometry is satisfied, and the rate of reaction of A is equal to the rate of formation of B or C; that is, $r_A = r_B = r_C$. The concept of the rate controlling step has been found to be most helpful in the analysis of reaction mechanisms composed of large numbers of reactions.

EXAMPLE 4-3

An experimental investigation of the liquid phase hydrochlorination of octyl and dodecyl alcohols in a batch reactor by Date et al. [8] revealed the following stoichiometry:

$$R_1OH + HCl \longrightarrow R_1Cl + H_2O \tag{1}$$

$$R_2OH + HCl \longrightarrow R_2Cl + H_2O \tag{2}$$

where the symbols R_1OH and R_1Cl are used to represent octyl alcohol and octyl chloride, respectively, and R_2OH and R_2Cl are used to represent dodecyl alcohol and dodecyl chloride, respectively. It was further found that the rates of reaction could be represented at 100.5°C as follows:

$$r_{R_1OH} = k_1[R_1OH][HCl] \tag{A}$$

$$r_{R_2OH} = k_2[R_2OH][HCl] \tag{B}$$

where
$$k_1 = 1.6 \times 10^{-3} \text{ liter/g mole min}$$

$$k_2 = 1.92 \times 10^{-3} \text{ liter/g mole min}$$

$$[A] = C_A = \text{concentration of compound } A$$

(a) Propose an ionic mechanism that satisfies both the stoichiometry and the rate expressions.

(b) On the basis of the initial concentrations in gram moles per liter,

$$[HCl]^0 = 1.3, \qquad [R_1OH]^0 = [R_2OH]^0 = 2.21$$

calculate the gram moles of dodecyl chloride and octyl chloride produced per liter of solution at the time 20% of the octyl alcohol has been consumed by reaction. Reactions (1) and (2) are carried out at 100.5°C in the liquid phase in a batch reactor, and it may be assumed that the density of the liquid phase remains essentially constant throughout the course of the reaction. Also, calculate the percentage of the HCl reacted when the 20% of the octyl alcohol has reacted.

SOLUTION

(a) The following mechanism was proposed by Date et al. [8] for the hydrochlorination of each alcohol:

$$\underset{k_3'}{\overset{k_3}{\rightleftharpoons}}$$

$$ROH + HCl \quad \overset{k_3}{\underset{k_3'}{\rightleftharpoons}} \quad R{-}\overset{\overset{\displaystyle H}{\displaystyle |}}{O}{-}H + Cl^- \tag{3}$$
$$\underset{+}{}$$

$$Cl^- + R{-}\overset{\overset{\displaystyle H}{\displaystyle |}}{O}{-}H \quad \overset{k_4}{\longrightarrow} \quad RCl + H_2O \tag{4}$$
$$\underset{+}{}$$

where R is used to represent either the octyl or the dodecyl group. It was further supposed that Reaction (3) was in equilibrium and that $K_3 \ll 1$. Reaction (4) was assumed to be the rate controlling step. Then the rate of appearance of $RCl(R_1Cl$ or $R_2Cl)$ is given by

$$r_{RCl} = k_4[Cl^-][ROH_2^+] \tag{C}$$

Since Reaction (3) is assumed to be at equilibrium,

$$[ROH_2^+][Cl^-] = K_3[ROH][HCl] \tag{D}$$

Equations (C) and (D) may be combined to give

$$r_{RCl} = k_4 K_3 [ROH][HCl] \qquad (E)$$

Since $K_3 \ll 1$, it follows that essentially all of the ROH is in the form of either ROH or RCl, but not ROH_2^+. Consequently the stoichiometry is satisfied with the result that the rate of formation of RCl must be equal to the rate of disappearance of ROH. Thus

$$r_{ROH} = r_{RCl} = k_4 K_3 [ROH][HCl] = k[ROH][HCl] \qquad (F)$$

Equation (F) is seen to be in agreement with Equations (A) and (B); the constant $k_4 K_3 = k$ in Equation (F) is of course different for each alcohol.

(b) Since the mass density is constant, the material balances on $R_1 OH$ and $R_2 OH$ in a batch reactor may be stated in the form:

$$r_{R_1 OH} = -\frac{d[R_1 OH]}{dt} \qquad (G)$$

$$r_{R_2 OH} = -\frac{d[R_2 OH]}{dt} \qquad (H)$$

Elimination of $r_{R_1 OH}$ and $r_{R_2 OH}$ from Equations (A), (B), (G), and (H) yields

$$-\frac{d[R_1 OH]}{dt} = k_1 [R_1 OH][HCl] \qquad (I)$$

$$-\frac{d[R_2 OH]}{dt} = k_2 [R_2 OH][HCl] \qquad (J)$$

By division of the members of Equation (I) by the corresponding members of Equation (J) and by integration of the result so obtained, it is found upon rearrangement that

$$\frac{[R_2 OH]}{[R_2 OH]^0} = \left(\frac{[R_1 OH]}{[R_1 OH]^0} \right)^{k_2/k_1} \qquad (K)$$

For 20% conversion of octyl alcohol, $[R_1 OH] = 0.8\,[R_1 OH]^0$. For this condition, Equation (K) gives

$$\frac{[R_2 OH]}{[R_2 OH]^0} = (0.8)^{1.92 \times 10^{-3}/1.6 \times 10^{-3}} = 0.8^{1.2} = 0.765$$

Thus

$$[R_2 OH] = 0.765[R_2 OH]^0 = (0.765)(2.21) = 1.69$$

Then on the basis of one liter of the reacting mixture, it follows that the gram moles of dodecyl chloride formed $= 2.21 - 1.69 = 0.52$.

The gram moles of octyl chloride formed $= (2.21)(0.2) = 0.442$.

The gram moles of dodecyl chloride formed per gram mole of octyl chloride formed $= 0.52/0.442 = 1.18$.

The gram moles of HCl reacted are equal to the gram moles of R_1Cl plus the gram moles of R_2Cl formed $= 0.52 + 0.442 = 0.962$.

The gram moles of HCl reacted per gram mole of HCl in the feed $= 0.962/1.30 = 0.74$.

In the interest of simplicity, relatively simple reaction mechanisms were used in the demonstration of the applications of the pseudo steady state assumption and the rate controlling step assumption. The student may demonstrate to himself the utility of these assumptions in the analysis of relatively complex reaction mechanisms by solving the problems listed at the end of this chapter.

C. Comparison of the Pseudo Steady State and the Rate Controlling Step Assumptions

In order to ascertain the accuracy of the results obtained by the pseudo steady state and the rate controlling step assumptions, the following reaction mechanism was selected for analysis because it could be treated by each of the approximate methods and because it also possessed an analytical solution. Suppose that A reacts to form R and S by the mechanism

$$A \underset{k_1'}{\overset{k_1}{\rightleftarrows}} R$$
$$R \overset{k_2}{\longrightarrow} S \tag{4-76}$$

in a batch reactor which is operated isothermally. Further suppose that the reaction is initiated with pure A. Thus the initial conditions are the same as those stated at the beginning of this chapter for the reaction given by Equation (4-1). The differential equations to be solved simultaneously are as follows:

$$\frac{-dN_A}{dt} = k_1 N_A - k_1' N_R \tag{4-77}$$

$$\frac{dN_R}{dt} = k_1 N_A - k_1' N_R - k_2 N_R \tag{4-78}$$

$$\frac{dN_S}{dt} = k_2 N_R \tag{4-79}$$

By following the same procedure as that demonstrated for Equations (4-5) through (4-7), the following results are obtained:

$$N_A = C_1 \exp(m_1 t) + C_2 \exp(m_2 t) \tag{4-80}$$

where
$$C_1 = \frac{-N_A^0(m_2 + k_1)}{m_1 - m_2}$$

$$C_2 = \frac{N_A^0(m_1 + k_1)}{m_1 - m_2}$$

$$m_1 = \frac{-b + \sqrt{b^2 - 4c}}{2}, \qquad b^2 > 4c$$

$$m_2 = \frac{-b - \sqrt{b^2 - 4c}}{2}, \qquad b^2 > 4c$$

$$b = k_1 + k_1' + k_2$$

$$c = k_1 k_2$$

and $$N_R = \frac{1}{k_1'}\left[(m_1 + k_1)C_1 \exp(m_1 t) + (m_2 + k_1)C_2 \exp(m_2 t)\right] \quad (4\text{-}81)$$

The value of N_S (the moles of S present at any time t) is found by use of the material balance $N_S = N_A^0 - N_A - N_R$.

Expressions will now be developed for N_A and N_R by use of the pseudo steady state and the rate controlling step assumptions. Suppose that the apparent stoichiometry of the reaction given by Equation (4-76) is

$$A \longrightarrow S \qquad\qquad (4\text{-}82)$$

and that the rate is given by

$$r_A = kC_A \qquad\qquad (4\text{-}83)$$

1. USE OF THE PSEUDO STEADY STATE ASSUMPTION. To apply this assumption, it will be supposed that the reaction occurs by the mechanism given by Equation (4-76) and that $k_1 \ll k_2$ and $dN_R/dt \cong 0$. On the basis of the assumption that $dN_R/dt \cong 0$, the differential equations given by Equations (4-77) and (4-78) may be solved simultaneously to give

$$N_A = N_A^0 \exp\left[-\left(\frac{k_1 k_2}{k_1' + k_2}\right)t\right] \qquad\qquad (4\text{-}84)$$

and $$N_R = \left(\frac{N_A^0 k_1}{k_1' + k_2}\right)\exp\left[-\left(\frac{k_1 k_2}{k_1' + k_2}\right)t\right] \qquad\qquad (4\text{-}85)$$

The expression for N_S is found by use of the material balance $N_S = N_A^0 - N_A - N_R$.

For relatively small values of k_1/k_2, say $\frac{1}{10}$ or smaller, the values given by Equations (4-84) and (4-85) for N_A and N_R are in good agreement with the correct values given by Equations (4-80) and (4-81), respectively, regardless of the size of the k_1' as shown in Table 4-1. To illustrate these characteristics,

TABLE 4-1

COMPARISON OF THE APPROXIMATE VALUES OF N_A AND N_R PREDICTED BY THE PSEUDO STEADY STATE ASSUMPTION WITH THE CORRECT VALUES FOR THE REACTIONS:

$$A \underset{k_1'}{\overset{k_1}{\rightleftarrows}} R \overset{k_2}{\longrightarrow} S$$

I. Case 1: $k_1 = k_1' = 1$, $k_2 = 10$, and $N_A^0 = 1$, $N_R^0 = N_S^0 = 0$.

t (time) (consistent units)	N_A (correct) [by Equation (4-80)]	N_A (approximate) [by Equation (4-84)]	N_R (correct) [by Equation (4-81)]	N_R (approximate) [by Equation (4-85)]
0.05	0.9522	0.9556	0.0374	0.0869
0.1	0.9082	0.9131	0.0573	0.0830
0.2	0.8280	0.8338	0.0712	0.0757
0.3	0.7576	0.7613	0.0713	0.0692
0.4	0.6907	0.6951	0.0672	0.0632
0.5	0.6312	0.6347	0.0621	0.0577
0.6	0.5768	0.5796	0.0569	0.0527
0.7	0.5271	0.5292	0.0520	0.0481
0.8	0.4816	0.4832	0.0477	0.0439
0.9	0.4402	0.4412	0.0436	0.0401
1.0	0.4022	0.4029	0.0398	0.0366

II. Case 2: $k_1' = k_2 = 10$, $k_1 = 1$, and $N_A^0 = 1$, $N_R^0 = N_S^0 = 0$.

t (time) (consistent units)	N_A (correct) [by Equation (4-80)]	N_A (approximate) [by Equation (4-84)]	N_R (correct) [by Equation (4-81)]	N_R (approximate) [by Equation (4-85)]
0.05	0.9601	0.9753	0.0308	0.0487
0.1	0.9313	0.9512	0.0411	0.0476
0.2	0.8843	0.9048	0.0445	0.0452
0.3	0.8412	0.8607	0.0430	0.0430
0.4	0.8018	0.8187	0.0411	0.0409
0.5	0.7636	0.7788	0.0391	0.0389
0.6	0.7273	0.7408	0.0373	0.0370
0.7	0.6927	0.7047	0.0355	0.0352
0.8	0.6597	0.6703	0.0338	0.0335
0.9	0.6283	0.6376	0.0322	0.0319
1.0	0.5974	0.6065	0.0307	0.0303

the correct and approximate values of N_A and N_R are compared for the two cases where $k_1' = k_1$ and $k_1' = k_2$.

In particular, for the first case, suppose that $N_A^0 = 1$, $N_R^0 = N_S^0 = 0$, $k_2 = 10 \text{ sec}^{-1}$, and $k_1' = k_1 = 1 \text{ sec}^{-1}$. Equation (4-80) gives

Correct values of $N_A = 0.99 \exp(-0.901t) + (0.00971)\exp(-11.1t)$

while Equation (4-84) gives

Approximate value of $N_A = 1.0 \exp(-0.909t)$

The values of N_R given by Equations (4-81) and (4-85) are:

Correct value of $N_R = 0.098 \exp(-0.901t) - 0.098 \exp(-11.1t)$

Approximate value of $N_R = 0.0909 \exp(-0.901t)$

Obviously, the approximate and correct values of N_A are in good agreement, while the maximum error in N_R occurs at $t = 0$.

For the second case, suppose that $N_A^0 = 1$, $N_R^0 = 0$, $k_1 = 1 \text{ sec}^{-1}$, $k_2 = 10 \text{ sec}^{-1}$, and $k_1' = k_2 = 10 \text{ sec}^{-1}$. Equations (4-80) and (4-84) give

Correct value of $N_A = 0.974 \exp(-0.488t) + (0.0256)\exp(-20.51t)$

Approximate value of $N_A = 1.0 \exp(-0.5t)$

while Equations (4-81) and (4-85) give

Correct value of $N_R = 0.05 \exp(-0.488t) - 0.05 \exp(-20.5t)$

Approximate value of $N_R = 0.05 \exp(-0.5t)$

A comparison of the approximate and correct values of N_A and N_R for different choices of t is shown in Table 4-1.

The exact expressions given by Equations (4-80) and (4-81) can be shown to reduce approximately to those given by Equations (4-84) and (4-85), respectively, for the case where $k_1 \ll 1$, $k_2 \gg 1$, and k_1' is finite and positive [see Problem 4-12(b)].

2. USE OF THE RATE CONTROLLING STEP ASSUMPTION. For the case where the experimental results are given by Equations (4-82) and (4-83) and the mechanism is given by Equation (4-76), the rate controlling step assump-

tion is applied by first making the following assumptions:

(1) The reaction $A \overset{k_1}{\underset{k_1'}{\rightleftharpoons}} R$ is in dynamic equilibrium, $K_1 = N_R/N_A$.

(2) Since the amount of R present at any time is negligible by Equation (4-82), it is assumed that $K_1 \ll 1$.

(3) The reaction $R \overset{k_2}{\rightarrow} S$ is the rate controlling step.

These assumptions imply that

$$k_2 \ll k_1 \ll k_1'$$

Because of the relatively high order of the approximations involved, it is possible to obtain more than one expression for N_A, N_R, and N_S (see Problem 4-12). The desired solution must satisfy the conditions that $N_A = N_A^0$ at $t = 0$, $N_R \cong 0$ for all t because it has been assumed that $K_1 \ll 1$, and all of A must eventually appear in the form of S. The equations obtained by the following approach satisfy these conditions. The expressions $N_R = K_1 N_A$ and $N_S \cong N_A^0 - N_A$ may be used to restate Equation (4-79) in terms of N_A as follows:

$$-\frac{dN_A}{dt} = k_2 K_1 N_A \tag{4-86}$$

Separation of the variables followed by integration and rearrangement yields

$$N_A = N_A^0 \exp\left[-k_2 K_1 t\right] \tag{4-87}$$

The equilibrium assumption may be used to obtain the following approximate expression for N_R:

$$N_R = K_1 N_A^0 e^{-k_2 K_1 t} \tag{4-88}$$

An improved approximation of N_S may now be found by use of the exact material balance $N_S = N_A^0 - N_A - N_R$.

The expression given by Equation (4-80) for N_A may be reduced in an approximate manner to the one given by Equation (4-87) by imposing the condition that $k_2 \ll k_1 \ll k_1'$ [see Problem 4-12(c)]. A comparison of the correct and approximate values of N_A and N_R for different choices of t is shown in Table 4-2.

It is of interest to note that in spite of the fact that the results obtained by each of the approximate methods satisfy the supposed experimental observations [Equations (4-82) and (4-83)], they are based in part on diametrically opposite assumptions. In particular, Equations (4-84) and (4-85) are based in part on the assumption that $k_1 \ll k_2$, while Equations (4-86) and (4-88) are based in part on the assumption that $k_1 \gg k_2$. This result is unique for this particular example."

TABLE 4-2

COMPARISON OF THE APPROXIMATE VALUES OF N_A AND N_R PREDICTED BY THE RATE CONTROLLING STEP ASSUMPTION WITH THE CORRECT VALUES FOR THE REACTION:

$$A \underset{k'_1}{\overset{k_1}{\rightleftarrows}} R \overset{k_2}{\longrightarrow} S$$

$k_1 = 10, k_2 = 1, k'_1 = 1000, K_1 = 0.01,$ and $N_A^0 = 1, N_R^0 = N_S^0 = 0.$

t (time) (consistent units)	N_A (correct) [by Equation (4-80)]	N_A (approximate) [by Equation (4-87)]	N_R (correct) $\times (10^2)$ [by Equation (4-81)]	N_R (approximate) $\times (10^2)$ [by Equation (4-88)]
10	0.8958	0.9048	0.8949	0.9048
30	0.7332	0.7408	0.7325	0.7408
50	0.6002	0.6065	0.5996	0.6065
70	0.4913	0.4966	0.4908	0.4966
90	0.4022	0.4066	0.4018	0.4066
110	0.3292	0.3328	0.3289	0.3328
130	0.2695	0.2725	0.2734	0.2725
150	0.2206	0.2231	0.2204	0.2231
170	0.1806	0.1827	0.1804	0.1827
190	0.1478	0.1496	0.1477	0.1496

The concept of the rate controlling step is used extensively in the simplification of catalytic mechanisms.

III. INTERPRETATION OF EXPERIMENTAL RESULTS

When only one reaction is involved and the reaction proceeds at a relatively slow rate, the reaction rate constant may be determined in a batch reactor operated at isothermal conditions. The mechanism may be established and the rate constant or constants determined by use of the integral expressions and plots presented in Chapter 1.

If the reaction proceeds too fast for an investigation of the reaction in a batch reactor to be feasible, a flow-type reactor may be employed. In the following analysis, batch reactors and plug-flow reactors are used in order to demonstrate some possible techniques which may be employed in the analysis of the experimental results for complex reactions.

If a single reaction is involved in an isothermally operated reactor in which a negligible drop in pressure occurs, then the integral expressions presented in Chapter 2 may be used for the determination of the mechanism and rate constant (or constants where reversible reactions are involved). Also, because of the simplicity of the rate expressions, perfectly mixed flow reactors (see Figure 2-7) could prove useful in the study of relatively fast reactions.

A. Determination of the Stoichiometry

Actually, there is no unique technique for establishing the stoichiometry of any arbitrary mechanism. For example, in the case of some relatively complex mechanisms, it may be necessary to determine the mechanism and stoichiometry simultaneously. Although the following techniques are not applicable for all types of reactions, they should prove helpful in the analysis of experimental results.

Suppose that data have been collected from a plug-flow reactor or a batch reactor in the form of product compositions as a function of t for batch reactors and $1/S_V$ for plug-flow reactors. Further suppose that only t (or $1/S_V$) has been varied and that all remaining variables, such as the composition of the feed, the reaction temperature, and the total pressure, have been held fixed for all experiments. First suppose that the single reaction

$$A \xrightarrow{k_1} 2B \qquad\qquad (4\text{-}89)$$

occurs. If this is the only reaction occurring in the system, a plot of the moles of product B formed per mole of A reacted versus t (or $1/S_V$) would give a horizontal line with an ordinate of 2 as shown in Figure 4-4.

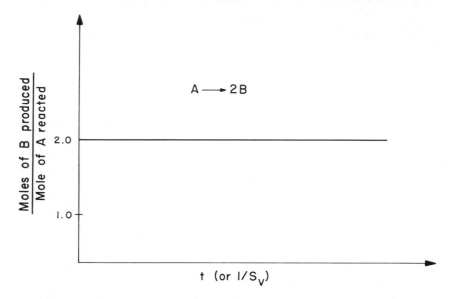

Figure 4-4. Determination of the stoichiometric numbers for a single reaction.

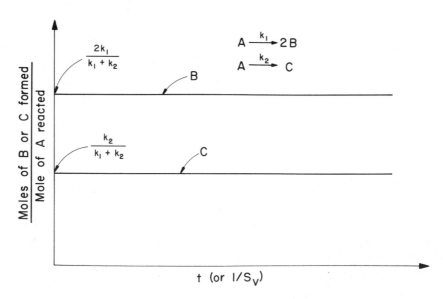

Figure 4-5. Determination of the stoichiometric numbers for the two simultaneous reactions.

Instead of a single reaction suppose that A also reacts to give $2B$ and C as follows:

$$A \xrightarrow{k_1} 2B$$
$$A \xrightarrow{k_2} C \tag{4-90}$$

For this case, plots of B and C formed per mole of A reacted would yield horizontal lines with ordinates having the values shown in Figure 4-5.

Next consider the case where B further reacts to a secondary product D; that is,

$$A \xrightarrow{k_1} 2B$$
$$A \xrightarrow{k_2} C \tag{4-91}$$
$$B \xrightarrow{k_3} D$$

Then the moles of B formed per mole of A reacted decrease as t or $1/S_V$ increases. Also, the plot of the moles of D formed per mole of A reacted begins at the origin and increases as t or $1/S_V$ increases as shown in Figure 4-6.

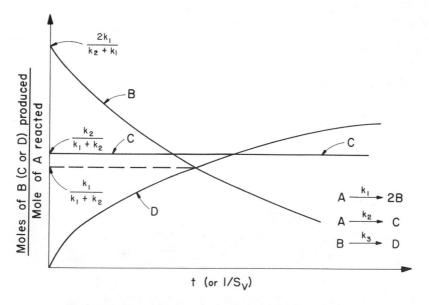

Figure 4-6. Determination of primary and secondary reactions.

The curves for C and B are typical of those for compounds produced by *primary* reactions and the curve for D is typical of those for compounds produced by *secondary* reactions. Graphs of this type are helpful in establishing the primary and secondary reactions involved in a particular reaction mechanism.

B. Interpretation of Integral Reactor Data

In the following analysis the parameters of temperature, pressure, and feed composition are held fixed for all runs. Suppose that a series of runs has been made in a plug-flow reactor and that product distributions have been determined for each run and plotted as indicated in Figure 4-7. Before further consideration of the particular reaction mechanism needed to satisfy the results presented in Figure 4-7, the relationships needed in the interpretation of *integral reactor* data are developed. At each value of V for a given run, the component-material balance on A is given by

$$r_A = -\frac{dn_A}{dV} \tag{4-92}$$

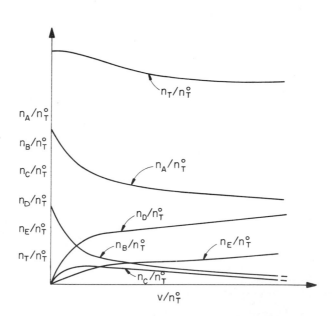

Figure 4-7. Results obtained in an integral plug-flow reactor at the conditions: (1) isothermal operation at the same temperature for all runs, (2) same pressure for all runs, and (3) same feed composition for all runs.

Then, for this run,

$$V = -\int_{n_A^0}^{n_A} \frac{dn_A}{r_A} \tag{4-93}$$

If the run under consideration is made at the feed rate n_T^0, then both sides of Equation (4-93) can be divided by the constant n_T^0 (for the run under consideration) to give

$$\frac{V}{n_T^0} = -\int_{n_A^0}^{n_A} \frac{dn_A}{n_T^0 r_A} = -\int_{y_A^0}^{n_A/n_T^0} \frac{d(n_A/n_T^0)}{r_A} \tag{4-94}$$

where $y_A^0 = n_A^0/n_T^0$. Now, Equation (4-94) may be regarded as representing the result achieved by a sequence of runs in which V/n_T^0 is varied. Note either or both V and n_T^0 may be varied from run to run but that n_A/n_T^0 depends upon only the ratio of V to n_T^0. The sequence of runs may be represented as follows:

$$\left(\frac{V}{n_T^0}\right)_1 = -\int_{y_A^0}^{(n_A/n_T^0)_1} \frac{d(n_A/n_T^0)}{r_A}$$

$$\left(\frac{V}{n_T^0}\right)_2 = -\int_{y_A^0}^{(n_A/n_T^0)_2} \frac{d(n_A/n_T^0)}{r_A}$$

$$\vdots \qquad \vdots \qquad \vdots \tag{4-95}$$

$$\left(\frac{V}{n_T^0}\right)_n = -\int_{y_A^0}^{(n_A/n_T^0)_n} \frac{d(n_A/n_T^0)}{r_A}$$

If V/n_T^0 is now regarded as a dependent variable and n_A/n_T^0 as an independent variable, Equation (4-94) may be differentiated to give

$$\frac{d(V/n_T^0)}{d(n_A/n_T^0)} = -\frac{1}{r_A}$$

or

$$r_A = -\frac{d(n_A/n_T^0)}{d(V/n_T^0)} \tag{4-96}$$

[Note that the result given by Equation (4-96) is based on the assumption that the lower limits in the integrals in Equation (4-95) remain constant for all runs.] Then the slope of the curve n_A/n_T^0 versus V/n_T^0 in Figure 4-7 gives the numerical value of r_A in a reactor in which the partial pressures of $A, B, C,$ and D are given by expressions of the form

$$p_A = \frac{n_A}{n_T} P = \frac{(n_A/n_T^0)P}{(n_T/n_T^0)} \tag{4-97}$$

n_A/n_T^0 and n_T/n_T^0 are read from the graph at the V/n_T^0 having the slope r_A [see Equation (4-96)].

Alternately, r_A may be stated in terms of the derivative of n_A/n_T^0 with respect to $1/S_V$. Since

$$S_V = \left(\frac{n_T^0}{V}\right)\frac{RT_s}{P_s}$$

it follows that

$$r_A = -\left(\frac{P_s}{RT_s}\right)\frac{d(n_A/n_T^0)}{d(1/S_V)} \tag{4-98}$$

Since r_A may be expressed in terms of the rate constants and partial pressures of the proposed mechanism, it is evident that the results of integral reactor tests may be used to determine the rate constants corresponding to a proposed mechanism. For example, suppose that the results presented in Figure 4-7 have been obtained by making a series of runs and that it is desired to determine the mechanism and rate constants. The following approach may be used. First the data shown in Figure 4-7 are plotted in the same form demonstrated in Figure 4-6. For example, for component C,

$$\frac{(n_C/n_T^0) - y_C^0}{y_A^0 - (n_A/n_T^0)} \quad \text{is plotted versus} \quad \frac{V}{n_T^0}$$

From such a plot it may be established that C and D are primary products and E is a secondary product. The fact that the curve for C in Figure 4-7 passes through a maximum and has a shape similar to compound B in Figure 4-6 further suggests that C is involved in the reaction that produces E. Further suppose that the reactions $A + B \rightarrow C + D$ and $2C \rightarrow E$ constitute balanced stoichiometric equations. Then a mechanism which is in agreement with stoichiometric experimental results is as follows:

$$A + B \underset{k_1'}{\overset{k_1}{\rightleftharpoons}} C + D \tag{4-99}$$

$$2C \underset{k_2'}{\overset{k_2}{\rightleftharpoons}} E \tag{4-100}$$

If a single set of four rate constants can be found which fits the experimental results over the range of interest, then it can be concluded that the mechanism given by Equations (4-99) and (4-100) is a satisfactory one. If sufficient thermodynamic data are available, the equilibrium constants K_1 and K_2 may be computed, and the number of rate constants to be determined experimentally may be reduced to two, say k_1 and k_2, since

$$k_1' = \frac{k_1}{K_1} \tag{4-101}$$

$$k_2' = \frac{k_2}{K_2} \tag{4-102}$$

The following differential equations may be stated for components A, B, C, D, and E:

$$-\frac{d(n_A/n_T^0)}{d(V/n_T^0)} = r_1 - r_1' \tag{4-103}$$

$$-\frac{d(n_B/n_T^0)}{d(V/n_T^0)} = r_1 - r_1' \tag{4-104}$$

$$\frac{d(n_C/n_T^0)}{d(V/n_T^0)} = (r_1 - r_1') - (2r_2 - 2r_2') \tag{4-105}$$

$$\frac{d(n_D/n_T^0)}{d(V/n_T^0)} = r_1 - r_1' \tag{4-106}$$

$$\frac{d(n_E/n_T^0)}{d(V/n_T^0)} = r_2 - r_2' \tag{4-107}$$

For a gas phase reaction,

$$\begin{aligned} r_1 &= k_1 p_A p_B, & r_1' &= k_1' p_C p_D \\ r_2 &= k_2 p_C^2, & r_2' &= k_2' p_E \end{aligned} \tag{4-108}$$

If the proposed mechanism is in agreement with the experimental results shown in Figure 4-7, then at each V/n_T^0, it follows from Equations (4-103), (4-104), and (4-106) that the following equalities must be satisfied:

$$-\frac{d(n_A/n_T^0)}{d(V/n_T^0)} = -\frac{d(n_B/n_T^0)}{d(V/n_T^0)} = \frac{d(n_D/n_T^0)}{d(V/n_T^0)} \tag{4-109}$$

Suppose that the experimental results are in agreement with Equation (4-109). Then, of the three expressions given by Equations (4-103), (4-104), and (4-106), only one of them is independent. Let Equation (4-103) be selected as the independent equation of the set. However, of the three remaining equations [Equations (4-103), (4-105), and (4-107)], only two of these at most are independent because Equation (4-105) may be obtained by multiplying both sides of Equation (4-107) by -2 and adding the result to Equation (4-103); that is,

$$-2\frac{d(n_E/n_T^0)}{d(V/n_T^0)} - \frac{d(n_A/n_T^0)}{d(V/n_T^0)} = r_1 - r_1' - 2(r_2 - r_2') \qquad (4\text{-}110)$$

The right-hand side of this expression is seen to be identical to the right-hand side of Equation (4-105). The left-hand side may be shown to be identical by means of material balances. Let z denote the moles of A that have reacted at any point in a reactor. Then

$$n_A = n_A^0 - z \qquad (4\text{-}111)$$

and the moles of C at any point in a reactor are given by

$$n_C = n_C^0 + z - 2(n_E - n_E^0) \qquad (4\text{-}112)$$

Addition of Equations (4-111) and (4-112) followed by rearrangement yields

$$n_C = (n_A^0 + n_C^0 + 2n_E^0) - 2n_E - n_A \qquad (4\text{-}113)$$

Division of each member of Equation (4-113) by n_T^0 followed by differentiation with respect to V/n_T^0 yields

$$\frac{d(n_C/n_T^0)}{d(V/n_T^0)} = -\frac{2d(n_E/n_T^0)}{d(V/n_T^0)} - \frac{d(n_A/n_T^0)}{d(V/n_T^0)} \qquad (4\text{-}114)$$

Therefore, the left-hand sides of Equations (4-110) and (4-105) are identical, and consequently only two, at most, of the three expressions [Equations (4-103), (4-105), and (4-107)] are independent. (For the general case of n rate equations, the theory of linear algebra may be used to determine the number of linearly independent equations.) Let Equations (4-103) and (4-107) be selected for consideration as the independent set. Obviously, neither of these expressions can be produced from the other. Consequently, they are independent. Since Equations (4-103) and (4-107) constitute two equations in four unknowns (k_1, k_1', k_2, and k_2'), each equation must be stated at each of two different values of V/n_T^0. The equations so obtained may be represented by the following matrix equations:

$$\begin{bmatrix} a_1 & -b_1 \\ a_2 & -b_2 \end{bmatrix} \begin{bmatrix} k_1 \\ k_1' \end{bmatrix} = \begin{bmatrix} m_1 \\ m_2 \end{bmatrix} \tag{4-115}$$

and

$$\begin{bmatrix} c_1 & -d_1 \\ c_2 & -d_2 \end{bmatrix} \begin{bmatrix} k_2 \\ k_2' \end{bmatrix} = \begin{bmatrix} m_3 \\ m_4 \end{bmatrix} \tag{4-116}$$

where $a_1 = (p_A p_B)_1$. [The subscript 1 means that the product enclosed by parentheses is to be evaluated at the particular value of V/n_T^0 denoted by $(V/n_T^0)_1$.]

$$a_1 = (p_A p_B)_1, \qquad a_2 = (p_A p_B)_2$$

$$b_1 = (p_C p_D)_1, \qquad b_2 = (p_C p_D)_2$$

$$c_1 = (p_C^2)_1, \qquad c_2 = (p_C^2)_2$$

$$d_1 = (p_E)_1, \qquad d_2 = (p_E)_2$$

$$m_1 = \left(-\frac{d(n_A/n_T^0)}{d(V/n_T^0)} \right)_1, \qquad m_2 = \left(-\frac{d(n_A/n_T^0)}{d(V/n_T^0)} \right)_2$$

$$m_3 = \left(\frac{d(n_E/n_T^0)}{d(V/n_T^0)} \right)_1, \qquad m_4 = \left(\frac{d(n_E/n_T^0)}{d(V/n_T^0)} \right)_2$$

Matrix Equation (4-115) is readily solved for k_1 and k_1', and k_2, and k_2' may be determined by solving matrix Equation (4-116). If after the procedure described has been repeated for other choices of V/n_T^0 within the range of interest and the values of the rate constants so obtained are in reasonable agreement, a suitable mechanism has been found. (Note that if equilibrium constants are available for each of the two reactions, the number of equations and unknowns is reduced to two, since k_1' and k_2' may be expressed in terms of k_1 and k_2, respectively.)

C. Interpretation of Data from Other Types of Reactors

At small values of V/n_T^0, where the conversion per pass through the reactor is small, the reactor is commonly called a *differential reactor*. The small conversion per pass in a differential reactor simplifies the evaluation of the integral appearing in Equation (4-93). In particular, Equation (4-93) may be restated as follows by use of the *mean value theorem of integral calculus*:

$$V = -\int_{n_A^0}^{n_A} \frac{dn_A}{r_A} = -\left(\frac{1}{r_A} \right)_m (n_A - n_A^0) \tag{4-117}$$

where the subscript m is used to denote the mean value of $1/r_A$. For small conversions per pass, the mean value of $1/r_A$ may be approximated with good accuracy by use of the arithmetic average of $1/r_A$ at n_A and n_A^0. That is,

$$\left(\frac{1}{r_A}\right)_m \cong \frac{1}{2}\left(\frac{1}{r_A}\bigg|_{n_A} + \frac{1}{r_A}\bigg|_{n_A^0}\right) \tag{4-118}$$

In the interest of simplicity, the subscript m is dropped in the following analysis of the case where the reactions given by Equations (4-99) and (4-100) are carried out in a differential reactor. For a differential reactor, the equations corresponding to Equations (4-103) and (4-107) are as follows:

$$\frac{n_A^0 - n_A}{V} = r_1 - r_1' \quad \text{or} \quad \frac{n_A^0/n_T^0 - n_A/n_T^0}{(V/n_T^0)} = r_1 - r_1' \tag{4-119}$$

$$\frac{n_E - n_E^0}{V} = r_2 - r_2' \quad \text{or} \quad \frac{n_E/n_T^0 - n_E^0/n_T^0}{V/n_T^0} = r_2 - r_2' \tag{4-120}$$

Since the feed composition is held fixed for all runs, it follows that n_A^0/n_T^0 and n_E^0/n_T^0 are constant for all choices of V/n_T^0. Equations (4-119) and (4-120) can be applied within their range of applicability to determine the rate constants in the same manner as described for Equations (4-103) and (4-107).

Data collected in batch reactors may be analyzed in a manner analogous to that described. In this case, Figure 4-7 would consist of a plot of the ratios of N_A, N_B, N_C, N_D, and N_E with respect to N_T^0 versus time. Data for perfectly mixed flow reactors are analyzed in a manner analogous to that shown for differential reactors except that the procedure is valid over all values of V/n_T^0.

To determine the variation of the rate constants with temperature, it is necessary to repeat the experiments required to plot Figure 4-7 for each of two or three other temperatures. The values of each k so obtained can generally be expressed as an exponential function of temperature of the form of Equation (1-29).

EXAMPLE 4-4

Propylene was oxidized with air by Billingsley et al. [9] over a copper oxide catalyst in a fixed-bed flow type reactor which is described in some detail in Chapter 8. Selected data obtained by Billingsley et al. are presented in Table 4-3. These data are to be used to establish the stoichiometry of the reactions involved in the catalytic oxidation of propylene by use of the techniques illustrated by Figures 4-4, 4-5, and 4-6. In this case,

TABLE 4-3

SELECTED EXPERIMENTAL RESULTS REPORTED BY BILLINGSLEY ET AL. [16] FOR THE PARTIAL OXIDATION OF PROPLYENE BY AIR OVER A COPPER OXIDE CATALYST

W/n_T^0	Partial Pressure (in. of Hg)		Feed Rates (g moles/hr)						Effluent Rates (g moles/hr)			
	O_2	C_3H_6	O_2	N_2	CO_2	C_3H_8	C_3H_6	O_2	CO_2	C_3H_8	C_3H_4	C_3H_4O
4.04	11.07	10.90	0.3819	1.5279	0.0006	0.0132	0.3663	0.3641	0.0109	0.0142	0.3606	0.0022
2.84	11.23	10.91	0.5440	2.1761	0.0007	0.0189	0.5217	0.5242	0.0120	0.0218	0.5151	0.0029
2.07	10.79	10.94	0.7404	2.9617	0.0010	0.0269	0.7437	0.7197	0.0130	0.0261	0.7368	0.0029
1.69	11.67	12.03	0.9023	3.6096	0.0013	0.0334	0.9213	0.8797	0.0146	0.0261	0.9142	0.0027
1.29	11.66	10.83	1.2032	4.8128	0.0016	0.0402	1.1099	1.1769	0.0169	0.0401	1.1015	0.0034
4.09	10.01	19.19	0.3240	1.2961	0.0006	0.0221	0.6105	0.3101	0.0073	0.0199	0.6045	0.0038
2.95	10.26	17.75	0.4629	1.8515	0.0008	0.0285	0.7881	0.4483	0.0079	0.0257	0.7819	0.0038
2.22	10.05	18.76	0.6017	2.4070	0.0010	0.0402	1.1100	0.5826	0.0105	0.0386	1.1020	0.0049
1.55	10.01	19.13	0.8563	3.4250	0.0015	0.0590	1.6316	0.8280	0.0160	0.0552	1.6204	0.0065
4.31	8.54	25.90	0.2660	1.0643	0.0004	0.0285	0.7881	0.2527	0.0060	0.0280	0.7823	0.0036
2.76	8.65	24.82	0.4210	1.6843	0.0008	0.0430	1.1876	0.4050	0.0080	0.0471	1.1800	0.0052
1.93	8.72	25.36	0.6015	2.4062	0.0010	0.0623	1.7204	0.5818	0.0102	0.0679	1.7114	0.0061
1.19	8.64	25.38	0.9717	3.8871	0.0017	0.1020	2.8194	0.9428	0.0154	0.1073	2.8064	0.0083
3.92	7.49	28.33	0.2660	1.0643	0.0005	0.0358	0.9879	0.2539	0.0056	0.0154	0.9818	0.0044
2.66	7.65	30.76	0.3817	1.5272	0.0007	0.0542	1.4985	0.3618	0.0090	0.0558	1.4883	0.0074
1.90	7.64	29.50	0.5437	2.1750	0.0010	0.0747	2.0646	0.5223	0.0097	0.0804	2.0534	0.0083
1.20	7.65	29.90	0.8560	3.4244	0.0015	0.1193	3.2967	0.8255	0.0138	0.1186	3.2805	0.0120
4.04	11.36	11.06	0.3816	1.5261	0.0007	0.0132	0.3663	0.3638	0.0110	0.0134	0.3606	0.0023
4.04	11.30	11.03	0.3813	1.5255	0.0007	0.0132	0.3663	0.3630	0.0112	0.0139	0.3601	0.0025
1.55	9.82	18.91	0.8552	3.4209	0.0016	0.0591	1.6316	0.8329	0.0124	0.0584	1.6220	0.0060
1.21	9.64	18.40	1.0863	4.3455	0.0020	0.0743	2.0535	1.0585	0.0160	0.0740	2.0420	0.0068
4.04	8.20	7.98	0.3812	1.5247	0.0007	0.0132	0.3663	0.3664	0.0092	0.0129	0.3614	0.0021
4.04	8.33	8.03	0.3812	1.5247	0.0007	0.0132	0.3663	0.3671	0.0087	0.0131	0.3615	0.0021

however, the variable W/n_T^0 [grams of catalyst (gram mole of feed/hr)] may be used as the independent variable rather than t or $1/S_V$.

    (a) By use of the data presented in Table 4-3, construct the following graphs:

        (1) Moles of acrolein produced per mole of propylene reacted versus W/n_T^0

        (2) Moles of carbon dioxide produced per mole of propylene reacted versus W/n_T^0

    (b) From the graphs obtained in (a), propose a stoichiometry for the oxidation of propylene, and give supporting arguments for the proposed stoichiometry.

SOLUTION

    (a) From the data presented in Table 4-3, the graphs presented in Figures 4-8 and 4-9 were constructed.

    (b) Comparison of Figures 4-8 and 4-9 with Figures 4-5 and 4-6 suggest that acrolein and carbon dioxide are produced by primary reactions. If a secondary reaction, such as the further oxidation of acrolein to carbon dioxide, were significant, then the curves in Figure 4-8 would have exhibited negative slopes and those in Figure 4-9 would have exhibited positive slopes. If the polymerization of acrolein to the dimer were significant, then the curves in Figure 4-8 would have exhibited negative slopes. The horizontal lines shown in Figures 4-8 and 4-9, plus the fact that other possible products did not appear in the effluent in significant amounts, suggest that the catalytic oxidation of propylene

$\dfrac{W}{n_T^0}$, Grams of catalyst per gram-mole of feed per hour

Figure 4-8. The horizontal lines suggest that acrolein is a primary product which does not undergo either further oxidation or polymerization to any significant extent. [Taken from D. S. Billingsley and C. D. Holland, *I&EC Fundamentals*, 2:252 (1963). Used with permission of the American Chemical Society.]

Figure 4-9. The horizontal lines suggest that carbon dioxide is produced by a primary reaction and that any carbon dioxide produced by secondary reactions is insignificant. [Taken from D. S. Billingsley and C. D. Holland, *I&EC Fundamentals*, 2:252 (1963). Used with permission of the American Chemical Society.]

over a copper oxide catalyst is adequately described by the following stoichiometric equations:

$$C_3H_6 + O_2 \rightleftharpoons CH_2CHCHO + H_2O$$
$$C_3H_6 + 4.5O_2 \rightleftharpoons 3\,CO_2 + 3\,H_2O$$

PROBLEMS

4-1. (a) Begin with Equation (4-17) and the initial conditions stated below it and develop the expressions given by Equations (4-18) and (4-19).

(b) Begin with Equations (4-5) and (4-17) and develop Equation (4-20).

(c) Begin with Equations (4-28), (3-58), and the initial condition that at $N_B = N_B^0$, $N_M = 0$, and obtain the result given by Equation (4-29).

(d) Beginning with Equations (4-30), (3-58), (4-29), and the initial condition that at $N_B = N_B^0$, $N_D = 0$, obtain the result given by Equation (4-31).

(e) Show that Equation (4-22) may be integrated to give Equation (4-32), provided that the moles of C are held fixed by feeding C to the reactor at the same rate at which it is consumed by the reaction.

4-2. For the case where the reaction given by Equation (4-1) is carried out isothermally in the gas phase in a plug-flow reactor at steady state operation, obtain n_A, n_R, and n_S as functions of V/v_T. Assume that the pressure drop is negligible and that the gaseous mixture obeys the perfect gas law.

4-3. If the complex reaction given by Equation (4-1) is carried out isothermally in the liquid phase in a perfectly mixed flow reactor at steady state operation, show that when the feed contains A alone ($n_R^0 = n_S^0 = 0$),

$$n_A = \frac{n_A^0[1/\theta + (k_1' k_2'/a)]}{1/\theta + k_1 - k_1'/a(k_1 - k_2')}$$

where $a = \dfrac{1}{\theta} + k_2' + k_2 + k_1'$,   and the rate constants are based on concentration units

$$\theta = \frac{V}{v_T}$$

4-4. The chloride-chlorate reaction for the production of chlorine dioxide was investigated by Hong et al. [10], who found that the stoichiometry of the reactions involved could be represented by the following equation:

$$2\,H^+ + ClO_3^- + Cl^- \longrightarrow ClO_2 + \tfrac{1}{2}Cl_2 + H_2O \tag{A}$$

in a strong acid solution at 25°C and at high ratios of chlorate (ClO_3^-) to chloride (Cl^-). Hong et al. [10] proposed the following mechanism

$$3\,H^+ + 2\,Cl^- + ClO_3^- \rightleftharpoons Cl_2 + HClO_2 + H_2O \tag{1}$$

$$HClO_2 + H^+ + ClO_3^- \longrightarrow 2ClO_2 + H_2O \tag{2}$$

$$HClO_2 + H^+ + Cl^- \longrightarrow 2HOCl \tag{3}$$

$$HOCl + H^+ + Cl^- \longrightarrow Cl_2 + H_2O \tag{4}$$

and assumptions:

1. The accumulation of $HClO_2$ and $HOCl$ with time is negligible.
2. $k_2[H^+][ClO_3^-] \gg k_3[H^+][Cl^-]$
3. $k_2[H^+][ClO_3^-] \gg k_1'[Cl_2]$

On the basis of the proposed reaction and assumptions show that

$$\frac{d[ClO_2]}{dt} = 2k_1[H^+]^3[Cl^-]^2[ClO_3^-]$$

and $$\frac{d[Cl_2]}{dt} = k_1[H^+]^3[Cl^-]^2[ClO_3^-]$$

4-5. Acrylonitrile is produced by reaction of propylene, ammonia, and oxygen over a bismuth phosphomolybdate catalyst [11, 12]. (This catalyst was developed by SOHIO for producing acrylonitrile.) The reaction rates were found to be independent of ammonia or oxygen concentrations and could be represented as

Byproducts: CO, CO_2 ethylene, and acetaldehyde

For a reaction temperature of 470°C, the following rate constants were reported:

$k_1 = 0.195 \text{ sec}^{-1}$

$k_2 = 0.005 \text{ sec}^{-1}$

$k_3 = 0.4 \text{ sec}^{-1}$

$k_4 = $ a small bimolecular rate constant $(r_4 = k_4[O_2][C_2H_3CHO])$

The rates of the first and second reactions are first order with respect to propylene, and the third is first order with respect to acrolein.

Acrylonitrile is to be produced by use of the SOHIO process in a plug-flow reactor. The reactor is to be operated isothermally at 470°C, and a space velocity $V/v_T^0 = 9.1$ sec. (Actually Farkas [11] and Callahan et al. [12] state that they used a residence time of 9.1 sec. Their residence time was taken to mean space velocity.) The feed to the reactor contains 6.6% propylene, 86.1% air, and 7.3% ammonia. Since the amount of propylene in the feed is relatively small, the change in the total number of moles resulting from the reaction may be neglected and the volumetric flow rate v_T may be assumed constant throughout the reactor volume V. If the byproduct reaction is neglected, calculate

(a) the percent of the propylene converted
(b) the moles of acrolein produced per mole of propylene reacted
(c) the moles of acrylonitrile produced per mole of propylene reacted.

Answer: **(a)** 83.8% **(b)** 0.00405 **(c)** 0.996.

4-6. Gulyaev et al. [13] proposed the following mechanism for the thermal decomposition of methane,

$$CH_4 \xrightarrow{k_1} \ddot{C}H_2 + H_2$$
$$\ddot{C}H_2 + CH_4 \xrightarrow{\overline{k_1}} C_2H_6 \tag{1}$$

$$C_2H_6 \xrightarrow{k_2} C_2H_4 + H_2 \tag{2}$$

$$C_2H_4 \xrightarrow{k_3} C_2H_2 + H_2 \tag{3}$$

$$C_2H_2 \xrightarrow{k_4} 2 C + H_2 \tag{4}$$

where
$$k_1 = 2.25 \times 10^{13} \exp\left(\frac{-91,000}{RT}\right) \text{sec}^{-1}$$

$$k_2 = 9 \times 10^{13} \exp\left(\frac{-69,000}{RT}\right) \text{sec}^{-1}$$

$$k_3 = 2.57 \times 10^{8} \exp\left(\frac{-40,000}{RT}\right) \text{sec}^{-1}$$

$$k_4 = 1.7 \times 10^{6} \exp\left(\frac{-30,000}{RT}\right) \text{sec}^{-1}$$

where T is in $°K$ and $R = 1.9872$.

To approximate the residence times required to maximize the conversions of methane to ethylene and to acetylene, respectively, in a plasma jet, the equations for isothermal operation of a constant volume batch reactor were used [13]. Carry out the analysis outlined below in (a) through (g) on the basis of a reaction temperature of 3000°K and a feed consisting of pure methane.

(a) On the basis of the assumption that the accumulation of $\ddot{C}H_2$ is negligible, show that $[\ddot{C}H_2] = k_1/\bar{k}_1$ where $[\ddot{C}H_2]$ denotes the concentration of $\ddot{C}H_2$ in moles per unit volume.

(b) Show that
$$[CH_4] = [CH_4]^0 \exp(-2k_1 t)$$

(c) If the accumulation of ethane is negligible, show that the concentration of ethane at any time t may be approximated as follows:

$$[C_2H_6] = \frac{k_1}{k_2}[CH_4]$$

(d) Show that

$$[C_2H_4] = \frac{k_1[CH_4]^0}{(2k_1 - k_3)}[\exp(-k_3 t) - \exp(-2k_1 t)]$$

(e) Show that

$$[C_2H_2] = \frac{k_1 k_3 [CH_4]^0}{(2k_1 - k_3)(2k_1 - k_4)(k_3 - k_4)}[(k_3 - k_4)\exp(-2k_1 t)$$
$$- (2k_1 - k_4)\exp(-k_3 t) + (2k_1 - k_3)\exp(-k_4 t)]$$

(f) Show that the maximum concentration of ethylene occurs at time

$$t = \frac{\log_e(2k_1/k_3)}{2k_1 - k_3}$$

(g) Calculate the moles of ethylene, ethane, acetylene, and carbon produced per mole of methane charged at 3000°K at the reaction time corresponding to the maximum production of ethylene.

Answer: $[C_2H_4]/[CH_4]^0 = 0.449$, $[C_2H_6]/[CH_4]^0 = 0.000166$,
$[C_2H_2]/[CH_4]^0 = 0.0365$, $[C]/[CH_4]^0 = 0.00196$

4-7. J. L. Bollard [14] proposed the following mechanism for the liquid phase oxidation of hydrocarbons:

$$\text{Initiation:} \quad x \xrightarrow{k_1} R^{\cdot}$$

$$\text{Propagation:} \quad R^{\cdot} + O_2 \xrightarrow{k_2} RO_2^{\cdot}$$

$$RO_2^{\cdot} + RH \xrightarrow{k_3} ROOH + R^{\cdot}$$

$$\text{Termination:} \quad 2R^{\cdot} \xrightarrow{k_4} R_2$$

$$R^{\cdot} + RO_2^{\cdot} \xrightarrow{k_5} \text{stable products}$$

$$2RO_2^{\cdot} \xrightarrow{k_6} \text{stable products}$$

where
- x = an initiator such as benzoyl peroxide
- R = any saturated hydrocarbon
- $R^{\cdot}$ = free radical of saturated hydrocarbon

On the assumptions that there is no appreciable accumulation of $[R^{\cdot}]$ and $[RO_2^{\cdot}]$ and that $k_5 = \sqrt{k_4 k_6}$, show that the rate of reaction of oxygen is given by

$$r_{O_2} = \frac{k_2[O_2]\{r_i\sqrt{k_6} + k_3[RH]\sqrt{r_i}\}}{k_2[O_2]\sqrt{k_6} + k_3[RH]\sqrt{k_4} + \sqrt{k_4 k_6 r_i}}$$

where r_i is the rate of initiation (the rate of formation of $R^{\cdot}$).

4-8. The following mechanism has been reported by Pacey et al. [15] for the pyrolysis ethane.

Initiation:	$C_2H_6 \longrightarrow$	$2CH_3^{\cdot}$	(1)
Propagation:	$CH_3^{\cdot} + C_2H_6 \longrightarrow$	$CH_4 + C_2H_5^{\cdot}$	(2)
	$C_2H_5^{\cdot} \longrightarrow$	$C_2H_4 + H^{\cdot}$	(3)
	$H^{\cdot} + C_2H_6 \longrightarrow$	$H_2 + C_2H_5^{\cdot}$	(4)
Termination:	$C_2H_5^{\cdot} + C_2H_5^{\cdot} \longrightarrow$	$n\text{-}C_4H_{10}$	(5)
	$C_2H_5^{\cdot} + C_2H_5^{\cdot} \longrightarrow$	$C_2H_6 + C_2H_4$	(6)
Propylene formation:	$C_2H_5^{\cdot} + C_2H_4 \longrightarrow$	$C_3H_6 + CH_3^{\cdot}$	(7)
Inhibition:	$H^{\cdot} + C_2H_4 \longrightarrow$	$C_2H_5^{\cdot}$	(8)

No significant accumulation of free radicals was observed experimentally, and thus the pseudo steady state assumption may be used in the analysis. Also, it was found experimentally that $k_5 = 7k_6$. Show that the rate of disappearance of ethane and the rate of appearance of ethylene are given by

$$r_{C_2H_6} = k_1[C_2H_6] + k_2[CH_3^{\cdot}][C_2H_6] + k_4[H^{\cdot}][C_2H_6] - \frac{k_6}{2}[C_2H_5^{\cdot}]^2$$

$$r_{C_2H_4} = k_3[C_2H_5^{\cdot}] - k_7[C_2H_5^{\cdot}][C_2H_4] - k_8[H^{\cdot}][C_2H_4] + \frac{k_6}{2}[C_2H_5^{\cdot}]^2$$

and show that

$$[CH_3^{\cdot}] = \frac{2k_1}{k_2} + \frac{k_7}{k_2}\frac{[C_2H_4][C_2H_5^{\cdot}]}{[C_2H_6]}$$

$$[H^{\cdot}] = \frac{k_3[C_2H_5^{\cdot}]}{k_4[C_2H_6] + k_8[C_2H_4]}$$

$$[C_2H_5^{\cdot}] = \frac{1}{2}\left\{\frac{k_1[C_2H_6]}{k_6}\right\}^{1/2}$$

4-9. The following free radical mechanism for the oxidation of hydrocarbons was proposed by Alagy et al. [16].

Initiation:	Initiator $\longrightarrow$	$R^{\cdot}$	(1)
	$R^{\cdot} + O_2 \longrightarrow$	$RO_2^{\cdot}$	(2)
		$ROOH + R^{\cdot}$	(3)
Propagation:	$RO_2^{\cdot} + RH$		
		$ROH + RO^{\cdot}$	(4)
	$RO^{\cdot} + RH \longrightarrow$	$ROH + R^{\cdot}$	(5)
Termination:	$RO_2^{\cdot} + RO_2^{\cdot} \longrightarrow$	stable products	(6)
	$RO_2^{\cdot} + R^{\cdot} \longrightarrow$	stable products	(7)
	$R^{\cdot} + R^{\cdot} \longrightarrow$	stable products	(8)

On the basis of the assumption that there is no appreciable accumulation of the free radicals, and the assumption that $k_7 = \sqrt{k_6 k_8}$, show that the rate of disappearance of RH and the rates of appearance of ROH and $ROOH$ are given by the following expressions:

$$r_{RH} = (k_3 + k_4)[RO_2^{\cdot}][RH] + k_5[RO^{\cdot}][RH]$$

$$r_{ROH} = k_4[RO_2^{\cdot}][RH] + k_5[RO^{\cdot}][RH]$$

$$r_{ROOH} = k_3[RO_2^{\cdot}][RH]$$

and show that

$$[RO_2^{\cdot}] = \sqrt{r_i/k_6} - (\sqrt{k_8/k_6})[R^{\cdot}]$$

$$[R^{\cdot}] = \frac{r_i + (k_3 + k_4)(\sqrt{r_i/k_6})[RH]}{k_2[O_2] + (k_3 + k_4)(\sqrt{k_8/k_6})[RH] + \sqrt{k_8 r_i}}$$

$$[RO^{\cdot}] = \frac{k_4}{k_5}[RO_2^{\cdot}]$$

4-10. For the reaction

$$A + B \longrightarrow 2D$$

it has been observed that at high concentrations of B relative to A the rate of reaction is given by

$$r_A = kC_A^2$$

which at high concentrations of A relative to B the rate of reaction is given by

$$r_A = \bar{k} C_A C_B$$

Propose a mechanism that will satisfy both the stoichiometry and the rate expressions.

4-11. Suppose that the following reactions were investigated in a perfectly mixed flow reactor:

$$A \xrightarrow{k_1} R \xrightarrow{k_2} S$$

$$A \xrightarrow{k_3} P$$

For a feed rate of 100 g moles/min of pure A and a residence time $\theta = V/v_T = 20$ min, 80% of A was converted. The product compositions in mole percent were as follows:

Component	%
A	20
R	50
S	20
P	10

(a) Find k_1, k_2, and k_3.
Answer: $k_1 = 0.175$ min^{-1}; $k_2 = 0.02$ min^{-1}; $k_3 = 0.025$ min^{-1}.
(b) For the set of rate constants obtained in (a), determine the value of θ which should be used in order to maximize the moles of R produced per mole of A fed. Calculate the composition of the product at this optimum value of θ.
Answer: $\theta = 15.8$ min, and the mole fraction of A, R, S, and P were: 0.240, 0.505, 0.160, and 0.0950, respectively.

4-12. (a) Because of the relative high order of approximations involved in the rate controlling step approach, more than one expression may be obtained for N_A, N_R, and N_S. For example, where $k_2 \ll k_1 \ll k_1'$ and $N_R = K_1 N_A$, show that by beginning with Equation (4-75) and by making use of the assumptions that $k_1 N_A - k_1' N_R \simeq 0$ (or $N_R = K_1 N_A$) that the following expressions are obtained for N_A and N_R:

$$N_A = N_A^0 \exp(-k_2 t)$$
$$N_R = K_1 N_A^0 \exp(-k_2 t)$$

(b) If $k_1 \ll 1, k_2 \gg 1$, and k_1' is finite and positive, show that the exact expressions given by Equations (4-80) and (4-81) for N_A and N_R, may be reduced to those given by Equations (4-84) and (4-85), respectively, by approximating the square root term appearing in m_1 and m_2 by the first two terms of the binomial series expansion; that is,

$$\sqrt{b^2 - 4c} \cong b - \frac{2c}{b}$$

(c) Begin with the expression for N_A as given by Equation (4-80) and impose the condition that $k_2 \ll k_1 \ll k_1'$ and show that the relationship given by Equation (4-87) is obtained.

Hint: Make use of the same approximation shown in Part (b).

4-13. Show that the ordinates for A and B have the values shown in Figure 4-5.

4-14. (a) Show that the intercepts for B, C, and D have the values shown in Figure 4-6.
(b) Show that at the point of intersection, the ordinates of B and C have the value of $k_2/(k_1 + k_2)$. Show that the ordinates of B and D at the point of intersection have the value shown in Figure 4-6.
(c) Show that in the limit as t (or $1/S_V$) approaches infinity, the y intercept of the curve for D in Figure 4-6 approaches $2k_1/(k_1 + k_2)$.

NOTATION

A^* = activated molecules or free radical

C_A^* = concentration of the activated molecules

M = concentration of the monomer

R_j = polymer molecule or the concentration of polymer molecules leaving j monomer units

$R\cdot$ = free radical

τ = defined by Equation (4-35) and has the units of (moles)(time)/volume

REFERENCES

1. MacMullin, R. B., *Chem. Eng. Prog.*, *44*:183 (1948).

2. Smith, J. M., *Chem. Eng. Kin.*, McGraw-Hill Book Company, New York (1972).

3. Aris, R., *Introduction to the Analysis of Chemical Reactors*, Prentice-Hall, Inc., Englewood Cliffs, N.J. (1965).

4. Allen, G., G. Gee, and C. Stretch, *J. Polymer Sci.*, *48*:189 (1960).

5. Bhattacharyya, D. N., J. Smid, and M. Szwarc, *J. Phys. Chem.*, *69*:624 (1965).

6. Lindermann, F. A., *Trans. Faraday Soc.*, *17*:598 (1922).

7. Hinshelwood, C. N., *Proc. Roy. Soc.*, *A113*:230 (1927).

8. Date, R. D., J. B. Butt, and H. Bliss, *I&EC Fund.*, *8*:687 (1960).

9. Billingsley, D. S., and C. D. Holland, *I&EC Fund.*, *2*:252 (1963).

10. Hong, C. C., F. Lenzi, and W. H. Rapson, *Canadian J. Chem. Eng.*, *45*:349 (1967).

11. Farkas, Adalbert, *Hydrocarbon Processing*, p. 121 (July 1970).

12. Callahan, J. C., R. K. Grasselli, E. C. Milberger, and H. A. Strecker, *Preprints of the Division of Petroleum Chemistry of American Chemical Society 14, No. 3*, C13 (Sept. 1969).

13. Gulyaev, G. V., and L. S. Polak, *Kinetika i Kataliz*, (in Russian), *6*:399 (1965); *Kinetics and Catalysis* (English trans.), *6*:352 (1965).

14. Bollard, J. L., *Proc. Roy. Soc.*, *A186*:218 (1946); *Quart. Rev. Chem. Soc.*, *31* (1949).

15. Pacey, P. D., and J. H. Purnell, *I&EC Fund.*, *11*:233 (1972).

16. Alagy, J., L. Asselineau, C. Busson, B. Cha, and H. Sandler, *Hydrocarbon Processing 47: No. 12*, 131 (1968).

Thermodynamics of
Chemical Reactions

5

Most chemical reactions are accompanied by the evolution or the absorption of heat. Since the rate of reaction depends strongly upon temperature, it is necessary to take the heat of reaction into account in the design of chemical reactors. In this chapter, the methods for calculating the heats of reaction as provided by chemical thermodynamics are presented. The effects of pressure and heats of mixing on the enthalpy of a mixture are treated in Chapter 11. Also needed in the analysis of the feasibility of carrying out chemical reactions is the free energy change for a reaction. The free energy change makes it possible to calculate the maximum conversion which is theoretically attainable.

The fundamental thermodynamic quantities of internal energy U, enthalpy H, Gibbs free energy G, Helmholtz free energy A, and the entropy function S, are related as follows:

$$H = U + Pv \tag{5-1}$$

$$G = H - TS \tag{5-2}$$

$$A = U - TS \tag{5-3}$$

where T is the absolute temperature and Pv is the pressure-volume product. Although the conversion factor for Pv has been omitted, it is supposed that the Pv product has the units of Btu/lb mole, cal/g mole or joules/kg mole. The quantities H, U, G, and A have the units of Btu/lb, Btu/lb mole, cal/g, cal/g mole, joules/kg, or joules/kg mole and entropy has the units of Btu/(lb mole °R), cal/(g mole °K), or joules/(kg mole °K).

For a pure component or for a mixture at constant composition, the first and second laws of thermodynamics are contained in the single expression:

$$dU = T \, dS - P \, dv \tag{5-4}$$

By use of this expression and the relationships given by Equations (5-1) through (5-3), the following differential expressions are obtained:

$$dH = T \, dS + v \, dP \tag{5-5}$$

$$dG = -S \, dT + v \, dP \tag{5-6}$$

$$dA = -S \, dT - P \, dv \tag{5-7}$$

The functions U, A, G, H, and S are called state functions because changes in these functions depend only upon the initial and final states of a system, and they are consequently independent of the path taken by a system in passing from the initial to the final state. The fact that the final values of these functions are independent of path is used extensively in the calculation of the heats of reaction and the free energy changes for reactions.

A. Heat of Reaction

The *standard heat of reaction* at the temperature T is defined as the sum of the enthalpies of the products in their respective standard states at the temperature T minus the sum of the enthalpies of the reactants in their respective standard states at the temperature T. The standard states may be selected arbitrarily, and two of the standard states which are commonly used are shown in Table 5-1.

TABLE 5-1
STANDARD STATES

Physical State	Standard State
Solid	The most stable form at 1 atm pressure and at the specified temperature
Gas	Perfect gas at 1 atm pressure and at the specified temperature

Standard States Used Herein

Substances	Standard State
All elements and compounds except carbon	Perfect gas at 1 atm pressure and at the specified temperature
Carbon	Graphite form at 1 atm pressure and at the specified temperature

Now consider the reaction

$$aA(g) + bB(g) = cC(s) + dD(g) \qquad (5\text{-}8)$$

where C denotes carbon. To compute the standard heat of reaction at 25°C, it is helpful to visualize each component as being in a separate container at its standard state as shown below.

$$aH_A^\circ \qquad\qquad bH_B^\circ \qquad\qquad\qquad cH_C^\circ \qquad\qquad dH_D^\circ$$

$$
\boxed{\begin{array}{l} a \text{ moles of } A \\ \text{perfect gas at} \\ 1 \text{ atm and } 25°C \end{array}}
+
\boxed{\begin{array}{l} b \text{ moles of } B \\ \text{perfect gas at} \\ 1 \text{ atm and } 25°C \end{array}}
\;\;\begin{array}{c} a\Delta H_{r\,298}^\circ \\ = \end{array}\;\;
\boxed{\begin{array}{l} c \text{ moles of } C \\ \text{pure graphite at} \\ 1 \text{ atm and } 25°C \end{array}}
+
\boxed{\begin{array}{l} d \text{ moles of } D \\ \text{perfect gas at} \\ 1 \text{ atm and } 25°C \end{array}}
$$

From the definition of the standard heat of reaction, it follows that heat of reaction per mole of A for the reaction given by Equation (5-8) is given by

$$\Delta H_{r298}^\circ = \left(\frac{1}{a}\right)\left[cH_c^\circ + dH_D^\circ - aH_A^\circ - bH_B^\circ\right] \qquad (5\text{-}9)$$

When the standard state of a perfect gas at 1 atm pressure is used for all substances except carbon, and the standard state of carbon is taken to be graphite at 1 atm pressure (see Table 5-1), the corresponding enthalpies are identified by the superscript $\circ$. When these enthalpies are evaluated at the temperature of 25°C (298.15°K), the subscript 298 is used. (In the examples and tables, 298 is used to mean 298.16°K, an old value for 25°C.) The use of separate containers for each of the substances involved in the reaction emphasizes the fact that the standard heat of reaction in no way accounts for any heat of solution effects. The standard heat of reaction is used in the calculation of the heat of reaction at any specified temperature as demonstrated in a subsequent section.

B. Heat of Formation

The standard heat of formation ΔH_f° of a compound at the temperature T is the *standard heat of reaction* when the given compound in its standard state at the temperature T is *formed from its elements* in their standard states at the temperature T. The elements in their standard states are taken as the reference state; that is, they are assigned an enthalpy of zero. In the case of gases such as oxygen and nitrogen, the standard state could be taken as either the atomic or the molecular forms of oxygen and nitrogen. The molecular forms are generally taken as the respective standard states because this choice generally leads to a simplification in the calculation of heats of reaction involving these gases. Typical heats of formation are given in Table 5-2. The heat of formation of methane per mole of methane formed from its elements by the reaction

$$C(s) + 2\,H_2(g) = CH_4(g) \qquad (5\text{-}10)$$

may be represented graphically as follows:

$$H_C^\circ \qquad\qquad 2H_{H_2}^\circ \qquad\qquad H_{CH_4}^\circ$$

1 mole of carbon: graphite at 1 atm and 25°C	+	2 moles of H_2: perfect gas at 1 atm and 25°C	$\Delta H_{r\,298}^\circ$ =	1 mole methane: perfect gas at 1 atm and 25°C

The heat of reaction is given by

$$\Delta H_{f\,298}^\circ = \Delta H_{r\,298}^\circ = \left[H_{CH_4}^\circ - H_C^\circ - 2H_{H_2}^\circ\right]_{298} \qquad (5\text{-}11)$$

Since $H_C^\circ = H_{H_2}^\circ = 0$, it follows that

$$\Delta H_{r\,298}^\circ = \Delta H_{f\,298}^\circ = H_{CH_4,\,298}^\circ \qquad (5\text{-}12)$$

Thus the standard heat of formation of CH_4 is equal to its enthalpy above its elements in their standard states.

TABLE 5-2
TYPICAL HEATS OF FORMATION AT 25°C
(Taken from [1] and [2])

Substance	ΔH_f^0 kcal/mole	Substance	ΔH_f^0 kcal/mole
H (g)	52.095	1-Butene (g)	-0.03
O (g)	59.553	Acetylene (g)	54.194
Cl (g)	28.989	Benzene (g)	19.820
CO (g)	-26.416	Toluene (g)	11.950
CO_2 (g)	-94.051	o-Xylene (g)	4.540
H_2O (g)	-57.798	m-Xylene (g)	4.120
H_2O (l)	-68.315	p-Xylene (g)	-4.290
Methane (g)	-17.889	Methanol (l)	-57.11
Ethane (g)	-20.236	Ethanol (l)	-66.20
Propane (g)	-24.820	Glycine (s)	-126.330
Ethylene (g)	12.496	Acetic acid (l)	-116.4
Propylene (g)	4.879	1,3 Butadiene (g)	26.33

* These heats of formation are based on the standard state of carbon in the solid state of graphite at 1 atm and 25°C, and molecular hydrogen, chlorine and oxygen in the standard state of a perfect gas at 1 atm and 25°C.

The standard heat of reaction for the production of water gas from methane and steam

$$CH_4(g) + H_2O(g) = CO(g) + 3H_2(g) \tag{5-13}$$

may be calculated from the heats of formation at 25°C as follows. Addition of the following reactions

$$CH_4(g) = C(s) + 2\,H_2(g), \qquad \Delta H = -\Delta H_f^\circ = 17.889 \text{ kcal}$$

$$H_2O(g) = \tfrac{1}{2}O_2(g) + H_2(g). \qquad \Delta H = -\Delta H_f^\circ = 57.7979 \text{ kcal}$$

$$C(s) + \tfrac{1}{2}O_2(g) = CO(g), \qquad \Delta H = \Delta H_f^\circ = -26.4157 \text{ kcal}$$

yields

$$CH_4(g) + H_2O(g) = CO(g) + 3\,H_2(g), \qquad \Delta H_{r298}^\circ = 49.2712 \text{ kcal}$$

.This calculation is a numerical demonstration of the general formula for the calculation of the heat of reaction from heats of formation; that is, for the general reaction,

$$aA + bB = cC + dD \tag{5-14}$$

the standard heat of reaction is given by

$$\Delta H_{r298}^\circ = \frac{1}{a}\left[c\,\Delta H_{fC}^\circ + d\,\Delta H_{fD}^\circ - a\,\Delta H_{fA}^\circ - b\,\Delta H_{fB}^\circ\right]_{298} \tag{5-15}$$

where it is understood that each heat of formation is evaluated at $T = 298.16°K$. Equation (5–15) may be used to calculate the standard heat of reaction at any temperature T, provided that the heats of formation are available.

Another method for calculating heats of reaction that is in common practice makes use of the difference

$$H_T^\circ - H_0^\circ \qquad \text{or} \qquad \frac{H_T^\circ - H_0^\circ}{T}$$

The enthalpy of a compound or element in its standard state at temperature T is denoted by H_T° and the corresponding enthalpy at 0°K is denoted by H_0°. To demonstrate the presentation of these data, an abbreviated set of data are shown in Table 5-3. The use of these data is illustrated by the calcula-

TABLE 5-3

$$\text{Selected Values of the Enthalpy Function } H_T^\circ - H_0^\circ \text{ (Taken from [1])}$$

Substance	ΔH_{f0}° kcal/mole	$H_T^\circ - H_0^\circ$ in cal/mole at $T°K$ indicated					
		298.16	400	600	800	1000	1500
H_2 (g)	0	2023.81	2731.0	4128.6	5537.4	6965.8	10,694.2
O_2 (g)	0	2069.78	2792.4	4279.2	5854.1	7397.0	11,776.4
C (graphite)	0	251.56	502.6	1198.1	2081.7	3074.6	5814
CO (g)	-27.2019	2072.63	2783.8	4209.5	5699.8	7256.5	11,358.8
CO_2 (g)	-93.9686	2238.11	3194.8	5322.4	7689.4	10,222	17,004
H_2O (g)	-57.107	2367.7	3194.0	4882.2	6689.6	8608.0	13,848
Methane (g)	-15.987	2397	3323	5549	8321	11,560	21,130
Ethane (g)	-16.571	2856	4296	8016	12,760	18,280	34,500
Propane (g)	-19.482	3512	5556	10,930	17,760	25,670	48,650
Ethylene (g)	14.522	2525	3711	6732	10,480	14,760	27,100
Acetylene (g)	54.329	2391.5	3541.2	6127	8999	12,090	20,541
Benzene (g)	24.000	3401	5762	12,285	20,612	30,163	57,350
Toluene (g)	17.500	4306	7269	15,334	25,621	37,449	71,250
o-Xylene (g)	11.096	5576	9291	19,070	31,386	45,531	85,960
m-Xylene (g)	10.926	5325	8925	18,563	30,817	44,933	85,330
p-Xylene (g)	11.064	5358	8929	18,499	30,690	44,755	85,080

tion of the standard heat of formation of methane by the reaction

$$C(298.16°K) + 2H_2(298.16°K) = CH_4(298.16°K)$$

The standard heat of formation of methane is obtained by adding the following reactions:

$C(0°K) + 2 H_2(0°K) = CH_4(0°K),$	$\Delta H_{f0}^\circ = -15.987,$	$\Delta H = \Delta H_{f0}^\circ$
$C(298.16°K) = C(0°K),$	$\Delta H = -0.2516,$	$\Delta H = -(H_T^\circ - H_0^\circ)_C$
$2 H_2(298.16°K) = 2 H_2(0°K),$	$\Delta H = -4.0476,$	$-2(H_T^\circ - H_0^\circ)_{H_2}$
$CH_4(0°K) = CH_4(298.16°K),$	$\Delta H = 2.3970,$	$\Delta H = (H_T^\circ - H_0^\circ)_{CH_4}$

$$C(298.16°K) + 2H_2(298.16°K) = CH_4(298.16°K), \qquad \Delta H_f^\circ = -17.889 \text{ kcal/g mole}$$

(5-16)

The general case of the formation of compound C in its standard state from its elements in their standard states, all at the temperature T, is represented by

$$aA + bB = cC \tag{5-17}$$

where A and B are elements. The formula for the heat of formation of compound C at temperature $T°K$ is obtained by adding the following equations:

$$aA(0°K) + bB(0°K) = cC(0°K), \qquad \Delta H = c\Delta H^°_{f0}$$
$$aA(T°K) = aA(0°K), \qquad \Delta H = -a(H^°_T - H^°_0)_A$$
$$bB(T°K) = bB(0°K), \qquad \Delta H = -b(H^°_T - H^°_0)_B$$
$$cC(0°K) = cC(T°K), \qquad \Delta H = c(H^°_T - H^°_0)_C$$

$$aA(T°K) + bB(T°K) = cC(T°K)$$

$$c\,\Delta H^°_{fC} = c\,\Delta H^°_{f0C} + c(H^°_T - H^°_0)_C - \left[a(H^°_T - H^°_0)_A + b(H^°_T - H^°_0)_B\right]$$

or

$$\Delta H^°_{fC} = \Delta H^°_{f0C} + (H^°_T - H^°_0)_C - \left[\frac{a}{c}(H^°_T - H^°_0)_A + \frac{b}{c}(H^°_T - H^°_0)_B\right]$$

$$(5\text{-}18)$$

Now suppose that compound C reacts to give compounds D and E by the equation

$$cC = dD + eE \qquad (5\text{-}19)$$

and that it is desired to find the heat of reaction at temperature T by use of the data in Table 5-3. Since the heat of reaction may be computed from the heats of formation by use of Equation (5-15) and since Equation (5-18) is applicable for each compound, it follows that the heat of reaction per mole of C is given by

$$\Delta H^°_r = \frac{1}{c}\left[d\,\Delta H^°_{f0D} + e\,\Delta H^°_{f0E} - c\,\Delta H^°_{f0C} + d(H^°_T - H^°_0)_D\right.$$
$$\left. + e(H^°_T - H^°_0)_E - c(H^°_T - H^°_0)_C\right]$$

$$(5\text{-}20)$$

Note that when each member involved in the reaction is a compound as in Equation (5-19), the terms involving the elements A and B in Equation (5-18) cancel in the development of Equation (5-20) because the same set of elements required to form the reactants is also required to form the products. This fact is vividly demonstrated when Equation (5-20) is derived by use of a path such as the one shown in Figure 5-1 for the reaction

$$CO(g) + H_2O(g) = H_2(g) + CO_2(g)$$

Figure 5-1. Use of an alternate path to relate the heat of reaction to the heats of formation.

C. Variation of Heat of Reaction with Temperature

The heat of reaction at any temperature T may be obtained directly from heat of formation and enthalpy data of the types presented in Tables 5-2 and 5-3 by use of Equation (5-15) and (5-20) respectively, provided, of course, that the data are available at the temperature T of interest. The variation of the heat of reaction with temperature may also be accounted for by use of heat capacity data. For the general reaction given by Equation (5-8) at any temperature T, Equation (5-9) is applicable, where H_C°, H_D°, H_A°, and H_B° are evaluated at the temperature T. Since the heat capacity of a pure component A is defined by

$$\left(\frac{\partial H_A^\circ}{\partial T}\right)_P = C_{pA}^\circ \tag{5-21}$$

Equation (5-9) may be differentiated to give

$$\left(\frac{\partial\ \Delta H_r^\circ}{\partial T}\right)_P = \frac{c}{a}\left(\frac{\partial H_C^\circ}{\partial T}\right)_P + \frac{d}{a}\left(\frac{\partial H_D^\circ}{\partial T}\right)_P - \left(\frac{\partial H_A^\circ}{\partial T}\right)_P - \frac{b}{a}\left(\frac{\partial H_B^\circ}{\partial T}\right)_P \tag{5-22}$$

and thus

$$\left(\frac{\partial\ \Delta H_r^\circ}{\partial T}\right)_P = \frac{c}{a}C_{pC}^\circ + \frac{d}{a}C_{pD}^\circ - C_{pA}^\circ - \frac{b}{a}C_{pB}^\circ = \Delta C_p^\circ \tag{5-23}$$

which holds for each T at the specified pressure P.

One of the advantages of the selection of a perfect gas at 1 atm pressure at a given temperature as the standard state is the fact that the heat capacity of any element or compound may be determined spectroscopically at conditions that approximate zero pressure. Since all substances approach perfect gases as the pressure goes to zero, these heat capacities may be used for perfect gases at any pressure because the change of C_p with pressure for a perfect gas is equal to zero [3, 4, 5]. Consequently, the change in ΔH_r° with temperature at any pressure may be computed by use of the heat capacities for the perfect gases. Tabular collections of these heat capacities are available (see Table 5-4).

Suppose that the heat of reaction is known at some temperature T_0. Then integration of Equation (5-23) over the temperature range from T_0 to T yields

$$\Delta H_r^\circ = \Delta H_r^\circ\bigg|_{T_0} + \int_{T_0}^T \Delta C_p^\circ\, dT \tag{5-24}$$

This expression may be derived by use of the path shown in Figure 5-2. Since ΔH_r° is independent of path, it may be computed by summing the ΔH's around the path shown in Figure 5-2. Thus, when ΔH_r° is based on one

TABLE 5-4
SELECTED VALUES AT THE INDICATED TEMPERATURE, IN CAL/G MOLE °K OF
HEAT CAPACITIES FOR PERFECT GAS STATE (Taken from [1])

Substance	298.16	400	600	800	1000	1500
H_2 (g)	6.892	6.975	7.009	7.080	7.219	7.720
O_2 (g)	7.020	7.196	7.670	8.063	8.336	8.739
C(monatomic) (g)	4.980	4.975	4.971	4.970	4.969	4.975
CO (g)	6.965	7.013	7.276	7.625	7.931	8.416
CO_2 (g)	8.874	9.876	11.310	12.293	12.980	13.954
H_2O (g)	8.025	8.186	8.676	9.245	9.850	11.233
Methane (g)	8.536	9.721	12.55	15.10	17.21	20.71
Ethane (g)	12.58	15.68	21.35	25.83	29.33	34.90
Propane (g)	17.57	22.54	30.88	37.08	41.83	49.26
Ethylene (g)	10.41	12.90	17.10	20.20	22.57	26.36
Acetylene (g)	10.499	11.973	13.728	14.933	15.922	17.704
Benzene (g)	19.52	26.74	37.74	45.06	50.16	57.67
Toluene (g)	24.80	33.25	46.58	55.72	62.19	71.78
o-Xylene (g)	31.85	41.03	55.98	66.64	74.35	85.93
m-Xylene (g)	30.49	40.03	55.51	66.41	74.23	85.89
p-Xylene (g)	30.32	39.70	55.16	66.14	74.02	85.79
1-Butene	20.47	26.04	35.14	41.80	46.82	54.62
1,3-Butadiene	19.01	24.29	31.84	36.84	38.81	46.34

mole of A, it follows from Figure 5-2 that

$$\Delta H_r^\circ = \frac{1}{a}\left[\int_T^{T_0} aC_{pA}^\circ \, dT + \int_T^{T_0} bC_{pB}^\circ \, dT + a\,\Delta H_r^\circ \Big|_{T_0} \right.$$

$$\left. + \int_{T_0}^T cC_{pC}^\circ \, dT + \int_{T_0}^T dC_{pD}^\circ \, dT \right] \tag{5-25}$$

which is readily reduced to the result given by Equation (5-24). If the heat capacities of the perfect gases in Equation (5-25) are expressed as functions of temperature as follows:

$$C_{pi}^\circ = \alpha_i + \beta_i T + \gamma_i T^2 + \delta_i T^3$$

then the integrals in Equation (5-25) may be evaluated and the resulting expression for ΔH_r° may be stated as follows:

$$\Delta H_r^\circ = \Delta H_r^\circ \Big|_{T_0} + \Delta\alpha(T - T_0) + \frac{\Delta\beta}{2}(T^2 - T_0^2)$$

$$+ \frac{\Delta\gamma}{3}(T^3 - T_0^3) + \frac{\Delta\delta}{4}(T^4 - T_0^4) \tag{5-26}$$

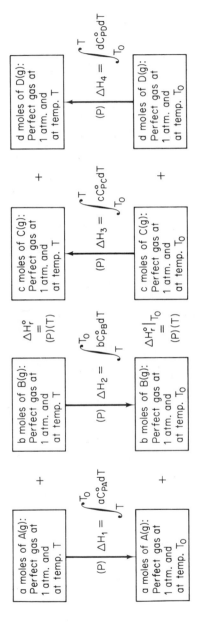

Figure 5-2. Path for calculating ΔH_r^0 at temperature T from a knowledge of ΔH_r^0 at T_0 and heat capacity data.

where

$$\Delta\alpha = \frac{1}{a}(c\alpha_C + d\alpha_D - a\alpha_A - b\alpha_B)$$

$$\Delta\beta = \frac{1}{a}(c\beta_C + d\beta_D - a\beta_A - b\beta_B)$$

$$\Delta\gamma = \frac{1}{a}(c\gamma_C + d\gamma_D - a\gamma_A - b\gamma_B)$$

$$\Delta\delta = \frac{1}{a}(c\delta_C + d\delta_D - a\delta_A - b\delta_B)$$

Since the heat capacities for perfect gases are independent of pressure, the same numerical value for ΔH is obtained if the specified pressure of 1 atm in Figure 5-2 is replaced by any arbitrary pressure P. Thus, when the standard states of all compounds involved in a reaction are taken to be perfect gases at 1 atm at the temperature of the reaction, the heat of reaction ΔH_r° is independent of pressure; that is,

$$\left(\frac{\partial \Delta H_r^\circ}{\partial P}\right)_T = 0 \tag{5-27}$$

or

$$\Delta H_r^\circ \big|_{P,T} = \Delta H_r^\circ \big|_{1,T}$$

If the constituents of the reacting mixture behave as perfect gases,

then

$$\Delta H_r \big|_{P,T} = \Delta H_r^\circ \big|_{P,T} = \Delta H_r^\circ \big|_{1,T} \tag{5-28}$$

If, on the other hand, the behavior of the constituents of the reaction mixture does depend upon pressure, the heat of reaction at P and T may be found as shown in Chapter 11.

EXAMPLE 5-1

Calculate the heat of reaction for the dehydrogenation of 1-butene to 1,3 butadiene at 900°K by use of the heat of formation data given in Table 5-2 and the heat capacities given in Table 5-4.

1-butene   1,3 butadiene

SOLUTION

For convenience, let the above reaction be represented as follows:

$$A \rightleftharpoons B + C$$

The heat of reaction at 25°C is computed by use of the heats of formation given in Table 5-2 as follows:

$$\Delta H_r^\circ = \Delta H_{fB}^\circ + \Delta H_{fC}^\circ - \Delta H_{fA}^\circ$$

$$= 26.33 + 0.0 - (-0.03) = 26.36 \text{ kcal/g mole}$$

By use of Equation (5-24)

$$\Delta H_{r900}^\circ = 26{,}360 + \int_{298.16}^{900} [C_{pB}^\circ + C_{pC}^\circ - C_{pA}^\circ] \, dT$$

The integrand is evaluated numerically by use of the heat capacities (cal/g mole °K) given in Table 5-4 as follows:

$T°K$	C_{pC}°	C_{pB}°	C_{pA}°	$\Delta C_p^\circ = C_{pB}^\circ + C_{pC}^\circ - C_{pA}^\circ$
298.16	6.892	19.01	20.47	5.432
300	6.895	19:11	20.57	5.435
400	6.975	24.29	26.04	5.225
500	6.994	28.52	30.93	4.584
600	7.009	31.84	35.14	3.709
700	7.036	34.55	38.71	2.876
800	7.080	36.84	41.80	2.120
900	7.142	38.81	44.49	1.462

The integral appearing in the above expression for ΔH_r° at 900°K is evaluated by use of the trapezoidal rule. For the first increment in temperature

$$\int_{298.16}^{300} \Delta C_p^\circ \, dT = [\Delta C_{p298}^\circ + \Delta C_{p300}^\circ](300 - 298.16)\tfrac{1}{2} = 9.998$$

From 300°K to 900°K, equal increments in temperature of 100°K are used, and

$$\int_{300}^{900} \Delta C_p^\circ \, dT = \left[\frac{\Delta C_{p300}^\circ}{2} + (\Delta C_{p400}^\circ + \Delta C_{p500}^\circ + \cdots + \Delta C_{p800}^\circ) + \frac{\Delta C_{p900}^\circ}{2} \right](100)$$

$$= 2196.25 \text{ cal/g mole}$$

Thus the heat of reaction at 900°K is given by

$$\Delta H_{r900}^\circ = 26{,}360 + 2196.25 + 9.998$$

$$= 28{,}568 \text{ cal/g mole} \quad \text{or} \quad 28.568 \text{ kcal/g mole}$$

214

D. Standard Free Energy Change
and Equilibrium Constants

The Gibbs free energy function G is particularly convenient for expressing how far a chemical reaction is away from equilibrium when the reactants and products are in their standard states. In the developments that follow, any arbitrary standard state may be employed, and a variety of standard states have been used in the past. In the interest of simplicity, only the standard states shown in Table 5-1 are employed. Expressions needed in the analysis of chemical equilibria are developed as follows.

At constant temperature, Equation (5-6) reduces to

$$dG = v \, dP \tag{5-29}$$

For one mole of a perfect gas ($Pv = RT$), this expression becomes

$$dG = \frac{RT}{P} dP = RT \, d \log_e P \tag{5-30}$$

The general form of this expression may be retained for any substance by defining the fugacity f by

$$dG = RT \, d \log_e f \qquad \text{(at constant } T) \tag{5-31}$$

where f is that function required to give the correct free energy change for a process carried out isothermally. For example, for the isothermal process where the pressure on a system is changed from P_1 to P_2 and the corresponding fugacities change from f_1 to f_2, the free energy change is found by integration of Equation (5-31)

$$G(T, P_2) - G(T, P_1) = RT \log_e \frac{f_2}{f_1} \tag{5-32}$$

Corresponding to the *standard heat of formation* there is a *standard free energy of formation* ΔG_f° of a substance, which is defined as the change in free energy that occurs when a substance in its standard state is formed from its elements in their standard states. Thus it is inferred by this definition that ΔG_f° for any element is zero.

The *standard free energy change* ΔG° is that free energy change that occurs when products in their standard states are formed from reactants in their standard states. Then for the reaction given by Equation (5-14), the standard free energy change is stated in terms of the free energies of formation as follows:

$$\Delta G^\circ = c \, \Delta G_{fC}^\circ + d \, \Delta G_{fD}^\circ - a \, \Delta G_{fA}^\circ - b \, \Delta G_{fB}^\circ \tag{5-33}$$

215

TABLE 5-5

Selected Values of the Free Energy Function, $(G° - H_0°)/T$ (Taken from [1])

$(G_T° - H_0°)/T$ in cal/(mole °K) at indicated T°K

Substance	298.16	400	600	800	1000	1500
H_2 (g)	−24.423	−26.422	−29.203	−31.186	−32.738	−35.590
O_2 (g)	−42.061	−44.112	−46.968	−49.044	−50.697	−53.808
C (graphite)	−0.5172	−0.8245	−1.477	−2.138	−2.771	−4.181
CO (g)	−40.350	−42.393	−45.222	−47.254	−48.860	−51.864
CO_2 (g)	−43.555	−45.828	−49.238	−51.895	−54.109	−58.481
H_2O (g)	−37.172	−39.508	−42.768	−45.131	−47.018	−50.622
Methane (g)	−36.46	−38.86	−42.39	−45.21	−47.65	−52.84
Ethane (g)	−45.27	−48.24	−53.08	−57.29	−61.11	−69.46
Propane (g)	−52.73	−56.48	−62.93	−68.74	−74.10	−85.86
Ethylene (g)	−43.98	−46.61	−50.70	−54.19	−57.29	−63.94
Acetylene (g)	−39.976	−42.451	−46.313	−49.400	−52.005	−57.231
Benzene (g)	−52.93	−56.69	−63.70	−70.34	−76.57	−90.45
Toluene (g)	−61.98	−66.74	−75.52	−83.79	−91.53	−108.75
o-Xylene (g)	−65.61	−71.74	−82.81	−93.01	−102.46	−123.30
m-Xylene (g)	−67.63	−73.50	−84.20	−94.18	−103.48	−124.11
p-Xylene (g)	−66.25	−72.15	−82.83	−92.76	−102.02	−122.59

Various tables are available that list the free energies of formation of various substances as functions of temperature. As a result of the development of statistical methods, free energy data are frequently tabulated as $(G_T° - H_0°)/T$ as demonstrated by Table 5-5.

At the temperature of absolute zero, it follows from the definition of G [Equation (5-2)] that

$$G_0° = H_0° \tag{5-34}$$

$$\Delta G_{f0}° = \Delta H_{f0}° \tag{5-35}$$

(This relationship is particularly important because it permits the values for $\Delta G_{f0}°$ to be obtained from Table 5-3 in which the values for $\Delta H_{f0}°$ are listed.)

Suppose that a compound C in its standard state is formed from its elements in their standard states at the temperature T according to the following reaction:

$$aA(g) + bB(s) = cC(g) \tag{5-36}$$

The free energy change for this reaction can be represented as follows:

a moles of element A: perfect gas at 1 atm and at the temperature T	+	b moles of element B: solid at 1 atm and at the temperature T	$\xrightarrow{c\Delta G°}$ =	c moles of compound C: perfect gas at 1 atm and at the temperature T

The following formula for the free energy of formation for C is developed in a manner analogous to that shown in the development of Equation (5-17).

$$\left(\frac{\Delta G_{fC}^{\circ}}{T}\right) = \left[\frac{\Delta H_{f0}^{\circ}}{T} + \frac{G_T^{\circ} - H_0^{\circ}}{T}\right]_{\text{compound } C}$$
$$- \frac{a}{c}\left(\frac{G_T^{\circ} - H_0^{\circ}}{T}\right)_{\text{element } A} - \frac{b}{c}\left(\frac{G_T^{\circ} - H_0^{\circ}}{T}\right)_{\text{element } B} \qquad (5\text{-}37)$$

Free energies of formation may be used to calculate the standard free energy change ΔG° for a reaction by use of Equation (5-33).

EXAMPLE 5-2

Calculate the free energy formation of benzene at 800°K by use of Equation (5-37) and the data given in Tables 5-3 and 5-5. The reaction is

$$6\,C(s) + 3\,H_2(g) = C_6H_6(g)$$

SOLUTION

Since $\Delta G_{f0}^{\circ} = \Delta H_{f0}^{\circ}$, the value of ΔG_{f0}° may be found by use of Table 5-3; namely,

$$\Delta G_{f0}^{\circ} = \Delta H_{f0}^{\circ} = 24{,}000 \text{ cal/g mole}$$

From Table 5-5, the following values are obtained:

Substance	$(G_T^{\circ} - H_0^{\circ})/T$(cal/g mole °K) at 800°K
C_6H_6	-70.34
H_2	-31.186
C	-2.138

Substitution of the above numerical values into Equation (5-37) gives

$$\frac{\Delta G_f^{\circ}}{800} = \left[\frac{24{,}000}{800} + (-70.34)\right] - 6(-2.138) - 3(-31.186)$$

$$= 66.046 \text{ (cal/g mole °K)}$$

Thus the free energy of formation of benzene at 800°K from its elements in their standard states at 800°K is given by

$$\Delta G_f^{\circ} = (66.046)(800) = 52{,}836.8 \text{ cal/g mole}$$

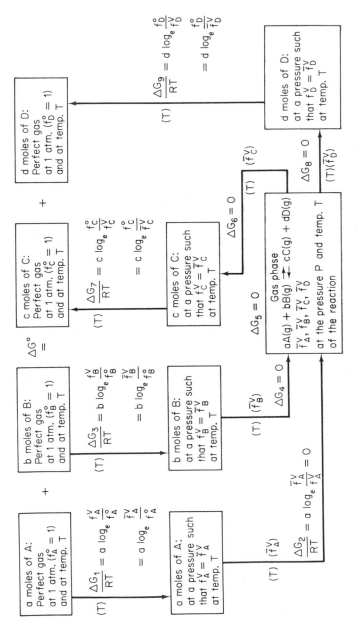

Figure 5-3. Use of a path for relating ΔG^0 and the equilibrium constant for a gas phase reaction.

1. RELATIONSHIP BETWEEN THE STANDARD FREE ENERGY CHANGE ΔG° AND THE EQUILIBRIUM CONSTANT FOR A GAS PHASE REACTION. Suppose compounds C and D are formed from compounds A and B by the following reaction at the pressure P and temperature T:

$$aA(g) + bB(g) \;\rightleftharpoons\; cC(g) + dD(g) \tag{5-38}$$

Since the free energy function G is independent of path, a path such as the one shown in Figure 5-3 may be devised which involves the standard free energy change ΔG° and the equilibrium constant. In this figure, the symbols $\bar{f}_A^V, \bar{f}_B^V, \bar{f}_C^V$, and $\bar{f}_D^V$ denote the fugacities of components A, B, C, and D, respectively, in the equilibrium gaseous mixture at temperature T and pressure P. The familiar concept of the Van't Hoff equilibrium box is used as part of the path. The box is regarded as being so large that a moles of A and b moles of B may be introduced and c moles of C and d moles of D withdrawn without upsetting the equilibrium state of the box; provided of course, that these compounds are introduced and withdrawn at their respective equilibrium fugacities, $\bar{f}_A^V, \bar{f}_B^V, \bar{f}_C^V$, and $\bar{f}_D^V$. Addition of the free energy changes around the path yields

$$\Delta G = -RT \log_e \frac{(\bar{f}_C^V)^c(\bar{f}_D^V)^d}{(\bar{f}_A^V)^a(\bar{f}_B^V)^b} + RT \log_e \frac{(f_C^\circ)^c(f_D^\circ)^d}{(f_A^\circ)^a(f_B^\circ)^b} \tag{5-39}$$

Equation (5-39) applies regardless of the standard states selected for the pure components. For the special case shown in Figure 5-3 where the standard state of each component (A, B, C, and D) is taken to be a perfect gas at 1 atm at the temperature of the mixture, the second term on the right-hand side of Equation (5-39) vanishes and Equation (5-39) reduces to

$$\Delta G^\circ = -RT \log_e \frac{(\bar{f}_C^V)^c(\bar{f}_D^V)^d}{(\bar{f}_A^V)^a(\bar{f}_B^V)^b} \tag{5-40}$$

where the superscript $^\circ$ has been added to ΔG to denote the particular set of standard states used to compute the free energy change.

For the particular set of standard states shown in Figure 5-3, Equation (5-39) may be stated in terms of the activities a_i and equilibrium constant K as follows:

$$\Delta G^\circ = -RT \log_e K \tag{5-41}$$

where $K = \dfrac{a_C^c a_D^d}{a_A^a a_B^b}$

$a_i = \bar{f}_i/f_i^\circ = \bar{f}_i$, for the standard states shown in Figure 5-3

For the standard state of a perfect gas at 1 atm at the specified temperature, the activity a_i (a dimensionless variable) is numerically equal to the fugacity $\bar{f}_i$ of component i in the mixture.

The behavior of many fluids may be approximated with good accuracy by use of the concept of an *ideal* solution. A gaseous mixture is said to form an *ideal* solution at a given temperature and pressure if the fugacity $\bar{f}_i^V$ of each component in the mixture is related to its fugacity in the pure state as follows:

$$\bar{f}_i^V = f_i^V y_i \tag{5-42}$$

where f_i^V = fugacity of the pure component i evaluated at the
                   temperature T and pressure P of the mixture

         y_i = mole fraction in gas

For such mixtures, Equation (5-40) reduces to

$$\Delta G^\circ = -RT \log_e K_f K_y \tag{5-43}$$

where the constants K_f and K_y are defined as follows:

$$K_f = \frac{(f_C^V)^c (f_D^V)^d}{(f_A^V)^a (f_B^V)^b} \qquad K_y = \frac{y_C^c y_D^d}{y_A^a y_B^b}$$

Comparison of Equations (5-41) and (5-43) shows that

$$K = K_f K_y \tag{5-44}$$

Various types of correlations of fugacities for pure components as functions of temperature and pressure have appeared in the literature.

For the case where each component of the mixture behaves as a perfect gas, it follows that $K = K_f K_y = K_p$, and thus

$$\Delta G^\circ = -RT \log_e K_p = -RT \log_e \left[\frac{p_C^c p_D^d}{p_A^a p_B^b} \right] \tag{5-45}$$

EXAMPLE 5-3

Calculate the conversion of pure methanol to dimethyl ether by the reaction

$$2\, CH_3OH \;\rightleftharpoons\; (CH_3)_2O + H_2O$$

when pure methanol is allowed to come to equilibrium at 1 atm pressure and at each of the following temperatures: 500°K, 600°K, and 700°K. Assume that at these conditions, the mixture obeys the perfect gas law. The following values of the free energy changes (obtained by use of data given in Reference [6]) may be used.

$T°K$	$\Delta G°$ (kcal per g mole of $(CH_3)_2O$ formed)
500	-2.95
600	-2.56
700	-2.18

SOLUTION

For convenience, let the above reaction be represented as follows:

$$2A \rightleftharpoons B + C$$

Let x be the moles of A converted per mole of A in the feed. Then the stoichiometry of the reaction requires that

$$n_A = n_A^0 - n_A^0 x$$
$$n_B = n_B^0 + \tfrac{1}{2}n_A^0 x$$
$$n_C = n_C^0 + \tfrac{1}{2}n_A^0 x$$
$$\overline{n_T = n_T^0}$$

Also, since the feed is to be pure methanol, $n_B^0 = n_C^0 = 0$, and thus $n_T = n_T^0 = n_A^0$.

Since it is given that the mixture obeys the perfect gas law, the expression given by Equation (5-45) is applicable. For the reaction given, the appropriate form of K_p is given by

$$K_p = \frac{p_C p_D}{p_A^2} = \frac{n_C n_D}{n_A^2} = \frac{(\tfrac{1}{2}n_A^0 x)^2}{(n_A^0 - n_A^0 x)^2} = \frac{\tfrac{1}{4}x^2}{(1-x)^2}$$

This expression is readily solved for x as a function of K_p to give

$$x = \frac{2\sqrt{K_p}}{1 + 2\sqrt{K_p}}$$

Thus, by use of Equation (5-45) and the above expression for the conversion, the desired results are obtained as summarized in the following table:

$T°K$	$K_p = \exp\left(\dfrac{-\Delta G°}{RT}\right)$	$x = \dfrac{2\sqrt{K_p}}{1 + 2\sqrt{K_p}}$
500	19.472	0.898
600	8.560	0.854
700	4.793	0.814

2. CHEMICAL REACTIONS IN THE LIQUID PHASE. Suppose that the reaction given by Equation (5-38) is carried out in the liquid phase at the total pressure P and temperature T; that is,

$$aA(l) + bB(l) = cC(l) + dD(l) \tag{5-46}$$

Again the standard state of each component i is taken to be a perfect gas at 1 atm pressure and the temperature T of the reaction. Thus ΔG° for the liquid phase reaction given by Equation (5-46) is exactly equal to the ΔG° for the gas phase reaction given by Equation (5-38). For ΔG° is always computed on the basis of the standard state and is independent of whether the reaction is carried out in the vapor phase, the liquid phase, or in two or more phases.

In order to relate ΔG° to the equilibrium constant, it is necessary, however, to take into account the precise manner in which the reaction is carried out. In this case, let the fugacities of components A, B, C, and D in the equilibrium mixture be denoted by $\bar{f}_A^L$, $\bar{f}_B^L$, $\bar{f}_C^L$, and $\bar{f}_D^L$, where the superscript L is used to denote that these fugacities are for components in the liquid phase. The free energy ΔG° may be related to the equilibrium constant by use of the path shown in Figure 5-4. Consider the path shown for compound A. First compound A is expanded isothermally as a perfect gas to pressure P_0. If the pressure P_0 is allowed to go to zero, the perfect gas may be regarded as an actual substance, because all substances become perfect gases as the pressure goes to zero. After the ΔG's for compound A have been summed, the limit of this sum is taken as P_0 is allowed to go to zero. In the limit as P_0 goes to zero, the gas withdrawn at pressure P_0 may be regarded as an actual gas. Thus this box acts as a "converter" in that a perfect gas enters it at 1 atm and an actual substance leaves it at pressure P_0. Then for the first step,

$$\Delta G_1 = aRT \log_e \frac{P_0}{1}$$

(The limit as P_0 approaches zero is imposed in a subsequent step.) Next the actual gas is compressed isothermally to a total pressure equal to the vapor pressure P_A of pure compound A at the temperature T. At this pressure, the fugacity of compound A is denoted by f_{A,P_A}^V, and for this step

$$\Delta G_2 = aRT \log_e \frac{f_{A,P_A}^V}{f_{A,P_0}^V}$$

In the third step, compound A is condensed at its vapor pressure P_A (at temperature T). Since the vapor and liquid phases of compound A are in a state of equilibrium at the P_A and T, it follows that

$$f_A^V \big|_{P_A} = f_A^L \big|_{P_A}$$

and thus
$$\Delta G_3 = aRT \log_e \frac{f_{A,P_A}^L}{f_{A,P_A}^V} = 0$$

Figure 5-4. Use of a path to relate ΔG^0 and the equilibrium constant for a liquid phase reaction.

Next, compound A is compressed isothermally to a pressure such that it has a fugacity f_A^L equal to its fugacity $\bar{f}_A^L$ in the equilibrium box, and for this step

$$\Delta G_4 = aRT \log_e \frac{\bar{f}_A^L}{f_{A,P_A}^L}$$

For the fifth step, the Van't Hoff equilibrium box is used again, where a moles of A and b moles of B are introduced and c moles of C and d moles of D are withdrawn from the equilibrium box at their respective equilibrium fugacities $\bar{f}_A^L$, $\bar{f}_B^L$, $\bar{f}_B^L$, and $\bar{f}_D^L$. For this step

$$\Delta G_5 = 0$$

Then the change in free energy for compound A around the entire path is given by

$$\Delta G_A^\circ = \lim_{P_0 \to 0} \left[\sum_{j=1}^5 \Delta G_j \right] = \lim_{P_0 \to 0} \left[aRT \log_e \left(\frac{P_0}{1} \right) \left(\frac{f_{A,P_A}^V}{f_{A,P_0}^V} \right) \left(\frac{\bar{f}_A^L}{f_{A,P_A}^L} \right) \right]$$

$$= aRT \log_e \frac{\bar{f}_A^L}{1}$$

For the entire path

$$\Delta G^\circ = \sum_{i=A,B,C,D} \Delta G_i^\circ = -RT \log_e \frac{(\bar{f}_C^L)^c (\bar{f}_D^L)^d}{(\bar{f}_A^L)^a (\bar{f}_B^L)^b}$$

Since

$$a_A = \frac{\bar{f}_A^L}{1}, \qquad a_B = \frac{\bar{f}_B^L}{1}$$

$$a_C = \frac{\bar{f}_C^L}{1}, \quad \text{and} \quad a_D = \frac{\bar{f}_D^L}{1} \tag{5-47}$$

it is possible to state Equation (5-47) in terms of the equilibrium constant K [see Equation (5-41)] for the reaction under consideration.

To state the equilibrium constant K in terms of the mole fractions in the liquid phase, the general expression for the fugacity of a component in a mixture,

$$\bar{f}_i^L = \gamma_i^L f_i^L x_i \tag{5-48}$$

is used. In this case f_i^L is evaluated at the temperature T and pressure P of the reacting mixture and the activity coefficient γ_i^L is a function of P, T, and the x_i's. Then, for the reaction given by Equation (5-46),

$$K = K_\gamma K_f K_x \tag{5-49}$$

The quantities K_γ, K_f, and K_x are defined as follows:

$$K_\gamma = \frac{\gamma_C^c \gamma_D^d}{\gamma_A^a \gamma_B^b}, \qquad K_f = \frac{(f_C^L)^c (f_D^L)^d}{(f_A^L)^a (f_B^L)^b}, \qquad K_x = \frac{x_C^c x_D^d}{x_A^a x_B^b} \tag{5-50}$$

For an ideal solution, $\gamma_A = \gamma_B = \gamma_C = \gamma_D = 1$, and thus $K = K_f K_x$. Thus, for an ideal solution,

$$\Delta G^\circ = -RT \log_e K_f K_x \tag{5-51}$$

3. EVALUATION OF THE FUGACITIES, f_A^L, f_B^L, f_C^L, AND f_D^L, $P > P_i$ FOR $i = A$, B, C, AND D. If the total pressure at which the reaction occurs is greater than the vapor pressures of the respective components at the temperature of the reaction, then f_A^L, f_B^L, f_C^L, and f_D^L at the temperature and pressure of the reaction may be evaluated as indicated by Equation (5-54). The development of this relationship follows. When pure component A in the liquid state is compressed from its vapor pressure at the temperature of the reaction to the total pressure P of the reaction, the following result is obtained by integration of Equation (5-29):

$$\Delta G = \int_{P_A}^{P} v \, dP \cong (P - P_A)v \tag{5-52}$$

Since the effect of pressure on the volume of a liquid is usually negligible, the approximate result given by Equation (5-52) represents the change in free energy with good accuracy. Also, for this same change in pressure at the temperature T of the reaction, Equation (5-32) gives

$$\Delta G = RT \log_e \frac{f_A^L}{f_{A,P_A}^L} = RT \log_e \frac{f_A^L}{f_{A,P_A}^V} \tag{5-53}$$

where f_A^L is the value of the fugacity of component A at the total pressure P and temperature T. After ΔG has been eliminated from Equations (5-52) and (5-53), the following result is obtained upon rearrangement:

$$f_A^L = f_{A,P_A}^V \exp\left[\frac{(P - P_A)v}{RT}\right] \tag{5-54}$$

The fugacity of A at its vapor pressure may be evaluated by use of an appropriate equation of state.

EXAMPLE 5-4

Calculate the liquid fugacity of n-butane in the liquid state at 350°K and 60 atm. The vapor pressure of n-butane at 350°K is 9.35 atm [1]. The molar volume of the liquid at the vapor pressure (or saturation pressure) at 350°K is 0.1072 liter per gram mole [7]. From the jb and jb-E tables of Reference [1], the fugacity coefficient ϕ at the vapor pressure at $T = 350$°K is 0.8340.

SOLUTION

The fugacity of the vapor at 350°K is computed as follows:

$$f^V_{i,P_i} = \phi P_i = \left(\frac{f^V_{i,P_i}}{P_i}\right) P_i = 0.8340 \times 9.35 = 7.7979 \text{ atm}$$

The fugacity of the liquid f^L_i at $P = 60$ atm may be estimated by use of Equation (5-54) as follows:

$$f^L_i = f^V_{i,P_i} \exp\left[\frac{(P - P_i)v}{RT}\right]$$

$$f^L_i = 7.7979 \exp\left[\frac{(60 - 9.35)(0.1072)}{(0.08205)(350)}\right] = 9.421 \text{ atm}$$

If the total pressure is less than the vapor pressure of one of the components, the liquid state at the pressure P and temperature T is a hypothetical state since the pure component cannot exist in the liquid state at the pressure P. Consequently, the volume v can no longer be regarded as a constant in the integration as was done in Equation (5-52). Thus, in order to evaluate ΔG when one or more of the pure components are in hypothetical states at the temperature T and pressure P of the system, the fugacities of the components in the hypothetical state must be found by extrapolation procedures.

E. Calculation of Fugacities of Components in Hypothetical States

Procedures which may be used to compute the fugacities of components in hypothetical vapor and liquid states are presented below—first for a component in a hypothetical liquid state and secondly for a component in a hypothetical vapor state at the temperature T and pressure P of the mixture.

1. CALCULATION OF f^L_i WHEN $P < P_i$ AT THE TEMPERATURE T. When the specified value of the total pressure P is less than the vapor pressure P_i of component i at the specified temperature T, component i cannot exist in the liquid phase. Thus the hypothetical liquid state of component i must be found or defined by an extrapolation procedure. The description of this procedure is made easier by use of the fugacity coefficient chart shown in Figure 5-5. The reduced temperature and reduced pressure used in this

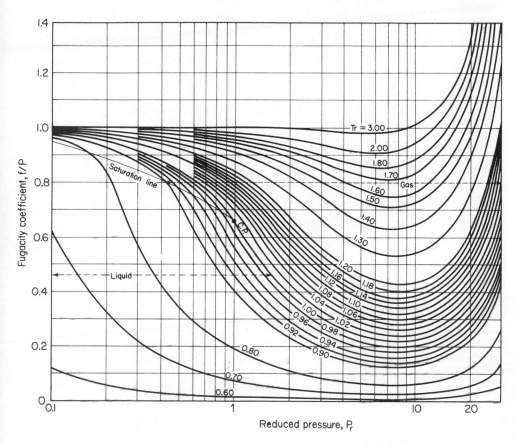

Figure 5-5. Fugacity coefficients of gases and liquids: $Z_c = 0.27$ [From *Chemical Engineers Handbook,* by Robt. H. Perry, C. H. Chilton and S. D. Kirkpatrick, 4th ed. pp. 4–53. © 1963 by McGraw-Hill Book Company. Used with permission of McGraw-Hill Book Company.]

chart are defined in the usual way,

$$P_r = \frac{P}{P_c}, \qquad T_r = \frac{T}{T_c} \tag{5-55}$$

Suppose, for example, that the specified temperature and pressure for component i gives a reduced pressure $P_{r0} = 0.5$ and a reduced temperature $T_{r0} = 1.0$. This point (P_{r0}, T_{r0}) is seen to lie in the vapor phase above the saturation line in Figure 5-5. The hypothetical liquid state at P_{r0} and T_{r0} may be defined by the extrapolation of the points (ϕ_1, T_{r1}), (ϕ_2, T_{r2}), ..., along the isobar P_{r0} to the hypothetical liquid state P_{r0} and T_{r0}. If data for a pure component are available, it is not necessary to use the reduced temperatures and pressures in the construction. An extrapolation procedure for predicting the liquid fugacity of a substance in a hypothetical liquid state is demonstrated by the following numerical example.

EXAMPLE 5-5

In this example the procedure described above is used to calculate the liquid fugacity of f_i^L of n-butane in a hypothetical liquid state at a pressure below its vapor pressure of 9.35 atm at the given temperature of 350°K. In particular, it is desired to determine the liquid fugacity of n-butane at 350°K and 4.52 atm. At 350°K, the molar volume of the saturated liquid is equal to 0.1072 liter per g mole [7]. The following values of the fugacity coefficient were taken from the jb-E tables of Reference [1].

$$\phi \Big|_{P_i} = \frac{f_i^V}{P_i}$$

T (°K)	(at the vapor pressure)	Vapor Pressure P_i (atm)
300	0.9219	2.55
310	0.9066	3.43
320	0.8900	4.52

SOLUTION

To carry out the extrapolation procedure described above, values of ϕ at different values of the reduced temperature along the isobar $P = 4.52$ are found by use of the above data.

First the given values of ϕ at the vapor pressure are used to compute the fugacity of the vapor at its vapor pressure, f_{i,P_i}^V. These vapor fugacities and Equation (5-54) are then used to compute the fugacities of the liquid in the hypothetical state of $P = 4.52$ atm and $T = 350$°K. Then the desired values of ϕ at $P = 4.52$ atm are computed.

T (°K)	$f_{i,P_i}^V = (\phi\|_{P_i})P_i$	f_i^L at $P = 4.52$ atm [by Equation (5-54)]	ϕ at ($P = 4.52$ atm) [$\phi = (f_i^L/4.52)$]
300	2.35	2.37	0.524
310	3.11	3.12	0.691
320	4.02	4.02	0.890

The graph of ϕ versus T at $P = 4.52$ atm used to find ϕ at $T = 350$°K is shown in Figure 5-6. The value of ϕ so obtained is

$$\phi = 1.5$$

Thus the liquid fugacity of n-butane in the hypothetical liquid state at $T = 350$°K and $P = 4.52$ atm is given by

$$f_i^L = \phi P = \left(\frac{f_i^L}{P}\right) P = (1.5)(4.52) = 6.78 \text{ atm}$$

Figure 5-6. Extrapolation procedure for the prediction of the liquid fugacity of n-butane in the hypothetical liquid state at $P = 4.52$ atm and $350°$K.

2. CALCULATION OF f_i^V WHEN $P > P_i$ AT THE TEMPERATURE T.   In this case component i cannot exist in the vapor phase because the total pressure is greater than the vapor pressure of component i at the temperature T of the mixture. For this component, the state P_{r0} and T_{r0} lies in the liquid region (below the saturation line in Figure 5-5). The fugacity coefficient in the hypothetical vapor state at P_{r0} and T_{r0} is found in a manner analogous to that demonstrated above for the hypothetical liquid state. In the present case, however, the points (ϕ_1, T_{r1}), (ϕ_2, T_{r2}), ..., are located in the vapor region at the reduced pressure P_{r0}. After these points have been plotted (ϕ versus T_r), the value of ϕ at T_{r0} and P_{r0} is found by extrapolation to T_{r0}. Again, if values of ϕ are available for a pure component, the extrapolation procedure may be carried out in terms of P and T instead of P_r and T_r.

EXAMPLE 5-6

Calculate the vapor fugacity of n-butane in the hypothetical vapor state at $374°$K and 20 atm. At $374°$K, the vapor pressure of n-butane is 15.4 atm. This vapor pressure was found by interpolation of the data given in the jb and jb-E tables of Reference [1].

From this same reference, the following data were obtained:

$T(^\circ K)$	ϕ at $P = 20$ atm
390	0.7570
392	0.7615
394	0.7659
396	0.7701
400	0.7782

SOLUTION

The data presented above were plotted in Figure 5-7. As shown, extrapolation to the temperature of 374°K at $P = 20$ atm gives

$$\phi = 0.725$$

Figure 5-7. Extrapolation procedure for the prediction of the vapor fugacity of n-butane in the hypothetical vapor state at $P = 20$ atm and 374°K.

Thus the vapor fugacity of *n*-butane in the hypothetical vapor state of 374°K and 20 atm is given by

$$f_i^V = (0.725)(20) = 14.5 \text{ atm}$$

F. Heterogeneous Chemical Reactions

If components in different phases participate in a chemical reaction, then the reaction is classified as a heterogeneous chemical reaction. To illustrate such a reaction, consider the case where the following reaction is carried out at the total pressure P and temperature T.

$$aA(g) + bB(l) = cC(s) + dD(g) \qquad (5\text{-}56)$$

Let the following standard states be selected.

| a moles of A:
perfect gas at
1 atm and
temperature T | $+$ | b moles of B:
perfect gas at
1 atm and
temperature T | $=$ | c moles of C:
solid at 1 atm
and temperature
T | $+$ | d moles of D:
perfect gas at
1 atm and
temperature T |

If C is an element such as carbon whose standard state is taken to be graphite while the standard states of all of the other elements are perfect gases at 1 atm at the temperature T, then the ΔG computed by use of the alternate path in Figure 5-8 will be equal to $\Delta G°$ as computed from the free energies of formation.

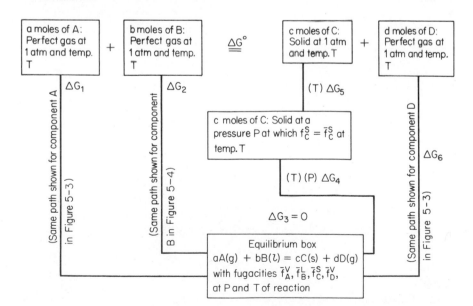

Figure 5-8. Use of a path to relate ΔG^0 and the equilibrium constant for a heterogeneous reaction.

For component A, the change in free energy in going from the standard state to the equilibrium box is

$$\Delta G_1 = aRT \log_e \frac{\bar{f}_A^V}{1}$$

as illustrated in Figure 5-3. In the same manner as shown for component B in Figure 5-4

$$\Delta G_2 = bRT \log_e \frac{\bar{f}_B^L}{1}$$

Since the reaction is in equilibrium, $\Delta G_3 = 0$. For the solid, the change in free energy in going from the equilibrium box to the standard state as shown in Figure 5-8 is given by

$$\Delta G_4 = cRT \log_e \frac{f_C^S}{\bar{f}_C^S} = 0$$

$$\Delta G_5 = cRT \log_e \frac{f_C^\circ}{f_C^S} = -cRT \log_e a_C$$

where f_C° is equal to the fugacity of component C in the standard state $(P = 1 \text{ atm}, T)$ and a_C is equal to the activity of component C [defined below Equation (5-41)].

The change in free energy of compound D in going from the equilibrium box to its standard state is given by

$$\Delta G_6 = dRT \log_e \frac{1}{\bar{f}_D^V}$$

Since ΔG° is equal to the sum of the free energy changes around the path shown in Figure 5-8, it follows that

$$\Delta G^\circ = -RT \log_e \frac{(a_C)^c (\bar{f}_D^V)^d}{(\bar{f}_A^V)^a (\bar{f}_B^L)^b} \tag{5-57}$$

Since the liquid phase is composed of pure compound B, it follows that

$$\bar{f}_B^L = f_B^L \big|_{P,T}$$

where the fugacity of the pure component B may be evaluated by use of Equation (5-54).

To evaluate a_C, another expression is obtained for ΔG_5 by use of Equation (5-52), namely,

$$\Delta G_5 = c \int_P^1 v_s \, dP \cong c(1 - P)v_s$$

where v_s is the volume per mole of C in the solid state. From these two expressions for ΔG_5, the following formula for computing a_C is obtained:

$$a_C = \exp\left[-\left(\frac{1 - P}{RT}\right)v_s\right]$$

Generally, the volume v_s for a solid is so small that its activity can be set equal to unity with good accuracy.

For illustrative purposes, suppose that the approximation $a_C = 1$ is valid and that the vapor phase forms an ideal solution. Then Equation (5-57) reduces to

$$\Delta G^\circ = -RT \log_e \frac{(f_D^V y_D)^d}{(f_A^V y_A)^a (f_B^L)^b}$$

If it is further supposed that the vapor behaves as a perfect gas and that the pressure correction for f_B^L [given by an equation of the form of Equation (5-54)] is insignificant, then the above expression for ΔG° further reduces to

$$\Delta G^\circ = -RT \log_e \frac{(P y_D)^d}{(P y_A)^a (P_B)^b} \tag{5-58}$$

where P_B is the vapor pressure of pure component B at the temperature T of the reaction.

EXAMPLE 5-7

The reaction

$$CO_2(g) + C(s) \;\rightleftharpoons\; 2CO(g)$$

occurs in the reducing zone of a coal gasification reactor. At 800°C, $K_p = 7.64633$ atm, and at 1000°C, $K_p = 149.886$ atm (see Reference [8]). If it is supposed that pure carbon dioxide in the gaseous state is present initially over pure carbon in the solid state, find the equilibrium mole fractions of carbon dioxide and carbon monoxide at each of the above temperatures at a pressure of 1 atm.

SOLUTION

Let the reaction be represented by the following symbols:

$$A(g) + B(s) \;\rightleftharpoons\; 2C(g)$$

Since B is a solid, the activity of B is approximately equal to unity, as discussed above. Thus assume $a_B = 1$. Then

$$K_p = \frac{p_C^2}{p_A} = \frac{P y_C^2}{y_A}$$

The stoichiometric relationships are as follows:

$$
\begin{aligned}
n_A &= n_A^0 - n_A^0 x \\
n_C &= \quad\quad 2n_A^0 x \\
\hline
n_T &= n_A^0 + n_A^0 x
\end{aligned}
$$

Then

$$y_A = \frac{1-x}{1+x} \quad \text{and} \quad y_C = \frac{2x}{1+x}$$

and

$$K_p = \frac{P(2x)^2(1+x)}{(1+x)^2(1-x)} = \frac{4x^2}{(1+x)(1-x)} = \frac{4x^2}{1-x^2}$$

Thus

$$x^2 = \frac{K_p}{4 + K_p}$$

and at 800°C,

$$x = \left(\frac{7.6433}{4 + 7.6433}\right)^{1/2} = 0.810$$

At 1000°C,

$$x = \left(\frac{149.886}{4 + 149.886}\right)^{1/2}$$

$$x = 0.987$$

G. Effect of Temperature, Pressure, and Concentration on Equilibrium Conversion

1. TEMPERATURE. The particular choice of the standard state of a perfect gas at 1 atm at the temperature of the reaction makes it possible to express $\Delta G°$ in terms of the specific heats of the reactants and products in the perfect gas state. The variation of $\Delta G°$ or the equilibrium constant with temperature is given by the Van't Hoff equation which relates $\Delta G°$ and $\Delta H_r°$. The Van't Hoff equation may be developed in the following manner. Division of each member of Equation (5-2) by T followed by partial differentiation with respect to temperature at constant pressure yields

$$\left(\frac{\partial(G/T)}{\partial T}\right)_P = -\frac{H}{T^2} + \frac{1}{T}\left(\frac{\partial H}{\partial T}\right)_P - \left(\frac{\partial S}{\partial T}\right)_P \tag{5-59}$$

From the definition of C_p given by Equation (5-21) and from Equation (5-5), it can be shown that

$$C_p = \left(\frac{\partial H}{\partial T}\right)_P = T\left(\frac{\partial S}{\partial T}\right)_P$$

In view of this result, it is seen that Equation (5-59) reduces to the following form of the Van't Hoff equation.

$$\left(\frac{\partial (G/T)}{\partial T}\right)_P = -\frac{H}{T^2} \tag{5-60}$$

Now observe that Equation (5-60) is applicable for each component that participates in the reaction, say the reaction given by Equation (5-38). Since

$$\Delta G^\circ = cG_C^\circ + dG_D^\circ - aG_A^\circ - bG_B^\circ \quad \text{and} \quad \Delta H_r^\circ = cH_C^\circ + dH_D^\circ - aH_A^\circ - bH_B^\circ$$

and since Equation (5-60) may be stated for each component in its standard state, the Van't Hoff relationship may be restated in the form

$$\left(\frac{\partial (\Delta G^\circ/T)}{\partial T}\right)_P = -\frac{\Delta H_r^\circ}{T^2} \tag{5-61}$$

Elimination of ΔG° from Equations (5-41) and (5-61) gives

$$R\left(\frac{\partial \log_e K}{\partial T}\right)_P = \frac{\Delta H_r^\circ}{T^2} \tag{5-62}$$

To express the variations of the functions ΔG° or K with T, let Equation (5-26) be restated in terms of an arbitrary constant of integration C_1 as follows

$$\Delta H_r^\circ = \Delta \alpha T + \frac{\Delta \beta}{2} T^2 + \frac{\Delta \gamma}{3} T^3 + \frac{\Delta \delta}{4} T^4 + C_1 \tag{5-63}$$

Substitution of this expression for ΔH_r° into Equation (5-61) followed by integration yields

$$-\frac{\Delta G^\circ}{T} = \Delta \alpha \log_e T + \frac{\Delta \beta}{2} T + \frac{\Delta \gamma}{6} T^2 + \frac{\Delta \delta}{12} T^3 - \frac{C_1}{T} + C_2 \tag{5-64}$$

where C_2 is the constant of integration. By use of Equation (5-41), it is possible to restate Equation (5-64) in the alternate form

$$R \log_e K = \Delta\alpha \log_e T + \frac{\Delta\beta}{2} T + \frac{\Delta\gamma}{6} T^2 + \frac{\Delta\delta}{12} T^3 - \frac{C_1}{T} + C_2 \quad (5\text{-}65)$$

By inspection of Equations (5-63) and (5-64), it is evident that the constants of integration C_1 and C_2 may be obtained if ΔH_r° and ΔG° are known either at the same or different temperatures or if ΔG° is known at two different temperatures.

Examination of Equation (5-62) shows that for exothermic reactions the equilibrium constant decreases as the temperature increases. Thus, for exothermic reactions, the equilibrium conversion decreases as the reaction temperature is increased. The converse of these statements may be made for endothermic reactions.

EXAMPLE 5-8

A commercial process for the production of 1,3 butadiene consists of the dehydro-genation of 1-butene in the presence of steam at high temperatures. It is desired to find the maximum conversion of 1-butene to 1,3 butadiene which can be expected at $900°K$ and 1 atm in a reactor in which the feed consists of 15 moles of steam per mole of 1-butene.

(a) Compute ΔG° and K for the dehydrogenation of 1-butene to 1,3 butadiene (see Example 5-2) by use of the Equations (5-63), (5-64), and (5-41).

(b) On the basis of the K found in part (a), calculate the fraction of 1-butene converted to 1,3 butadiene at equilibrium. The following data are available.

Curve Fits of the Heat Capacities (taken from [9]):

$$C_p = \alpha + \beta T + \gamma T^2 + \delta T^3 \text{ (cal/g mole °K)}$$

Component	α	$\beta \times 10^2$	$\gamma \times 10^5$	$\delta \times 10^9$
Hydrogen	6.424	0.1039	−0.00780	
1,3 Butadiene	−1.29	8.350	−5.582	14.24
1-Butene	−0.24	8.650	−5.110	12.04

Other data (taken from [6]):

$$\Delta G_f^\circ \text{ of 1-butene at } 25°C = 17.09 \text{ (kcal/g mole)}$$

$$\Delta G_f^\circ \text{ of 1,3-butadiene at } 25°C = 36.01 \text{ (kcal/g mole)}$$

$$\Delta H_r^\circ \text{ at } 25°C \text{ (see Example 5-1)} = 26.36 \text{ (kcal/g mole)}$$

SOLUTION

(a) The free energy of formation of 1,3 butadiene by the dyhydrogenation of 1-butene by the reaction at 25°C,

$$C_4H_8 \rightleftharpoons C_4H_6 + H_2$$
$$\text{1-butene} \qquad \text{1,3 butadiene}$$

or

$$A \rightleftharpoons B + C$$

is computed as follows:

$$\Delta G° = \Delta G°_{fB} - \Delta G°_{fA} = 36.01 - 17.09 = 18.92 \text{ (kcal/g mole)}$$

Since $\Delta H°_r$ is known at 25° and the curve fits for the heat capacities are available, the constant C_1 in Equation (5-63) may be evaluated:

$$C_1 = \Delta H°_r - \left[\Delta\alpha T + \frac{\Delta\beta}{2} T^2 + \frac{\Delta\gamma}{3} T^3 + \frac{\Delta\delta}{4} T^4 \right]$$

where

$$\Delta\alpha = \alpha_B + \alpha_C - \alpha_A, \qquad \Delta\beta = \beta_B + \beta_C - \beta_A$$
$$\Delta\gamma = \gamma_B + \gamma_C - \gamma_A, \qquad \Delta\delta = \delta_B + \delta_C - \delta_A$$

By use of the data given:

$$C_1 = 26{,}360 - \left[5.374(298.16) - \frac{0.1961}{2}(10^{-2})(298.16)^2 \right.$$

$$\left. - \frac{0.4798}{3}(10^{-5})(298.16)^3 + \frac{2.17(10^{-9})}{4}(298.16)^4 \right]$$

Thus

$$C_1 = 2.4887 \times 10^4$$

This value of C_1 and the data given at 25°C may be used to compute C_2 in Equation (5-64); that is,

$$C_2 = -\left[\frac{18{,}920}{298.16} + 5.374(\log_e 298.16) - \frac{0.1961}{2}(10^{-2})(298.16) \right.$$

$$\left. - \frac{0.4798(10^{-5})}{6}(298.16)^2 + \frac{2.17}{12}(10^{-9})(298.16)^3 - \frac{2.4884}{298.16}(10^4) \right]$$

$$C_2 = -10.2483$$

Equation (5-64) may now be used to evaluate ΔG° at 900°K,

$$-\frac{\Delta G^\circ_{900}}{900} = 5.374 \log_e 900 - \frac{0.1961}{2}(10^{-2})(900) - \frac{0.4798}{6}(10^{-5})(900)^2$$

$$+ \frac{2.17(10^{-9})(900)^3}{12} - \frac{2.4887(10^4)}{900} - 10.2483$$

$$= -2.743$$

Thus

$$\Delta G^\circ_{900} = (900)(2.735) = 2462 \text{ (cal/g mole)}$$

The equilibrium constant K at 900°K may be computed by use of Equation (5-41); namely,

$$K = \exp\left[-\frac{\Delta G^\circ}{RT}\right] = \exp\left[\frac{-2468}{(1.9872)(900)}\right]$$

$$K = 0.252$$

(b) The stoichiometry of the dehydrogenation reaction [see Part (a)] may be used to express the molar flow rates in terms of the conversion x as follows:

$$n_A = n_A^0 - n_A^0 x$$
$$n_B = n_A^0 x$$
$$n_C = n_A^0 x$$
$$n_I = n_I^0$$
$$\overline{n_T = n_T^0 + n_A^0 x}$$

where n_I is used to represent the steam. Since it is to be assumed that the mixture behaves as a perfect gas at 900°K and 1 atm, $K = K_f K_y = K_p$,

and

$$K_p = \frac{p_B p_C}{p_A} = \left(\frac{n_B n_C}{n_A n_T}\right) P$$

If n_A, n_B, n_C, and n_T are stated in terms of the conversion x by use of the above stoichiometric relationships, a quadratic equation in x is obtained. The solution of this equation for positive values of x is given by

$$x = \frac{-K_p(1 - y_A^0) + \sqrt{[(1 - y_A^0)K_p]^2 + 4K_p y_A^0(P + K_p)}}{2y_A^0(P + K_p)}$$

where $y_A^0 = n_A^0/n_T^0$. Since $y_A^0 = \frac{1}{16}$, $K_p = 0.252$ and $P = 1$ atm,

$$x = \frac{(-0.252)(0.9375) + \sqrt{[(0.9375)(0.252)]^2 + 4(0.252)(0.0625)(1.252)}}{2(0.0625)(1.252)}$$

$$x = 0.8355$$

For endothermic reactions the equilibrium constant increases as the temperature is increased. Thus the equilibrium conversion for an endothermic reaction increases as the temperature is increased.

2. EFFECT OF TOTAL PRESSURE AND INITIAL CONCENTRATIONS. Although the free energy change $\Delta G°$ and, hence, the corresponding equilibrium constant K are independent of the pressure at which the reaction is carried out, the equilibrium conversion may depend on the pressure.

For the gas phase reaction,

$$2A \;\rightleftharpoons\; R \tag{5-66}$$

$$K = \frac{\bar{f}_R^V}{(\bar{f}_A^V)^2} \tag{5-67}$$

Suppose that $K = 0.4$, which would correspond to a $\Delta G°$ greater than zero. Further, suppose that R and A are perfect gases so that the fugacities may be replaced by partial pressures. Then

$$K = K_f K_y = K_p = \frac{P_R}{P_A^2} = \frac{y_R P}{y_A^2 P^2} = \frac{y_R}{y_A^2 P} \tag{5-68}$$

Since K is not a function of pressure, the value of y_R can be increased by increasing the pressure. As P increases, y_R/y_A^2 must increase since K is fixed. Thus, for reactions in which the total number of moles decrease as the reaction progresses, an increase in the pressure increases the equilibrium conversion. Conversely, for reactions in which the number of moles increase, a decrease in the pressure produces an increase in the equilibrium conversion.

For the case of an ideal solution, Equation (5-50) shows that at a given temperature and pressure, K_x is fixed. Consequently, K_x is independent of conversion. Suppose for example, that the reaction given by Equation (5-66) occurs in the liquid phase and that the liquid phase is an ideal solution. Then

$$K = K_f K_x = K_f \frac{x_R}{x_A^2} \tag{5-69}$$

where

$$x_A = \frac{n_A}{n_T}, \qquad x_R = \frac{n_R}{n_T}$$

$$n_T = n_A + n_R + n_S$$

$$n_S = \text{moles of solvent}$$

Then

$$K_x = \frac{n_R n_T}{n_A^2} \tag{5-70}$$

From Equation (5-70), it is evident that as the total number of moles n_T is decreased, the equilibrium conversion of A to R increases. Thus, as the relative amount of solvent is decreased, the equilibrium conversion of A to R is increased. Conversely, for reactions in which the total number of moles increase (such as $A \rightleftarrows 2R$), an increase in the relative amount of solvent increases the equilibrium conversion of A to R.

H. Relationship between the Equilibrium Constants
K, K_p, K_c, and K_x

If the reactants and products of the reaction given by Equation (5-66) are perfect gases, then

$$K = K_p = \frac{p_R}{p_A^2} \tag{5-71}$$

Since $p_R = C_R RT$ and $p_A = C_A RT$ for a perfect gas, then Equation (5-71) reduces to

$$K_p = \frac{C_R RT}{C_A^2 (RT)^2} = \frac{C_R}{C_A^2}(RT)^{-1}$$

$$K_p = K_c (RT)^{-1} \tag{5-72}$$

In general, $K_p = K_c(RT)^{\Delta n}$, where Δn is equal to the sum of stoichiometric coefficients of the products minus the sum of the stoichiometric coefficients of the reactants. For the liquid phase, consider again the reaction given by Equation (5-66). From Equations (5-49) and (5-69), it follows that

$$K = K_\gamma K_f K_x = K_\gamma K_f \frac{x_R}{x_A^2} \tag{5-73}$$

The mole fractions appearing in the right-hand side of Equation (5-73) may be stated in terms of concentrations as follows:

$$K_x = \frac{(C_T x_R) C_T}{(C_T x_A)^2} = K_c C_T \tag{5-74}$$

where C_T = molar density of the equilibrium mixture

In general then

$$K = K_\gamma K_f K_x = C_T^{-\Delta n} K_\gamma K_f K_c \tag{5-75}$$

where Δn is defined below Equation (5-72).

I. Equilibrium Conversions for Multiple Reactions

Consider the two parallel reactions

$$A \rightleftharpoons R$$
$$A \rightleftharpoons S$$

(5-76)

Sufficient data are generally available [1] for the calculation of $\Delta G°$ for each reaction, and from these values of $\Delta G°$, the corresponding values of K may be computed by use of Equation (5-41). Consider the case where the reactions occur in the gas phase and the gas can be treated as a perfect gas. Then two independent equations at a given temperature T and pressure P may be stated; namely,

$$K_{p1} = \frac{p_R}{p_A}$$

(5-77)

$$K_{p2} = \frac{p_S}{p_A}$$

(5-78)

For a given set of initial conditions (the moles of A, R, and S initially), these equations may be solved simultaneously.

EXAMPLE 5-9

For the gas phase reactions,

$$A \rightleftharpoons R \qquad K_{p1} = 4$$
$$A \rightleftharpoons S \qquad K_{p2} = 1$$

calculate the equilibrium composition for the case where the products are not present initially.

SOLUTION

(a)
$$K_{p1} = \frac{p_R}{p_A} = \frac{y_R P}{y_A P} = \frac{n_R/n_T}{n_A/n_T}$$

$$K_{p2} = \frac{p_S}{p_A} = \frac{y_S P}{y_A P} = \frac{n_S/n_T}{n_A/n_T}$$

$$n_A = n_A^0 - n_1 - n_2$$

$$n_R = n_R^0 + n_1$$

$$n_S = n_S^0 + n_2$$

241

Since $n_R^0 = n_S^0 = 0$, then

$$4 = \frac{n_1}{n_A^0 - n_1 - n_2}$$

$$1 = \frac{n_2}{n_A^0 - n_1 - n_2}$$

When these two equations are solved simultaneously for n_1 and n_2, one obtains

$$n_R = n_1 = \tfrac{2}{3}n_A^0$$

$$n_S = n_2 = \tfrac{1}{6}n_A^0$$

The moles of A converted per mole of A in the feed are then given by

$$\frac{n_A^0 - n_A}{n_A^0} = \frac{n_1 + n_2}{n_A^0} = \frac{5}{6}$$

Most problems involving simultaneous reactions are more difficult to solve than the one shown in Example 5-9. Generally, it is necessary to find the equilibrium composition for a set of multiple reactions by use of a trial and error procedure such as the Newton-Raphson method [10] as demonstrated in the next example.

EXAMPLE 5-10

The reactions

$$C(s) + 2\,H_2 \; \rightleftharpoons \; CH_4 \tag{1}$$

$$C(s) + CO_2 \; \rightleftharpoons \; 2CO \tag{2}$$

occur in the reduction of carbon. On the basis of the following data given by Gumz [8], calculate the equilibrium composition at $700°C$ and 10 atm. The feed consists of 30% CO_2 and 70% hydrogen and the K_p's for the respective reactions at this temperature are $K_{p1} = 0.13237$ atm^{-1} and $K_{p2} = 1.07266$ atm.

SOLUTION

For convenience, let reactions (1) and (2) be represented as follows:

$$C + 2A \; \rightleftharpoons \; B \tag{1a}$$

$$C + D \; \rightleftharpoons \; 2E \tag{2a}$$

Let n_1 and n_2 be equal to the moles of C that react by the first and second reactions, respectively.

Then

$$
\begin{aligned}
n_A &= n_A^0 - 2n_1 \\
n_B &= n_1 \\
n_D &= n_D^0 - n_2 \\
n_E &= 2n_2 \\
\hline
n_T &= n_T^0 - n_1 + n_2
\end{aligned}
$$

Since carbon is a solid at these conditions, its activity may be taken equal to unity, and

$$
K_{p1} = \frac{p_B}{p_A^2} = \frac{n_1(n_T^0 - n_1 + n_2)}{(n_A^0 - 2n_1)^2 P}
$$

$$
K_{p2} = \frac{p_E^2}{p_D} = \frac{(2n_2)^2 P}{(n_T^0 - n_1 + n_2)(n_D^0 - n_2)}
$$

To solve for the two unknowns n_1 and n_2, the above equations are first restated in functional notation and then solved by use of the Newton-Raphson method [10]. Let

$$
f_1(n_1, n_2) = \frac{n_1(n_T^0 - n_1 + n_2)}{(n_A^0 - 2n_1)^2 P K_{p1}} - 1
$$

$$
f_2(n_1, n_2) = \frac{4n_2^2 P}{(n_T^0 - n_1 + n_2)(n_D^0 - n_2)K_{p2}} - 1
$$

As a basis, take $n_T^0 = 1$. Then $n_A^0 = 0.7$, $n_D^0 = 0.3$, $P = 10$ atm, $K_{p1} = 0.13237$, and $K_{p2} = 1.07266$. The Newton-Raphson method consists of the successive solution of the following equations for Δn_1 and Δn_2.

$$
\frac{\partial f_1}{\partial n_1} \Delta n_1 + \frac{\partial f_1}{\partial n_2} \Delta n_2 = -f_1
$$

$$
\frac{\partial f_2}{\partial n_1} \Delta n_1 + \frac{\partial f_2}{\partial n_2} \Delta n_2 = -f_2
$$

where the partial derivatives and the functions are evaluated at $n_1 = n_{1,k}, n_2 = n_{2,k}$, and

$$
\Delta n_1 = n_{1,k+1} - n_{1,k}
$$

$$
\Delta n_2 = n_{2,k+1} - n_{2,k}
$$

The values assumed to make the given trial are denoted by the subscript k and those to be used for the next trial by the subscript $k + 1$.

The solution values obtained for n_1 and n_2 by this procedure are as follows:

$$
n_1 = 0.1773
$$

$$
n_2 = 0.0739
$$

The solution set is, of course, that set of positive numbers that makes $f_1 = f_2 = 0$. (The values listed above were taken to be the solution set because the corresponding values of f_1 and f_2 were approximately zero.)

The equilibrium composition of the gas computed on the basis of the above values of n_1 and n_2 is

Component	Moles	Mole %
H_2	0.3434	38.52
CH_4	0.1773	19.77
CO_2	0.2261	25.22
CO	0.1478	16.49
	0.8966	100.00

Another method which may be used to solve this problem is called *interpolation regula falsi* [10]. For a single variable function the interpolation formula for this method is

$$x_3 = \frac{x_1 f(x_2) - x_2 f(x_1)}{f(x_2) - f(x_1)} \tag{5-79}$$

This procedure may be applied to the above set of two simultaneous equations as follows. Take either n_1 or n_2 to be the independent variable, say n_1. Then set either f_1 or f_2 equal to zero, say f_1, and solve for the dependent variable n_2. The assumed value of n_1 and the corresponding calculated value of n_2 are then substituted in f_2. If f_2 is equal to zero, the correct value of n_1 was assumed. If f_2 is unequal to zero for the first choice of n_1 (denoted by $n_{1,1}$), it is evaluated from some arbitrarily selected second choice of n_1 (denoted by $n_{1,2}$). Then Equation (5-79) is applied,

$$n_{1,3} = \frac{n_{1,1} f_2(n_{1,2}) - n_{1,2} f_2(n_{1,1})}{f_2(n_{1,2}) - f_2(n_{1,1})} \tag{5-80}$$

After the calculational procedure has been repeated for $n_{1,3}$, the next best value, $n_{1,4}$, is found by interpolating between the points $[n_{1,3}, f_2(n_{1,3})]$ and $[n_{1,2}, f_2(n_{1,2})]$ in a manner analogous to that demonstrated by Equation (5-80) for the points $[n_{1,2}, f_2(n_{1,2})]$ and $[n_{1,1}, f_2(n_{1,1})]$.

To initiate the calculational procedure for the above example, two values are selected for n_1, say

$$n_{1,1} = 0.18 \quad \text{and} \quad n_{1,2} = 0.165$$

After f_1 has been set equal to zero and solved for n_2, one obtains

$$n_2 = n_1 - n_T^0 + n_1 \left(\frac{n_A^0}{n_1} - 2 \right)^2 PK_{p_1}$$

For $n_{1,1} = 0.18$,

$$n_{2,1} = 0.18 - 1 + 0.18 \left(\frac{0.7}{0.18} - 2 \right)^2 (10)(0.13237) = 0.03011$$

For $n_{1,2} = 0.165$,

$$n_{2,2} = 0.165 - 1 + 0.165 \left(\frac{0.7}{0.165} - 2 \right)^2 (10)(0.13237) = 0.26327$$

When f_2 is evaluated on the basis of $n_{1,1}$ and $n_{2,1}$, one obtains

$$f_2(n_{1,1}) = \frac{4(0.03011)^2(10)}{(1.0 - 0.18 + 0.03011)(0.3 - 0.03011)(1.07266)} - 1 = -0.85265$$

Evaluation of f_2 on the basis of $n_{1,2}$ and $n_{2,2}$ gives

$$f_2(n_{1,2}) = \frac{4(0.26327)^2(10)}{(1.0 - 0.165 + 0.26327)(0.3 - 0.26327)(1.07266)} - 1 = 63.0736$$

Then Equation (5-80) is used to obtain the next best value for n_1; namely,

$$n_{1,3} = \frac{(0.18)(63.0736) - (0.165)(-0.85265)}{63.0736 - (-0.85265)} = 0.1798$$

This value of $n_{1,3}$ is used to compute $n_{2,3}$ in the same manner demonstrated above for $n_{2,1}$ and $n_{2,2}$. Next f_2 is evaluated on the basis of $n_{1,3}$ and $n_{2,3}$. Then $n_{1,4}$ is found by interpolation between the most recent pair of points as described above. This process is continued until the value of f_2 is equal to or less than some small preassigned number. The use of search techniques for solving problems involving systems of complex reactions at chemical equilibrium has been presented by Anthony et al [11].

The techniques demonstrated above for the calculation of the equilibrium constants and equilibrium yields are useful in both the analysis of experimental results and in the design of reactors in which equilibrium conditions prevail. The techniques demonstrated for the calculation of the heat of reaction are useful in the design of chemical reactors because of the necessity to provide for an appropriate amount of heat transfer.

PROBLEMS

5-1. To determine the effect of the ratio of steam to 1-butene on the equilibrium conversion of 1-butene to 1,3-butadiene, repeat Example 5-8 for the following steam to 1-butene ratios:
(a) zero moles of steam and 1 mole of 1-butene,
(b) 6 moles of steam per mole of 1-butene, and
(c) 12 moles of steam per mole of 1-butene.
Answer: (a) $x = 0.4486$, (b) $x = 0.7279$, (c) $x = 0.8111$

5-2. Calculate the equilibrium composition at 900°C and 40 atm for the following reactions:

$$C(s) + 2H_2 \ \rightleftharpoons \ CH_4 \tag{1}$$

$$C(s) + CO_2 \ \rightleftharpoons \ 2CO \tag{2}$$

The feed composition is the same as Example 5-10 and the values of K_p taken from Gumz [8] are

$$K_{p1} = 0.019845 \text{ atm}^{-1}$$

$$K_{p2} = 38.6164 \text{ atm}$$

Answer: 40.87,   13.27,   33.94,   11.92 mole % H_2, CH_4, CO, and CO_2 respec-

5-3. The primary reactions in a coal gasifier are as follows:

$$C(s) + 2\,H_2 \ \rightleftharpoons \ CH_4 \tag{1}$$

$$C(s) + CO_2 \ \rightleftharpoons \ 2\,CO \tag{2}$$

$$C(s) + H_2O(g) \ \rightleftharpoons \ H_2 + CO \tag{3}$$

Calculate the equilibrium composition of the gas at 700°C and 20 atm for an initial gas composition of 50% CO_2 and 50% H_2O. The equilibrium constants taken from Gumz [8] are as follows:

$$K_{p1} = 0.13237 \text{ atm}^{-1}$$

$$K_{p2} = 1.07266 \text{ atm}$$

$$K_{p3} = 1.6618 \text{ atm}$$

Answer: 22.1,   3.52,   13.03,   40.22,   20.32 mole % H_2, CH_4, CO, CO_2, and H_2O respectively.

5-4. In the production of methane from water gas, the following reactions occur:

$$CO + 3 H_2 \rightleftharpoons CH_4 + H_2O \tag{1}$$

$$CO + H_2O \rightleftharpoons CO_2 + H_2 \tag{2}$$

At 550°C, the equilibrium constants given by Gumz [8] are as follows:

$$K_{p1} = 12.460 \text{ atm}^{-2}$$

$$K_{p2} = 3.45381$$

Calculate the equilibrium composition for an initial composition of 4 moles of hydrogen per mole of carbon monoxide and a reactor pressure of 5 atm.
Answer: 30.40, 38.71, 0.4889, 1.272, 29.13 mole % CH_4, H_2, CO, CO_2, and H_2O respectively.

5-5. For the reactions given in Problem 5-3, calculate ΔH_r°, and K at 1000°K and 1 atm by use of the data given in Tables 5-3 and 5-5.

Answer: (1) $\Delta H_r^\circ = -21.433$ kcal, $K = 0.09829$
(2) $\Delta H_r^\circ = 40.783$ kcal, $K = 1.029$
(3) $\Delta H_r^\circ = 32.447$ kcal, $K = 2.488$

5-6. Methanol may be reacted with oxygen over a catalyst to produce formaldehyde at reaction temperatures in the range of 400 to 600°C. The following reactions occur simultaneously.

$$CH_3OH + \tfrac{1}{2}O_2 \longrightarrow CH_2O + H_2O \tag{1}$$

$$CH_3OH \longrightarrow CH_2O + H_2 \tag{2}$$

(a) On the basis of the following data taken from Reference [6] calculate ΔG° and ΔH_r° at 700°K and 800°K for each reaction.

Component	ΔH_f° (kcal/g mole) 700°K	800°K	ΔG_f° (kcal/g mole) 700°K	800°K
CH_3OH	−50.88	−51.31	−24.84	−21.10
O_2	0	0	0	0
CH_2O	−29.17	−29.44	−23.59	−22.77
H_2O	−58.71	−58.91	−49.92	−48.65
H_2	0	0	0	0

(b) In (a) it will be found that the first reaction tends to go to completion and is highly exothermic, whereas the second reaction will be found to have an equilibrium constant of the order of unity and to be highly endothermic. Calculate the equilibrium composition for a feed consisting of 40 mole % CH_3OH and 60 mole % air for a reactor pressure of 1 atm and a reaction temperature of 700°K.

(c) Use the results of (b) to compute the heat which must be added or removed per mole of feed to the reactor in order to maintain the reaction temperature at 700°K.

Answer: (a) At 700°K, $\Delta H^\circ_{r1} = -37$, $\Delta H^\circ_{r2} = 21.71$, $\Delta G^\circ_1 = -48.67$, $\Delta G^\circ_2 = 1.25$ kcal/g mole. At 800°K, $\Delta H^\circ_{r1} = -37.04$, $\Delta H^\circ_{r2} = 21.87$, $\Delta G^\circ_1 = -50.32$, $\Delta G^\circ_2 = -1.67$ kcal/g mole. (b) 4.97, 27.99, 20.76, 7.23, 39.05 mole % CH_3OH, CH_2O, H_2O, H_2, and N_2 respectively. (c) 7.42 kcal must be removed per mole of CH_3OH fed.

5-7. (a) Use the data given in Tables 5-3 and 5-5 to compute ΔG° and ΔH°_r for the reaction

$$C_2H_6 \rightleftharpoons C_2H_4 + H_2$$

at 1000°K.

(b) Use the value of ΔG° found in (a) to compute the maximum conversions which can be achieved at the pressures of 1 atm and 60 Torr when pure ethane is fed to the reactor.

Answer: (a) $\Delta H^\circ_r = 34.539$, $\Delta G^\circ = 2.175$ kcal/g mole, (b) $x = 0.5008$, 0.8996

5-8. In the cracking of ethane, some acethylene is produced. The acetylene produced by this reaction is removed by hydrogenation over a catalyst, which is represented by

$$C_2H_2 + H_2 \rightleftharpoons C_2H_4$$

(a) Calculate the equilibrium constants for the hydrogenation of acetylene at 298.16°K, 600°K, and 1000°K.

(b) For a feed consisting of 90% inerts, 8% hydrogen, and 2% acetylene, calculate the equilibrium conversions of hydrogen at 600°K and 1000°K at a pressure of 5 atm.

Answer: (a) $K = 5.193 \times 10^{24}$, 1.194×10^9, and 501.4 atm^{-1}, (b) $x = 0.25$, 0.2484

5-9. A possible reaction for the production of methanol is

$$CO_2 + 3 H_2 \rightleftharpoons CH_3OH + H_2O$$

Carbon dioxide is available from fossil fuel electric generating plants. Some of the capacity of an electric generating plant could be used to produce hydrogen by the electrolysis of water.

(a) For the above reaction, calculate the heat of reaction, ΔH°_r, at 298.16°K and 600°K.

(b) Calculate ΔG° at 298.16 and at 600°K.

(c) Compute the conversion at 600°K for an operating pressure of 300 atm. Hydrogen and carbon dioxide are fed to the reactor in the ratio of three moles of hydrogen per mole of carbon dioxide. In addition to the thermodynamic data given in the tables in this chapter, the following data, which were taken from [6], are available. For methanol:

$$\Delta H_f^\circ = -48.08 \text{ kcal/g mole at } 25°C$$

$$\Delta H_f^\circ = -50.34 \text{ kcal/g mole at } 600°K$$

$$\Delta G_f^\circ = -38.8 \text{ kcal/g mole at } 25°C$$

$$\Delta G_f^\circ = -28.52 \text{ kcal/g mole at } 600°K$$

Answer: **(a)** $\Delta H_r^\circ = -11.827$, -14.71 kcal/g mole, **(b)** $\Delta G^\circ = 0.8221$, 14.769 kcal/g mole, **(c)** $x = 0.3789$

5-10. For the hydrogenation of acetylene to ethylene,

$$C_2H_2 + H_2 \rightleftharpoons C_2H_4$$

calculate K_c at 1000°K. Assume that the gas behaves as a perfect gas.
Answer: $K_c = 4.111 \times 10^4$ liters/(g mole).

5-11. Toluene is to be hydrogenated to methylcyclohexane at a reaction temperature of 600°K. Calculate ΔH_r°, ΔG°, and K. For methylcyclohexane, the following data at 600°K were taken from Reference [6].

$$\Delta H_f^\circ = -44.49 \text{ kcal/g mole}$$

$$\Delta G_f^\circ = 69.79 \text{ kcal/g mole}$$

Answer: $\Delta H_r^\circ = -52.4249$, $\Delta G^\circ = 21.432$ kcal/g mole, $K = 1.5586 \times 10^{-8}$

5-12. Methanol may be reformed to produce methane by the following reaction:

$$4 \text{ CH}_3\text{OH} \rightleftharpoons 3 \text{ CH}_4 + \text{CO}_2 + 2 \text{ H}_2\text{O}$$

Calculate ΔH_r° and ΔG° for this reaction at 600°K. For the data needed for methanol (see Problem 5-9).
Answer: $\Delta H_r^\circ = -69.4294$, $\Delta G^\circ = -99.1492$ kcal/g mole

5-13. Ethylene may be produced from carbon monoxide and hydrogen by the reactions:

$$2 \text{ CO} + 4 \text{ H}_2 \rightleftharpoons C_2H_4 + 2 \text{ H}_2\text{O}$$

$$\text{CO} + 2 \text{ H}_2 \rightleftharpoons C_2H_4 + 2 \text{ CO}_2$$

Calculate ΔG° and ΔH_r° for each of these reactions at 600°K and 800°K.

Answer: At $600°K$: $\Delta H_{r1}^{\circ} = -54.913$, $\Delta H_{r2}^{\circ} = -72.324$ kcal/g mole, $\Delta G_1^{\circ} = -2.6762$, $\Delta G_2^{\circ} = -10.5416$ kcal/g mole. At $800°K$: $\Delta H_{r1}^{\circ} = -54.978$, $\Delta H_{r2}^{\circ} = -103.380$ kcal/g mole, $\Delta G_1^{\circ} = 14.552$, $\Delta G_2^{\circ} = -10.1188$ kcal/g mole

5-14. Ethylene may be produced from methanol by the following reaction

$$2\,CH_3OH \rightleftharpoons C_2H_4 + 2\,H_2O$$

Calculate $\Delta G°$, $\Delta H_r°$, and K for this reaction at $600°K$ and $800°K$. Use the following data, which were taken from Reference (6).

Component	ΔH_f° (kcal/g mole)		ΔG_f° (kcal/g mole)	
	$600°K$	$800°K$	$600°K$	$800°K$
CH_3OH	-50.34	-51.31	-28.52	-21.10
C_2H_4	10.60	9.77	20.92	24.49
H_2O	-58.91	-58.50	-51.16	-48.65

Answer: At $600°K$: $\Delta H_r° = -6.54$ kcal, $\Delta G° = -24.36$ kcal. At $800°K$: $\Delta H_r° = -4.61$ kcal, $\Delta G° = -30.61$ kcal.

NOTATION

A = Helmholtz free energy.

a_i = activity of component i at the temperature and pressure of the system.

C_p° = heat capacity of a perfect gas; defined by Equation (5-21).

f_i = fugacity of pure component i at the temperature and pressure of the system.

$\bar{f}_i$ = fugacity of component i in a mixture at the temperature and pressure of the mixture.

f_i° = fugacity of pure component i in its standard state at temperature of the system.

G = Gibbs free energy.

ΔG_f° = standard free energy of formation which is equal to the change in free energy when a compound in its standard state is formed from its elements in their standard state, all at the temperature T, and the standard states are taken to be as stated in Table 5-1.

ΔG_{f0}° = the value of ΔG_f° at the temperature $0°K$.

$\Delta G°$ = standard free energy change which is equal to the change in free energy which occurs when products in their standard states are formed from reactants in their standard states, all at the temperature T.

G_T° = free energy of a compound or element in its standard state at the temperature T, and G_0° denotes its free (see Table 4-1) energy at the temperature $0°K$.

H = enthalpy; also used to denote the enthalpy of one mole of mixture.

$\Delta H_r^\circ =$ standard heat of reaction which is defined as the sum of the enthalpies of the products in their standard states minus the sum of the enthalpies of the reactants in their standard states (see Table 5-1), all at the temperature T.

$\Delta H_f^\circ =$ standard heat of formation which is defined as the standard heat of reaction when a compound in its standard state is formed from its elements in their standard state, all at the temperature T. ΔH_{f0}° is the value of ΔH_f° at $0^\circ K$.

$H_T^\circ =$ enthalpy of a compound or element in its standard state at the temperature T, and H_0° is the corresponding enthalpy at $0^\circ K$.

$K =$ equilibrium constant.

$K_y, K_p =$ equilibrium constants for the gas phase.

$K_x =$ equilibrium constant for the liquid phase.

$K_f, K_\gamma =$ ratios of fugacities and activities respectively.

$n_i =$ moles of component i (or molar flow rate of component i).

$n_T =$ total moles of mixture (or total molar flow rate).

$p_i =$ partial pressure of component i.

$P =$ total pressure.

$P_c =$ critical pressure.

$P_i =$ vapor pressure of component i.

$P_r =$ reduced pressure.

$R =$ gas constant in consistent units.

$S =$ entropy.

$T =$ temperature, degrees absolute.

$T_c =$ critical temperature, degrees absolute.

$T_r =$ reduced temperature.

$T_0 =$ temperature at which the heat of reaction is known.

$U =$ internal energy.

$v =$ molar volume, volume per mole.

$x_i =$ mole fraction of component i in the liquid phase.

$y_i =$ mole fraction of component i in the gas phase.

Greek Letters

$\gamma_i =$ activity coefficient for component i.

$\phi =$ fugacity coefficient.

Superscripts

$L =$ liquid phase.

$S =$ solid phase.

$V =$ vapor phase.

REFERENCES

1. "Selected Values of Physical and Thermodynamic Properties of Hydrocarbons and Related Compounds," API Research Project 44, Thermodynamics Research Center, Texas A & M University, College Station, Texas (1977). (Loose-leaf data sheets.)

2. Wagman, D. D., *Tables of Selected Values of Chemical Properties*, National Bureau of Standards (July 1, 1973).

3. Denbigh, K. G., *The Principles of Chemical Equilibrium*, Cambridge University Press, New York (1955).

4. Klotz, I. M., *Chemical Thermodynamics*, Prentice-Hall, Inc., Englewood Cliffs, N.J. (1950).

5. Smith, J. M., and H. C. Van Ness, *Introduction to Chemical Engineering Thermodynamics*, McGraw-Hill Book Company, New York (1959).

6. Stull, D. R., E. F. Westrum, Jr., and G. C. Sinke, *The Chemical Thermodynamics of Organic Compounds*, John Wiley & Sons, Inc., New York (1969).

7. Perry, Robt. H., Cecil H. Chilton, and Sidney D. Kirkpatrick, *Chemical Engineers' Handbook*. 4th Ed., pg. 4–53, McGraw-Hill Book Company, New York (1963).

8. Gumz, W., Gas *Producers and Blast Furnaces, Theory and Methods of Calculation*, John Wiley & Sons, Inc., New York (1950).

9. Hougen, O. A., K. M. Watson, and R. A. Ragatz, *Chem. Proc. Princ.*, *Part I, Material and Energy Balances*, John Wiley & Sons, New York (1959).

10. Carnahan, B., H. A. Luther, and J. O. Wilkes, *Applied Numerical Methods*, John Wiley & Sons, Inc., New York (1969).

11. Anthony, R. G., and D. M. Himmelblau, *J. Physical Chem. 67*, 1080 (1963).

Energy Balances

6

Equations needed to take heat effects into account in the design of various types of reactors are presented in this chapter. First the general expression for an energy balance on an element of fluid in a plug-flow reactor is developed in Part I, and then various methods for evaluating the enthalpy of the reacting mixture are presented. In Parts II and III, the energy-balance equations for perfectly mixed flow reactors and batch reactors are developed. In this chapter, the effects of pressure and composition on the heats of reaction are neglected. These effects are included in the advanced treatment in Chapter 11.

I. DEVELOPMENT OF ENERGY-BALANCE EQUATIONS FOR PLUG-FLOW REACTORS

The first law of thermodynamics asserts that the energy of the universe is constant. Consequently, the total amount of energy entering minus that leaving the system must be equal to the accumulation of energy within the system. (The word "system" is used to mean that particular part of the universe under consideration.) The following form of the energy balance is readily applied to systems at unsteady state operation.

$$\int_{t_n}^{t_n + \Delta t} \left[\begin{pmatrix} \text{input of energy} \\ \text{to the system} \\ \text{per unit time} \end{pmatrix} - \begin{pmatrix} \text{output of energy} \\ \text{from the system} \\ \text{per unit time} \end{pmatrix} \right] dt$$
$$= \begin{pmatrix} \text{energy within} \\ \text{the system} \end{pmatrix} \Bigg|_{t_n + \Delta t} - \begin{pmatrix} \text{energy within} \\ \text{the system} \end{pmatrix} \Bigg|_{t_n} \quad (6\text{-}1)$$

In accounting for all of the energy entering and leaving a system, the energy equivalents of the net heat absorbed and the net work done on the system must be taken into account. The terms *heat* and *work* represent energy in the state of transition between the system and its surroundings. A system that has work done on it experiences the conversion of mechanical energy into internal energy. Let the internal energy contained by a unit mass of fluid be denoted by U. The internal energy is the energy associated with the structure and molecular motion of the molecules that make up each unit mass of fluid. Let KE denote the kinetic energy of the mass motion of a unit mass of fluid. The potential energy PE is equal to the work required to raise a unit mass of fluid a given distance above a specified datum level, against the force of gravity. Finally let the total energy possessed by a unit mass of fluid be denoted by U_T. Then

$$U_T = U + \text{KE} + \text{PE} \tag{6-2}$$

where all of these quantities are stated on a mass basis rather than the mole basis. For convenience, let H_T be defined as follows:

$$H_T = H + \text{KE} + \text{PE} \tag{6-3}$$

where $\qquad H = $ enthalpy in Btu/lb mass

Thus $H_T = U + Pv + \text{KE} + \text{PE} = U_T + Pv$, where v is volume of fluid per unit mass.

Throughout all of the developments that follow, it is supposed that the reactor shown in Figure 6-1 is flowing full and that the reacting mixture is in plug flow. Let z_j, z_{j+1}, t_n, and t_{n+1} be arbitrarily selected in the space and

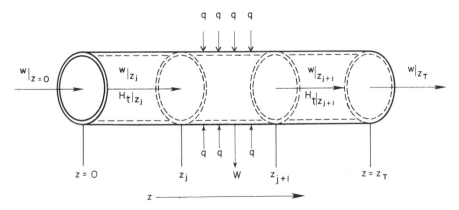

Figure 6-1. Energy balance on the element of volume from z_j to z_{j+1} of a plug-flow reactor. [Taken from Charles D. Holland, *I&EC Fundamentals*, 16:143 (1977). Used with the permission of the American Chemical Society.]

time domains of interest. Then Δz and Δt are fixed as follows:

$$\Delta z = z_{j+1} - z_j$$

$$\Delta t = t_{n+1} - t_n$$

The formulation of the energy balance for the element of volume from z_j to z_{j+1} over the time period from t_n to t_{n+1} follows. The energy entering the element per unit time in the fluid at z_j is given by

$$\left\{\begin{array}{l}\text{Input of energy} \\ \text{per unit time} \\ \text{by flow}\end{array}\right\} = (wU_T)\Big|_{z_j} \tag{6-4}$$

At any time $t(t_n \le t \le t_{n+1})$, the work required to force one unit mass of fluid into the element of volume is given by

$$\begin{array}{l}\text{Work per} \\ \text{unit mass}\end{array} = \int_0^v P\,dv\Big|_{z_j} = (Pv)\Big|_{z_j} \tag{6-5}$$

Note, this work Pv may vary with time throughout the time period Δt. (In this equation and those which follow, it is understood of course that the Pv product is to be stated in energy units which are consistent with the remaining terms in the equations.) At any time t,

$$\left\{\begin{array}{l}\text{Rate at which work} \\ \text{is done on the element} \\ \text{of volume by the entering} \\ \text{fluid}\end{array}\right\} = (wPv)\Big|_{z_j} \tag{6-6}$$

Let q (energy per hour per foot, say Btu/hr ft) denote the rate of heat transfer to the system from the surroundings at each z ($z_j \le z \le z_{j+1}$), where it is understood that q varies in a continuous manner with respect to z at any t. Then

$$\left\{\begin{array}{l}\text{Heat transferred across} \\ \text{the boundary of the} \\ \text{element of volume} \\ \text{per hr}\end{array}\right\} = \int_{z_j}^{z_{j+1}} q\,dz \tag{6-7}$$

With regard to the shaft work done by the system on the surroundings, two cases are considered. In the first case, the work leaves the system at a point z lying between z_j and z_{j+1} as shown in Figure 6-1, and the rate at which the system does work on the surroundings is denoted by W(energy/time, say Btu/hr). In the second case, it is supposed that work is done by the system in a continuous manner at each point on the boundary, and that the rate at which work is done per unit length is denoted by $\mathscr{W}$ (energy per unit time per foot, say Btu/hr ft). For the second case,

$$\left\{\begin{array}{l}\text{Shaft work done} \\ \text{by the element} \\ \text{of volume per hr}\end{array}\right\} = \int_{z_j}^{z_{j+1}} \mathscr{W}\,dz \tag{6-8}$$

The integral difference equation is set up for the first case from which the final result for the second case is readily obtained. The input terms that appear in Equation (6-1) are as follows:

$$\begin{Bmatrix}\text{Input of energy} \\ \text{to the element} \\ \text{of volume during} \\ \text{the time period } \Delta t\end{Bmatrix} = \int_{t_n}^{t_{n+1}} \left\{ (wU_T)\Big|_{z_j} + (wPv)\Big|_{z_j} + \int_{z_j}^{z_{j+1}} q\, dz \right\} dt \quad (6\text{-}9)$$

The output terms are

$$\begin{Bmatrix}\text{Output of energy} \\ \text{from the element} \\ \text{of volume during} \\ \text{the time period } \Delta t\end{Bmatrix} = \int_{t_n}^{t_{n+1}} \left\{ (wU_T)\Big|_{z_{j+1}} + (wPv)\Big|_{z_{j+1}} + W \right\} dt \quad (6\text{-}10)$$

The accumulation of energy [the right-hand side of Equation (6-1)] is given by

$$\begin{Bmatrix}\text{Accumulation of energy} \\ \text{within the element of} \\ \text{volume during the} \\ \text{time period } \Delta t\end{Bmatrix} = \int_{z_j}^{z_{j+1}} \rho S U_T\, dz\Big|_{t_{n+1}} - \int_{z_j}^{z_{j+1}} \rho S U_T\, dz\Big|_{t_n} \quad (6\text{-}11)$$

where ρ is the density (mass per unit volume) of the fluid and S is the cross-sectional area of the element volume as shown in Figure 6-1. Since $\rho = 1/v$, and $H_T = U_T + Pv$, it follows from Equations (6-2) and (6-3) that

$$\rho U_T = \rho H_T - \rho(Pv) = \rho H_T - P \quad (6\text{-}12)$$

Then Equation (6-11) may be restated in terms of H_T as follows:

$$\begin{Bmatrix}\text{Accumulation of} \\ \text{energy during} \\ \text{time } \Delta t\end{Bmatrix} = \int_{z_j}^{z_{j+1}}\left[\rho H_T\Big|_{t_{n+1}} - \rho H_T\Big|_{t_n}\right]S\, dz - \int_{z_j}^{z_{j+1}}\left[P\Big|_{t_{n+1}} - P\Big|_{t_n}\right]S\, dz$$

$$(6\text{-}13)$$

Also, when Equation (6-3) is used to state the inputs and outputs in terms of H_T, the final result for the energy balance is given by

$$\int_{t_n}^{t_{n+1}} \left\{ (wH_T)\Big|_{z_j,t} - (wH_T)\Big|_{z_{j+1},t} + \int_{z_j}^{z_{j+1}} q\, dz - W \right\} dt$$

$$= \int_{z_j}^{z_{j+1}}\left[(\rho H_T)\Big|_{t_{n+1},z} - (\rho H_T)\Big|_{t_n,z}\right]S\, dz$$

$$- \int_{z_j}^{z_{j+1}}\left[P\Big|_{t_{n+1},z} - P\Big|_{t_n,z}\right]S\, dz \quad (6\text{-}14)$$

(Note in the application of this equation that all terms must be expressed in appropriate energy units.) Examination of the second integral on the right-hand side of Equation (6-14) shows that it has the physical significance of being the difference between the amount of work required to sweep out the element of volume at times t_{n+1} and t_n.

If the element of volume does shaft work on the surroundings at each point along the boundary, then W in Equation (6-14) is replaced by the expression given by Equation (6-8).

In dealing with systems involving chemical reactions, it is generally more convenient to work in terms of molar flow rates rather than mass flow rates because enthalpies are generally stated in tables on a mole basis rather than a mass basis. Since mass flow rates are constant for many systems for which the corresponding values of the molar flow rates vary, it might appear simpler to use mass flow rates. However, this is not generally the case, and molar flow rates are used in most of the subsequent developments. Since the same amount of energy is contained in a given amount of material regardless of the units employed, it follows that

$$w \left[\frac{\text{mass}}{\text{time}} \right] H \left[\frac{\text{energy}}{\text{mass}} \right] = n_T \left[\frac{\text{moles}}{\text{time}} \right] H \left[\frac{\text{energy}}{\text{mole}} \right]$$

and

$$S(\text{length}^2)\rho \left[\frac{\text{mass}}{\text{length}^3} \right] H \left[\frac{\text{energy}}{\text{mass}} \right] = S(\text{length}^2)\rho \left[\frac{\text{mole}}{\text{length}^3} \right] H \left[\frac{\text{energy}}{\text{mole}} \right]$$

Thus, when molar flow rates and densities are used, Equation (6-14) takes the form

$$\int_{t_n}^{t_{n+1}} \left[(n_T H_T) \Big|_{z_j,t} - (n_T H_T) \Big|_{z_{j+1},t} + \int_{z_j}^{z_{j+1}} q \, dz - W \right] dt$$

$$= \int_{z_j}^{z_{j+1}} \left[(\rho H_T) \Big|_{t_{n+1},z} - (\rho H_T) \Big|_{t_n,z} \right] S \, dz$$

$$- \int_{z_j}^{z_{j+1}} \left[P \Big|_{t_{n+1},z} - P \Big|_{t_n,z} \right] S \, dz \tag{6-15}$$

where H_T is now stated on a mole basis.

At steady state operation, Equation (6-15) for a plug-flow reactor reduces to

$$n_T H_T \Big|_{z_j} - n_T H_T \Big|_{z_{j+1}} + \int_{z_j}^{z_{j+1}} q \, dz - W = 0 \tag{6-16}$$

Generally the changes in kinetic and potential energies in a reactor are negligible relative to the heat effects associated with a chemical reaction.

Also, the work W can be disregarded in most cases because the energy introduced into the reacting mixture by any device such as a stirrer is generally small relative to the heat of reaction. Thus the approximation $\Delta KE = 0$, $\Delta PE = 0$, and $W = 0$ are made in all subsequent developments, and on this basis Equation (6-16) reduces to

$$-\left[(n_T H)\Big|_{z_{j+1}} - (n_T H)\Big|_{z_j} \right] + \int_{z_j}^{z_{j+1}} q \, dz = 0 \tag{6-17}$$

By application of the mean value theorems and the limiting process described in Chapter 1 to Equation (6-17), the following differential equation is obtained

$$-\frac{d(n_T H)}{dz} + q = 0 \tag{6-18}$$

A. Energy-Balance Equations for Reactors in Which the Reacting Mixtures Form Ideal Solutions and Have Enthalpies Which Are Independent of Pressure

The enthalpy difference $[(n_T H)\big|_{z_{j+1}} - (n_T H)\big|_{z_j}]$ which appears in Equation (6-17) may be evaluated by use of a *path* which can be made much simpler than the actual path followed by the reaction between z_j and z_{j+1}. An alternate path may be used to evaluate the enthalpy difference because the enthalpy per mole of mixture as well as the enthalpy of the mixture, $n_T H$, depends upon only the initial and final states of the system. First the enthalpy difference appearing in Equation (6-17) is evaluated for the case where a single reaction occurs.

1. ENERGY-BALANCE EQUATIONS FOR REACTORS IN WHICH A SINGLE REACTION OCCURS—USE OF THE PATH SHOWN IN FIGURE 6-2. In the formulation of the path shown in Figure 6-2, it was supposed that the single reaction occurring in the reactor was of the form

$$aA + bB = cC + dD \tag{6-19}$$

Furthermore, as implied by the above title, it was assumed that all mixtures involved formed ideal solutions and had enthalpies which were independent of pressure. In the path shown in Figure 6-2, the conversion x of component A at any z in the reactor is used. The conversion x is defined as the moles of A converted per mole of A in the feed [see Equation (2-19)]. Then for the general reaction given by Equation (6-19), the molar flow rates at any z in

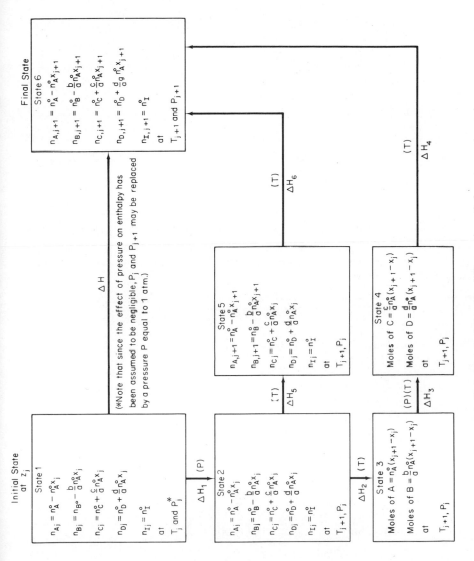

Figure 6-2. Path for calculating the difference in enthalpy at z_j and z_{j+1} in Figure 6-1.

the reactor may be stated in terms of the conversion x as follows:

$$n_A = n_A^0 - n_A^0 x$$

$$n_B = n_B^0 - \frac{b}{a} n_A^0 x$$

$$n_C = n_C^0 + \frac{c}{a} n_A^0 x \tag{6-20}$$

$$n_D = n_D^0 + \frac{d}{a} n_A^0 x$$

$$n_I = n_I^0$$

$$n_T = n_T^0 + \left[\frac{c + d - a - b}{a}\right] n_A^0 x = n_T^0 + \delta n_A^0 x$$

where n_I is the molar flow rate of all inert components (components which do not participate in the reaction). Instead of x, all of the flow rates may be expressed in terms of one of the other flow rates, say n_A. When the definition of x [Equation (2-19)] is substituted into Equation (6-20), the following expressions are obtained:

$$n_A = n_A^0 - (n_A^0 - n_A)$$

$$n_B = n_B^0 - \frac{b}{a}(n_A^0 - n_A)$$

$$n_C = n_C^0 + \frac{c}{a}(n_A^0 - n_A) \tag{6-21}$$

$$n_D = n_D^0 + \frac{d}{a}(n_A^0 - n_A)$$

$$n_I = n_I^0$$

$$n_T = n_T^0 + \delta(n_A^0 - n_A)$$

For convenience, the values of the variables at z_j and z_{j+1} are identified by the subscripts j and $j + 1$, respectively; that is,

$$n_A\Big|_{z_j} = n_{Aj}, \qquad T\Big|_{z_j} = T_j, \qquad x\Big|_{z_j} = x_j$$

The first step of the path shown in Figure 6-2 consists of a heating process wherein the mixture is heated at constant pressure from the temperature T_j

to the temperature T_{j+1}. Thus

$$\Delta H_1 = \int_{T_j}^{T_{j+1}} n_{Tj} C_{pj}^\circ \, dT = n_{Tj} \int_{T_j}^{T_{j+1}} C_{pj}^\circ \, dT \qquad (6\text{-}22)$$

where

$$n_{Tj} = n_{Aj} + n_{Bj} + n_{Cj} + n_{Dj} + n_{Ij}$$

The heat capacity of the perfect gas mixture at the temperature T is given by

$$C_{pj}^\circ = \frac{1}{n_{Tj}} [n_{Aj} C_{pA}^\circ + n_{Bj} C_{pB}^\circ + n_{Cj} C_{pC}^\circ + n_{Dj} C_{pD}^\circ + n_{Ij} C_{pI}^\circ] \quad (6\text{-}23)$$

where the heat capacities of individual components are, of course, a function of temperature alone.

The moles of A that react in the element of volume $S(z_{j+1} - z_j)$ are equal to

$$n_{Aj} - n_{A,j+1} = n_A^0(x_{j+1} - x_j)$$

This amount of A is withdrawn from the mixture in State 2 and becomes one of the reactants in State 3. The moles of B required to react with $n_A^0(x_{j+1} - x_j)$ moles of A is equal to

$$\frac{b}{a} n_A^0(x_{j+1} - x_j)$$

This amount of B is withdrawn from the mixture in State 2 and becomes the second reactant in State 3. Since it has been assumed that the mixture forms an ideal solution and since H has been assumed independent of pressure,

$$\Delta H_2 = 0, \qquad \Delta H_4 = 0, \qquad \Delta H_5 = 0, \qquad \Delta H_6 = 0$$

The change in enthalpy ΔH_3 in going from Step 3 to Step 4 is computed as follows on the basis of a knowledge of the heat of reaction $\Delta H_{r,j+1}^\circ$ per mole of A reacted at temperature T_{j+1}.

$$\Delta H_3 = n_A^0(x_{j+1} - x_j) \, \Delta H_{r,j+1}^\circ$$

Then, for the complete path,

$$n_{T,j+1} H_{j+1} - n_{Tj} H_j = \sum_{k=1}^{6} \Delta H_k = n_{Tj} \int_{T_j}^{T_{j+1}} C_{pj}^\circ \, dT$$

$$+ \, n_A^0(x_{j+1} - x_j) \, \Delta H_{r,j+1}^\circ \qquad (6\text{-}24)$$

and Equation (6-17) becomes

$$-n_{Tj} \int_{T_j}^{T_{j+1}} C_{pj}^\circ \, dT - [n_A^0(x_{j+1} - x_j) \Delta H_{r,j+1}^\circ] + \int_{z_j}^{z_{j+1}} q \, dz = 0 \quad (6\text{-}25)$$

Equation (6-25) may be stated in the form of a differential equation by first applying the mean value theorems of differential and integral calculus as demonstrated in Chapter 1 to obtain

$$-n_{Tj} \left[C_{pj} \Big|_{T_j + \alpha \Delta T} \right] \Delta T - n_A^0 \, \Delta H_{r,j+1} \left[\frac{dx}{dz} \Big|_{z_j + \beta \Delta z} \right] \Delta z + \left[q \Big|_{z_j + \alpha \Delta z} \right] \Delta z = 0$$

$$(6\text{-}26)$$

where $0 \leq \alpha \leq 1, 0 < \beta < 1, 0 \leq \gamma \leq 1$. Let each term of Equation (6-26) be divided by Δz. Then in the limit as Δz approaches zero, the following result is obtained:

$$-n_T C_p^\circ \frac{dT}{dz} - n_A^0 \, \Delta H_r^\circ \frac{dx}{dz} + q = 0 \quad (6\text{-}27)$$

for any z $(0 < z < z_T)$. Since

$$Sr_A = -\frac{dn_A}{dz} = n_A^0 \frac{dx}{dz} \quad (6\text{-}28)$$

Equation (6-27) may be restated in the following alternate form:

$$-n_T C_p^\circ \frac{dT}{dz} - \Delta H_r^\circ r_A S + q = 0 \quad (6\text{-}29)$$

This energy balance is commonly stated in terms of the independent variable V (the volume of the reactor) rather than z. Since the volume $V = Sz$, it follows that

$$-n_T C_p^\circ \frac{dT}{dV} - r_A \Delta H_r^\circ + \frac{q}{S} = 0 \quad (6\text{-}30)$$

It should be observed that in going from the integral difference equation form of the energy balance [Equation (6-25)] to the differential equation [Equation (6-27)], the fact that $n_{Tj} C_{pj}^\circ$ may be evaluated at the conversion x_j and that the heat of reaction may be evaluated at the temperature T_{j+1} is lost. Thus, if the energy-balance equation is to be solved numerically, it would appear to be advantageous to use Equation (6-25) rather than Equation (6-27).

Since the enthalpy is independent of path, any number of alternate paths may be used for its calculation. Also, instead of beginning with the integral difference equation [Equation (6-17)], one may begin with the differential equation [Equation (6-18)]. An expression for $n_T H$ as a function of x and T may be obtained by use of an appropriate path (see Problem 6-1).

2. ENERGY-BALANCE EQUATIONS FOR REACTORS IN WHICH ANY NUMBER OF REACTIONS OCCUR. For relatively simple reactions and for steady state operation, the techniques demonstrated above and in Problem 6-1 are satisfactory. However, for complex reactions and for unsteady state operation, the use of the elements at a reference state for the calculation of the enthalpy of a compound offers many advantages. The enthalpy of component i above this reference state, denoted by H°_{fi}, is defined as the enthalpy of component i at a given temperature T in the perfect gas state at 1 atm above its elements in their standard states at some arbitrary datum temperature. For example, consider the case where the elements A and B form compound C, and the reference temperature for the elements is taken to be $0°K$. Then the enthalpy of compound C is given by

$$H^\circ_{f,C} = \Delta H^\circ_{f0,C} + (H^\circ_T - H^\circ_0)_C \qquad (6\text{-}31)$$

Values for $\Delta H^\circ_{f0,C}$ and $(H_T - H^\circ_0)$ are available from standard thermodynamic tables (see, for example, Table 5-3). For the case of element A, the enthalpy at temperature T is given by

$$H^\circ_{f,A} = (H^\circ_T - H^\circ_0)_A$$

For the case where the reference state of the elements is taken equal to the temperature of compound C, the enthalpy becomes equal to the heat of formation

$$H^\circ_{f,C} = \Delta H^\circ_{f,C}$$

When the heats of mixing and the effect of pressure on enthalpy are negligible, then the enthalpy of each component i in the reacting mixture at the temperature T and pressure P can be taken equal to its enthalpy in the perfect gas state at the temperature T and a pressure of 1 atm above its elements in their standard states at a given reference temperature.

Thus, when enthalpies are calculated as outlined above, the enthalpy $n_T H$ of a gaseous mixture at any z in the reactor is given by

$$n_T H = \sum_{i=1}^{c} n_i H^\circ_{fi} \qquad (6\text{-}32)$$

Similarly, if the reaction occurs in the liquid phase, then the enthalpy, $n_T H$, of the liquid mixture at any z in the reactor is given by

$$n_T H = \sum_{i=1}^{c} n_i h_{fi}^{\circ} \qquad (6\text{-}33)$$

where h_{fi}° is the enthalpy of formation of component i in the liquid state at temperature T from its elements in their standard states at the reference temperature. The enthalpies h_{fi}° and H_{fi}° differ by $\lambda_i(T)$, the latent heat of vaporization of component i at the temperature T; that is,

$$h_{fi}^{\circ} = H_{fi}^{\circ} - \lambda_i(T) \qquad (6\text{-}34)$$

For convenience, the reacting mixture is taken to be in the gaseous state in the developments which follow.

When the enthalpy of the mixture is given by Equation (6-32), the energy balance given by Equation (6-17) for a plug-flow reactor takes the form

$$\sum_{i=1}^{c} n_i H_{fi}^{\circ} \Big|_{z_j} - \sum_{i=1}^{c} n_i H_{fi}^{\circ} \Big|_{z_{j+1}} + \int_{z_j}^{z_{j+1}} q \, dz = 0 \qquad (6\text{-}35)$$

where the same reference state is used to compute H_{fi}° at z_j and z_{j+1}.

Next the expression given by Equation (6-32) for $n_T H$ is used to evaluate $d(n_T H)/dz$ in Equation (6-18). Since the right-hand side of Equation (6-32) is a function of the complete set of n_i's and the temperature T, it may be represented in functional notation as follows:

$$n_T H = f(n_1, n_2, \ldots, n_c, T) \qquad (6\text{-}36)$$

where the function f is defined by Equation (6-32). Then

$$\frac{d(n_T H)}{dz} = \sum_{i=1}^{c} \frac{\partial f}{\partial n_i} \frac{dn_i}{dz} + \frac{\partial f}{\partial T} \frac{dT}{dz} \qquad (6\text{-}37)$$

and by use of Equation (6-32),

$$\frac{d(n_T H)}{dz} = \sum_{i=1}^{c} H_{fi}^{\circ} \frac{dn_i}{dz} + \left(\sum_{i=1}^{c} n_i \frac{\partial H_{fi}^{\circ}}{\partial T} \right) \frac{dT}{dz} \qquad (6\text{-}38)$$

Let

$$C_{pi}^{\circ} = \frac{\partial H_{fi}^{\circ}}{\partial T} \qquad (6\text{-}39)$$

Then the second summation of Equation (6-38) reduces to $n_T C_p^\circ$. For

$$\sum_{i=1}^{c} n_i \frac{\partial H_{fi}^\circ}{\partial T} = \sum_{i=1}^{c} n_i C_{pi}^\circ = n_T \sum_{i=1}^{c} \left(\frac{n_i}{n_T}\right) C_{pi}^\circ = n_T C_p^c \qquad (6\text{-}40)$$

where C_p° is the heat capacity of the perfect gas mixture. When the results given by Equations (6-38) and (6-40) are substituted into Equation (6-18), one obtains

$$-n_T C_p^\circ \frac{dT}{dz} - \sum_{i=1}^{c} H_{fi}^\circ \frac{dn_i}{dz} + q = 0 \qquad (6\text{-}41)$$

As shown in Chapter 2, the derivatives of n_i with respect to z are related to the net rates of reaction r_i. If all of the rates are defined in terms of disappearance, then the material balance for component i becomes

$$S r_i = -\frac{dn_i}{dz} \qquad (6\text{-}42)$$

When each of the c components present in the mixture are involved in a set of reactions, the energy-balance expression may be stated as follows:

$$-n_T C_p^\circ \frac{dT}{dz} + S \sum_{i=1}^{c} H_{fi}^\circ r_i + q = 0 \qquad (6\text{-}43)$$

For the case where the single reaction given by Equation (6-19) occurs in the reactor, the rates of reaction r_i are related as follows:

$$r_B = \frac{b}{a} r_A, \qquad r_C = -\frac{c}{a} r_A, \qquad r_D = -\frac{d}{a} r_A \qquad (6\text{-}44)$$

where all of the rates are defined in terms of disappearance. Thus the second term of Equation (6-43) becomes

$$S \sum_{i=1}^{c} H_{fi}^\circ r_i = -S r_A \left[\frac{c}{a} H_{fC}^\circ + \frac{d}{a} H_{fD}^\circ - H_{fA}^\circ - \frac{b}{a} H_{fB}^\circ \right] = -S r_A \, \Delta H_r^\circ$$

$$(6\text{-}45)$$

where ΔH_r° is the standard heat of reaction per mole of A reacted at the temperature T; the superscript $^\circ$ denotes the fact that each member of the mixture is taken to be in its standard state of a perfect gas except for the element carbon, which, if present, is taken to be the solid, graphite.

When the result given by Equation (6-45) is substituted into Equation (6-43), the energy-balance expression given by Equation (6-29) is obtained.

B. Energy Balances for Plug-Flow Reactors at Unsteady State Operation

An energy balance on the reacting mixture contained in the element of volume $S(z_{j+1} - z_j)$ shown in Figure 6-1 is represented by Equation (6-15). Suppose that the shaft work is done continuously on the surroundings at each point along the boundary. To represent this situation, W in Equation (6-15) must be replaced by the integral expression given by Equation (6-8). Further suppose that all of the variables appearing in Equation (6-15) are continuous and have continuous derivatives. The following partial differential equation corresponding to the modified form of Equation (6-15) may be obtained by use of the mean value theorems and limiting process as demonstrated in Chapter 1.

$$-\frac{\partial(n_T H_T)}{\partial z} + q - \mathcal{W} = S\left[\frac{\partial(\rho H_T)}{\partial t} - \frac{\partial P}{\partial t}\right] \tag{6-46}$$

Since $\rho = n_T/v_T$ (where v_T is the total volumetric flow rate), Equation (6-46) may be expressed as follows for the case where the kinetic and potential energy effects are negligible.

$$-\frac{\partial(n_T H)}{\partial z} + q - \mathcal{W} = S\left[\frac{1}{v_T}\frac{\partial(n_T H)}{\partial t} - \frac{n_T H}{v_T^2}\frac{\partial v_T}{\partial t} - \frac{\partial P}{\partial t}\right] \tag{6-47}$$

For the general case where any number of reactions occur in the reacting mixture and the enthalpy of the mixture is independent of the heats of mixing and pressure, the enthalpy of the mixture may be represented by Equation (6-32). By use of this expression for $n_T H$, the partial derivatives of $n_T H$ with respect to z and t in Equation (6-47) may be evaluated. The first term on the left-hand side of Equation (6-47) may be evaluated in the same manner as demonstrated for $d(n_T H)/dz$ [see Equation (6-37)]. The result so obtained is

$$\frac{\partial(n_T H)}{\partial z} = n_T C_p^\circ \frac{\partial T}{\partial z} + \sum_{i=1}^c H_{fi}^\circ \frac{\partial n_i}{\partial z} \tag{6-48}$$

Evaluation of $\partial(n_T H)/\partial t$ gives

$$\frac{\partial(n_T H)}{\partial t} = \frac{\partial(n_T H)}{\partial T}\frac{\partial T}{\partial t} + \sum_{i=1}^c \frac{\partial(n_T H)}{\partial n_i}\frac{\partial n_i}{\partial t} \tag{6-49}$$

Utilization of the relationship given by Equation (6-32) for $n_T H$ gives

$$\frac{\partial(n_T H)}{\partial t} = n_T C_p^\circ \frac{\partial T}{\partial t} + \sum_{i=1}^{c} H_{fi}^\circ \frac{\partial n_i}{\partial t} \tag{6-50}$$

The partial derivative of n_i with respect to z is related to its partial derivative with respect to t by the component-material balance, Equation (2-104), which is restated in terms of z as follows,

$$-\frac{\partial n_i}{\partial z} - Sr_i = S \frac{\partial(n_i/v_T)}{\partial t} \tag{6-51}$$

where n_i/v_T represents the concentration of component i. Thus, when Equation (6-51) is used to eliminate $\partial n_i/\partial z$ from Equation (6-48), the following result is obtained:

$$\frac{\partial(n_T H)}{\partial z} = n_T C_p^\circ \frac{\partial T}{\partial z} - S \sum_{i=1}^{c} H_{fi}^\circ r_i - \frac{S}{v_T} \sum_{i=1}^{c} H_{fi}^\circ \frac{\partial n_i}{\partial t} + \frac{S}{v_T^2} \sum_{i=1}^{c} H_{fi}^\circ n_i \frac{\partial v_T}{\partial t} \tag{6-52}$$

Evaluation of the partial derivatives appearing in Equation (6-47) by use of Equations (6-50) and (6-52) gives the following form of the energy balance for a plug-flow reactor at unsteady state operation.

$$-n_T C_p^\circ \frac{\partial T}{\partial z} + S \sum_{i=1}^{c} H_{fi}^\circ r_i + q - \mathscr{W} = S \left[\frac{n_T}{v_T} C_p^\circ \frac{\partial T}{\partial t} - \frac{\partial P}{\partial t} \right] \tag{6-53}$$

(Note in the application of this equation, $\mathscr{W}$ and $S\,\partial P/\partial t$ must be expressed in the consistent units of energy per unit time per unit length.) For the case where the single reaction given by Equation (6-19) occurs and where $\mathscr{W} = 0$, and the change of pressure with time is negligible, Equation (6-53) reduces to

$$-n_T C_p^\circ \frac{\partial T}{\partial z} - Sr_A \Delta H_r^\circ + q = \frac{S n_T C_p^\circ}{v_T} \frac{\partial T}{\partial t} \tag{6-54}$$

The use of the enthalpy H_{fi}° [defined by Equation (6-31)] for the evaluation of the expression for $n_T H$ [Equation (6-32)] is applicable for reactors at both steady state and unsteady state operation. However, the paths shown in Figures 6-2 and P6-1 are not necessarily meaningful when the feed rates n_A^0, n_B^0, n_C^0, n_D^0, and n_I^0 vary with time. For any given time t, the flow rates n_A, n_B, n_C, n_D, and n_I at a given z cannot necessarily be formed by the reaction of the feed at the same instant. Actually, the flow rates at a given z and t are the result of the reaction which has occurred since the feed entered the reactor at some earlier time. For further clarification, suppose that n_A, n_B, n_C, n_D, and n_I at a given z and t are known. Let the actual value of n_A^0 at time t be picked to define the conversion x given by Equation (6-20). Although the resulting value of n_A given by the first expression of Equation (6-21) is obviously correct, the remaining expressions do not necessarily give the correct values of n_B, n_C, and n_D when the actual values of n_B^0, n_C^0, and n_D^0 at time t are used in these expressions. These obvious difficulties are avoided by use of the enthalpy H_{fi}° and the molar flow rates for each component in the mixture.

II. DEVELOPMENT OF ENERGY-BALANCE EQUATIONS FOR PERFECTLY MIXED FLOW REACTORS

Typical of the perfectly mixed flow reactors is the one shown in Figure 6-3. Energy-balances equations for steady state and unsteady state operation are developed below.

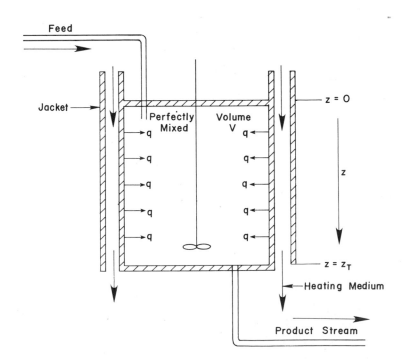

Figure 6-3. Sketch of a perfectly mixed flow reactor.

A. Steady State Operation

Suppose that the reactor shown in Figure 6-3 is operated at steady state and that any number of reactions occur within the reactor. Generally, the changes in the kinetic and potential energies of the entering and leaving streams are negligible as well as the energy equivalent of the work done by the stirrer on the reacting mixture. Under these conditions, the energy balance on the reacting mixture contained in the reactor at steady state operation is given by

$$n_T^\circ H(T_0) - n_T H + \int_0^{z_T} q\, dz = 0 \qquad (6\text{-}55)$$

where $\quad q = Ua(T - T_c)$, T_c is the temperature of the heat-transfer medium at any z

$\quad H(T_0) =$ enthalpy of the reactants, evaluated at the feed composition and at the feed temperature T_0 and pressure P_0 at the inlet to the reacting mixture

For the case where any number of reactions occur and the effect of the heats of mixing and the pressure on the enthalpy of the mixture is negligible, the enthalpy terms appearing in Equation (6-55) may be evaluated by use of Equation (6-32). The result so obtained is given by

$$\sum_{i=1}^c n_i^0 H_{fi}^\circ(T_0) - \sum_{i=1}^c n_i H_{fi}^\circ(T) + \int_0^{z_T} q\, dz = 0 \qquad (6\text{-}56)$$

Use of the component-material balance expression

$$Vr_i = n_i^0 - n_i \qquad (6\text{-}57)$$

(where r_i is defined in terms of disappearance for all components) to eliminate the n_i's from Equation (6-56) gives

$$\sum_{i=1}^c n_i^0 [H_{fi}^\circ(T_0) - H_{fi}^\circ(T)] + V \sum_{i=1}^c H_{fi}^\circ(T) r_i + \int_0^{z_T} q\, dz = 0 \quad (6\text{-}58)$$

For the case where the single reaction given by Equation (6-19) occurs, Equation (6-58) reduces to

$$\sum_{i=1}^c n_i^0 [H_{fi}^\circ(T_0) - H_{fi}^\circ(T)] - V \Delta H_r^\circ r_A + \int_0^{z_T} q\, dz = 0 \qquad (6\text{-}59)$$

269

B. Unsteady State Operation

If it is supposed that the kinetic and potential energies as well as work contributions are negligible, then the energy balance on the reacting mixture in the perfectly mixed reactor over the time period from t_n to t_{n+1} may be represented as follows:

$$\int_{t_n}^{t_{n+1}} \left[n_T^0 H_0 - n_T H + \int_0^{z_T} q \, dz \right] dt = (\rho V U) \Big|_{t_{n+1}} - (\rho V U) \Big|_{t_n} \quad (6\text{-}60)$$

where H_0 is used to denote $H(T_0)$.

This expression may be reduced to the following integral-difference equation by use of the mean value theorems and limiting processes as demonstrated in Chapter 1.

$$n_T^0 H_0 - n_T H + \int_0^{z_T} q \, dz = \frac{d(\rho V U)}{dt} \quad (6\text{-}61)$$

Since $U = H - Pv$, $\rho = n_T / v_T$, Equation (6-61) may be restated in terms of the enthalpy function $n_T H$ as follows:

$$n_T^0 H_0 - n_T H + \int_0^{z_T} q \, dz = \frac{d[(V/v_T)n_T H]}{dt} \quad (6\text{-}62)$$

In order to simplify the presentation, suppose that V, P, and v_T are constant. These assumptions are good approximations for most systems. On the basis of these assumptions, Equation (6-62) reduces to

$$n_T^0 H_0 - n_T H + \int_0^{z_T} q \, dz = \frac{V}{v_T} \frac{d(n_T H)}{dt} \quad (6\text{-}63)$$

where $n_T^0 H_0$ and $n_T H$ have the values given above [see Equations (6-55) and (6-56)]. Evaluation of the derivative $d(n_T H)/dt$ is effected in a manner analogous to that demonstrated by Equation (6-50). The result is

$$\frac{d(n_T H)}{dt} = n_T C_p^\circ \frac{dT}{dt} + \sum_{i=1}^c H_{fi}^\circ(T) \frac{dn_i}{dt} \quad (6\text{-}64)$$

Use of the component-material balance given by Equation (2-117) and the assumptions enumerated above,

$$n_i^0 - n_i - V r_i = \frac{d(V n_i / v_T)}{dt} = \frac{V}{v_T} \frac{dn_i}{dt} \quad (6\text{-}65)$$

After dn_i/dt has been eliminated from Equations (6-64) and (6-65), the following result is obtained:

$$\frac{d(n_T H)}{dt} = \frac{v_T}{V} \sum_{i=1}^{c} H_{fi}^{\circ}(T)[n_i^0 - n_i - V r_i] + n_T C_p^{\circ} \frac{dT}{dt} \qquad (6\text{-}66)$$

After the result given by Equation (6-66) has been used to eliminate $d(n_T H)/dt$ in Equation (6-63), and after $n_T^0 H_0$ and $n_T H$ have been replaced by their equivalents as given by Equation (6-32), the following form of the energy-balance expression is obtained:

$$\sum_{i=1}^{c} n_i^0[H_{fi}^{\circ}(T_0) - H_{fi}^{\circ}(T)] + V \sum_{i=1}^{c} H_{fi}^{\circ} r_i + \int_{0}^{z_T} q \, dz = \left(\frac{V n_T C_p^{\circ}}{v_T}\right) \frac{dT}{dt}$$

$$(6\text{-}67)$$

III. DEVELOPMENT OF ENERGY BALANCE EQUATIONS FOR BATCH REACTORS

A typical batch reactor is shown in Figure 6-4. Generally, the kinetic energy effects as well as the work done by the stirrer on the reacting mixture are negligible relative to the heat effects associated with the reaction. Thus the energy balance on the reacting mixture of volume V over the time period

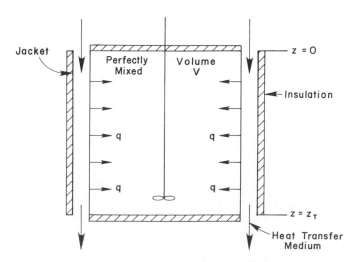

Figure 6-4. A typical batch reactor.

from t_n to t_{n+1} is given by

$$\int_{t_n}^{t_{n+1}} Q \, dt = (\rho V U) \Big|_{t_{n+1}} - (\rho V U) \Big|_{t_n} \qquad (6\text{-}68)$$

where U is the internal energy per mole of reacting mixture, ρ is the molar density of the mixture, and Q is equal to the rate of heat transfer to the reacting mixture. If the rate of heat transfer differs at each point along the boundary, Q in the above equation may be expressed in terms of the point value q (energy per unit time per unit length) as:

$$Q = \int_0^{z_T} q \, dz \qquad (6\text{-}69)$$

Since enthalpies are more frequently tabulated than are internal energies, it is desirable to restate $\rho V U$ in terms of the enthalpy as:

$$\rho V U = \rho V(H - Pv) = \rho V H - PV \qquad (6\text{-}70)$$

where it is, of course, understood that the PV product is to be expressed in the same energy units as the other terms appearing in this equation. Since the molar density $\rho = N_T/V$ (where N_T is the total number of moles in the reacting mixture at any time t), Equation (6-70) may be restated as follows:

$$\rho V U = N_T H - PV \qquad (6\text{-}71)$$

Thus, when $\rho V U$ in Equation (6-68) is replaced by its equivalent as given by Equation (6-71), one obtains

$$\int_{t_n}^{t_{n+1}} Q \, dt = [N_T H - PV] \Big|_{t_{n+1}} - [N_T H - PV] \Big|_{t_n} \qquad (6\text{-}72)$$

This expression for the energy balance may be used to obtain the following differential equation by use of the mean value theorems and limiting processes as demonstrated in Chapter 1.

$$Q = \frac{d(N_T H)}{dt} - \frac{d(PV)}{dt} \qquad (6\text{-}73)$$

The expression for the total enthalpy of the mixture $N_T H$ is obtained by replacing the molar flow rates $\{n_i\}$ in Equation (6-32) with the moles of each component present in the reacting mixture $\{N_i\}$. The resulting expression is

$$N_T H = \sum_{i=1}^{c} N_i H_{fi}^{\circ} \qquad (6\text{-}74)$$

Differentiation of this expression with respect to time gives

$$\frac{d(N_TH)}{dt} = N_TC_p^\circ \frac{dT}{dt} + \sum_{i=1}^{c} H_{fi}^\circ \frac{dN_i}{dt} \tag{6-75}$$

where the molar heat capacity of the mixture is defined by

$$C_p^\circ = \sum_{i=1}^{c} \left(\frac{N_i}{N_T}\right) C_{pi}^\circ \tag{6-76}$$

If the rate of reaction r_i is defined in terms of disappearance for each component i, then the component-material balance for each component may be expressed as follows:

$$r_i = -\frac{1}{V}\frac{dN_i}{dt} \tag{6-77}$$

After dN_i/dt in Equation (6-75) has been eliminated by use of Equation (6-77) and the expression so obtained has been substituted into Equation (6-73), the following result is obtained upon rearrangement:

$$N_TC_p^\circ \frac{dT}{dt} - \frac{d(PV)}{dt} - V\sum_{i=1}^{c} H_{fi}^\circ r_i - Q = 0 \tag{6-78}$$

For the case where the single reaction occurs and the pressure and reactor volume do not vary appreciably with time, Equation (6-78) reduces to

$$N_TC_p^\circ \frac{dT}{dt} + V\,\Delta H_r^\circ r_A - Q = 0 \tag{6-79}$$

The differential equations were developed in terms of the enthalpy functions because thermodynamic data are more commonly stated in terms of enthalpies rather than internal energies. When internal energies rather than enthalpies are used (see Problem 6-10), the following expression is obtained for the energy balance for a batch reactor in which any number of reactions occur.

$$N_TC_v^\circ \frac{dT}{dt} - V\sum_{i=1}^{c} U_{fi}^\circ r_i - Q = 0 \tag{6-80}$$

where U_{fi}° = the internal energy of component i in the standard state of a perfect gas at the temperature T above its elements in their standard states at some arbitrary datum temperature

If only one reaction occurs, say the one given by Equation (6-19), then each r_i may be expressed in terms of r_A and Equation (6-80) reduces to the following form:

$$N_T C_v^\circ \frac{dT}{dt} + V\,\Delta U_r^\circ r_A - Q = 0 \qquad (6\text{-}81)$$

where

$$\Delta U_r^\circ = \frac{c}{a}U_{fC}^\circ + \frac{d}{a}U_{fD}^\circ - U_{fA}^\circ - \frac{b}{a}U_{fB}^\circ$$

Energy-balance equations for other types of reactors may be developed in a manner analogous to that demonstrated above for plug-flow, perfectly mixed flow reactors, and batch reactors. When the heat of reaction depends upon pressure and composition, the above equations must be modified as described in Chapter 11.

PROBLEMS

6-1. An expression for the enthalpy $n_T H$ of the reacting mixture at any z in the reactor may be obtained for the case where a single reaction occurs by use of the alternate path shown in Figure P6-1.

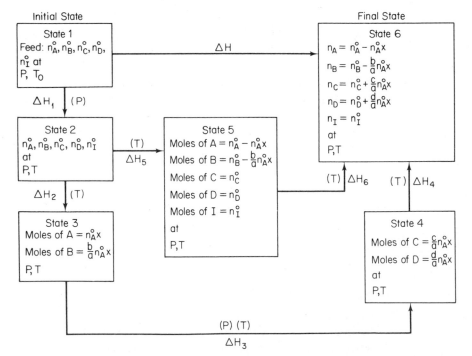

Figure P6-1. Path for the calculation of the enthalpy of the reacting mixture as a function of temperature and conversion.

(a) Let the feed be taken as the reference state; that is, $H_{feed} = 0$. Then use the path shown in Figure P6-1 to show that the enthalpy of the reacting mixture at any z is given by

$$n_T H = n_T^0 \int_{T_0}^{T} (C_p^\circ)_{feed} \, dT + n_A^0 x \, \Delta H_r^\circ \qquad (A)$$

where $(C_p^\circ)_{feed} = \sum_{feed} y_i^0 C_{pi}^\circ, \quad y_i^0 = \dfrac{n_i^0}{n_T^0} \quad$ and $\quad i = A, B, C, D, I$

$\Delta H_r^\circ =$ heat of reaction per mole of A reacted, evaluated at the temperature T [see Equation (5-24)]

$x =$ fraction of A converted; defined by Equation (6-20)

(b) Since the right-hand side of Equation (A) is a function of x and T, let it be denoted by $f(x, T)$. Then $n_T H = f(x, T)$, and

$$\frac{d(n_T H)}{dz} = \left[\frac{\partial f(x, T)}{\partial x} \frac{dx}{dz} + \frac{\partial f(x, T)}{\partial T} \frac{dT}{dz} \right] \qquad (B)$$

Show that

$$\frac{\partial f(x, T)}{\partial x} = n_A^0 \, \Delta H_r^\circ \qquad (C)$$

and that

$$\frac{\partial f(x, T)}{\partial T} = n_T^0 (C_p^\circ)_{feed} + n_A^0 x \frac{\partial(\Delta H_r^\circ)}{\partial T} \qquad (D)$$

By use of the above definition of $(C_p^\circ)_{feed}$ and the expression given by Equation (5-24) for ΔH_r° as a function of T, show that Equation (D) may be reduced to

$$\frac{\partial f(x, T)}{\partial T} = n_T C_p^\circ \qquad (E)$$

(c) Show that when the final expression obtained above for $d(n_T H)/dz$ is substituted into Equation (6-18), the expression given by Equation (6-29) is obtained.

6-2. For an adiabatic reactor, $q = 0$ for all z. Then for a plug-flow reactor the enthalpy balance enclosing the entrance and any position z is given by

$$n_T H \Big|_{z=0} - n_T H \Big|_{z} = 0$$

For the case where a single reaction occurs in the perfect gas phase, show that the conversion x and temperature T at the position z are related as follows:

$$x = -\frac{\int_{T_0}^{T} (C_p^\circ)_{feed} \, dT}{y_A^0 \, \Delta H_r^\circ}$$

where T_0 is the temperature of the feed, y_A^0 is the mole fraction of A in the feed, and the ΔH_r° is the heat of reaction at the temperature T per mole of A reacted.

6-3. Suppose that the following reactions occur in the gas phase in a plug-flow reactor:

$$A \longrightarrow 2C \tag{1}$$

$$2A \longrightarrow D \tag{2}$$

Let n_1 denote the moles of A per unit time that have reacted at a given z by the first reaction, and let n_2 denote the moles of A per unit time that have reacted by the second reaction at a given z. Let r_{A1} denote the rate of disappearance of A by the first reaction and r_{A2} the rate of disappearance of A by the second reaction. Then show that

$$r_{A1} = -\tfrac{1}{2}r_C, \qquad r_{A1} + r_{A2} = r_A$$

$$r_{A2} = -2r_D$$

where r_C and r_D are the rates of disappearance of C and D. Then show that Equation (6-43) may be restated as follows:

$$-n_T C_p^\circ \frac{dT}{dz} - S[r_{A1}\,\Delta H_{r1}^\circ + r_{A2}\,\Delta H_{r2}^\circ] + q = 0$$

where $\quad \Delta H_{r1}^\circ = 2H_{fC}^\circ - H_{fA}^\circ, \qquad \Delta H_{r2}^\circ = \tfrac{1}{2}H_{fD}^\circ - H_{fA}^\circ$

6-4. Supply the missing steps required to obtain Equation (6-65) from Equation (6-63).

6-5. Obtain the partial differential equation given by Equation (6-46) by use of the mean value theorems and the limiting processes as demonstrated in Chapter 1.

6-6. The "heat-source" method for making enthalpy balances is based on the separation of the enthalpy of the mixture into a sensible heat term and a heat of reaction term. In this case, let H represent the sensible heat per unit mass of the reacting mixture at any z in the reactor. Let Q_r° denote the heat evolved at temperature T per mole of A reacted; that is, let

$$Q_r^\circ = -\Delta H_r^\circ \tag{A}$$

(a) Show that the energy balance on the element of volume $S(z_{j+1} - z_j)$ of the tubular reactor shown in Figure 6-1 is given by

$$wH\Big|_{z_j} - wH\Big|_{z_{j+1}} + \int_{z_j}^{z_{j+1}} r_A Q_r^\circ S\, dz + \int_{z_j}^{z_{j+1}} q\, dz = 0 \tag{B}$$

where r_A is defined in terms of the disappearance of A.

(b) Although the sensible heat of the reacting mixture depends upon both conversion and temperature, the separation of the sensible heat effects from the heat of reaction effects makes it necessary to define the derivative of the sensible heat with respect to z as follows:

$$\frac{dH}{dz} = C_p^\circ \frac{dT}{dz} \tag{C}$$

where C_p° is the heat capacity of the mixture on a mass basis. Show that after the mean value theorems have been applied to Equation (B) as demonstrated in Chapter 2 and after the limit has been taken as Δz goes to zero, the following result is obtained:

$$-wC_p^\circ \frac{dT}{dz} + r_A Q_r^\circ S + q = 0 \tag{D}$$

(c) Since

$$w \left[\frac{\text{mass}}{\text{time}}\right] C_p^\circ \left[\frac{\text{energy}}{(\text{mass})(\text{degree of temp})}\right]$$

$$= n_T \left[\frac{\text{moles}}{\text{time}}\right] C_p^\circ \left[\frac{\text{energy}}{(\text{moles})(\text{degree of temp})}\right]$$

and in view of the definition of Q_r° given by Equation (A), show that Equation (D) may be restated in the form given by Equation (6-29). [The definition given by Equation (C) can lead to confusion in the treatment of nonideal solutions, where the enthalpies of the components in the reacting mixture depend upon composition.]

6-7. For the case where the reactions are carried out in the liquid phase in a plug-flow reactor, use Equation (6-33) in the evaluation of $n_T H$ in the energy balance given by Equation (6-18) to show that

$$-n_T c_p^\circ \frac{dT}{dz} + S \sum_{i=1}^{c} h_{fi}^\circ r_i + q = 0$$

where $h_{fi}^\circ = H_{fi}^\circ - \lambda_i$, enthalpy of the liquid at the temperature T

$$c_p^\circ = \sum_{i=1}^{c} \frac{n_i}{n_T} \frac{\partial h_{fi}^\circ}{\partial T} = \sum_{i=1}^{c} \frac{n_i}{n_T}\left(\frac{\partial H_{fi}^\circ}{\partial T} - \frac{\partial \lambda_i}{\partial T}\right)$$

6-8. Repeat Problem 6-7 for the case where the single reaction given by Equation (6-19) occurs in the liquid phase, and show that the corresponding energy balance may be stated in the following form:

$$-n_T c_p^\circ \frac{dT}{dz} - r_A (\Delta H_r^\circ)_{\text{liq}} S + q = 0$$

where $(\Delta H_r^\circ)_{\text{liq}} = \frac{c}{a} h_{fC}^\circ + \frac{d}{a} h_{fD}^\circ - h_{fA}^\circ - \frac{b}{a} h_{fB}^\circ$

6-9. Repeat Problem 6-8 for the case of a perfectly mixed flow reactor at steady state operation and show that the energy balance may be stated as follows:

$$\sum_{i=1}^{c} n_i^0 [h_{fi}^\circ(T_0) - h_{fi}^\circ(T)] + V \sum_{i=1}^{c} h_{fi}^\circ(T) r_i + \int_0^{z_T} q\, dz = 0$$

6-10. (a) Begin with Equation (6-68) and the generalized enthalpy function given by Equation (6-74) and develop the energy-balance expression given by Equation (6-80).

Hints:

(1) Since $PV = N_T Pv$ [where v is the molar volume of the mixture (volume/mole)] and $U = H - Pv$, show that Equation (6-74) may be reduced to

$$N_T U = \sum_{i=1}^{c} N_i U_{fi}^{\circ}$$

where U_{fi}° is the internal energy of formation of the mixture in the perfect gas state at the temperature of the mixture.

(2) Since $\rho = N_T/V$, show that Equation (6-68) may be reduced to the following differential equation:

$$Q = \frac{d(N_T U)}{dt}$$

(b) For the case where the single reaction

$$aA + bB \longrightarrow cC + dD$$

occurs, show that Equation (6-80) reduces to Equation (6-81).

6-11. The single reaction

$$aA + bB \rightleftharpoons cC + dD$$

is carried out in a perfectly mixed flow reactor. For this case, show that Equation (6-58) reduces to Equation (6-59).

NOTATION

(See also Chapter 5)

a = heat transfer area, heat-transfer surface area per unit length.

C_p° = heat capacity (at constant pressure) of a perfect gas or perfect gas mixture; defined by Equation (6-40).

C_v° = heat capacity (at constant volume) of a perfect gas or perfect gas mixture.

h_{fi}° = the enthalpy of component i in the liquid state at temperature T above its elements in their perfect gas states at a given reference temperature; defined by Equation (6-34).

H_T = enthalpy plus the kinetic and potential energy contributions; defined by Equation (6-3).

H°_{fi} = the enthalpy of component i in the gaseous state of a perfect gas at the temperature T and at a pressure of 1 atm above its elements in their standard states at a given reference temperature.

n_i = molar flow rate of component i.

n_T = total molar flow rate.

N_i = moles of component i.

N_T = total moles of mixture.

Q = total rate of heat transfer; energy per unit time.

q = point value of the rate of heat transfer; energy transferred per unit time per unit length.

r_i = rate of disappearance of component i by reaction, moles per unit time per unit volume of the reacting mixture.

n_i = molar flow rate of component i.

n_T = total molar flow rate of component i.

N_T = total moles of mixture.

S = cross-sectional area.

t = time.

U = internal energy; also used to denote the overall heat-transfer coefficient.

U_T = internal energy plus the kinetic and potential energy contributions; defined by Equation (6-2).

v_T = total volumetric flow rate.

v = molar volume of the reacting mixture, volume per mole.

V = volume of the reactor filled by the reacting mixture.

w = mass flow rate.

W = work done by the system on the surroundings.

$\mathscr{W}$ = work done by the system on the surroundings per unit length of boundary.

x = conversion; defined by Equation (6-20).

y_i = mole fraction of component i in the gas phase.

z = length.

$\lambda_i(T)$ = latent heat of vaporization as defined by Equation (6-34). Since the effect of pressure on enthalpy is neglected in the text, $\lambda_i(T)$ can be taken equal to the latent heat of vaporization at the saturation temperature and pressure.

Section II:
Design of Thermal
and Catalytic Reactors

Design of

Thermal Reactors

7

Thermal reactors belong to that class of reactors in which the energy of activation required for the reaction to take place at an appreciable rate is provided by heating the reaction mixture. The transfer of the appropriate amount of heat to and/or from the reacting mixture is one of the major problems to be solved in the design of thermal reactors.

The design of thermal reactors is demonstrated in Part I of this chapter by solving several relatively simple examples. Since the analysis of rate data is simplified by carrying a reaction out isothermally, many experimental reactors are designed for this type operation as demonstrated in Examples 7-1 and 7-2. Most industrial reactors are not operated isothermally and the design of these reactors involves the simultaneous solution of the material- and energy-balance equations. Numerical examples are presented for the purpose of demonstrating the design of batch reactors, tubular reactors, and perfectly mixed flow reactors. In Part II, the general behavior of selected design equations is demonstrated through the use of the concept of the reaction phase plane.

I. REACTOR DESIGN

To begin the design of a reactor, answers must be found to several questions, such as: What types of materials of construction are inert to the reacting system at the temperatures and pressures being considered? What method is to be used to transfer heat to and from the reacting mixture? What pressure drop across the reactor should be permitted? What volume (or time) is required to effect the desired conversion? Will the load bearing properties of the ground or building support the reactor? Many of the questions which must be answered are the same questions which must be answered in the design of any structure. Of these questions, only the ones concerning heat transfer, fluid flow, and chemical reactions are considered in the following analysis.

To effect the necessary heat transfer, several types of reactors have been developed. Cracking reactions such as the cracking of propane and ethane to ethylene are commonly carried out in direct-fired reactors. In these reactors, the reactants are passed through tubes which are surrounded by a direct-fired combustion furnace. In these furnaces, heat is transferred to the heated side of the wall at approximately the same rate at all points.

In another class of reactors, the latent heat of vaporization of the heat-transfer medium is either transferred to or removed from the reacting mixture. An example of this type of reactor is a steam jacketed reactor in which heat is supplied to the reacting mixture by the condensing steam in the jacket.

A third type of reactor is a heat-exchanger reactor in which the reactants pass through the reactor either in the tubes or on the outside of the tubes. The heat-transfer medium passes through the reactor in a direction counter-current or parallel (cocurrent) with respect to the reacting mixture. When the reacting mixture is used to preheat the feed, the reactor is sometimes called an autothermal reactor.

A. Design of Batch Reactors

In order to maintain the reacting mixture at the desired temperature throughout the course of the reaction cycle, it is necessary to provide for an appropriate amount of heat transfer either to or from the reacting mixture. The design of batch reactors in which various mechanical arrangements are used for the transfer of heat from (or to) the reacting mixture is shown by the solution of several illustrative examples. To demonstrate that a given mechanical and geometrical arrangement provides the desired amount of heat transfer, it is necessary to solve the material and energy balances for each time t of the reaction cycle.

To reduce the calculations involved in the design of reactors only one reaction is assumed to occur in the illustrative examples which follow. The material and energy balances [see Equations (1-40) and (6-81), respectively] developed in Chapters 1 and 6 for the reactor are restated here for convenience; namely,

$$Material\ balance:\quad r_A = -\frac{1}{V}\frac{dN_A}{dt} \tag{7-1}$$

$$Energy\ balance\ on\ the\ reactants:\quad Q - r_A V\, \Delta U_r = N_T C_v \frac{dT}{dt} \tag{7-2}$$

where Q is equal to the rate of transfer of heat from the heat-transfer medium to the reacting mixture. As shown in Chapter 11, the energy-balance equations for systems which form nonideal solutions are of the same general form as those developed in Chapter 6 for ideal solutions and may be obtained formally by omitting the superscript $°$ in the equations in Chapter 6.

For the case where the heat-transfer medium is best described as being perfectly mixed in the space provided for it (for example, in the jacket shown in Figure 7-1), then

$$Q = U_h A(T_c - T) \tag{7-3}$$

where A is the total area of the heating surface in contact with the reacting mixture. If the heat-transfer medium is passed through any number of tubes in parallel which are in contact with the reacting mixture (see Figures 7-2 and 7-3), then

$$Q = \int_0^L q \, dz = \int_0^L U_h a(T_c - T) \, dz \tag{7-4}$$

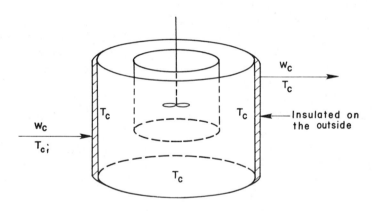

Figure 7-1. The heat-transfer medium is perfectly mixed.

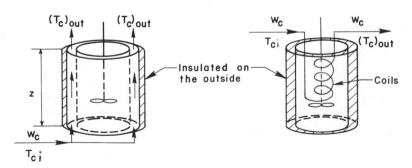

Figure 7-2. Heat-transfer medium passes through the jacket.

Figure 7-3. Heat-transfer medium passes through the coils.

where a is equal to the total surface of heat-transfer area per foot of length; that is, $a = N\pi D$, where N is the number of tubes of diameter D which are connected in parallel. When the reactants are perfectly mixed, the length z is measured in the direction of flow of the heat-transfer medium. The total length of the tubes or coils exposed to the reacting mixture is denoted by L. The assumption that the heat-transfer medium is in plug flow is generally regarded as being valid, provided that the Reynolds number for the fluid is equal to or greater than 10^4.

Since the development of the differential equations describing the heat-transfer medium for various types of mechanical arrangements was not presented in Chapter 6, a brief development of these equations for the cases (1) where the heat-transfer medium is perfectly mixed and (2) where it is in plug flow is shown below.

Consider first the case where the heat-transfer medium is perfectly mixed as indicated in Figure 7-1. The energy balance on the perfectly mixed heat-transfer medium of mass $\mathscr{M}_c$ which is contained in the jacket space over the time period from time t_n to $t_n + \Delta t$ is given by

$$\int_{t_n}^{t_n + \Delta t} \left[w_c(H_{ci} - H_c) - Q \right] dt = \mathscr{M}_c H_c \Big|_{t_n + \Delta t} - \mathscr{M}_c H_c \Big|_{t_n} \qquad (7\text{-}5)$$

where H_{ci} = enthalpy of the heat-transfer medium entering the jacket at any time t, Btu/lb

$\qquad\quad\ H_c$ = enthalpy of the heat-transfer medium in the jacket and also leaving the jacket at any time t, Btu/lb

$\qquad\quad\ w_c$ = mass flow rate of the heat-transfer medium as it enters and leaves the jacket, lb/hr

Equation (7-5) applies for fluids that form either ideal or nonideal solutions. By use of the mean value theorems followed by a limiting process as demonstrated in Chapter 1, the above integral-difference equation may be reduced to the following differential equation:

Energy balance on heat-transfer

medium—perfectly mixed: $\quad w_c(H_{ci} - H_c) - Q = \mathscr{M}_c C_{pc} \dfrac{dT_c}{dt} \qquad (7\text{-}6)$

The appropriate expression for Q is given by Equation (7-3). Although Equation (7-6) actually represents the limit of the energy balance given by Equation (7-5) as the time period over which this balance was made is allowed to go to zero, Equation (7-6) is referred to simply as an "energy balance."

Consider next the case where the heat-transfer medium passes in plug flow through one or more tubes in parallel or one or more coils in parallel as shown in Figure 7-2. The energy balance on the heat-transfer medium

contained in all of the parallel tubes in the element Δz over the time period
from t_n to $t_n + \Delta t$ (see Figure 7-2) is given by

$$\int_{t_n}^{t_n + \Delta t} \left[w_c H_c \bigg|_{z_j,t} - w_c H_c \bigg|_{z_j + \Delta z,t} - \int_{z_j}^{z_j + \Delta z} q\, dz \right] dt$$

$$= \int_{z_j}^{z_j + \Delta z} \left[S_c \rho_c H_c \bigg|_{t_n + \Delta t,z} - S_c \rho_c H_c \bigg|_{t_n,z} \right] dz \qquad (7\text{-}7)$$

where w_c is the total mass flow rate of the heat-transfer medium through the
parallel tubes, S_c is the total cross-sectional area of all parallel tubes, ρ_c is
the mass density of the heat-transfer medium, q is defined by Equation (7-4),
and z is positive in the direction of flow of the heat-transfer medium. Again
by use of the procedure demonstrated in Chapter 1, Equation (7-7) may be
reduced to the following partial differential equation:

> *Energy balance on heat-transfer*
>
> *medium—plug flow:* $\quad -w_c C_{pc} \dfrac{\partial T_c}{\partial z} - q = S_c \rho_c C_{pc} \dfrac{\partial T_c}{\partial t} \qquad (7\text{-}8)$

Equations (7-7) and (7-8) are also based on the assumption that the axial
transfer of heat through the flowing stream is negligible.

In addition to the above equations, the Fanning equation [1] is needed to
calculate the pressure drop

$$-\frac{dP}{dz} = \frac{2fG^2}{D\rho g_c} = \frac{2fu^2 \rho}{Dg_c} \qquad (7\text{-}9)$$

where
$$P = \text{pressure in } \mathrm{lb_f/ft^2}$$
$$D = \text{inside diameter of the tube, ft}$$
$$G = \text{mass flux, } \mathrm{lb_m/ft^2 \ sec}$$
$$g_c = 32.17 \ (\mathrm{lb_m \ ft})/\mathrm{lb_f \ sec^2}$$
$$f = \text{friction factor; dimensionless}$$
$$z = \text{direction of flow, ft}$$
$$\rho = \text{density, } \mathrm{lb_m/ft^3}$$
$$u = \text{average velocity, ft/sec}$$

(In the above definitions, the symbol $\mathrm{lb_m}$ is used to mean pounds mass, and
the symbol $\mathrm{lb_f}$ is used to mean pounds force. In all other equations, only
mass units are involved, and consequently the subscript m is omitted in the
interest of simplicity.)

In summary, the design equations required to describe the batch reactors considered herein are given by Equations (7-1), (7-2), (7-6), (7-8), and (7-9). The design of batch reactors is demonstrated by numerical examples which follow.

1. ISOTHERMAL OPERATION: THE HEAT-TRANSFER MEDIUM IS PERFECTLY MIXED. To illustrate the design of reactors of this type, two design problems are solved. In Example 7-1, styrene is to be polymerized isothermally in a batch reactor. Water is to be used as the coolant. Reactors in which both the reactants and the coolant are perfectly mixed are described by Equations (7-1), (7-2), (7-3), and (7-6). In addition to the assumptions listed in the development of these equations, it is also assumed that the heat capacities and the overall heat-transfer coefficient remain constant throughout the course of the reaction. The assumption of constant heat capacities permits the first term of Equation (7-6) to be restated as follows:

$$w_c(H_{ci} - H_c) = w_c C_{pc}(T_{ci} - T_c) \tag{7-10}$$

Since the reaction is to be carried out isothermally, $dT/dt = 0$, and Equations (7-2) and (7-3) may be combined to give

$$U_h A(T_c - T) = r_A V \, \Delta U_r \tag{7-11}$$

Since r_A is generally a function of time [for example, for a first-order reaction, $r_A = k_c C_A^0 \exp(-k_c t)$], it is evident from Equation (7-11) that T_c must vary with time in order for the reaction temperature to remain constant. By inspection of Equation (7-6), it is evident that the outlet temperature T_c of the coolant also depends upon its inlet temperature T_{ci}, its mass flow rate w_c, and other variables. When Equation (7-11) is used to eliminate T_c from Equation (7-6), the following expression is obtained:

$$w_c C_{pc}(T_{ci} - T) - \left[\frac{w_c C_{pc}}{U_h A} + 1 \right] r_A V \, \Delta U_r = \left[\frac{\mathcal{M}_c C_{pc} V \, \Delta U_r}{U_h A} \right] \frac{dr_A}{dt} \tag{7-12}$$

This expression may be used to compute the flow rates w_c required to maintain the temperature of the reactants constant at a specified variation of the inlet temperature, T_{ci}, with time. Alternately, the inlet temperatures T_{ci} required to maintain T constant at specified values of w_c may be computed by use of Equation (7-12).

EXAMPLE 7-1

Styrene is to be polymerized isothermally in a batch reactor at a reaction temperature of 20°C. An alkyllithium initiator is to be used, and the corresponding rate expression and rate constant k_c, which were determined by Worsfold and Bywater [2], are to be used. Water is to be used as the heat-transfer medium. It may be assumed that the water in the jacket surrounding the reaction vessel is perfectly mixed. On the basis of the data given below, find the inlet temperature of the cooling water T_{ci}, the flow rate w_c, and the outlet temperature required to carry the reaction out isothermally.

Given:

C = total polymer concentration (g moles/liter)

C_A^0 = 2 g moles/liter, initial concentration of styrene in the solvent benzene

V = 400 ml, volume of the reactor occupied by the reacting mixture

C_p = 0.42 cal/g°C, heat capacity of the reacting mixture

C_{pc} = 1 cal/g°C, heat capacity to be used for water

k_c = 0.387 (liter/g mole)$^{1/2}$/min

U_h = 25 Btu/(hr ft^2 °F), based on the area A defined below

A = 0.35 ft^2, the heat-transfer area based on the inside diameter of the reactor

ΔH_r = -16.6 kcal/g mole of styrene polymerized

$r_A = k_c C^{1/2} C_A$, g moles of styrene reacted per liter per minute

C_A = concentration of styrene (g moles/liter) at any time t

$\mathscr{M}_c$ = 100 g, mass of coolant in jacket

Initial concentration of the initiator = 0.01 g mole/liter

Assumptions:
1. Assume that the reaction of the initiator (sec–butyllithium) with the monomer styrene is exceedingly fast, relative to the polymerization of styrene, and that the initiator reaction goes to completion [3]. Thus C = 0.01 g mole/liter for all time t.
2. The change in density of the reacting mixture and of the coolant may be neglected.
3. $\Delta H_r \cong \Delta U_r$ for this liquid phase reaction.

SOLUTION

For a batch reactor in which the density is constant, it was shown in Chapter 2 that Equation (7-1) reduces to $r_A = -dC_A/dt$. Thus

$$-\frac{dC_A}{dt} = k_c C^{1/2} C_A = (0.387)(0.01)^{1/2} C_A = 0.0387 C_A$$

Integration of this expression followed by rearrangement gives

$$C_A = C_A^0 e^{-0.0387t} = 2e^{-0.0387t}$$

Thus

$$r_A = (0.0774)e^{-0.0387t} \tag{A}$$

The numerical value of $U_h A$, which is needed in subsequent calculations, is found as follows:

$$U_h A = \left(\frac{25 \text{ Btu}}{\text{ft}^2 \text{ hr } ^\circ\text{F}}\right)(0.35 \text{ ft}^2)\left(\frac{1.8^\circ\text{F}}{^\circ\text{C}}\right)\left(\frac{252 \text{ cal}}{\text{Btu}}\right)\left(\frac{1 \text{ hr}}{60 \text{ min}}\right) = 66.15 \text{ cal/}^\circ\text{C min} \tag{B}$$

By use of this result and the data given above, the variation of T_c with time may be found by use of Equation (7-11); namely,

$$T_c = T + \frac{r_A V \,\Delta U_r}{U_h A} = 20 + \frac{[0.0774e^{-0.0387t}](0.4)(-16{,}600)}{66.15}$$

Thus

$$T_c = 20 - 7.77e^{-0.0387t} \tag{C}$$

This expression for T_c was used to prepare the following table.

Time (min)	0	5	10	15	20	30	40	50	60
T_c (°C)	12.2	13.6	14.7	15.7	16.4	17.6	18.3	18.9	19.2

In order for the outlet temperature to take on the values listed in this table, it is necessary to pick values of the flow rate w_c and inlet temperature T_{ci} which satisfy Equation (7-12). To evaluate dr_A/dt, which appears in Equation (7-12), the expression given by Equation (A) is differentiated to give

$$\frac{dr_A}{dt} = -(0.0774)(0.0387)e^{-0.0387t} \tag{D}$$

With the aid of this result and other data presented above, it is possible to express the flow rate w_c as a function of time by use of Equation (7-12) as follows:

$$w_c = \frac{V \,\Delta U_r\,[(r_A/C_{pc}) + (\mathscr{M}_c/U_h A)(dr_A/dt)]}{(T_{ci} - T) - \dfrac{r_A V \,\Delta U_r}{U_h A}}$$

Thus

$$w_c = \frac{-484e^{-0.0387t}}{(T_{ci} - 20) + 7.77e^{-0.0387t}} \tag{E}$$

Since the flow rate of the coolant is positive, the inlet temperature T_{ci} must be selected such that

$$0 < (T_{ci} + 7.77e^{-0.0387t}) < 20$$

If the value $T_{ci} = 10°C$ is selected, then the corresponding flow rates w_c required to achieve isothermal operation are as follows:

Time (min)	0	5	10	15	20	30	40	50	60
w_c (g/min)	217	124	70	48	35	20	12	8	5

In the design of an isothermal reactor, careful consideration should be given to the specification of the initial concentration of the reactants. To achieve the variation in flow rates computed in the above example would require the use of a very fast acting controller on the flow rate w_c of the water. By carrying this reaction out at a lower temperature and at a lower initial concentration of the monomer, $(T_c - T)$ is smaller than in the above example and isothermal operation is easier to achieve (see Problem 7-9).

2. ISOTHERMAL OPERATION—USE OF COOLING COILS.   In order to obtain a greater heat-transfer area than is available in a jacketed reactor, cooling coils are often mounted inside batch reactors. The operation and design of such reactors are described by Equations (7-1), (7-2), (7-4), and (7-8). In many instances, the accumulation term on the right-hand side of Equation (7-8) is insignificant relative to the other terms and can be neglected. For such reactors, Equation (7-8) becomes

$$w_c C_{pc} \frac{dT_c}{dz} + q = 0 \qquad (7\text{-}13)$$

which is recognized as the dynamic form of the steady state equation for the transfer of heat from a flowing stream to the wall of the pipe. This differential equation may be solved by first eliminating q by use of the relationship $q = U_h a(T_c - T)$ followed by the separation of variables, and then integrating from $T_c = T_{ci}$ at $z = 0$ to $(T_c)_{out}$ at $z = z_T$.

$$(T_c)_{out} - T = (T_{ci} - T)e^{-\alpha} \qquad (7\text{-}14)$$

where it has been assumed that the ratio $\alpha = U_h A / w_c C_{pc}$ is independent of the position z. Also, Equation (7-13) may be integrated termwise with respect to z as follows:

$$\int_0^L w_c C_{pc} \frac{dT_c}{dz} dz = - \int_0^L q \, dz = -Q$$

to give $\qquad\qquad Q = w_c C_{pc} [T_{ci} - (T_c)_{out}] \qquad (7\text{-}15)$

Equations (7-14) and (7-15) may be combined to give the well-known expression

$$Q = U_h A \, \Delta T_{lm} \tag{7-16}$$

where

$$\Delta T_{lm} = \frac{[(T_c)_{\text{out}} - T] - [T_{ci} - T]}{\log_e \{[(T_c)_{\text{out}} - T]/[T_{ci} - T]\}}$$

An equivalent but perhaps a more convenient expression to use for Q in the problem that follows may be obtained by eliminating $[(T_c)_{\text{out}} - T_{ci}]$ from Equations (7-14) and (7-15) to give

$$Q = w_c C_{pc}[T_{ci} - T][1 - e^{-\alpha}] \tag{7-17}$$

When the reaction is carried out isothermally, $dT/dt = 0$, and Equation (7-2) reduces to

$$Q = r_A V \, \Delta U_r \tag{7-18}$$

Since r_A can be expressed as a function of time, Equation (7-18) serves to give the total rate of heat transfer through the coil at any time t. The use of the above equations in the design of a reactor is illustrated by the following example.

EXAMPLE 7-2

Instead of using an external jacket on the reactor in Example 7-1, suppose that a cooling coil is to be used and that the outside of the reactor is to be insulated. The insertion of the cooling coil in the reaction space (the volume V) reduces the volume available for the reactants by 25 cc. The overall heat-transfer coefficient for the coil is estimated to be 100 Btu/hr ft^2 °F. (This coefficient is based on the outside surface area of the tube.) The tubing has an outside diameter of $\frac{3}{16}$ in. and a wall thickness of 0.032 in. The total length of the coil is 33 in. For a cooling water flow rate of 450 ml/min, calculate the inlet and outlet temperatures of the cooling water required to maintain the reaction temperature at 20°C throughout the course of the reaction. Assume that the heat loss from the outer shell of the reactor to the surroundings is negligible.

SOLUTION

When the expression given by Equation (A) of Example 7-1 is substituted into Equation (7-18), one obtains

$$Q = [(0.0774)e^{-0.0387t}]V \, \Delta U_r$$

$$Q = [0.0774e^{-0.0387t}](0.375)(-16,600)$$

$$Q = -482e^{-0.0387t} \text{ (cal/min)} \tag{A}$$

When this expression for Q is substituted into Equation (7-17), an expression for computing the inlet temperature of the colling water at any time t is obtained; namely,

$$T_{ci} = T - \frac{482e^{-0.0387t}}{w_c C_{pc}(1 - e^{-\alpha})} \tag{B}$$

where $\alpha = \dfrac{U_h A}{w_c C_{pc}} = \dfrac{\left(100 \dfrac{Btu}{hr\ ft^2\ °F}\right)\left(\dfrac{1\ hr}{60\ min}\right)(0.1349\ ft^2)\left(1.8 \dfrac{°F}{°C}\right)\left(252 \dfrac{cal}{Btu}\right)}{(450\ g/min)(1\ cal/g\ °C)}$

$$\alpha = 0.227$$

and

$$1 - e^{-\alpha} = 0.203$$

Thus Equation (B) reduces to

$$T_{ci} = 20 - \frac{482e^{-0.0387t}}{(450)(0.203)} = 20 - 5.28e^{-0.0387t} \tag{C}$$

To find the outlet temperature of the coolant, Equation (7-15) is first solved for $(T_c)_{out}$ to give

$$(T_c)_{out} = T_{ci} - \frac{Q}{w_c C_{pc}}$$

Elimination of Q by use of Equation (A) and substituting for $w_c C_{pc}$ gives

$$(T_c)_{out} = T_{ci} + \frac{482e^{-0.0387t}}{450} = T_{ci} + 1.071e^{-0.0387t} \tag{D}$$

Values of the inlet and outlet temperatures computed by use of Equations (C) and (D) are presented in the following table.

t (min)	0	5	10	15	20	30	40	50	60
T_{ci} (°C)	14.72	15.65	16.41	17.05	17.57	18.35	18.88	19.24	19.48
$(T_c)_{out}$ (°C)	15.79	16.53	17.14	17.65	18.08	18.69	19.11	19.39	19.59

B. Design of Tubular Reactors

The manner in which heat is transferred to (or from) the reacting mixture serves to distinguish the various types of tubular reactors from one another. The heat-transfer medium may be passed through the reactor cocurrently or countercurrently with respect to the reacting stream. Alternately, the heating may be effected by use of a condensing vapor such as steam. In other reactors, such as those used in thermal cracking, the tubes that contain the reactants are heated by passing them through a direct-fired furnace.

A summary of the equations needed in the design of the tubular reactors considered herein follows. These equations are applicable when the reactants and the heat-transfer medium make a single pass through the reactor, the fluids are in plug flow, and when the reactor is at the condition of steady state operation.

$$Material\ balance:\quad r_A = -\frac{dn_A}{dV} = n_A^0 \frac{dx}{dV} = \frac{n_A^0}{S}\frac{dx}{dz} \tag{7-19}$$

$$Energy\ balance\ on\ reactants—plug\ flow:\quad wC_p\frac{dT}{dz} + r_A S\,\Delta H_r - q = 0$$

$$\tag{7-20}$$

Energy balances on heat-transfer medium:

$$1.\ Cocurrent—plug\ flow:\quad w_c C_{pc}\frac{dT_c}{dz} + q = 0 \tag{7-21}$$

$$2.\ Countercurrent—plug\ flow:\quad -w_c C_{pc}\frac{dT_c}{dz} + q = 0 \tag{7-22}$$

In the above equations, the positive direction of z is taken to be the direction of flow of the reactants. For cocurrent, countercurrent, and steam-heated reactors, the heat-transfer rate q (Btu per hour per foot of length) is given by

$$q = U_h a(T_c - T) \tag{7-23}$$

For direct-fired reactors, only the first two of the above equations are needed, and q is usually given as an estimated numerical value in Btu per hour per square foot of heat transfer area. Also, it should be pointed out that the length variable z may be replaced by the corresponding volume V at any z, since $V = Sz$. In addition to the above equations, the Fanning equation [Equation (7-9)] may be needed to compute the pressure drop across a given length of pipe.

If an appropriate correspondence exists between the operating variables in a batch reactor and in a tubular reactor, then the material-balance equations for tubular reactors may be obtained from those for a batch reactor. For example, if both reactors are operated isothermally, the fluid density is constant, the batch reactor is perfectly mixed, and plug flow prevails throughout the length of the tubular reactor, then the variable t in the equations for the batch reactor may be replaced by the variable θ (the true residence time, $\theta = V/v_T$) to give the material-balance equations for the tubular reactor. The residence time $\theta = V/v_T$ required to achieve a specified conversion may be found by use of the material-balance equations. Even though the residence time gives no explicit information about the tube diameter, the computed value of the residence time does depend upon the assumption of plug flow. To achieve plug flow, an appropriate number of tubes having a given diameter must be selected. The selection of the number of tubes of a given diameter must also be made in a manner such that the heat-transfer requirements and the pressure drop limitations are all satisfied simultaneously. The inter-relationships of the variables involved in the design of a reactor are demon-strated by the following example.

EXAMPLE 7-3

It is desired to carry out the first-order unidirectional reaction $A \rightarrow R$ in the liquid phase in a tubular reactor at a temperature of 120°F. The reaction is exothermic, and a heat-exchanger reactor is to be used. The reacting medium is to be passed through the tubes and the cooling medium through the shell side of the exchanger. Water is to be used as the heat-transfer medium, and the transfer of heat from the outer shell to the surroundings may be neglected. The following data are available:

$C_p = 8$ Btu/lb mole °F, for the reacting mixture

$C_{pc} = 1.0$ Btu/lb °F for the cooling water

$C_A^0 = 0.0245$ lb mole/ft^3, initial concentration of the feed

$k = 0.128$ sec^{-1}, rate constant

$v_T = 360$ ft^3/hr, flow rate of the feed to the reactor

$U_h = 150$ Btu/ft^2 hr °F

$\Delta H_r = -30,600$ Btu/lb mole of A reacted

$\mu = 0.44$ centipoise or 1.06 lb/ft hr, viscosity of the reacting mixture

$\rho = 56.16$ lb/ft^3

(a) Calculate the reactor volume required to obtain a 90% conversion of A per pass.
(b) If 1-in. (20 BWG) reactor tubes are used, find the number and length of the tubes required to satisfy the following conditions:

    1. The reactor volume found in (a).
    2. The pressure drop across the reactor is not to exceed 20 lb/in.^{2}
    3. To approximate plug flow, the Reynolds number in each tube is not to be less than 10^4.

(c) Should parallel or countercurrent flow be used? Why? Find the inlet temperature and the flow rate of the cooling water required for isothermal operation.
(d) Construct a graph of the temperature of the cooling water versus the residence time.

SOLUTION

(a) Since the reaction is first order and isothermal, Equations (2-13), (2-16), and (2-19) may be used to compute first θ and then the reactor volume.

$$\theta = -\frac{1}{k} \log_e (1 - x)$$

$$\theta = -\frac{1}{0.128} \log_e (1 - 0.9) = 18 \text{ sec}$$

$$V = \theta v_T = (18)(0.1 \text{ ft}^3/\text{sec}) = 1.8 \text{ cubic ft}$$

(b) From page 11-11 of Reference [1], the following data were obtained for 20 BWG tubes:

$$D \text{ (inside diameter)} = 0.93 \text{ in.} = 0.0775 \text{ ft}$$

$$S \text{ (internal cross-sectional area)} = 4.717 \times 10^{-3} \text{ ft}^2$$

$$a \text{ (internal heat-transfer area per foot of tube)} = 0.2435 \text{ ft}^2/\text{ft}$$

The conditions stated may be satisfied by use of three reactor tubes with a length of 127.2 ft. For

$$V = NSL = (3)(4.717 \times 10^{-3})(127.2) = 1.8 \text{ ft}^3$$

The velocity u per tube is given by

$$u = \frac{L}{\theta} = \frac{127.2}{18} = 7.07 \text{ ft/sec}$$

Then

$$N_{Re} = \frac{Du\rho}{\mu} = \frac{(0.0775)(7.07)(56.16)}{(1.06)(1/3600)} = 1.045 \times 10^5$$

From Figure 5-25 of Reference [1], the Fanning friction factor $f = 0.0044$. Then by use of the integrated form of Equation (7-9),

$$(P)_{\text{inlet}} - (P)_{\text{outlet}} = \frac{(2)(0.0044)(127.2)(7.07)^2(56.16)}{(0.0775)(32.2)(144)} = 8.74 \text{ psi}$$

Thus the reactor should be constructed as shown in Figure 7-4 with three 180° bends. The pressure drop should not exceed the allowable drop of 20 psi, since the pressure

295

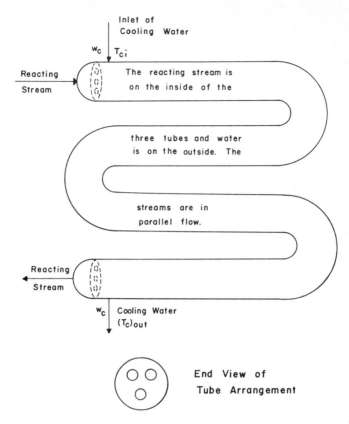

Figure 7-4. Proposed configuration of the reactor designed in Example 7-3.

drop resulting from entrance effects and return bends should be less than 7 psi. Consequently, the total pressure drop should not exceed 16 psi, which is less than the permissible drop of 20 psi.

(c) Since the rate of reaction has its maximum value at the inlet of the reactor, the maximum rate of heat transfer must occur at the inlet of the reactor. This condition can be achieved when the coolant flows parallel with respect to the reactants. Isothermal operation is also possible by use of parallel flow for the case of a first-order reaction which takes place in the gas phase at constant density; whereas, isothermal operation is impossible (unless $\Delta H_r = 0$) when countercurrent flow is used (see Problem 7-6).

The equations needed to demonstrate that isothermal operation is possible when parallel flow is used and to compute the required inlet temperature and flow rate of the coolant are one and the same. The equations needed may be developed in the following manner. Since $dT/dz = 0$, Equation (7-20) reduces to

$$q = r_A S \Delta H_r \tag{A}$$

When q is replaced by its equivalent as given by Equation (7-23), the following expression is obtained upon rearrangement:

$$(T_c - T) = \frac{r_A S \, \Delta H_r}{U_h a} \tag{B}$$

Since

$$r_A = kC_A = kC_A^0 e^{-k\theta}$$

it is possible to state Equation (B) in terms of θ as follows:

$$(T_c - T) = \frac{kSC_A^0 \, \Delta H_r e^{-k\theta}}{U_h a} \tag{C}$$

Since

$$T_{ci} - T = \frac{kSC_A^0 \, \Delta H_r}{U_h a} \tag{D}$$

at $\theta = 0$, Equation (C) may be restated as follows:

$$T_c - T = (T_{ci} - T)e^{-k\theta} \tag{E}$$

When Equation (7-21) is integrated on the basis of the assumption that the temperature T of the reaction does not vary with position, the result so obtained may be rearranged and stated in the form

$$T_c - T = (T_{ci} - T)\exp\left[-\left(\frac{U_h a}{w_c C_{pc}}\right)z\right]$$

Since $\theta = V/v_T = Sz/v_T$, it follows that

$$T_c - T = (T_{ci} - T)\exp\left[-\left(\frac{U_h a}{w_c C_{pc}}\right)\left(\frac{v_T}{S}\right)\theta\right] \tag{F}$$

Comparison of Equations (E) and (F) shows that isothermal operation is possible provided that the following relationship exists between the rate constant k and the other variables; namely,

$$k = \left(\frac{U_h a}{C_{pc} S}\right)\left(\frac{v_T}{w_c}\right) = \left(\frac{4U_h}{C_{pc} D}\right)\left(\frac{v_T}{w_c}\right) \tag{G}$$

The inlet temperature of the cooling water may be computed by use of Equation (D).

$$T_{ci} = T + \frac{k \, DC_A^0 \, \Delta H_r}{4U_h}$$

$$T_{ci} = 120 + \frac{(0.128)(3,600)(0.0775)(0.0245)(-30,600)}{(4)(150)} = 75.38°F$$

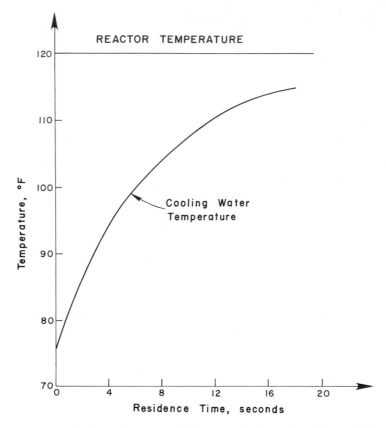

Figure 7-5. Isothermal operation of the reactor in Example 7-3 by parallel flow of the reacting stream and the coolant.

The flow rate w_c of the cooling water may be computed by solving Equation (G) for w_c to give

$$w_c = \left(\frac{4U_h}{C_{pc}D}\right)\left(\frac{v_T}{k}\right) = \frac{(4)(150)(0.1)}{(1)(0.0775)(0.128)} = 6048 \text{ lb/hr}$$

Since all of the variables (k, T, and T_{ci}) in Equation (E) are now known, it may be used to compute the temperature T_c at any θ. A graph of these results is shown in Figure 7-5.

1. USE OF CONDENSING VAPORS AS THE HEAT-TRANSFER MEDIUM. The use of condensing steam to supply the necessary heat to carry out an endothermic reaction is illustrated by the numerical example solved by Billingsley et al. [4] and by Logan [5]. Typical steam-heated reactors are depicted in Figure 7-6.

Figure 7-6. Sketches of reactors heated by use of condensing vapors. [Taken from D. S. Billingsley, W. S. McLaughin, Jr., N. E. Welch and C. D. Holland *Ind. Eng. Chem.*, 50:741 (1958). Used with permission of the American Chemical Society.]

EXAMPLE 7-4

The reaction $A \rightarrow$ products is to be carried out in a steam-heated heat-exchanger reactor. The charge rate is 10,000 lb per hr per tube. The feed, pure A, enters the reactor at a temperature of 70°F. It is desired to determine the volume of reactor required for 90% conversion of A. The internal diameter of the reactor tubes may be taken as 1 in. Steam at 240°F is available for heating purposes. The rate of the reaction may be taken to be first order with respect to A, and the rate constant may be taken as: $k(1/\text{hr}) = 203 \times 10^{15}e^{-46,846/RT}$, where T is in °R. The physical properties of the system, which may be assumed to remain constant throughout the reactor, are as follows:

$\rho = 80 \text{ lb/cu ft}$

$M_w = 200 \text{ lb/lb mole, molecular weight of the reacting stream}$

$U_h = 400 \text{ Btu/(hr sq ft °F) based on the inside diameter of the reactor tube}$

$C_p = 0.75 \text{ Btu/(lb °F)}$

$\Delta H_r = 40,000 \text{ Btu/lb mole}$

$E = 46,846 \text{ Btu/lb mole}$

$A = 203 \times 10^{15} (1/\text{hr})$

SOLUTION

Since the reaction is first order, the rate expression may be stated in the form:

$$r_A = kC_A = k\frac{n_A}{v_T} = \frac{kn_A^0}{v_T}(1 - x) \tag{A}$$

Also, since the variation of k with T is given by the Arrhenius expression ($k = Ae^{-E/RT}$), it is possible to express k at any T in terms of k_1 (the value of k at $T = T_1$) as follows:

$$k = k_1 e^{b(1 - 1/\phi)} \tag{B}$$

where

$$b = \frac{E}{RT_1}$$

$$\phi = \frac{T}{T_1}$$

Elimination of r_A and k from Equations (A), (B), and (7-19) followed by arrangement yields

$$\frac{dx}{dV} = \frac{k_1 e^{b(1 - 1/\phi)}(1 - x)}{v_T}$$

or

$$\frac{dx}{dZ} = e^{b(1 - 1/\phi)}(1 - x) \tag{C}$$

where

$$Z = \frac{k_1 V}{v_T}, \text{ dimensionless}$$

Since $a/S = N\pi D/(N\pi D^2/4)$, it is evident that Equations (7-20) and (7-23) may be combined and restated as follows:

$$-wC_p\frac{dT}{dV} + \frac{4U_h}{D}(T_c - T) - r_A\,\Delta H_r = 0 \tag{D}$$

where it is, of course, understood that a, S, and U are all based on the same tube diameter. When r_A in Equation (D) is replaced by its equivalent as given by Equations (A) and (C), and the resulting expression is restated in terms of the dimensionless variables ϕ, Z, and Φ (where $\Phi = T_c/T_1$), the following result is obtained upon rearrangement:

$$\phi + \frac{m}{s}\frac{d\phi}{dZ} + \frac{c}{s}\frac{dx}{dZ} = \Phi \tag{E}$$

300

TABLE 7-1
SYMBOLS IN EQUATIONS (C) AND (E) OF EXAMPLE 7-4
FOR VARIOUS TYPES OF REACTORS

Type and Arrangement	s	m/s	c/s	Z
Flow				
Reactants inside tubes	$\dfrac{v_T}{k_1}$	$\dfrac{\rho C_p S k_1}{U_h a}$	$\dfrac{n_A^0\,\Delta H_r S k_1}{v_T U_h a T_1}$	$\dfrac{k_1 V}{v_T}$
Reactants outside tubes	$\dfrac{v_T}{k_1}$	$\dfrac{\rho C_p S_o k_1}{U_h a}$	$\dfrac{n_A^0\,\Delta H^r S_o k_1}{v_T U_h a T_1}$	$\dfrac{k_1 V}{v_T}$
Batch				
Reactants inside tubes	$\dfrac{1}{k_1}$	$\dfrac{\rho C_v S k_1}{U_h a}$	$\dfrac{N_A^0\,\Delta U_r S k_1}{V U_h a T_1}$	$k_1 t$
Reactants outside tubes	$\dfrac{1}{k_1}$	$\dfrac{\rho C_v S_o k_1}{U_h a}$	$\dfrac{N_A^0\,\Delta U_r S_o k_1}{V_o U_h a T_1}$	$k_1 t$

where S_o, V_o = cross-sectional area and volume, respectively, between the outside of the tubes and the shell of the heat-exchanger reactor

The symbols m/s and c/s are defined in Table 7-1 for various types of reactors. The selection of the temperature T_1 is arbitrary. In the problem under consideration, T_1 was taken equal to the steam temperature, $700°R$, which for this problem is also the maximum possible temperature.

Several numerical methods are available for solving nonlinear differential equations [6]. It was elected to solve Equations (C) and (E) simultaneously by use of a combination of the trapezoidal method [6] and the Newton-Raphson method [6]. The trapezoidal method is a special case of the more general implicit method [6] in which the weight factor μ is taken equal to $\frac{1}{2}$; that is,

$$\int_{Z_j}^{Z_j+\Delta Z_j} f(x)\,dZ = \left[\mu f(x_{j+1}) + (1-\mu)f(x_j)\right]\Delta Z_j \qquad (7\text{-}24)$$

where x_j is the value of x at $Z = Z_j$ and x_{j+1} is the value of x at Z_{j+1}. For $\mu = \frac{1}{2}$, the implicit method reduces to the trapezoidal rule; namely,

$$\int_{Z_j}^{Z_j+\Delta Z_j} f(x)\,dZ = \frac{\Delta Z_j}{2}\left[f(x_{j+1}) + f(x_j)\right] \qquad (7\text{-}25)$$

The first step of the suggested numerical procedure for solving the problem at hand consists of integrating Equations (C) and (E) with respect to Z from Z_j to $Z_j + \Delta Z_j$

(where $\Delta Z_j = Z_{j+1} - Z_j$ is fixed at some preselected value) as follows:

$$0 = \frac{\Delta Z_j}{2}\left[e^{b(1-1/\phi)}(1-x) + e^{b(1-1/\phi_j)}(1-x_j)\right] - (x - x_j) \qquad \text{(F)}$$

$$0 = \frac{m}{s}(\phi - \phi_j) + \frac{c}{s}(x - x_j) + \frac{\Delta Z_j}{2}(\phi + \phi_j) - \Phi\,\Delta Z_j \qquad \text{(G)}$$

In the interest of simplicity, the subscript $j + 1$ has been omitted on the unknown values of x and ϕ at Z_{j+1}.

On the basis of known values of ϕ_j and x_j at Z_j, it is desired to find the positive values of ϕ and x which satisfy Equations (F) and (G). To find this solution set of values of ϕ and x by the Newton-Raphson method, the first step is to replace the zeros on the left-hand sides of Equations (F) and (G) by $F_1(\phi, x)$ and $F_2(\phi, x)$. Then the problem is to find the positive values of ϕ and x which make

$$F_1(\phi, x) = 0$$

$$F_2(\phi, x) = 0$$

simultaneously. The Newton-Raphson method consists of the repeated use of the linear terms of the Taylor series expansion of the functions F_1 and F_2 about an assumed set of values ϕ_n and x_n.

$$0 = F_1(\phi_n, x_n) + \frac{\partial F_1(\phi_n, x_n)}{\partial \phi}\Delta\phi + \frac{\partial F_1(\phi_n, x_n)}{\partial x}\Delta x \qquad \text{(H)}$$

$$0 = F_2(\phi_n, x_n) + \frac{\partial F_2(\phi_n, x_n)}{\partial \phi}\Delta\phi + \frac{\partial F_2(\phi_n, x_n)}{\partial x}\Delta x \qquad \text{(I)}$$

where
$$\Delta\phi = \phi_{n+1} - \phi_n$$

$$\Delta x = x_{n+1} - x_n$$

After these equations have been solved simultaneously for $\Delta\phi$ and Δx, the next set of values to be assumed are found by use of the definition of $\Delta\phi$ and Δx.

To demonstrate the use of this method, the calculations are shown for the first increment at the entrance of the reactor. The parameters are evaluated as follows:

$$b = \frac{E}{RT_1} = \frac{46,846}{(1.9872)(700)} = 33.677$$

$$k_1 = Ae^{-E/RT_1} = Ae^{-b} = 203 \times 10^{15}e^{-33.677} = 480.6 \text{ hr}^{-1}$$

$$Z = \frac{k_1 V}{v_T} = \frac{(480.6V)(80 \text{ lb/ft}^3)}{(10,000 \text{ lb/hr})} = 3.84V$$

where V is in cubic feet.

$$\frac{m}{s} = \frac{\rho C_p S k_1}{U_h a} = \frac{\rho C_p D k_1}{4U_h} = \frac{(80)(0.75)(\frac{1}{12})(480.6)}{(4)(400)} = 1.502$$

$$\frac{c}{s} = \frac{n_A^0 \, \Delta H_r S k_1}{v_T U_h a T_1} = \frac{n_A^0 \, \Delta H_r D k_1}{4 v_T U_h T_1} = \frac{(10{,}000/200)(40{,}000)(\frac{1}{12})(480.6)}{4(10{,}000/80)(400)(700)} = 0.572$$

$$\Phi = \frac{T_c}{T_1} = \frac{700}{700} = 1.0$$

For the first increment, let $\Delta Z_j = 1$. At $Z = 0$, $T = T_0 = 530°R$, and $x = x_0 = 0$. Thus

$$\phi_0 = \frac{530}{700} = 0.757$$

$$x_0 = 0$$

For the first trial, assume $T = 615°R$ at Z_1. Then

$$\phi_1 = \frac{615}{700} = 0.8786$$

Assume

$$x_1 = 0.005$$

For the first increment,

$$F_1(\phi, x) = \frac{\Delta Z_1}{2} \left[e^{b(1 - 1/\phi)}(1 - x) + e^{b(1 - 1/\phi_0)}(1 - x_0) \right] - (x - x_0)$$

Then

$$F_1(\phi_1, x_1) = 0.5 \left[e^{33.677(1 - 1/0.8786)}(1 - 0.005) + e^{33.677(1 - 1/0.757)}(1) \right] - 0.005$$

$$= -2.5 \times 10^{-4}$$

Similarly, for the first increment,

$$F_2(\phi, x) = \frac{m}{s}(\phi - \phi_0) + \frac{c}{s}(x - x_0) + \frac{\Delta Z_1}{2}(\phi + \phi_0) - \Phi \Delta Z_1$$

$$F_2(\phi, x) = 1.502(0.8786 - 0.757) + (0.572)(0.005) + 0.5(0.8786 + 0.757) - (1)(1)$$

$$= 0.0033$$

The partial derivatives appearing in the Newton-Raphson equations are evaluated as follows:

$$\frac{\partial F_1}{\partial \phi} = \frac{\Delta Z_1}{2} \left[\frac{b}{\phi^2} e^{b(1 - 1/\phi)}(1 - x) \right]$$

$$= 0.5 \left[\frac{33.677}{(0.8786)^2} e^{33.677(1 - 1/0.8786)}(1 - 0.005) \right] = 0.2068$$

$$\frac{\partial F_1}{\partial x} = -\frac{\Delta Z_1}{2} \left[e^{b(1 - 1/\phi)} \right] - 1$$

$$= -0.5 \left[e^{33.677(1 - 1/0.8786)} \right] - 1 = -1.005$$

Next

$$\frac{\partial F_2}{\partial \phi} = \frac{m}{s} + \frac{\Delta Z_1}{2} = 1.502 + 0.5 = 2.002$$

$$\frac{\partial F_2}{\partial x} = \frac{c}{s} = 0.572$$

When the values of the functions F_1, F_2 and their partial derivatives at the point ϕ_1, x_1 are substituted in the Newton-Raphson equations [Equations (H) and (I)], the following set of linear equations in the two unknowns $\Delta \phi$ and Δx is obtained:

$$0 = -2.5 \times 10^{-4} + 0.2068 \, \Delta \phi - 1.005 \, \Delta x$$

$$0 = 33.0 \times 10^{-4} + 2.002 \, \Delta \phi + 0.572 \, \Delta x$$

These two equations may be solved simultaneously for $\Delta \phi$ and Δx to give

$$\Delta \phi = -0.001489$$

$$\Delta x = -0.0005552$$

Thus the values of ϕ and x to be assumed for the next trial for the first increment ΔZ are given by the expressions for any trial n; namely,

$$\phi_{n+1} = \phi_n + \Delta \phi = 0.8786 - 0.001489 = 0.8771$$

$$x_{n+1} = x_n + \Delta x = 0.005 - 0.0005552 = 0.00445$$

This procedure is repeated for the first increment ΔZ_1 until the difference between the assumed and calculated values of ϕ and x are less than some small preassigned number. When the solution set satisfying this criterion has been found, the Newton-Raphson equations are applied to the second increment, the quantities ϕ_j and x_j in Equations (H) and (I) are replaced by solution set (ϕ_1, x_1) at Z_1.

The solution sets (ϕ, x) or (T, x) versus the reactor volume obtained by the procedure described above are displayed in Figure 7-7. It is to be observed that very little of A is converted in the first 0.43 ft^3 of the reactor. In this section of the reactor, the reactants are being heated to a temperature at which the rate constant k becomes significant. As in any numerical method, the choice of the increment size ΔZ_j has some affect on the numerical results [6] as demonstrated in Table 7-2.

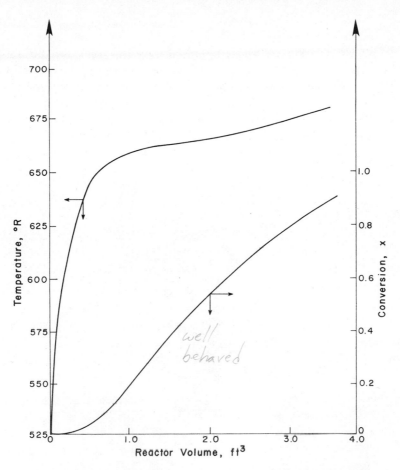

Figure 7-7. Temperature and conversion profiles in the steam-heated flow reactor designed in Example 7-4.

TABLE 7-2
EFFECT OF INCREMENT SIZE ΔZ ON THE SOLUTION OF EXAMPLE 7-4 [5]

Volume (ft³)	Conversion			Temperature (°R)		
	$\Delta Z = 0.1$	0.01	0.001	$\Delta Z = 0.1$	0.01	0.001
0.264	0.005	0.002	0.002	614.9	613.1	613.0
0.792	0.132	0.123	0.123	657.9	656.7	656.7
1.320	0.326	0.316	0.315	660.9	660.7	660.7
1.848	0.503	0.493	0.492	664.4	664.2	664.2
2.376	0.657	0.649	0.648	668.6	668.3	668.2
2.903	0.786	0.779	0.778	673.4	673.1	673.0
3.431	0.885	0.880	0.879	679.1	678.8	678.7
3.56	0.903	0.900	0.900	680.7	680.3	680.2

305

2. Design of a Direct-Fired Tubular Reactor for Carrying Out a Gas Phase Reaction. One of the best known examples of the use of direct-fired tubular reactors is the production of ethylene and propylene by the pyrolysis of hydrocarbon feedstocks. To achieve improved yield of olefins, contact times in these reactors have been reduced while the outlet temperatures have been increased. A recent development in the design of these reactors is the *Kellogg-Idemitsu Millisecond Furnace* shown in Figure 7-8.

Figure 7-8. The Kellogg-Idemitsu millisecond furnace for the manufacture of olefins by the pyrolysis of hydrocarbon feedstocks (Courtesy of Pullman-Kellogg).

By use of reaction temperatures of 1600–1700°F and contact times less than 0.1 sec, 33% (by weight) of ethylene may be produced from naphtha in this furnace [7]. (The contact time may be approximated by dividing the holdup volume of the reactor by the log mean of the volumetric flow rate, evaluated at the inlet and outlet conditions of the reactor.) While it has been established that pyrolysis proceeds by interacting free radical mechanisms [8, 9], the pyrolysis reactions may be approximated with good accuracy by a first-order system [7].

To illustrate the design of direct-fired tubular reactors, the problem solved by Murdoch et al. [10, 11] will be used. Although Murdoch et al. presented a design method based on an approximate analytical solution to the equations describing the reactor, a numerical method will be used below.

As the term is used here, a direct-fired tubular reactor consists essentially of straight tubes connected in series by return bends. Most but not all of the straight portion is heated on its outside by flue gas. The rate of heat transfer to the tubes is assumed to be constant, at different levels, in the radiant and convection sections. The number of straight lengths of tubes is equal to the number of return bends. The unit upon which the calculations will be based is therefore a hook shaped section consisting of one tube and one 180-degree return bend. The actual reactor consists of n of these hook shaped sections in series. Thus the reactor is equal in length to a long straight pipe of length $n(L_s + L_b)$, where L_s is equal to the length of straight pipe and L_b is equal to the length of the bend. Since the bends result in a greater pressure drop than an equal length of straight pipe, the friction factor must be modified accordingly. This may be done by defining a modified friction factor f for the Fanning equation [Equation (7-9)] as follows:

$$ f = \frac{Bf_0}{N_{Re}^{0.2}} \tag{7-26} $$

where $\qquad B = \dfrac{L_{ep}}{L_s + L_b}$

f_0 = coefficient for a straight pipe for which $B = 1$

L_{ep} = equivalent length of pipe for pressure drop

$N_{Re} = DG/\mu$, Reynolds number

For the case of direct-fired tubes, the heat flux in Btu per hour per square foot of heating surface is generally known rather than the heat transfer rate per foot of tube. To distinguish between these two rates of heat transfer, a script q will be used to represent the heat flux.*

Suppose that the heat-input rate q_a (Btu/hr ft² of inside area) is constant over the heated length L_h. The actual input rate q over the entire length of pipe may be computed as follows:

$$q = q_a \left(\frac{L_h}{L_s + L_b} \right) \tag{7-27}$$

It is customary to take

$$L_b = 4D \tag{7-28}$$

and

$$L_{ep} = L_s + 60D \tag{7-29}$$

where D denotes the inside diameter of the pipe, and where consistent units are employed. Therefore,

$$B = \frac{L_s + 60D}{L_s + 4D}$$

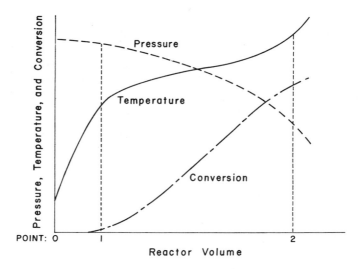

Figure 7-9. Pressure, temperature, and conversion profiles in a fired reactor with a constant heat input rate. [Taken from P. G. Murdoch and C. D. Holland, *Petroleum Refiner*, 33:159 (1954). Used with permission of the Gulf Publishing Company.]

---

* This script q (Btu/hr ft² of surface area) differs from the q (Btu/hr ft of length) used in other sections of this book. The two rates are related as follows:

$$\int_{z_j}^{z_j+\Delta z} q \, dz = \int_{z_j}^{z_j+\Delta z} q_a \, dz = \int_{z_j}^{z_j+\Delta z} q \left(\frac{4S}{D} \right) dz = \int_{V_j}^{V_j+\Delta V} \frac{4q}{D} \, dV \quad \text{or} \quad q = \frac{4Sq}{D}$$

Let an endothermic reaction occur in the reactor and suppose, first, that q is constant throughout. Then the variation, along the tube, of temperature, pressure, and conversion will be qualitatively as indicated in Figure 7-9. The feed enters at a relatively low temperature such that the reaction rate is very small. In the first portion of the reactor the feed is preheated to a temperature high enough to cause the reaction to occur at a small, but measurable rate. This is normally referred to as the *preheat section*; it is bounded by points 0 and 1 of Figure 7-9.

As the reaction commences, the rate of temperature rise diminishes because some of the heat input is utilized as heat of reaction, but unless the heat of reaction is very large the temperature rise continues until a predetermined outlet value is reached, at point 2. The portion of the reactor between points 1 and 2 will be called the *reaction section*. The reactor may, of course, be ended at any desired length, so that point 2 may in a specific case be either nearer to or farther from point 1 than indicated by the figure.

For the case where a single reaction occurs in the gas phase, three equations in the three unknowns P, T, and x are required to describe the reacting system. The pressure at any point along the reactor may be computed by replacing f in the Fanning equation [Equation (7-9)] by its equivalent given by Equation (7-26) to give

$$-\frac{dP}{dz} = \frac{2Bf_0 G^2}{DN_{Re}^{0.2} g_c \rho} \tag{7-30}$$

By use of the definition of Reynolds number and the gas law ($Pv = zRT$) it is possible to restate the above equation in the following form:

$$-P\frac{dP}{dV} = \beta T(1 + \delta y_A^0 x) \tag{7-31}$$

where P = absolute pressure, lb/in^2

T = temperature of the reacting mixture, °R

V = internal volume of the reactor tube; the internal volume of the straight lengths plus the return bends, ft^3

y_A^0 = mole fraction of the base component A in the feed; $y_A^0 = n_A^0/n_T^0$

$x = (n_A^0 - n_A)/n_A^0$

$\beta = \left(\frac{41.2}{M_w}\right)\left[\frac{zBf_0}{(6D)^{6.8}}\right]\left[\frac{w}{1000}\right]^{1.8} \mu^{0.2}$, $(psi)^2/(ft^3)(°R)$

δ = change in the number of moles per mole of A reacted [For the reaction: $aA + bB \rightleftarrows cC + dD$, $\delta = (c + d - a - b)/a$]

M_w = molecular weight of the feed

z = compressibility factor for the reacting mixture

D = internal diameter of a reactor tube, ft

w = feed rate to the reactor, $w = n_T^o M_w$, lb/hr

μ = viscosity, centipoise.

For the case where the reaction is first order with respect to A,

$$r_A = kp_A \tag{7-32}$$

Elimination of r_A from the material balance (7-19) by use of Equation (7-32) followed by the restatement of the expression so obtained in terms of pressure and conversion gives

$$n_T^o \frac{dx}{dV} = \frac{k(1 - x)P}{(1 + \delta y_A^o x)} \tag{7-33}$$

The enthalpy balance on the reactants [Equation (7-20)] may be restated in the following form:

$$\frac{dT}{dV} = m - s \frac{dx}{dV} \tag{7-34}$$

where

$$m = \frac{4q}{DwC_p}$$

$$s = \frac{y_A^o \, \Delta H_r}{M_w C_p}$$

In order to design the reactor, it is necessary to solve Equations (7-31), (7-33), and (7-34) simultaneously. When the equations are integrated with respect to volume by use of the trapezoidal rule (where needed) and the expressions so obtained are restated in functional form, the following results are obtained:

$$F_1(P, T, x) = \frac{\Delta V}{2} [\beta T(1 + \delta y_A^o x) + \beta T_j(1 + \delta y_A^o x_j)] + \frac{1}{2}[P^2 - P_j^2]$$

$$\tag{7-35}$$

$$F_2(P, T, x) = \frac{\Delta V}{2} \left[\frac{k(1 - x)P}{1 + \delta y_A^0 x} + \frac{k_j(1 - x_j)P_j}{1 + \delta y_A^0 x_j} \right] - n_T^0(x - x_j) \qquad (7\text{-}36)$$

$$F_3(P, T, x) = m \, \Delta V - s(x - x_j) - (T - T_j) \qquad (7\text{-}37)$$

For each element of reactor tube, Equations (7-35) through (7-37) may be solved simultaneously for values of P, T, and x at the end of the increment by use of the Newton-Raphson method in a manner analogous to that demonstrated in Example 7-4. This procedure is repeated for each increment until the desired conversion has been obtained.

In computer programs of the Newton-Raphson method, the functions and all variables are customarily normalized. Although matrix methods exist for performing this operation [12], the following algebraic procedure is generally satisfactory for relatively small problems. The variables of temperature and pressure may be normalized by stating them in terms of dimensionless variables T/T_b and P/P_b, where T_b and P_b are arbitrarily selected base values. After the variables have been restated in dimensionless form, the functions (or the original Taylor series expansions) should be restated such that the individual terms have values lying within the interval 0 to 1 or as close as possible to it. For example, instead of using the function F_2 as formulated above, a new function F_2/n_T^0 would be more suitable. In the interest of keeping all of the actual variables in view, the functions and variables in Equations (7-35) through (7-37) are used in the solution of the following illustrative example.

EXAMPLE 7-5

Many cracking reactions such as those shown in Example 2-5 may be represented by a single reaction of the form

$$A \longrightarrow 2B$$

Suppose that such a reaction is to be carried out in a fired tubular reactor which may be represented by the plug-flow model. The rate of reaction is first order with respect to A,

$$r_A = kp_A$$

The feed contains 95% of reactant A on a molar basis ($y_A^0 = 0.95$). The charge rate w is 8000 lb per hour per tube. The inlet temperature of the reacting stream is 600°F. The inlet pressure is 100 lb/in² (absolute). For the preheat section, the heat input rate is 6000 Btu/ft² hr; for the reactor section, the heat input rate is 11,000 Btu/ft² hr. The internal diameter of the tube is 0.28 ft. (The preheat section is defined for this problem as that reactor volume required to achieve a 1% conversion of the base reactant A.)

Determine the reactor volume required to convert 94.3% of A. Also, determine the outlet temperature and pressure of the reacting mixture. The physical properties are as follows:

$C_p = 0.75$ Btu/lb °R, heat capacity of the reacting mixture

$k = 4 \times 10^{11} e^{-46,500/T}$ [lb mole/(hr)(ft³)(lb/in²)], where T is in °R

$M_w = 60$, molecular weight of the reacting mixture

$\Delta H_r = 36,000$ Btu/(lb mole of A reacted)

$\mu = 0.02$ centipoise, viscosity of the reacting mixture

$zBf_0 = 0.072$

SOLUTION

Since the problem may be solved by use of the same numerical procedure used to solve Example 7-4, an abbreviated presentation of the trial procedure for the first increment of reactor volume is given. For the preheat section,

$$m = \frac{4q}{DwC_p} = \frac{(4)(6,000)}{(0.28)(8000)(0.75)} = 14.286°\text{R}$$

For the reaction section,

$$m = \left(\frac{11}{6}\right)(14.286) = 26.191°\text{R}$$

and
$$s = \frac{y_A^0 \, \Delta H_r}{M_w C_p} = \frac{(0.95)(36,000)}{(60)(0.75)} = 760°\text{R}$$

$$\beta = \left(\frac{41.2}{M_w}\right)\left[\frac{zBf_0}{(6D)^{6.8}}\right]\left[\frac{w}{1000}\right]^{1.8} \mu^{0.2} = 0.02804$$

$$\delta = \frac{2-1}{1} = 1$$

Take the first increment of volume $\Delta V = 2.0$ ft³. For the first trial for this increment of volume, assume:

$$P_1 = 99.1, \qquad T_1 = 1102 \quad \text{and} \quad x_1 = 2 \times 10^{-7}$$

Then, the functions F_1, F_2, and F_3 have the values

$$F_1(P, T, x) = -28.97$$
$$F_2(P, T, x) = 8.95 \times 10^{-6}$$
$$F_3(P, T, x) = -13.43$$

The partial derivatives needed in the Newton-Raphson method are evaluated at P_1,

T_1, and x_1 as follows:

$$\frac{\partial F_1}{\partial P} = P = 99.1$$

$$\frac{\partial F_1}{\partial T} = \left(\frac{\Delta V}{2}\right)[\beta(1 + \delta y_A^0 x)] = 0.02804$$

$$\frac{\partial F_1}{\partial x} = \left(\frac{\Delta V}{2}\right)[\beta T \, \delta y_A^0] = 29.355$$

$$\frac{\partial F_2}{\partial P} = \left(\frac{\Delta V}{2}\right)\left[\frac{k(1 - x)}{1 + \delta y_A^0 x}\right] = 1.89 \times 10^{-7}$$

$$\frac{\partial F_2}{\partial T} = \left(\frac{\Delta V}{2}\right)\left[\frac{(1 - x)P}{1 + \delta y_A^0 x}\right]\frac{\partial k}{\partial T} \quad \text{where} \quad \frac{\partial k}{\partial T} = \left[\frac{46,500}{T^2}\right]k$$

$$\frac{\partial F_2}{\partial T} = 7.17 \times 10^{-7}$$

$$\frac{\partial F_2}{\partial x} = \frac{\Delta V}{2}\left[\frac{-k(1 - x)P\delta y_A^0}{[1 + \delta y_A^0 x]^2} - \frac{kP}{[1 + \delta y_A^0 x]}\right] - n_T^0 = -133.3$$

$$\frac{\partial F_3}{\partial P} = 0$$

$$\frac{\partial F_3}{\partial T} = 1$$

$$\frac{\partial F_3}{\partial x} = -760$$

The Newton-Raphson equations for the first trial reduce to

$$0 = -28.97 + 99.1 \, \Delta P + 0.028 \, \Delta T + 29.4 \, \Delta x$$
$$0 = -8.95 \times 10^{-6} + 1.89 \times 10^{-7} \, \Delta P + 7.17 \times 10^{-7} \, \Delta T - 133.3 \, \Delta x$$
$$0 = -13.43 + 0.0 \, \Delta P - 1.0 \, \Delta T - 760 \, \Delta x$$

Solution of these equations for ΔP, ΔT, and Δx gives

$$\Delta P = 0.296$$
$$\Delta T = -13.43$$
$$\Delta x \cong 0$$

The trial values for the second trial for the first increment are then computed as follows:

$$P_2 = P_1 + \Delta P = 99.40$$
$$T_2 = T_1 + \Delta T = 1088.6$$
$$x_2 = x_1 + \Delta x = 2 \times 10^{-7}$$

TABLE 7-3

CONVERSION, TEMPERATURE, AND PRESSURE PROFILES FOR THE FIRED
TUBULAR REACTOR DESIGNED IN EXAMPLE 7-5

Volume (ft^3)	Conversion	Temperature (°R)	Pressure (psia)	Heat Flux (Btu/hr ft^2)
2.000	0.0000001	1089.998	99.365	6000.00
4.000	0.0000004	1118.567	98.740	6000.00
6.000	0.0000013	1147.136	98.094	6000.00
8.000	0.0000038	1175.705	97.428	6000.00
10.000	0.0000103	1204.269	96.740	6000.00
12.000	0.0000261	1232.826	96.031	6000.00
14.000	0.0000638	1261.366	95.300	6000.00
16.000	0.0001497	1289.871	94.546	6000.00
18.000	0.0003381	1318.297	93.769	6000.00
20.000	0.0007359	1346.564	92.968	6000.00
22.000	0.0015447	1374.519	92.143	6000.00
24.000	0.0031224	1401.889	91.292	6000.00
26.000	0.0060570	1428.227	90.415	6000.00
28.000	0.0112678	1457.598	89.510	11000.00
30.000	0.0232743	1500.852	88.563	11000.00
32.000	0.0483613	1534.164	87.564	11000.00
34.000	0.0881695	1556.288	86.504	11000.00
36.000	0.1385463	1570.380	85.374	11000.00
38.000	0.1942797	1580.402	84.167	11000.00
40.000	0.2521445	1588.803	82.878	11000.00
42.000	0.3106262	1596.735	81.501	11000.00
44.000	0.3690593	1604.703	80.030	11000.00
46.000	0.4271251	1612.952	78.461	11000.00
48.000	0.4846281	1621.627	76.787	11000.00
50.000	0.5414043	1630.855	74.999	11000.00
52.000	0.5972794	1640.769	73.090	11000.00
54.000	0.6520435	1651.526	71.049	11000.00
56.000	0.7054300	1663.330	68.864	11000.00
58.000	0.7570879	1676.449	66.519	11000.00
60.000	0.8065413	1691.242	63.997	11000.00
62.000	0.8531300	1708.213	61.296	11000.00
64.000	0.8959184	1728.072	58.326	11000.00
66.000	0.9335703	1751.834	55.111	11000.00
66.800	0.9451888	1761.336	53.913	11000.00

After the solution set of values for P, T, and x at V_1 has been found, the same procedure
is repeated for the second and all subsequent elements. The conversion, pressure, and
temperature profiles obtained on the basis of the specified values of the tube diameter
(0.28 ft) and the heat input rates are tabulated in Table 7-3.

The problem stated as Example 7-5 is easier to solve than is the problem which
commonly confronts the designer in which the diameter and the heat input rates to
the Preheat and Reaction sections are to be picked for a specified conversion such that
the outlet temperature and the pressure drop are equal to or less than the design specifications [10, 11]. One way to solve a problem of this type is as follows. Values of D

and q are assumed and the volume required to achieve the specified conversion is found by the numerical procedure illustrated in the above example. If the calculated values of the outlet temperature and pressure do not satisfy the specifications on the outlet temperature and pressure, another set of values for q and D are assumed and the corresponding outlet temperature and pressure at the required conversion are computed. Picking the tube diameter is simplified by the fact that the pressure drop is inversely proportional to the tube diameter raised to the 6.8 power. Thus a slight change in D has a significant effect on ΔP. Obviously, the picking of q and D may be formulated as a problem in optimization [13]. Alternately, the approximate method of Murdoch et al. [10, 11] may be used.

C. Design of Perfectly Mixed Flow Reactors

Typical reactors of this type are shown in Figures 2-6 and 2-7. A summary of the equations needed to describe reactors of this type follow for the case of steady state operation.

$$\text{Material balance:} \quad r_A = \frac{n_A^0 - n_A}{V} \tag{7-38}$$

$$\text{Energy balance on the reactants:} \quad -w \int_{T_0}^{T} (C_p)_{\text{feed}} \, dT - r_A V \, \Delta H_r + Q = 0 \tag{7-39}$$

where $(C_p)_{\text{feed}}$ is evaluated on the basis of the composition of the feed

Energy balance on the heat-transfer medium:

$$1. \ \text{Perfectly mixed:} \ w_c(H_{ci} - H_c) + Q = 0 \tag{7-40}$$

$$2. \ \text{Plug flow:} \ w_c C_{pc} \frac{dT_c}{dz} + q = 0 \tag{7-41}$$

The total rate of heat transfer (Btu/hr) from the heat-transfer medium to the reacting mixture is computed by use of Equation (7-3) for the case where the heat-transfer medium is perfectly mixed and by Equation (7-4) for the case where the heat-transfer medium is in plug flow.

In the first problem presented in this section, a perfectly mixed flow reactor is designed to operate isothermally. For such a reactor, "isothermal operation" is used to mean that the temperatures of the reacting mixture entering and leaving the reactor are equal.

EXAMPLE 7-6

A batch reactor is sometimes converted to a perfectly mixed flow reactor by introducing the feed continuously and removing the product continuously. To illustrate this type of operation, suppose that the batch reactor described in Example 7-1 is to be operated at steady state as a perfectly mixed flow reactor. The initial concentrations of styrene and initiator are the same as was stated in Example 7-1. Also, as in Example 7-1, the rate of reaction of styrene may again be represented by the pseudo first-order rate expression

$$r_A = \bar{k}C_A = 0.0387 C_A$$

If the reaction is to be carried out isothermally ($T_0 = T$) at 20°C and a conversion of 80% is to be obtained, find the volumetric flow rate of the feed required to achieve the desired conversion in a reactor having a volume of 400 ml.

Cooling water at 15°C is available for use as the heat-transfer medium. Find the cooling water rate w_c for the isothermal operation of the reactor at the specific conversion of 80%.

SOLUTION

Elimination of r_A from the material-balance expression [Equation (7-38)] and the experimental expression for the rate of reaction yields

$$\frac{n_A^0 x}{V} = \frac{n_A^0 - n_A}{V} = \bar{k}C_A = \bar{k}C_A^0(1 - x) \tag{A}$$

Elimination of n_A^0 from Equation (A) by use of the relationship

$$n_A^0 = C_A^0 v_T$$

followed by rearrangement yields

$$v_T = \frac{\bar{k}(1 - x)V}{x} \tag{B}$$

Thus

$$v_T = \frac{0.0387(1 - 0.8)(0.4)}{0.8}$$

$$= 0.00387 \text{ liter/min} = 3.87 \text{ cc/min}$$

Since the reaction is to be carried out isothermally, $T_0 = T$, and Equation (7-39) reduces to

$$Q = r_A V \Delta H_r = x n_A^0 \Delta H_r = x C_A^0 v_T \Delta H_r$$

Thus

$$Q = \left(\frac{2 \text{ g moles}}{\text{liter}}\right)\left(\frac{0.00387 \text{ liter}}{\text{min}}\right)(0.8)\left(\frac{-16{,}600 \text{ cal}}{\text{g mole}}\right)$$

$$= -102.79 \text{ cal/min}$$

The temperature T_c of the cooling water may be computed by use of Equation (7-3) as follows:

$$T_c = T + \frac{Q}{U_h A}$$

Since $U_h A = 66.15$ cal/°C min [see Equation (B) of Example 7-1], it follows that

$$T_c = 20°C + \left[\frac{-102.79 \text{ cal/min}}{66.15 \text{ cal/min °C}} \right] = 18.45°C$$

The flow rate w_c and the inlet temperature of T_{ci} of the cooling water are related by Equation (7-40). Since $w_c(H_{ci} - H_c) = w_c C_{pc}(T_{ci} - T_c)$, Equation (7-40) may be rearranged to give

$$w_c = \frac{Q}{C_{pc}(T_{ci} - T_c)}$$

Thus

$$w_c = \frac{-102.79}{15 - 18.45} = 29.8 \text{ g/min} = 29.8 \text{ cc/min}$$

Generally exothermic reactions are more easily controlled in a perfectly mixed flow reactor than in other types of reactors because, in the former, the reaction rate is proportional to the smallest (the final) concentration of the reactant.

EXAMPLE 7-7

Suppose that the reactor described in Example 7-1 is to be operated adiabatically at steady state as a perfectly mixed flow reactor. The inlet temperature of the reacting mixture is 25°C. Styrene is to be polymerized to a conversion of 80%. The concentration of styrene in the feed is 0.65 g mole per liter and that of the initiator is 0.01 g mole per liter. The remainder of the feed is the solvent, cyclohexane, which has a concentration of 8.58 g moles per liter. (Again it may be assumed as in Example 7-1 that the initiator has been completely consumed by reaction by the time the feed enters the reactor and that the total polymer concentration C remains constant at 0.01 g mole per liter.) The rate of polymerization of styrene is given by the following rate equation [2]:

$$r_A = k_c C^{1/2} C_A$$

where

$$k_c = 1.72 \times 10^{13} e^{-18,788/RT} \left(\frac{1}{\text{min}} \right) \left[\frac{\text{liter}}{\text{g mole}} \right]^{1/2}$$

Since the polymer remains relatively dilute in the reacting mixture throughout the course of the reaction, the density of the mixture may be assumed to remain constant. The molecular weight M_w of the feed is 85.4 g/g mole, the heat capacity of the feed is 0.42 cal/g °C, the molar density of the feed is 9.23 g moles/liter, and the mole fraction y_A^0 of styrene in the feed is 0.0704.

Calculate the outlet temperature of the reacting stream and the volumetric flow rate of the feed required to achieve the desired conversion in a reactor having a volume of 400 ml.

SOLUTION

The outlet temperature T of the reacting mixture may be found by first solving Equation (7-39) for T to give

$$T = T_0 - \frac{r_A V \Delta H_r}{w(C_p)_{\text{feed}}} \tag{A}$$

By use of Equation (7-38), $r_A V = n_A^0 - n_A = n_A^0 x$, and the fact that $w = n_T^0 M_w$, Equation (A) may be restated in the form

$$T = T_0 - \frac{y_A^0 x \Delta H_r}{M_w(C_p)_{\text{feed}}} \tag{B}$$

where $y_A^0 = n_A^0/n_T^0$

$$T = 25 - \frac{(0.0704)(0.8)(-16,600)}{(85.4)(0.42)} = 51.1^\circ C \tag{C}$$

The total volumetric flow rate of the feed may be computed by use of Equation (B) of Example 7-6; namely,

$$v_T = k\left(\frac{1-x}{x}\right) V$$

At $51.1^\circ C$, the pseudo first-order rate constant k has the following value:

$$k = kC^{1/2} = (1.72 \times 10^{13})(0.01)^{1/2} \exp\left[\frac{-18,778}{(1.9872)(324.1)}\right]$$

$$= 0.374 \ (1/\text{min})$$

Then

$$v_T = (0.374)\left[\frac{1-0.8}{0.8}\right](0.4) = 0.0374 \ \text{liter/min}$$

$$= 37.4 \ \text{cc/min}$$

and

$$\theta = \frac{V}{v_T} = \frac{400}{37.4} = 10.7 \ \text{min}$$

D. Design of a Reactor in which Any Number of Reactions Occur

In all of the above design examples, only one reaction occurred. In most commercial reactors, however, more than one reaction usually occurs. The term "reaction" is used to represent either a reversible or an irreversible reaction. For each reaction which occurs, there exists one independent

318

component material balance. Thus, instead of only one material-balance equation such as the ones shown above for batch, tubular, and perfectly mixed reactors, there exist instead one material-balance equation for each reaction. Likewise, in the energy-balance equation for the reacting stream, either the enthalpies for each component [see Equations (6-41), (6-58), and (6-78)] must be included or a heat of reaction term must be included for each reaction. The design of reactors in which multiple reactions occur is illustrated by use of the following specific example.

EXAMPLE 7-8

Methane is to be chlorinated in a brick-lined reactor which is operated adiabatically as a perfectly mixed flow reactor. The composition of the feed is 80% methane and 20% chlorine on a mole basis. The feed enters the reactor at 25°C. The reactor is to be operated at a residence time such that essentially all of the chlorine in the feed reacts to form one of the following chlorinated products:

$$CH_4 + Cl_2 \longrightarrow CH_3Cl + HCl \tag{1}$$

$$CH_3Cl + Cl_2 \longrightarrow CH_2Cl_2 + HCl \tag{2}$$

$$CH_2Cl_2 + Cl_2 \longrightarrow CHCl_3 + HCl \tag{3}$$

$$CHCl_3 + Cl_2 \longrightarrow CCl_4 + HCl \tag{4}$$

By use of the equations for a perfectly mixed flow reactor, calculate the temperature of the reacting mixture leaving the reactor and the moles of each chlorinated product produced per mole of methane fed.

It may be assumed that the reactions are unidirectional, and that the respective rates of disappearance of chlorine by each of the reactions are as follows:

$$r_1 = k_1 p_{CH_4} p_{Cl_2}, \qquad r_2 = k_2 p_{CH_3Cl} p_{Cl_2},$$

$$r_3 = k_3 p_{CH_2Cl_2} p_{Cl_2}, \qquad r_4 = k_4 p_{CHCl_3} p_{Cl_2}$$

The ratios of the rate constants are as follows [14]:

$$\frac{k_2}{k_1} = 0.424 \exp\left(\frac{1960}{RT}\right)$$

$$\frac{k_3}{k_1} = 1.0$$

$$\frac{k_4}{k_1} = 2.2 \exp\left(-\frac{2000}{RT}\right)$$

where $R = 1.9872$ and T is in °K.

The heats of reactions per mole of chlorine reacted at 25°C are as follows:

$$\Delta H_{r1} = -24{,}740 \text{ cal/g mole}$$

$$\Delta H_{r2} = -24{,}170 \text{ cal/g mole}$$

$$\Delta H_{r3} = -23{,}400 \text{ cal/g mole}$$

$$\Delta H_{r4} = -21{,}300 \text{ cal/g mole}$$

These values were computed by use of heats of formation data given in Reference [15].
The following curve fits for the heat capacities were taken from Hougen et al. [16] and the heats of formation from Reference [15].

Component	ΔH_f° at 298°K	α	$\beta \times 10^2$	$\gamma \times 10^5$	$\delta \times 10^9$
CH$_4$	-17.89	4.75	1.200	0.303	-2.630
CH$_3$Cl	-20.63	3.05	2.596	-1.244	2.300
CH$_2$Cl	-22.80	4.20	3.419	-2.350	6.068
CHCl$_3$	-24.20	7.61	3.461	-2.668	7.344
CCl$_4$	-24.00	12.24	3.4	-2.995	8.828
HCl	-22.00	7.244	-0.1824	0.3170	-1.036
Cl$_2$	0.0	6.8214	0.57095	-0.5107	1.547

$C_p = \alpha + \beta T + \gamma T^2 + \delta T^3$, T is in °K, and C_p has the units of cal/g mole °K

SOLUTION

For convenience, let the four reactions and their rates be represented as follows:

$$(1) \quad A + B \longrightarrow C + D, \quad r_1 = \frac{n_1}{V} = k_1 p_A p_B$$

$$(2) \quad C + B \longrightarrow E + D, \quad r_2 = \frac{n_2}{V} = k_2 p_C p_B$$

$$(3) \quad E + B \longrightarrow F + D, \quad r_3 = \frac{n_3}{V} = k_3 p_E p_B \tag{A}$$

$$(4) \quad F + B \longrightarrow G + D, \quad r_4 = \frac{n_4}{V} = k_4 p_F p_B$$

where $A = $ CH$_4$, $B = $ Cl$_2$, $C = $ CH$_3$Cl, $D = $ HCl, $E = $ CH$_2$Cl$_2$, $F = $ CHCl$_3$, and $G = $ CCl$_4$. The moles of chlorine reacted per unit time by Reactions (1), (2), (3), and (4) are denoted by $n_1, n_2, n_3,$ and n_4, respectively. The flow rates $n_A, n_B, n_C, n_D, n_E, n_F,$ and n_G may be expressed in terms of the rates $n_1, n_2, n_3,$ and n_4 by use of the stoichiometry of the four reactions as follows:

$$n_A = n_A^0 - n_1$$

$$n_B = n_B^0 - \sum_{k=1}^{4} n_k$$

$$n_C = n_1 - n_2 \qquad\qquad\qquad\qquad\qquad \text{(B)}$$

$$n_D = \sum_{k=1}^{4} n_k$$

$$n_E = n_2 - n_3$$

$$n_F = n_3 - n_4$$

$$\underline{n_G = n_4}$$

$$n_T = n_T^0$$

Since a reactor volume is to be used such that essentially all of the chlorine is to be consumed by the reaction,

$$n_B \cong 0$$

Thus the problem to be solved consists of finding the values of T, n_A, n_C, n_D, n_E, n_F, and n_G which satisfy (1) the rate expressions, (2) the stoichiometric relationships, and (3) the energy-balance equation. This problem will be formulated in terms of two equations in two unknowns.

For a perfectly mixed flow reactor which is operated adiabatically, Equation (6-58) reduces to

$$\sum_{i=1}^{c} n_i^0 [H_i(T_0) - H_i(T)] + V \sum_{i=1}^{c} H_i(T) r_i = 0 \qquad\qquad \text{(C)}$$

where $i = A, B, C, D, E, F,$ and G. For convenience, the symbol H_{fi}° has been replaced by H_i.

First consider the second sum in Equation (C). To restate this sum in terms of the heats of reaction, the following relationships between the net rates of disappearance of $A, B, \ldots, G$ (namely, $r_A, r_B, \ldots, r_G$) and the rates of disappearance of B by each reaction (namely, r_1, r_2, r_3, r_4) are needed. The stoichiometry of the four reactions requires that

$$r_A = r_1, \qquad\qquad r_D = -\sum_{k=1}^{4} r_k$$

$$r_B = \sum_{k=1}^{4} r_k, \qquad\qquad r_E = r_3 - r_2 \qquad\qquad \text{(D)}$$

$$r_C = r_2 - r_1, \qquad\qquad r_F = r_4 - r_3$$

$$r_G = -r_4$$

Since

$$V \sum_{i=1}^{c} H_i(T) r_i = V[H_A r_A + H_B r_B + H_C r_C + H_D r_D + H_E r_E + H_F r_F + H_G r_G]$$

the following result is obtained upon replacing $r_A, r_B, \ldots, r_G$ by their equivalents as given by Equation (D).

$$V \sum_{i=1}^{c} H_i(T) r_i = -V \sum_{k=1}^{4} \Delta H_{rk} r_k$$

where

$$\Delta H_{r1} = H_C + H_D - H_A - H_B$$

$$\Delta H_{r2} = H_E + H_D - H_C - H_B$$

$$\Delta H_{r3} = H_F + H_D - H_E - H_B$$

$$\Delta H_{r4} = H_G + H_D - H_F - H_B$$

By use of the definition of heat capacity [Equation (5-21)], it is possible to restate the first summation of Equation (C) in the following form:

$$\sum_{i=1}^{c} n_i^0 [H_i(T_0) - H_i(T)] = -n_T^0 \int_{T_0}^{T} (C_p)_{\text{feed}} \, dT \qquad (E)$$

Since the feed contains components A and B alone, the heat capacity of the feed is given by

$$(C_p)_{\text{feed}} = \frac{1}{n_T^0} [n_A^0 C_{pA} + n_B^0 C_{pB}]$$

Thus Equation (6-58) may be stated in the following equivalent form:

$$n_T^0 \int_{T_0}^{T} (C_p)_{\text{feed}} \, dT + V \sum_{k=1}^{4} \Delta H_{rk} r_k = 0 \qquad (F)$$

In the solution of the problem at hand, it was elected to replace $r_k V$ in Equation (F) by its equivalent n_k [see Equation (A)]. The corresponding functional expression may be formulated:

$$F = \int_{T_0}^{T} (C_p)_{\text{feed}} \, dT + \frac{1}{n_T^0} \sum_{k=1}^{4} \Delta H_{rk} n_k \qquad (G)$$

where each ΔH_{rk} is evaluated at the temperature T. The heat of reactions as a function of temperature for each reaction is found by use of Equation (5-24). For example, for the first reaction,

$$\Delta H_{r1} = \Delta H_{r1} \Big|_{T_0} + \int_{T_0}^{T} \Delta C_{p_1} \, dT$$

where
$$\Delta C_{p1} = C_{pC} + C_{pD} - C_{pA} - C_{pB}$$

By use of the heat capacities given, the integration implied in the above expression may be carried out. Use of the resulting expression so obtained together with the value of ΔH_{r1} at T_0 yields the desired functional expression [Equation (5-63)],

$$\Delta H_{rk} = C_{1k} + \Delta \alpha_k T + \frac{\Delta \beta_k}{2} T^2 + \frac{\Delta \gamma_k}{3} T^3, \qquad (k = 1, 2, 3, 4) \qquad \text{(H)}$$

where ΔH_{rk} is in cal gal per g mole, T is in °K, and

Reaction No.	C_{1k}	$\Delta \alpha_k$	$\Delta \beta_k \times 10^2$	$\Delta \gamma_k \times 10^5$	$\Delta \delta_k \times 10^9$
1	$-24{,}459$	-1.2774	0.6426	0.7193	2.347
2	$-24{,}647$	1.5726	0.06965	-0.2783	1.185
3	$-24{,}269$	3.8326	-0.7114	0.5097	-1.307
4	$-23{,}346$	5.0526	-0.8144	0.5007	-1.102

After the integration implied in the first term of Equation (G) has been carried out, the following result is obtained:

$$\int_{T_0}^{T} (C_p)_{\text{feed}} \, dT = 5.16428 + 0.5371(10^{-2})T^2 + 0.04675(10^{-5})T^3$$

$$- 0.44865(10^{-9})T^4 - 2024.7 \qquad \text{(I)}$$

where T is in °K.

The moles of B (chlorine) reacted by each reaction may be expressed in terms of the ratio n_A/n_1 and the temperature T as follows. From the stoichiometric relationship given by Equation (B),

$$n_1 = \frac{n_A^0}{1 + n_A/n_1} \qquad \text{(J)}$$

Since perfect gas behavior is assumed, the following expressions are obtained by division of r_2, r_3, and r_4 by r_1 [see Equation (A)]:

$$\frac{k_2 n_C}{k_1 n_A} = \frac{n_2}{n_1}$$

$$\frac{k_3 n_E}{k_1 n_A} = \frac{n_3}{n_1} \qquad \text{(K)}$$

$$\frac{k_4 n_F}{k_1 n_A} = \frac{n_4}{n_1}$$

By use of these results and the stoichiometric relationships of Equation (B), the following expressions for n_2, n_3, and n_4 as a function of n_A/n_1 and T are obtained:

$$n_2 = \frac{n_1}{1 + \dfrac{k_1}{k_2}(n_A/n_1)} \tag{L}$$

$$n_3 = \frac{n_2}{1 + \dfrac{k_1}{k_3}(n_A/n_1)} \tag{M}$$

$$n_4 = \frac{n_3}{1 + \dfrac{k_1}{k_4}(n_A/n_1)} \tag{N}$$

Thus the problem reduces to finding a set of values n_A/n_1 and T such that $F = 0$ and such that the sum of n_1, n_2, n_3, and n_4 is equal to n_B^0; that is, such that $n_B = 0$. Thus the second function to be satisfied may be stated as follows:

$$G = 1 - \frac{1}{n_B^0}\left[n_1 + n_2 + n_3 + n_4\right] \tag{O}$$

This problem may be solved by use of an interpolation procedure wherein T is regarded as the independent variable. For each choice of T, the value of n_A/n_1 that makes $G = 0$ is found. Then an improved choice of T is found by interpolation on the function F. On the basis of 100 g moles of feed, the calculations involved in making the first trial follow:

Trial No. 1: Assume $T_1 = 725°\text{K}$.

Since $n_T^0 = 100$ g moles and the feed consists of 80% methane and 20% chlorine, it follows that:

$$n_A^0 = 80, \qquad n_B^0 = 20$$

At 725°K,

$$\frac{k_1}{k_2} = 0.605, \qquad \frac{k_1}{k_3} = 1, \qquad \frac{k_1}{k_4} = 1.822$$

For the first trial on G, take

$$\left(\frac{n_A}{n_1}\right)_1 = 4.5$$

Then

$$n_1 = \frac{n_A^0}{1 + n_A^0/n_1} = \frac{80}{1 + 4.5} = 14.5455$$

$$n_2 = \frac{n_1}{1 + (k_1/k_2)(n_A/n_1)} = \frac{14.5455}{1 + (0.605)(4.5)} = 3.9075$$

$$n_3 = \frac{n_2}{1 + (k_1/k_3)(n_A/n_1)} = \frac{3.9075}{1 + (1)(4.5)} = 0.7105$$

$$n_4 = \frac{n_3}{1 + (k_1/k_4)(n_A/n_1)} = \frac{0.7105}{1 + (1.822)(4.5)} = 0.0772$$

and thus

$$G_1 = 1 - \tfrac{1}{20}[14.5455 + 3.9075 + 0.7105 + 0.0772]$$

$$G_1 = 0.03797$$

For the second trial on G, take

$$\left(\frac{n_A}{n_1}\right)_2 = 4.0$$

By repeating the same procedure shown above, the following results are obtained:

$$n_1 = 16.000, \qquad n_2 = 4.6784, \qquad n_3 = 0.9357, \qquad n_4 = 0.1129$$

and

$$G_2 = -0.08635$$

By use of the method of *interpolation regula falsi* [12], the next best value of (n_A/n_1) is found,

$$\left(\frac{n_A}{n_1}\right)_3 = \frac{(4.0)(0.03799) - (-0.08635)(4.5)}{0.03799 - (-0.08635)} = 4.347$$

A summary of the iterations on G at $T = 725°K$ follows:

Trial No.	n_A/n_k	n_1	n_2	n_3	n_4	G_k
1	4.5	14.5454	3.9074	0.7104	0.0772	0.0379
2	4.0	16.0000	4.6784	0.9357	0.1129	-0.0864
3	4.347	14.9617	4.1218	0.7709	0.0864	0.0029
4	4.335	14.9950	4.1393	0.7759	0.0872	0.0001

Next the value of F at $T = 725°K$ and $n_A/n_1 = 4.335$ is computed. The first term of the function F [Equation (G)] is evaluated by use of Equation (I),

$$\int_{298.16}^{725} (C_p)_{feed} dT = 4596$$

The second term $(1/n_T^0) \sum_{k=1}^{4} \Delta H_{rk} n_k$ of the function F is evaluated by use of Equation (H) and the solution set of n_k's at $n_A/n_1 = 4.335$ (given above).

Reaction No.	ΔH_{rk}	$\dfrac{1}{n_T^0}[n_k \Delta H_{rk}]$
1	$-24,448$	-3666
2	$-23,595$	-977
3	$-22,803$	-177
4	$-21,262$	-18
		-4838

Thus

$$F_1(725) = 4596 - 4839 = -242$$

Trial No. 2: Assume $T_2 = 750°$K.
At 750°K,

$$\frac{k_1}{k_2} = 0.6331, \qquad \frac{k_1}{k_3} = 1, \qquad \frac{k_1}{k_4} = 1.739$$

At $T = 750°$K, the value of n_A/n_1 needed to make $G = 0$ was found to be $n_A^0/n_1 = 4.3$. The iterative procedure demonstrated in Trial No. 1 was used. In summary, at $T = 750°$K, and $n_A/n_1 = 4.3$, the following result was obtained:

$$n_1 = 15.0943, \qquad n_2 = 4.0556, \qquad n_3 = 0.7652, \qquad n_4 = 0.0903$$

and $G = -0.0002$

The function F is now evaluated at $T = 750°$K and $n_A/n_1 = 4.3$. First, by Equation (I),

$$\int_{298.16}^{750} (C_p)_{feed} \, dT = 4925$$

By use of the above results and Equation (H),

Reaction No.	ΔH_{rk}	$\dfrac{1}{n_T^0}[n_k \Delta H_{rk}]$
1	$-24,439$	-3689
2	$-23,576$	-956
3	$-22,792$	-174
4	$-21,239$	-19
		-4838

Then

$$F_2(75) = 4925 - 4838 = 87$$

By interpolation on the functional values F_1 and F_2 at the corresponding values T_1 and T_2 gives T_3, the value of T to be assumed for the third trial; namely,

$$T_3 = \frac{725(87) - 750(-242)}{87 - (-242)} = 743.4$$

Trial No. 3: Assume $T_3 = 743.4$.
   At this temperature,

$$\frac{k_1}{k_2} = 0.6257, \qquad \frac{k_1}{k_2} = 1, \qquad \frac{k_1}{k_4} = 1.76$$

and at $(n_A/n_1) = 4.31$, $G \cong 0$. More precisely at $T_3 = 743.4$ and $(n_A/n_1) = 4.31$

$$n_1 = 15.066, \qquad n_2 = 4.0754, \qquad n_3 = 0.7675$$

$$n_4 = 0.0894 \quad \text{and} \quad G = 0.00009$$

Next F is evaluated. First

$$\int_{298.16}^{743.4} (C_p)_{\text{feed}} \, dT = 4838$$

and in a manner analogous to that described above, the following results are obtained:

Reaction No.	ΔH_{rk}	$\dfrac{1}{n_T^0}[n_k \, \Delta H_{rk}]$
1	$-24{,}439$	-3682
2	$-23{,}576$	-981
3	$-22{,}792$	-175
4	$-21{,}239$	-19
		-4837

Thus

$$F_3 = 4838 - 4837 = 1$$

Since this difference is within the accuracy of the calculations, $F_3 \cong 0$. The solution set of values of the variables follows:

$$T = 743.4°\text{K}, \qquad \frac{n_A}{n_1} = 4.31$$

$$n_A = 64.934$$

$$n_C = n_1 - n_2 = 10.991$$

$$n_E = n_2 - n_3 = 3.3079$$

$$n_F = n_3 - n_4 = 0.6781$$

$$n_G = n_4 = 0.0894$$

$$n_D = \sum_{k=1}^{4} n_k = 19.9983$$

$$n_B = 20 - \sum_{k=1}^{4} n_k = 0.0077$$

II. THE REACTION PHASE PLANE

This section was included in order to demonstrate that, for certain types of reactor problems, more than one solution may exist. In particular, it is shown that for the design of an adiabatic perfectly mixed flow reactor in which a first-order reversible, exothermic reaction is to be carried out, more than one steady state solution to the material and energy balances may exist. Thus the designer or operator of a reactor in which such an exothermic reaction occurs could obtain different conversions at the same residence time. Researchers van Heerden [17] and Bilous and Amundson [18] were among the first to point out the importance of analyses of the following type.

To provide some further insight into the design of reactors, an analysis of the material- and energy-balance equations for the case of a single reversible reaction is presented. The rate of reaction r for the case where a single reaction occurs may be represented as a function of conversion and temperature; that is, $r = r(x, T)$. The conversion-temperature plane (the x-T plane) is defined as the *reaction phase plane*. For example, consider the reaction

$$A \; \rightleftharpoons \; S \tag{7-42}$$

The rate of reaction of A is given by

$$r = k_1 C_A - k_2 C_S \tag{7-43}$$

where $\qquad k_1 = A_1 e^{-E_1/RT}, \qquad k_2 = A_2 e^{-E_2/RT}$

The notation appearing in these expressions is a simplification of that introduced in Chapter 1 in that k_1 and k_2 are used to represent k_{c1} and k_{c2}, E_1, and E_2 are used to represent E_{A1} and E_{A2}, and r is used to represent r_A.

The rate of reaction r may be expressed as a function of temperature T and conversion x as follows:

$$r = C_A^0[k_1(1 - x) - k_2 x] \tag{7-44}$$

From Figure 12-1 of Chapter 12, it is evident that exothermic and endothermic reactions are characterized by the following relationships between the activation energies.

$$E_1 < E_2 \qquad \text{(exothermic)} \tag{7-45}$$

$$E_1 > E_2 \qquad \text{(endothermic)} \tag{7-46}$$

Suppose that the initial concentrations of A and S are such that the reaction takes place from left to right. That is,

$$r(0, T) = k_1 C_A^0 - k_2 C_S^0 > 0 \tag{7-47}$$

At equilibrium, $r = 0$ and $x = x_e$ (the equilibrium conversion), and Equation (7-44) may be solved for the equilibrium conversion; namely,

$$x_e = \frac{1}{1 + k_2/k_1} \tag{7-48}$$

Then

$$\frac{dx_e}{dT} = -\left[\frac{1}{(1 + k_2/k_1)^2}\right]\left[\left(\frac{a_2}{RT^2}\right)\frac{k_2}{k_1}\right] \tag{7-49}$$

where

$$a_2 = E_2 - E_1$$

The above relationships may be used to show that the limiting values of x_e and dx_e/dT for an exothermic reaction are as follows:

$$\lim_{T \to 0} x_e = 1$$

$$\lim_{T \to \infty} x_e = \frac{1}{1 + A_2/A_1}$$

$$\lim_{T \to 0} \frac{dx_e}{dT} = 0 \tag{7-50}$$

$$\lim_{T \to \infty} \frac{dx_e}{dT} = 0$$

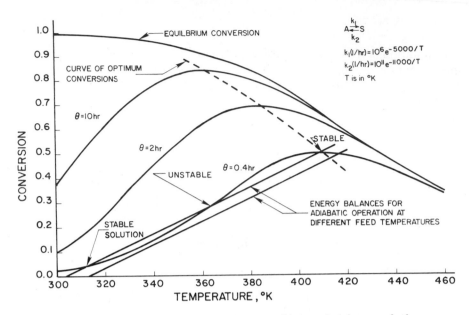

Figure 7-10. An exothermic, first-order reversible reaction in a perfectly mixed flow reactor.

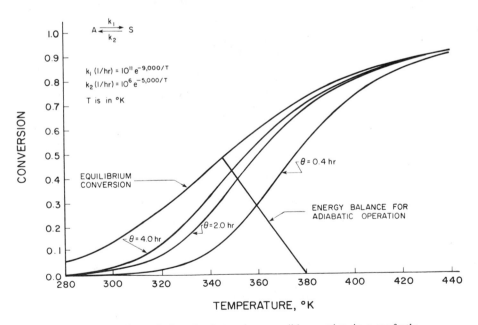

Figure 7-11. An endothermic, first-order reversible reaction in a perfectly mixed flow reactor.

For an exothermic reaction, $a_2 = E_2 - E_1 > 0$, and consequently by Equation (7-49), $dx_e/dT < 0$. A typical curve of x_e versus T is shown in Figure 7-10 for a first-order reversible, exothermic reaction. For a first-order reversible, endothermic reaction, $E_2 - E_1 < 0$. A typical graph of x_e versus T for these reactions is shown in Figure 7-11.

Suppose that the reaction represented by Equation (7-42) is carried out in a perfectly mixed flow reactor. Then the material balance given by Equation (7-38) may be stated in the form

$$x = \mathscr{R}\theta \qquad (7\text{-}51)$$

where

$$\mathscr{R} = \frac{r}{C_A^0}$$

$$\theta = \frac{V}{v_T}$$

For the special case where the rate of reaction r is given by Equation (7-44), the following expression for x as a function of θ and T is readily obtained by eliminating $\mathscr{R}$ from Equations (7-44) and (7-51) to give

$$x = \frac{k_1}{k_1 + k_2 + 1/\theta} \qquad (7\text{-}52)$$

Although the shapes of the curves of x versus T at parameters of θ may be deduced directly by use of Equation (7-52), a more general method is presented for deducing the shapes of these curves. Instead of choosing a specific reaction for making the analysis, the general case is considered in which the rate of reaction is given by any arbitrary continuous function which may be represented symbolically as $\mathscr{R} = \mathscr{R}(x, T)$. The conversion x which may be achieved in a perfectly mixed flow reactor is known from experiment to depend on the residence time θ and the temperature T of the reacting mixture; that is,

$$x = x(\theta, T)$$

This dependency of x on θ and T is also implied by Equation (7-51). Thus the total differential of $\mathscr{R}$ may be represented by

$$d\mathscr{R} = \left(\frac{\partial \mathscr{R}}{\partial x}\right)_T dx + \left(\frac{\partial \mathscr{R}}{\partial T}\right)_x dT$$

The partial derivative of $\mathcal{R}$ with respect to T with θ held fixed may be computed by use of the expression

$$\left(\frac{\partial \mathcal{R}}{\partial T}\right)_\theta = \left(\frac{\partial \mathcal{R}}{\partial x}\right)_T \left(\frac{\partial x}{\partial T}\right)_\theta + \left(\frac{\partial \mathcal{R}}{\partial T}\right)_x \tag{7-53}$$

By partial differentiation of each member of Equation (7-51) with respect to T with θ held fixed gives

$$\left(\frac{\partial \mathcal{R}}{\partial T}\right)_\theta = \frac{1}{\theta}\left(\frac{\partial x}{\partial T}\right)_\theta \tag{7-54}$$

Elimination of $(\partial \mathcal{R}/\partial T)_\theta$ from Equations (7-53) and (7-54) followed by rearrangement gives

$$\left(\frac{\partial x}{\partial T}\right) = \frac{\theta \left(\dfrac{\partial \mathcal{R}}{\partial T}\right)_x}{1 - \theta \left(\dfrac{\partial \mathcal{R}}{\partial x}\right)_T} \tag{7-55}$$

By application of the chain rule to the members of the Equation (7-53), the following expression for the second derivative of $\mathcal{R}$ with respect to T with θ held fixed is obtained:

$$\left(\frac{\partial^2 \mathcal{R}}{\partial T^2}\right)_\theta = \left(\frac{\partial^2 x}{\partial T^2}\right)_\theta \left(\frac{\partial \mathcal{R}}{\partial x}\right)_T + \left(\frac{\partial x}{\partial T}\right)_\theta^2 \left(\frac{\partial^2 \mathcal{R}}{\partial x^2}\right)_T + 2\left(\frac{\partial x}{\partial T}\right)_\theta \left(\frac{\partial^2 \mathcal{R}}{\partial x\, \partial T}\right) + \left(\frac{\partial^2 \mathcal{R}}{\partial T^2}\right)_x \tag{7-56}$$

But, by Equation (7-54),

$$\left(\frac{\partial^2 \mathcal{R}}{\partial T^2}\right)_\theta = \frac{1}{\theta}\left(\frac{\partial^2 x}{\partial T^2}\right)_\theta \tag{7-57}$$

From these two equations [(7-56) and (7-57)], the following expression for the second derivative of x with respect to T with θ held fixed is obtained:

$$\left(\frac{\partial^2 x}{\partial T^2}\right)_\theta = \frac{\theta \left[\left(\dfrac{\partial x}{\partial T}\right)_\theta^2 \left(\dfrac{\partial^2 \mathcal{R}}{\partial x^2}\right)_T + 2\left(\dfrac{\partial x}{\partial T}\right)_\theta \left(\dfrac{\partial^2 \mathcal{R}}{\partial x\, \partial T}\right) + \left(\dfrac{\partial^2 \mathcal{R}}{\partial T^2}\right)_x\right]}{1 - \theta \left(\dfrac{\partial \mathcal{R}}{\partial x}\right)_T} \tag{7-58}$$

For the special case of the first-order reversible reaction given by Equation (7-42), the following expressions for the partial derivatives of $\mathscr{R}$ appearing in Equation (7-58) may be found by use of Equation (7-44).

$$\left(\frac{\partial \mathscr{R}}{\partial x}\right)_T = -(k_1 + k_2)$$

$$\left(\frac{\partial^2 \mathscr{R}}{\partial x^2}\right)_T = 0$$

$$\left(\frac{\partial \mathscr{R}}{\partial T}\right)_x = \frac{1}{RT^2}\left[E_1 k_1 (1 - x) - E_2 k_2 x\right] \tag{7-59}$$

$$\left(\frac{\partial^2 \mathscr{R}}{\partial T^2}\right)_x = -\frac{2}{RT^3}\left[E_1 k_1 (1 - x) - E_2 k_2 x\right] + \frac{1}{RT^4}\left[E_1^2 k_1 (1 - x) - E_2^2 k_2 x\right]$$

$$\left(\frac{\partial^2 \mathscr{R}}{\partial x\, \partial T}\right) = -\frac{1}{RT^2}\left[E_1 k_1 + E_2 k_2\right]$$

Consider first the case of an exothermic, first-order reversible reaction for which $E_1 < E_2$. Since $(\partial \mathscr{R}/\partial x)_T < 0$ as shown above, it follows that the denominator of the expression for $(\partial x/\partial T)_0$ [Equation (7-55)] is always positive. However, for an exothermic reaction, the derivative $(\partial \mathscr{R}/\partial T)_x$ which appears in the numerator of Equation (7-55) may change signs. Let T_k denote the temperature at which a supposed change in signs occurs; that is, at $T = T_k$,

$$\left(\frac{\partial \mathscr{R}}{\partial T}\right)_x = 0$$

and thus

$$\left(\frac{\partial x}{\partial T}\right) = 0 \tag{7-60}$$

At $(\partial \mathscr{R}/\partial T)_x = 0$,

$$E_k k_1 (1 - x) = E_2 k_2 x$$

and thus

$$\left(\frac{\partial^2 \mathscr{R}}{\partial T^2}\right)_x = \frac{E_2 k_2 x}{RT^4}(E_1 - E_2) \tag{7-61}$$

Since $E_1 - E_2 < 0$, it follows that at $T = T_k$,

$$\left(\frac{\partial^2 \mathscr{R}}{\partial T^2}\right)_x < 0 \qquad (7\text{-}62)$$

By use of these results at $T = T_k$ and the fact that $(\partial^2 \mathscr{R}/\partial T^2)_T = 0$ for all T, it follows from Equation (7-56) that at $T = T_k$,

$$\left(\frac{\partial^2 x}{\partial T^2}\right)_\theta < 0 \qquad (7\text{-}63)$$

From the calculus, it is known that if the second derivative of a function is negative at the value of the independent variable for which the first derivative is equal to zero, then the function passes through a maximum. Thus, for each choice of θ, x passes through a maximum as shown in Figure 7-10. Since a maximum value of x exists for each θ for the first-order reversible, exothermic reaction, there exists an optimum operating line (or optimum curve) which passes through the maximums of all x versus T curves as indicated by the broken line in Figure 7-10.

For the case of an endothermic, reversible reaction for which $E_1 > E_2$, it follows from Equation (7-59) that for all $x < x_e$,

$$\left(\frac{\partial \mathscr{R}}{\partial T}\right)_x > \frac{\mathscr{R}}{RT^2} \qquad (7\text{-}64)$$

Since the initial conditions were selected such that $\mathscr{R}(0, T) > 0$, then $\mathscr{R}(x, T) > 0$ for all $x < x_e$ at any given T. Then it is evident that for the endothermic, reversible reaction

$$\left(\frac{\partial \mathscr{R}}{\partial T}\right) > 0 \qquad (7\text{-}65)$$

for all $x < x_e$ at any given T, and for these reactions Equations (7-55) and (7-59) lead to the result

$$\left(\frac{\partial x}{\partial T}\right) > 0 \qquad (7\text{-}66)$$

Typical curves of x versus T at fixed values of θ are shown in Figure 7-11.

From an analysis similar to that outlined above, the curves for irreversible reactions in perfectly mixed flow reactors may be deduced. Curves for an exothermic reaction are shown in Figure 7-12.

Figure 7-12. An exothermic, first-order irreversible reaction in a perfectly mixed flow reactor.

The graph of the equation for the energy balance on the reaction phase diagram is sometimes called the *reaction path*. For purposes of illustration, suppose that the perfectly mixed flow reactor shown in Figure 6-3 is to be operated adiabatically. For this type of operation, Equation (7-39) may be solved for x to give

$$x = -\frac{wC_{pm}(T - T_0)}{n_A^0 \, \Delta H_r} \tag{7-67}$$

where C_{pm} is the mean value of the heat capacity of the feed over the temperature interval between T_0 and T. If, however, the variation of the ratio $wC_{Pm}/n_A^0 \, \Delta H_r$ with temperature is neglected, then Equation (7-67) is a straight line with a positive slope for an exothermic reaction and a negative slope for an endothermic reaction (see Figures 7-10 through 7-12). For the exothermic, reversible reaction considered, the three intersections of the energy balance [Equation (7-67)] with the material balance [Equations (7-51) and (7-44)] shown in Figure 7-12 suggest that as many as three possible solutions (three sets of values of x and T at a given θ) exist. Whether or not one would obtain these solutions for a specified θ would depend upon several factors such as the inlet temperature of the feed and the shapes of the curves for the material- and energy-balance equations.

The "unstable solution" shown in Figures 7-10 and 7-12 is sometimes called the "ignition point" because at this point a slight increase in the temperature leads to an increase in the rate and the conversion which results in a further increase in the temperature until the upper solution point is reached. Similarly, if at the unstable solution point the temperature is decreased, the conversion and temperature will tend to decrease until the lower solution point is reached. Thus a minor upset of a reactor operating at the unstable solution point would cause it to move to either the upper or lower solution point. If, on the other hand, the reactor is being operated at either the upper or lower solution point, it tends to return to these respective points after minor upsets. The behavior of reactors for other types of reactions may be deduced by means of an analysis similar to the one shown for the first-order reversible reaction.

For a first-order reversible, endothermic reaction, the energy- and material-balance lines intersect at only one point for any given θ, and reactors in which endothermic reactions are carried out are sometimes referred to as being inherently stable.

A summary of reactor models and the conditions under which multiple solutions exist has been presented by Hlavacek et al. [19]. In particular, the plug-flow model does not exhibit multiple solutions at steady state operation.

PROBLEMS

7-1. The reactor described in Example 7-1 is to be used to produce the substance R in the following reaction:
$$A \longrightarrow R \qquad r_A = k_1 C_A^2$$

where $k_1 = 0.04$ liter/(g mole min) at 20°C and $C_A^0 = 2$ g moles/liter. The heat of the reaction is -16.6 kcal/g mole. All other data are the same as stated in Example 7-1. The reactor is to be operated isothermally at 20°C.
(a) At the selected times of $t = 0, 5, 10, 15, 20,$ and 25 min, calculate the temperature that the cooling water must possess in order for isothermal operation to be achieved. Assume that the cooling water in the jacket is perfectly mixed.
(b) Cooling water at an inlet temperature of 0°C is available. At the selected times of $t = 0, 5, 10, 15, 20,$ and 25 min, calculate the flow rate of the cooling water required for isothermal operation. What problem do you envision in the operation of the reactor?
Answer: (a) $T_c = 3.94, 11.81, 15.04, 16.68, 17.62, 18.22$°C
(b) $w_c = 204.65, 37.98, 18.87, 11.71, 8.09, 5.96$ g/min

7-2. The reactor described in Example 7-1 is to be operated adiabatically to polymerize styrene. The initial temperature is 5°C. Cyclohexane is to be used as the solvent. Find the times at which the reacting mixture takes on the temperatures of 10°, 20°, 30°, 40°, and 50°C, given
$$r_A = k_1 C^{1/2} C_A$$

C_A = concentration of styrene C = concentration of polystyryllithium

$C = 0.005$ g mole/liter $C_A^0 = 1$ mole/liter

The variation of k_1 with temperature is presented in Example 7-7. The molar density of the feed is 9.58 g moles/liter, and the specific heat of the feed is 0.42 cal/g°C. Neglect the variation of N_T, C_V, and ΔU_r with temperature throughout the course of the reaction.

Answer: $t \cong 0.1919, 1.17, 3.934, 11.237, 29.42$ min

7-3. Obtain the partial differential equation given by Equation (7-8) from Equation (7-7).

7-4. Verify the results presented in Table 7-1.

7-5. Begin with the functional relationships

$$\mathscr{R} = \mathscr{R}(x, T)$$
$$x = x(\theta, T)$$

and Equation (7-51)

$$x = \mathscr{R}\theta$$

and develop the expression for $(\partial^2 x/\partial T^2)_\theta$ which is given by Equation (7-58).

7-6. In Example 7-3, it was shown that for the case of an exothermic, first-order reaction, the reaction stream could be maintained at constant temperature in a heat-exchanger reactor by passing an appropriate cooling medium through the exchanger in the cocurrent direction.

(a) For the first-order irreversible reaction, show that isothermal operation is impossible if countercurrent flow is used in the heat-exchanger reactor, where $\Delta H_r \neq 0$.

(b) For second- and higher order irreversible reactions, show that isothermal operation is impossible in a heat-exchanger reactor, where $\Delta H_r \neq 0$.

7-7. In studying reactions in the laboratory, it is common practice to immerse the reactor in a large, perfectly mixed constant-temperature bath. Suppose the reaction presented in Example 7-1 is to be carried out in a 400 cc reactor with a heat-transfer area of 0.35 ft². The initial temperature of the reacting mixture is 20°C. The initial concentrations and the heat-transfer coefficient are the same as those given in Example 7-1. The reactor is immersed in the bath which is maintained at 20°C throughout the course of the reaction. Compute the reaction temperature and the conversion at selected time intervals. The variation of the reaction rate constant k with temperature is given in Problem 1-6 of Chapter 1.

Answer: At $t = 4, 10, 14, 18$ min, $T = 28.16, 28.87, 25.96, 23.92$°C, and $x = 0.185$, 0.48, 0.596, and 0.671

7-8. If the rate of reaction for the first-order exothermic, reversible reaction $A \rightleftarrows R$ is given by

$$r = C_A^0 \left[A_1(1 - x) \exp\left(\frac{-E_1}{RT}\right) - A_2 x \exp\left(\frac{-E_2}{RT}\right) \right]$$

show that the maximum conversion at a given residence time θ for a perfectly mixed flow reactor (see Figure 2-7) occurs at that temperature given by the following expression.

$$T = \frac{-E_2}{R \log_e \left[E_1/A_2\theta(E_2 - E_1)\right]}$$

7-9. Rework Example 7-1 for the case where the initial concentrations are taken to be the following set.

$$C_A^0 = 0.5 \text{ g mole/liter}$$

$$C = 0.001 \text{ g mole/liter}$$

Answer:

Time (min)	0	5	10	20	30	40	50	60
T_c (°C)	19.39	19.42	19.46	19.52	19.575	19.62	19.67	19.71
w_c (g/min)	3.988	3.98	3.73	3.28	2.88	2.54	2.24	2.01

NOTATION

(See also Chapters 1, 2, 3, 5, and 6)

a = surface area for heat transfer per foot of length of pipe. For a single pipe $a = \pi D$, and for N pipes connected in parallel, $a = N\pi D$.

B = a factor used in the definition of a modified friction factor for the Fanning equation [see Equation (7-26)].

c = a parameter used in the description of heat-exchanger reactors (see Table 7-1).

C = used in Example 7-1 to represent the concentration of all polymers at any time t, moles/unit volume.

C_v, C_p = heat capacities in consistent units, say Btu/lb °F or Btu/lb mole °F.

D = inside diameter.

f = Fanning friction factor [see Equation (7-26)].

g_c = 32.174 (lb$_m$ ft)/(lb$_f$ sec^2). (The symbol lb$_m$ represents pounds mass and the symbol lb$_f$ represents pounds force.)

G = mass flux, lb$_m$/ft^2 sec.

H_c = enthalpy of the heat-transfer medium.

L_b = length of bend.

L_s = length of straight pipe.

L_{ep} = equivalent length of pipe for pressure drop.

m = a parameter. For heat-exchanger reactors, m is defined in Table 7-1, and for direct-fired reactors, m is defined below Equation (7-34).

M_w = molecular weight.

$\mathcal{M}_c$ = mass of heat-transfer medium in the jacket or holdup space.

n = number of hookshaped sections connected in series in a direct-fired reactor.

N = number of tubes connected in parallel.

N_{Re} = Reynolds number; $N_{Re} = DG/\mu$.

P = absolute pressure, in consistent units.

Q = total rate of heat transfer across the heat-transfer surface A in consistent units, say Btu/hr [Equations (7-3) and (7-4)].

q = rate of heat transfer per unit length in consistent units, say Btu/hr ft [see Equation (7-4)].

$\mathcal{q}$ = rate of heat transfer per unit of heat-transfer area in consistent units, say Btu/hr ft^2 [see Equations (7-27) and (7-54)].

$\mathscr{R}$ = a rate of reaction used in the reaction phase plane analysis; $\mathscr{R} = r_A/C_A^\circ$.

s = a parameter. For heat-exchanger reactors, s is defined in Table 7-1, and for direct-fired reactors s is defined below Equation (7-34).

S = cross-sectional area based on the inside diameter. S_o is the cross-sectional area based on the outside area.

S_c = cross-sectional area of the space occupied by the heat-transfer medium.

T = temperature of the reacting mixture.

T_c = temperature of the heat-transfer medium. T_{ci} is the inlet, and $(T_c)_{out}$ is the outlet temperature of the medium.

U_h = overall heat-transfer coefficient in consistent units, say Btu/hr ft^2 °F.

v = volume per mole.

w_c = mass flow rate of the heat-transfer medium in consistent units, say lb/hr.

x_e = equilibrium conversion.

y_A^0 = mole fraction of A in the feed.

z = length of the path followed by the reacting mixture, and the positive direction of z is taken to be the direction of flow of the reacting mixture. If the reacting mixture is perfectly mixed in the reactor, then the positive direction of z is taken to be the direction of flow of the heat-transfer medium.

Z = a dimensionless parameter used in the description of heat-exchanger reactors (see Table 7-1).

z = compressibility factor (For any actual gas, $z = Pv/RT$).

Greek Letters

$\alpha = U_h A/w_c C_{pc}$ [see Equation (7-14)].

δ = change in the number of moles per mole of the base reactant A every time the reaction goes one time.

μ = viscosity in consistent units, say centipoise.

ρ = mass density in consistent units, say lb/cu ft.

ϕ = a dimensionless variable used in the design of heat-exchanger reactors, $\phi = T/T_1$.

$\Phi = T_c/T_1$.

REFERENCES

1. Perry, R. H., C. H. Chilton, and S. D. Kirkpatrick, editors, *Chemical Engineering Handbook*, 4th Ed., McGraw-Hill Book Company, New York (1963).

2. Worsfold, D. J., and S. Bywater, *Canadian J. of Chem. Eng.*, *38*:1891 (1960).

3. Hsieh, H., *J. Polymer Sci.*, *A3*:153 (1965).

4. Billingsley, D. S., W. S. McLaughlin, Jr., N. E. Welch, and C. D. Holland, *I&EC*, *50*:741 (1958).

5. Logan, G. F., Master of Engineering Report, Texas A&M University (Aug. 1970).

6. Carnahan, B., H. A. Luther, and J. O. Wilkes, *Applied Numerical Methods*, John Wiley & Sons, Inc., New York (1969).

7. Ennis, B. P., H. B. Boyd, and R. Orriss, *Chemtech*, 693 (Nov. 1975).

8. Buckens, A. B., and G. F. Froment, *Ind. Eng. Chem. Proc. Des. Develop.*, *7*:435 (1968).

9. Purnell, J. H., and D. A. Leathard, *Proc. Roy. Soc.*, *A305*:517 (1968).

10. Murdoch, P. G., and C. D. Holland, *Petroleum Refiner*, *33*:159 (1954).

11. Murdoch, P. G., and C. D. Holland, *Petroleum Refiner*, *33*:163 (1954).

12. Holland, C. D., *Fundamentals and Modeling of Separation Processes, Absorption, Distillation, Evaporation, and Extraction*, Prentice-Hall, Inc., Englewood Cliffs, N.J. (1975).

13. Wilde, D. J., *Optimum Seeking Methods*, Prentice-Hall, Inc., Englewood Cliffs, N.J. (1964).

14. Johnson, P. R., J. L. Parsons, and J. B. Roberts, *Ind. Eng. Chem.*, *51*:499 (1959).

15. Stull, D. R., E. F. Westrum, Jr., and G. C. Sinke, *The Chemical Thermodynamics of Organic Compounds*, John Wiley & Sons, Inc., New York (1969).

16. Hougen, O. A., K. M. Watson, and R. A. Ragatz, *Chem. Proc. Princ.*, *Vol. I*, John Wiley & Sons, Inc., New York (1943).

17. Van Heerden, C., *Ind. Eng. Chem.*, 45:1242 (1953); *Chem. Eng. Sci.*, *8*:113 (1958).

18. Bilous, O., and N. R. Amundson, *AIChE J.*, *1*:513 (1955).

19. V. Hlavacek and J. Votruba, Ch. 6, p. 314, *Chemical Reactor Theory, A Review*, Leon Lapidus and Neal R. Amundson, eds., Prentice-Hall, Inc., Englewood Cliffs, N.J., 1977.

Fundamentals of
Heterogeneous Catalysis

8

A catalyst is generally defined as a substance which alters the speed of a reaction but does not itself undergo any chemical change. In reality, most substances classified as catalysts are eventually destroyed by their subsequent combination with products produced by the reaction in which the catalyst participates. Frost *et al.* [1] suggests that, from a practical point of view, a catalyst should be defined as a substance which alters the speed of a given reaction, regardless of the final fate of the catalyst.

Since most catalysts are employed for the purpose of increasing the rate of a particular reaction, it follows that the presence of the catalyst leads to a mechanism having a lower energy barrier than the barrier which exists when the reaction occurs in the absence of the catalyst. The primary role of the catalyst is to change the mechanism to one with a lower activation energy. It follows that if the forward rate of a given reaction is increased, the reverse rate must be increased by the same proportion because the thermodynamic equilibrium is unaltered by the presence of the catalyst.

The mechanisms of heterogeneous catalysis are very complex. Most catalysts are prepared by one of two methods. The first is the impregnation of an active or inactive support with a material which is catalytic. Some supports are activated alumina, silica gels, silica aluminas, Fuller's earth, and activated charcoal. The support material is used because of its high internal surface area per unit mass. In the second method, catalyst supports are not used; instead the solid chemicals are slurried, mixed, pelleted, and then dried.

A certain amount of heat treatment of the catalyst pellet is required in both methods. Also, catalyst preparation may involve a pellettizing step which affects the final pore structure of the catalyst. The interior pore structure is commonly subdivided into the micropore and macropore structure or small and large pores. Two parameters used to characterize the interior of a catalyst are surface area and pore size distribution. Other parameters which have been considered are the crystal structure, the electronic potential, and semiconductivity and photoconductivity of the catalyst. Instruments which are used in catalytic research are electron microscopes, nuclear magnetic resonance (NMR), gas chromatography, mass spectroscopy, electron spin resonance, and others.

This chapter is devoted to the development of rate equations for catalytic reactor design. The development is based on the postulate that the following steps are required for a chemical reaction to occur.

1. Mass transfer by film diffusion of the reactants from the flowing stream of the reacting fluid to the exterior surface of the catalyst
2. Molecular diffusion of the molecules into the interior of the catalyst, pore diffusion
3. Adsorption of the reactants on the surface of the catalyst
4. Reaction between adsorbed molecules (or between an adsorbed molecule and a molecule in the gas phase). Once the reactants have been adsorbed, surface migration may occur. The effect or extent of surface migration (or surface diffusion) is difficult to characterize.
5. Desorption of product molecules from the surface of the catalyst
6. Molecular diffusion of the products from the interior to the exterior of the catalyst surface, pore diffusion
7. Mass transfer by film diffusion of the products from the exterior of the catalyst surface to the flowing stream

These seven steps are seen to occur in series, and for a flow process to be at steady state operation, the individual rates must be equal; provided, of course, that each rate is stated on the same basis. Thus it might appear possible to develop rate expressions involving the individual rate constants (or resistances) and the overall potential (or driving force) in a manner analogous to that used to develop the heat-transfer equation: $Q = UA \, \Delta T_{lm}$. However, it is generally impossible to obtain such an expression because of the impossibility of stating the individual rate expressions in the explicit forms needed to derive such an expression. Because of the complexity of the process, working expressions for the reaction rates are commonly based on the rate expression for the "rate controlling step," the step having the smallest rate constant. (This step is sometimes called the *slowest rate* in spite of the fact that the rates of the individual steps are equal.)

Rate expressions for steps 3 through 5 are developed in this chapter. The rate expressions presently used for chemical adsorption have grown out of the theory of physical adsorption. Also, experimental methods that give a measure of the effectiveness of a catalyst or a catalyst support, such as the measurement of surface area, have grown out of the theory of physical adsorption. Thus Part I is devoted primarily to the development of the theory of physical adsorption. Part II considers chemical adsorption, reaction, and desorption, and Part III is concerned with reactor design. The effect of pore diffusion and mass transfer to and from the reacting stream and the interface at the surface are treated in the next chapter.

I. PHYSICAL ADSORPTION

When a gas is brought into contact with an evacuated solid (such as charcoal) and part of it is taken up by the solid, any one of several processes may have occurred. If the gas molecules occupy the void space within the solid, the process is called *absorption*. If the molecules become attached to the surface of the adsorbent, the process is known as *adsorption*. If the interactions between the gas and the solid are weak, similar to those involved in condensation, the process is called *physical adsorption*, and if the interaction between the adsorbed molecules and the surface is strong, similar to chemical bonding, the process is called *chemical adsorption*. Physical adsorption is also called *van der Waals adsorption*, which implies that the van der Waals forces which are active in condensation are also involved in physical adsorption.

All physical adsorption and most chemical adsorption processes are *exothermic*, a result which has been verified experimentally time and again. However, in the case of chemical adsorption, two processes have been found to be endothermic; namely, the chemisorption of molecular hydrogen on glass and the adsorption of molecular hydrogen (followed by dissociation) on iron surfaces which have been contaminated with sulfur. That one should expect physical adsorption to be exothermic can be deduced from thermodynamic considerations in the following manner. An atom of the adsorbent that is on the surface of the adsorbent is subjected to an internal pull that is greater than the outward forces, which results in a tendency to decrease the surface. When a molecule is adsorbed, a balance of some of the inward forces is achieved, which in turn decreases the surface tension. Thus the surface energy (the product of surface tension and surface area) is decreased by adsorption. Consequently, adsorption results in a decrease in free energy for the system; $\Delta G < 0$. Prior to adsorption, the gas molecules are free to move in three-dimensional space, and following adsorption they are free to move in at most the two-dimensional space along the surface. Thus adsorption is accompanied by a decrease in entropy for the system; $\Delta S < 0$. Since adsorption is accompanied both by a decrease in free energy and a decrease in entropy, it follows that the process is always exothermic, $\Delta H < 0$, since $\Delta H = \Delta G + T \Delta S < 0$. The heats of physical adsorption are of the same order of magnitude as the heats of condensation of gases, and the heats of chemical adsorption are of the same order of magnitude as those for chemical reactions.

The amount of a gas adsorbed by physical adsorption at a given pressure increases as the saturation temperature is approached. At a given temperature and pressure, the amount of a gas adsorbed increases with the normal boiling point of the gas or with the critical temperature. Chemical adsorption, on the other hand, does not generally occur at relatively low temperatures, which is demonstrated by data taken by Holland et al. [2] and presented in Figure 8-1. Also, the initial amounts adsorbed increase as the temperature is increased. The rate of chemical adsorption is seen to be relatively fast at

Figure 8-1. Chemical adsorption of oxygen on a chromium catalyst supported on aluminum oxide. [Taken from C. D. Holland and P. G. Murdoch, *AIChE Journal* 3:386 (1957). Used with permission of the American Institute of Chemical Engineers.]

first and then very slow. An equilibrium was never achieved at the temperatures shown in Figure 8-1.

Physical adsorption is readily reversible with respect to temperature and
pressure; whereas, chemically adsorbed gases are difficult to remove even by
evacuation and heating. In fact, the only way the oxygen adsorbed (see
Figure 8-1) could be removed was to react it with hydrogen [2].

Furthermore, the amount of gas chemically adsorbed does not alter the
amount which can be physically adsorbed. For example, the same amount of
nitrogen was adsorbed in surface area determinations on the reduced adsorbent as was adsorbed by the adsorbent in each of the three states of oxidation
shown in Figure 8-1. Furthermore, the adsorbed nitrogen could be easily
removed by heating and evacuating, which did not, however, remove the
adsorbed oxygen. In effect, the chemically adsorbed oxygen becomes a
part of the surface and is removable only by chemical reaction.

A. Types of Physical Adsorption

Since the initial observations of C. K. Scheele in 1773 of the adsorption of
gases by solids, a wide variety of both adsorbents and adsorbates have been
investigated. The amount of a pure gas adsorbed by a unit mass of a given
adsorbent is a function of temperature and pressure alone,

$$v_s = f(P, T) \qquad (8\text{-}1)$$

where v_s = cc of gas adsorbed at STP ($0°C$ and 1 atm) per gram of adsorbent

The results of adsorption experiments are most commonly presented in the
form of *adsorption isotherms*, volume adsorbed as a function of pressure at
constant temperature.

$$v_s = f(P), \quad (\text{at constant } T) \qquad (8\text{-}2)$$

Sometimes the results are presented in the form of *adsorption isobars*, the
volume of gas adsorbed as a function of temperature at constant pressure.

$$v_s = f(T) \quad (\text{at constant } P) \qquad (8\text{-}3)$$

Occasionally, results are presented as *adsorption isosteres*, equilibrium pressure as a function of temperature at a fixed amount of gas adsorbed.

$$P = f(T), \quad (\text{at constant } v_s) \qquad (8\text{-}4)$$

A variety of shapes of curves have been observed by the various investigators who have studied the adsorption of many different gases by many different types of adsorbents. Brunauer [3] suggested the classification of these results according to the five types of isotherms shown in Figure 8-2. Adsorption isotherms of Type I are generally attributed to unimolecular adsorption. These curves are also referred to as Langmuir isotherms because they are described by the model proposed by Langmuir [4, 5, 6], which is presented in a subsequent section. The *S-shaped* or *sigmoid* isotherms, Type II, are generally regarded as being descriptive of multimolecular adsorption. Brunauer [3] suggests that Type III isotherms represent the formation of multimolecular layers before a unimolecular layer has been adsorbed. This behavior is attributed to the fact that the attraction between the adsorbent surface and the gas is less than the attraction between liquid molecules. Brunauer [3] showed that Types IV and V could be represented by equations that took into account the effect of capillary condensation.

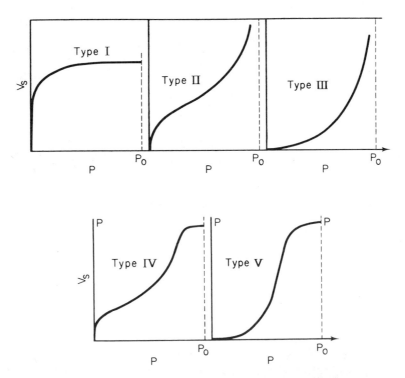

Figure 8-2. The five types of physical adsorption as proposed by Brunauer. Taken from Stephen Brunauer, L. S. Deming, W. E. Deming, and Edward Teller, *J. Amer. Chem. Soc.*, 52:1723 (1940). Used with permission of the American Chemical Society.]

B. Adsorption Models

In an attempt to explain the wide variety of experimental results characterized by Figure 8-2 many theories and models have been proposed. Of
these, only those needed to provide continuity in the development of the
expressions employed in the description of adsorption equilibria of multicomponent mixtures are presented.

1. HENRY'S LAW. Frequently, for adsorptions carried out isothermally
at low pressures, the amount of gas adsorbed can be described by Henry's law,

$$v = k_0 P \tag{8-5}$$

where k_0 = Henry's law constant

P = adsorption equilibrium pressure

At high pressures, the volume adsorbed in many instances becomes independent of pressure [7]; that is,

$$v = k_0' \tag{8-6}$$

Thus the power of the pressure for some systems ranges from 0 to 1. For intermediate pressures, the Freundlich equation is commonly used.

2. THE FREUNDLICH EQUATION. This empirical expression is of the form

$$v = k_1 P^{1/n} \tag{8-7}$$

where $n > 1$. More recently, this expression has been developed theoretically
on the basis of a logarithmic distribution of adsorption sites [8, 9]. This
expression often gives the best fit for isotherms of Type I [10].

3. THE LANGMUIR EQUATION. Brunauer [3] considered the Langmuir
equation to be, perhaps, the most important single equation in the field of
adsorption. Three derivations of this equation have been presented; the
original kinetic derivation of Langmuir [4, 5, 6], the thermodynamic derivation of Volmer [11], and statistical derivations by Fowler [12] and others.
Of these, only the kinetic derivation is presented here.

When a molecule strikes the surface of an adsorbent, it may be either
elastically reflected from the surface without any energy exchange taking
place or it may be elastically adsorbed with the release of energy. Most frequently, the collision is inelastic, and the molecule remains in contact with

347

the surface. Langmuir [4, 5, 6] attributed the phenomenon of adsorption to the average time that a molecule resides on the surface of an adsorbent. In summary, the postulates of Langmuir are as follows:

1. Of the molecules striking the surface, only those that strike a bare surface are candidates for adsorption. That is, molecules that strike an adsorbed molecule are elastically reflected.
2. The probability of evaporation of a molecule from the surface is the same whether or not the neighboring positions on the surface are empty or filled by other molecules. This amounts to assuming that the interaction between adsorbed molecules is negligible.

Let μ be equal to the number of molecules striking a unit of surface area per unit time. Let θ be equal to the fraction of the surface covered by adsorbed molecules. Then the candidates for adsorption by Postulate 1 are given by $(1 - \theta)\mu$. Let α denote the fraction of the molecules striking the bare surface which are condensed. Then

$$\text{Rate of adsorption} \left(\frac{\text{molecules}}{\text{sec cm}^2} \right) = \alpha(1 - \theta)\mu \tag{8-8}$$

Let v denote the rate of evaporation (or desorption) from a completely covered surface. Then by Postulate 2,

$$\text{Rate of desorption} \left(\frac{\text{molecules}}{\text{sec cm}^2} \right) = v\theta \tag{8-9}$$

Then at equilibrium, the fraction of surface covered by adsorbed molecules is given by

$$\alpha(1 - \theta)\mu = v\theta \tag{8-10}$$

or

$$\theta = \frac{(\alpha/v)\,\mu}{1 + (\alpha/v)\,\mu} \tag{8-11}$$

The following expression for μ, the number of molecules striking one cm^2 of surface per second, is given by the kinetic theory of gases [13],

$$\mu = \frac{P}{(2\pi mkT)^{1/2}} \tag{8-12}$$

where m = mass of a molecule

               k = Boltzmann constant

               T = temperature of the gas, $^\circ$K

An expression for v may be deduced from the concepts of the kinetic theory. Let q denote the heat given off when a molecule is adsorbed. Then to be desorbed, a molecule must possess an energy equal to or greater than q. If it is supposed that the adsorbed molecules possess a Maxwellian energy distribution in two degrees of freedom, then it may be shown that the fraction of molecules having an energy equal to or greater than q is given by $e^{-q/kT}$. Thus Equation (8-11) may be restated as follows:

$$\theta = \frac{bP}{1 + bP} \tag{8-13}$$

The dependence of b upon temperature is given by

$$b = \frac{\alpha e^{q/kT}}{(2\pi m k T)^{1/2}} \tag{8-14}$$

Since θ may be expressed as the ratio of the volume of gas adsorbed at pressure P to the volume required to form a unimolecular layer at the same temperature T, Equation (8-13) is commonly stated as

$$\frac{v}{v_m} = \frac{bP}{1 + bP} \tag{8-15}$$

where $v =$ the volume of gas adsorbed

$v_m =$ volume of gas adsorbed when the adsorbent is covered with a complete unimolecular layer

If $bP \ll 1$, then Equation (8-15) reduces to the form of Henry's law given by Equation (8-5), and if $bP \gg 1$, the form of Henry's law given by Equation (8-6) is obtained.

When the adsorption consists of a partially filled unimolecular layer, it is generally possible to obtain a satisfactory fit with Equation (8-15), the Langmuir equation. Also, this equation has been used with some success in the interpretation of chemical adsorption data. However, the development of the Langmuir equation was presented here, primarily, because it represents the starting point for the development of the BET method, the theory of multimolecular adsorption as proposed by Brunauer, Emmett, and Teller [14].

4. THE BET EQUATION. The multimolecular adsorption theory proposed by Brunauer, Emmett, and Teller [14] was the first attempt to present a

unified theory of physical adsorption of pure gases. The equations resulting from this theory may be used to correlate the five types of adsorption shown in Figure 8-2. The multimolecular theory of adsorption constitutes a generalization of Langmuir's theory in that the restriction of unimolecular adsorption is removed. In addition, the following postulates are made.

1. Let s_0, s_1, s_2, ..., s_n, ... represent the surface area covered by 0, 1, 2, ..., n, ... layers of adsorbed molecules. Postulate that the rate of condensation on s_n is equal to the rate of evaporation from surface s_{n+1}, $(n = 0, 1, 2, ...)$.
2. Postulate that the evaporation-condensation properties of the molecules in the second and higher adsorbed layers are the same as those of the lower layers.

By Postulate 1, the rate of adsorption on the bare surface is equal to the rate of evaporation from the first layer,

$$a_1 P s_0 = b_1 s_1 e^{-E_1/RT} \tag{8-16}$$

where E_1 is the heat of adsorption for the first layer, and a_1 and b_1 are constants. The relationship between the theory for multimolecular adsorption and the theory of Langmuir's adsorption is shown as follows. The rate of adsorption on the bare surface is equal to $a_1 P s_0$, which is proportional to $\alpha(1 - \theta)\mu$. The rate of desorption from the surface, which is covered by one layer of adsorbed molecules, is equal to $b_1 s_1 \exp(-E_1/RT)$, which is proportional to $\nu\theta$. Thus Equation (8-16) consists of an alternate statement of Langmuir's equation for unimolecular adsorption, and involves the assumption that a_1, b_1, and E_1 are independent of adsorbed molecules already present in the first layer. Similarly, the rate of condensation on top of the first layer is equal to the rate of evaporation from the second layer,

$$a_2 P s_1 = b_2 s_2 e^{-E_2/RT}$$

Continuation of this argument yields

$$a_3 P s_2 = b_3 s_3 e^{-E_3/RT}$$
$$\vdots \qquad \vdots$$
$$a_j P s_{j-1} = b_j s_j e^{-E_j/RT} \tag{8-17}$$
$$\vdots \qquad \vdots$$
$$a_n P s_{n-1} = b_n s_n e^{-E_n/RT}$$

(It is of interest to note that in spite of the fact that Langmuir's name is commonly associated with unimolecular adsorption, he also formulated a set of equations in 1918 [6] for the case where the adsorption spaces may hold more than one adsorbed molecule. These equations were of the same form as those given by Equation (8-17), but their summation was handled in a manner different from that proposed by Brunauer, Emmett, and Teller [14].) The summation procedure used by Brunauer, Emmett and Teller follows. The total surface of an adsorbent is given by

$$A = \sum_{j=0}^{n} s_j \tag{8-18}$$

where n is equal to the total number of adsorbed layers. The total volume adsorbed is given by:

$$v = v_0 \sum_{j=0}^{n} j s_j \tag{8-19}$$

where v_0 is equal to the volume adsorbed per unit area when the adsorbent surface is covered with a unimolecular layer. Then it follows that

$$\frac{v}{A v_0} = \frac{v}{v_m} = \frac{\displaystyle\sum_{j=0}^{n} j s_j}{\displaystyle\sum_{j=0}^{n} s_j} \tag{8-20}$$

where v_m is equal to the volume adsorbed when the adsorbent is covered with a complete unimolecular layer. By Postulate 2,

$$E_2 = E_3 = \cdots = E_n = E_L$$
$$\frac{b_2}{a_2} = \frac{b_3}{a_3} = \cdots = \frac{b_n}{a_n} = g \tag{8-21}$$

where g is a constant and E_L is equal to the heat of condensation. Each of the areas, $s_1, s_2, \ldots, s_j, \ldots$ may be expressed in terms of s_0 in the following manner. Let

$$y = \left(\frac{a_1}{b_1}\right) P e^{E_1/RT} \quad \text{and} \quad x = \left(\frac{P}{g}\right) e^{E_L/RT} \tag{8-22}$$

Then

$$s_1 = y s_0$$

$$s_2 = x s_1$$

$$s_3 = x s_2 = x^2 s_1 \tag{8-23}$$

$$\vdots \qquad \vdots \qquad \vdots$$

$$s_j = x s_{j-1} = x^{j-1} s_1 = y x^{j-1} s_0 = c x^j s_0$$

where

$$c = \frac{y}{x} = \left(\frac{a_1 g}{b_1}\right) e^{(E_1 - E_L)/RT}$$

This result may be used to compute v/v_m as given by Equation (8-20) as follows:

$$\frac{v}{v_m} = \frac{c s_0 \displaystyle\sum_{j=0}^{n} j x^j}{s_0 \left[1 + c \displaystyle\sum_{j=1}^{n} x^j\right]} \tag{8-24}$$

The sum of the geometric series appearing in the denominator is given by

$$\sum_{j=1}^{n} x^j = \frac{x - x^{n+1}}{1 - x} \tag{8-25}$$

The summation in the numerator of Equation (8-24) is evaluated in the following manner. First observe that

$$\sum_{j=1}^{n} j x^j = x \frac{d\left[\displaystyle\sum_{j=1}^{n} x^j\right]}{dx} \tag{8-26}$$

Then by use of the result obtained from Equation (8-25), it follows that

$$\sum_{j=1}^{n} j x^j = x \frac{d[(x - x^{n+1})/(1 - x)]}{dx}$$

Thus

$$\sum_{j=1}^{n} j x^j = \frac{x}{(1 - x)^2} [1 - (n + 1)x^n + n x^{n+1}] \tag{8-27}$$

Substitution of the results given by Equations (8-25) and (8-27) into Equation (8-24) followed by rearrangement yields

$$\frac{v}{v_m} = \left(\frac{cx}{1 - x}\right) \left[\frac{1 - (n + 1)x^n + n x^{n+1}}{1 + (c - 1)x - c x^{n+1}}\right] \tag{8-28}$$

Brunauer, Emmett, and Teller [14] suggest that the width of the pores, cracks, and capillaries of the adsorbent sets a limit on the maximum number of layers that can be adsorbed.

A physical interpretation of x is obtained from the following considerations. At $P \geq P_0$ (the saturation pressure of the given pure component at the temperature T of the adsorption), any amount of vapor may be condensed. The condensed vapor will appear to have been adsorbed. Consequently, the volume adsorbed becomes unbounded at the saturation pressure. As x approaches unity, these same characteristics are exhibited by Equation (8-28). By repeated application of l'Hôpital's rule, the following result is obtained:

$$\lim_{x \to 1} \frac{v}{v_m} = \frac{c(n^2 + n)}{2(1 + cn)} \tag{8-29}$$

Then at $x = 1$, it follows that v/v_m is unbounded as n increases without bound. Agreement between the physical considerations and Equation (8-28) is achieved by the condition that

$$\text{at} \quad P = P_0, \qquad x = 1 \tag{8-30}$$

From Equation (8-22),

$$\frac{x}{x_0} = \frac{P}{P_0} \tag{8-31}$$

where

$$x_0 = \frac{P_0}{g} e^{E_L/RT}$$

Comparison of Equations (8-30) and (8-31) shows that $x_0 = 1$, or

$$x = \frac{P}{P_0} \tag{8-32}$$

For the special case where $n = 1$, Equation (8-28) reduces to

$$\frac{v}{v_m} = \frac{cx}{1 + cx}$$

which is recognized as Langmuir's equation

$$\frac{v}{v_m} = \frac{c(P/P_0)}{1 + c(P/P_0)} \tag{8-33}$$

For $x < 1$, it is readily shown that the limit of v/v_m [given by Equation (8-28)] as the number of layers n is allowed to increase without bound is given by the following relationship:

$$\frac{v}{v_m} = \frac{cx}{(1 - x)(1 - x + cx)} \qquad (8\text{-}34)$$

or

$$\frac{v}{v_m} = \frac{cP}{(P_0 - P)[1 + (c - 1)(P/P_0)]} \qquad (8\text{-}35)$$

This expression is called the BET equation (after Brunauer-Emmett-Teller [14]). In the application of this expression for the determination of the surface area on an adsorbent, the following linear form may be employed.

$$\frac{P}{v(P_0 - P)} = \left(\frac{c - 1}{v_m c}\right)\frac{P}{P_0} + \frac{1}{v_m c} \qquad (8\text{-}36)$$

Then for multimolecular adsorption of the type described by Equation (8-36), a plot of $P/v(P_0 - P)$ versus P/P_0 (where $P/P_0 < 1$) should yield a straight line having a slope of $(c - 1)/v_m c$ and an intercept of $1/v_m c$. From the values obtained for the slope and intercept, the volume v_m required to cover the surface with a unimolecular layer is computed. After v_m has been determined, the surface area of the adsorbent may be calculated as demonstrated in Example 8-1, which is given below.

It is now fairly common practice to use nitrogen isotherms for the determination of the surface areas of catalysts (or adsorbents). These isotherms are determined at a temperature at or near the normal boiling point of nitrogen. Between relative pressures P/P_0 of 0.05 to 0.35, the plots of Equation (8-36) are approximately linear for Type II isotherms. For other types of isotherms, either the general expression given by Equation (8-28) or a similar one [3] may be employed.

Although the theoretical basis of the BET equation has been questioned by several authors, it is nevertheless generally accepted as giving reliable values for the surface area of an adsorbent. A typical surface area determination is demonstrated by the following example.

EXAMPLE 8-1

The following data were taken from Run 183 of Reference [2]. These data were obtained for a chromium catalyst (which was supported on aluminum oxide) by use of a low temperature adsorption apparatus which was similar to the one recommended by Brunauer [3]. Evaluate the surface area.

Data:

The temperature of the nitrogen adsorption is $-319.4°F$, and at this temperature the vapor pressure P_0 of nitrogen is 81.11 mm of Hg.

Adsorption Pressure P^*	Volume of Nitrogen Adsorbed $v^\dagger$
1.145	11.38
18.130	18.17
32.870	23.07
41.640	26.85
46.900	29.88

* P is in cm of Hg absolute
† v is in milliliters of nitrogen (at 0°C and 1 atm) adsorbed per gram of adsorbent

To estimate the area of surface covered by an adsorbed molecule of N_2, the formula used by Brunauer et al. [14] is available,

$$\sigma_m = 1.091 \left(\frac{M}{N\rho}\right)^{2/3} \tag{A}$$

where M = molecular weight of nitrogen

N = Avogadro's number

ρ = density of liquified nitrogen in grams per cubic centimeter = 0.808

σ_m = area occupied per molecule in square centimeters

SOLUTION

A plot of these data in the form of Equation (8-36) is shown in Figure 8-3. The slope was found to be

$$\text{slope} = 0.072 = \frac{c-1}{v_m c}$$

Since the intercept $1/v_m c$ is very nearly equal to zero for this example, it follows that

$$\frac{c-1}{v_m c} = \frac{1}{v_m} - \frac{1}{v_m c} \cong \frac{1}{v_m}$$

and thus $v_m = 13.9$ ml (at 0°C and 1 atm) per gram of adsorbent. The area per molecule may be estimated by substituting $M = 28$, $N = 6.023 \times 10^{23}$, and $\rho = 0.808$ g/cm^3 in Equation (A). The result so obtained is $\sigma_m = 16.2 \times 10^{-16}$ (cm^2 per molecule). By converting v_m to molecules adsorbed per gram of adsorbent and multiplying this result by σ_m, the surface area A_s in square centimeters per gram of catalyst is given.

$$A_s = \left(13.9 \frac{\text{cm}^3}{\text{g}}\right)\left(\frac{\text{g mole}}{22.4 \times 10^3 \text{ cm}^3}\right)\left(\frac{6.023 \times 10^{23} \text{ molecules}}{\text{g mole}}\right)\left(\frac{16.2 \times 10^{-16} \text{ cm}^2}{\text{molecule}}\right)$$

$$A_s = 6.05 \times 10^5 \text{ cm}^2/\text{g}$$

or

$$A_s = 60.5 \text{ m}^2/\text{g}$$

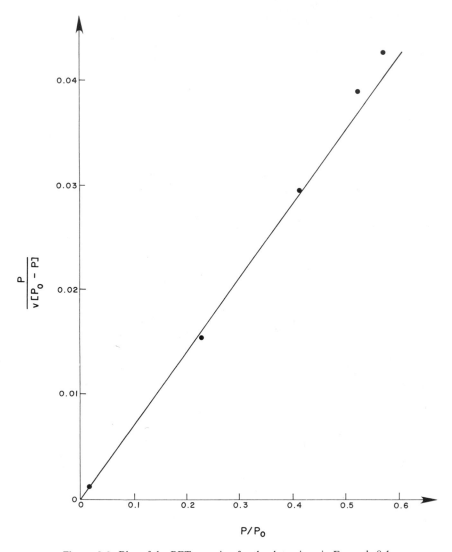

Figure 8-3. Plot of the BET equation for the data given in Example 8-1.

Livingston [15] recommended that a $\sigma_m = 15.4 \times 10^{-16}$ (cm^2 per molecule) be used for nitrogen instead of the value computed above.

The large surface areas exhibited by many adsorbents suggests that an adsorbent is made up of an intricate network of pores, and that most of the surface area lies in the interior of the adsorbent. Since the diameters of these pores may be of the same order of magnitude as that of molecules involved in a chemical reaction, considerable attention has been given to the determination of pore volume in recent years [16, 17, 18]. An extension of the BET theory of multimolecular adsorption of pure gases to include the adsorption of mixtures of gases was recently presented by Gonzales et al [19].

II. CHEMICAL ADSORPTION, REACTION, AND DESORPTION

In contrast to physical adsorption, chemical bonds are involved in chemical adsorption [20]. A further division of this type of adsorption into chemisorption and activated adsorption is common practice. Although the precise distinctions vary somewhat among authors, the general distinction usually made is that activated adsorption is a slower process and has a higher degree of reversibility than chemisorption. For convenience, all adsorption other than physical is referred to herein as *chemical adsorption*. Most of the past experimentation involving this type of adsorption has been pointed toward showing either the heterogeneity or homogeneity of catalyst surfaces.

H. S. Taylor and coworkers [21, 22, 23] have interpreted their investigations, which involved the adsorption of hydrogen by industrial catalysts, as showing the heterogeneity of industrial catalyst surfaces. On the other hand, Roberts [24], Beeck [7], and Eucken [25] have investigated pure metal catalysts, usually in the form of films. They found that all adsorption sites of these films behaved in essentially the same manner and concluded that such surfaces possessed a high degree of homogeneity. However, such films rarely make good commercial catalysts [23].

In the development of rate expressions for catalystic reactions, it is supposed that most of the chemical reaction which occurs in a flow system at steady state operation can be accounted for on the basis of only those sites which have extremely fast rates relative to the other sites. These sites were called *active centers* by Taylor et al. [23]. The concept of active centers was applied to industrial catalytic reactions by Hougen and Watson [26]. More recently, a classification of catalytic reactions was presented by Burwell [27]. For the oxygen adsorption shown in Figure 8-1, the sites which could be classified as the active sites would be among those that appear to have instantaneous rates in a batch system.

A. Formulation of the Rates of Chemical Adsorption, Desorption, and Reaction

Rate expressions for the three rate processes, adsorption, reaction, and desorption (steps 3, 4, and 5 of the introduction of this chapter), are developed for the special case of heterogeneous systems consisting of a gas phase and a solid catalyst.

TABLE 8-1

RESTRICTED CLASSIFICATION OF ELEMENTARY REACTIONS

(Taken from R. L. Burwell Jr., *Chemical & Eng. News* (Aug. 22, 1966). Used with permission of the American Chemical Society.)

Reaction	Broken Bonds	Bonds Made
1. Adsorption and its reverse, desorption		
(a) $S + NH_3(g) \rightleftharpoons H_3^+ NS^-$	None	$A-S$
(b) $S + H(g) \rightleftharpoons HS$	None	$A-S$
2. Dissociative adsorption and its reverse, associative desorption		
(a) $2S + H_2(g) \rightleftharpoons 2HS$	$A-A$	$2(A-S)$
(b) $2S + CH_4(g) \rightleftharpoons CH_3S + HS$	$A-B$	$A-S, B-S$
(c) $2S + CH_2{=}CH_2(g) \rightleftharpoons SCH_2CH_2S$	$A-A$	$2(A-S)$
3. Dissociative surface reaction and its reverse, associative surface reaction		
(a) $2S + C_2H_5S \rightleftharpoons HS + SCH_2CH_2S$	$A-B-S$	$A-S, B-S$
(b) $2S + SCH_2CH_2CH_2CH_2S \rightleftharpoons 2(SCH_2CH_2S)$	$S-A-A-S$	$2(A-S)$
4. Reactive adsorption and its reverse, reactive desorption		
(a) $HS + C_2H_4(g) \rightleftharpoons C_2H_5S$	$A-S, B-B$	$A-BS, B-S$
(b) $H_2C{=}CH_2 + D_2(g) + S \rightleftharpoons SCH_2CH_2D + DS$	$A-A$	$A-BS, B-S, A-S$
$\underset{\displaystyle S}{|}$		
(c) $SCH_2CH_2S + H_2(g) + S \rightleftharpoons SC_2H_5 + S + HS$	$B-S, A-A$	$A-BS, A-S$
5. Quasisorbed reactions		
(a) $H(g) + HS \rightleftharpoons H_2(g) + S$	$A-S$	$A-A$
(b) $2HS + C_2H_4(g) \rightleftharpoons 2S + C_2H_6(g)$	$2(A-S), B-B$	$2(A-B)$
(c) $HS + D_2(g) + S \rightleftharpoons S + HD(g) + DS$	$A-S, B-C, B-B$	$E-S, A-B, B-S$
(d) $DS + H_2C{=}CHCH_3(g) \rightleftharpoons DH_2CCH{=}CH_2(g) + HS$	$D-E$	$C-D$

1. MONOMOLECULAR SURFACE REACTIONS. Consider first the simple case where compound A is transformed to compound B in the presence of a catalyst,

$$A \; \rightleftharpoons \; B \tag{8-37}$$

One mechanism for such a reaction is the following one:

$$A(g) + S \; \underset{k_1'}{\overset{k_1}{\rightleftharpoons}} \; AS \tag{8-38}$$

$$AS \; \underset{k_2'}{\overset{k_2}{\rightleftharpoons}} \; BS \tag{8-39}$$

$$BS \; \underset{k_3'}{\overset{k_3}{\rightleftharpoons}} \; B(g) + S \tag{8-40}$$

where S = active sites

AS = chemically adsorbed A

BS = chemically adsorbed B

In the first step of the mechanism [Equation (8-38)], molecule A is adsorbed on the catalyst. In the second step of the mechanism [Equation (8-39)], the adsorbed molecule A obtains sufficient energy to cause it to form the product molecule B, all of which occurs on the single site. In the final step, molecule B is desorbed [Equation (8-40)] to the gas phase. Some of the ways in which molecules adsorb and react on catalytic surfaces are illustrated in Table 8-1.

The rate of chemical adsorption is formulated on the same basis as Langmuir's theory of physical adsorption. Thus the rate of chemical adsorption is proportional to the number of molecules of type A that strike the surface per unit time times the fraction of the surface that contains vacant active sites. By Equation (8-12), the total number of molecules striking a unit surface in unit time is proportional to the total pressure. Consequently, the number of molecules of type A that strike a unit of surface in unit time is proportional to p_A, the partial pressure of A. Let the fraction of the total number of active sites occupied by molecules of type A be denoted by θ_A, the fraction of those covered by molecules of type B by θ_B. Then $1 - \theta_A - \theta_B$ represents that fraction of the total number of sites which are vacant. If the condensation coefficient in Equation (8-8) is replaced by the proportionality or rate constant k_1, then the rate of chemical adsorption may be expressed as follows:

$$(r_1)_{\text{forward}} = k_1 p_A (1 - \theta_A - \theta_B) \tag{8-41}$$

where p_A is the partial pressure of component A at any point in the pore of a catalyst particle at any given location in a reactor. Again, as in physical desorption, the rate of chemical desorption A is taken to be proportional to θ_A, the fraction of the surface covered by A,

$$(r_1)_{\text{reverse}} = k_1'\theta_A \tag{8-42}$$

Then the net rate r_1 (molecules of A adsorbed per unit time per unit of surface area) is given by

$$r_1 = k_1 p_A(1 - \theta_A - \theta_B) - k_1'\theta_A \tag{8-43}$$

It has become customary because of convenience in the analysis of processes to express the rate r_1 in the units of

$$\frac{\text{moles of } A \text{ adsorbed}}{\text{(unit time)(unit mass of catalyst)}} \tag{8-44}$$

instead of those used in the above analysis. From a theoretical point of view, r_1 could have been based either on a unit of reactor volume or on a unit of surface area rather than on a unit mass of catalyst.

The forward rate at which the surface reaction proceeds may be taken proportional to the amount of A in the adsorbed state, AS, or the fraction of the active sites covered by adsorbed molecules of A,

$$(r_2)_{\text{forward}} = k_2\theta_A \tag{8-45}$$

and the reverse rate by

$$(r_2)_{\text{reverse}} = k_2'\theta_B \tag{8-46}$$

Thus the net rate is given by

$$r_2 = k_2\theta_A - k_2'\theta_B \tag{8-47}$$

The net rate of reaction for the desorption of the product molecule B from the surface is given by

$$r_3 = k_3\theta_B - k_3'p_B(1 - \theta_A - \theta_B) \tag{8-48}$$

Since θ_A and θ_B are difficult to determine experimentally, it is desirable to eliminate these variables from the rate expressions. Elimination of these variables may be effected by making use of the fact that at steady state operation, any set of rate processes that are in series must occur at the same rate. For if it is supposed that the rates were not equal, then there would be an accumulation or depletion with respect to time, which is contrary to the steady state assumption. Thus

$$r_1 = r_2 = r_3 = r \tag{8-49}$$

and Equations (8-43), (8-47), and (8-48) may be regarded as three equations in the three unknowns θ_A, θ_B, and r. Since these equations are linear in these variables they may be stated in matrix notation as follows:

$$\begin{bmatrix} K_2 & -1 & -1/k_2' \\ (K_1 p_A + 1) & K_1 p_A & 1/k_1' \\ p_B/K_3 & (1 + p_B/K_3) & -1/k_3 \end{bmatrix} \begin{bmatrix} \theta_A \\ \theta_B \\ r \end{bmatrix} = \begin{bmatrix} 0 \\ K_1 p_A \\ p_B/K_3 \end{bmatrix} \tag{8-50}$$

where $K_1 = k_1/k_1'$, $K_2 = k_2/k_2'$, and $K_3 = k_3/k_3'$. This matrix equation may be solved for θ_A, θ_B, and r by Gaussian elimination. The rate expression so obtained follows:

$$r = \frac{k_1 p_A - f_1[k_1' p_B/K_3]}{1 - (k_1 p_A/k_2') + f_1 f_2} \tag{8-51}$$

The functions f_1 and f_2 are defined as follows:

$$f_1 = \frac{1 + K_1 p_A(1 + K_2)}{K_2(1 + p_B/K_3) + p_B/K_3} \tag{8-52}$$

$$f_2 = \left[\frac{k_1'}{k_3} + \left(1 + \frac{p_B}{K_3}\right)\left(\frac{k_1'}{k_2'}\right) \right] \tag{8-53}$$

The use of the notation θ_A and θ_B to represent the fractions of the active sites covered by molecules of types A and B, respectively, follows the original notation suggested by Langmuir [4, 5, 6]. More recently, this notation was employed by Walas [28]. However, instead of this notation, concentration-type units are most commonly employed in the chemical engineering literature to represent the number of active sites covered by molecules of a given type.

The formulation of the concept of concentration of active sites may be effected by regarding a gram mole simply as the number 6.023×10^{23}. Thus one gram mole of active sites is equal to 6.023×10^{23} sites, and one pound mole of sites is equal to $454 \times 6.023 \times 10^{23}$ sites. For metal catalysts Boudart [29] suggests the use of 10^{15} sites per square centimeter. The area referred to is the BET area obtained by nitrogen adsorption. This number of sites corresponds to the number of metal atoms on the surface of the catalyst. For acidic catalysts, such as those used in cracking reactions, there are approximately 10^{13} sites per square centimeter [30]. On the basis of the numbers of sites per square centimeter and the BET surface area, the number of sites per unit mass of catalyst may be computed. The mass of catalyst required to obtain one mole of sites may then be computed. Then the total concentration of sites C_T may be defined as follows:

$$C_T = \frac{\text{total moles of sites}}{\text{unit mass of catalyst}} \qquad (8\text{-}54)$$

Obviously, the concentration could have been defined on the basis of surface area or a unit volume of catalyst bed rather than on the basis of a unit mass of catalyst. However, because of convenience, not only the concentrations but also the rates of adsorption, desorption, and reaction are defined on the basis of a unit mass of catalyst. Thus θ_A and θ_B may be stated in terms of a ratio of concentration units as follows:

$$\theta_A = \frac{C_{AS}}{C_T}, \qquad \theta_B = \frac{C_{BS}}{C_T} \qquad (8\text{-}55)$$

The quantities C_{AS} and C_{BS} are defined as follows:

$$C_{AS} = \frac{\text{moles of } A \text{ adsorbed}}{\text{unit mass of catalyst}} \qquad (8\text{-}56)$$

$$C_{BS} = \frac{\text{moles of } B \text{ adsorbed}}{\text{unit mass of catalyst}} \qquad (8\text{-}57)$$

The definitions of C_{AS}, C_{BS}, and C_T suppose that only one molecule is adsorbed per active site.

Equations (8-43), (8-47), and (8-48) may be restated in terms of concentration units as follows:

$$r_1 = k_1 p_A C_S - k_1' C_{AS} \qquad (8\text{-}58)$$

$$r_2 = k_2 C_{AS} - k_2' C_{BS} \qquad (8\text{-}59)$$

$$r_3 = k_3 C_{BS} - k_3' p_B C_S \qquad (8\text{-}60)$$

where $C_S = C_T - C_{AS} - C_{BS}$, the concentration of vacant sites
The rates r_1, r_2, r_3 are defined as the moles of A adsorbed, the moles of A reacted, and the moles of B desorbed, respectively, per unit time per unit

mass of catalyst. As a matter of convenience, the same symbols were employed for the rate constants in Equations (8-43), (8-47), and (8-48) and Equations (8-58) through (8-60). Again $r_1 = r_2 = r_3 = r$, and Equations (8-58), (8-59), and (8-60) may be solved to give

$$r = \frac{C_T[k_1 p_A - f_1(k'_1 p_A/K_3)]}{1 - (k_1 p_A/k'_2) + f_1 f_2} \tag{8-61}$$

where the functions f_1 and f_2 have the same formal definitions given by Equations (8-52) and (8-53).

B. Approximate Rate Expressions

In the same manner as demonstrated in the treatment of the mechanisms of homogeneous reactions the rate equations can be simplified by use of the concept of the "rate controlling step." In the development presented below, which follows that of Hougen and Watson [26], one reaction is regarded as the rate controlling step and the remaining reactions are taken to be in equilibrium.

To illustrate this method, suppose first that the adsorption of A given by Equation (8-38) is the "rate controlling step" of the mechanism. By this statement it is meant that k_1 and k'_1 are small relative to the other rate constants, and that almost as soon as A is adsorbed, it reacts to form compound B which is desorbed immediately. That is, suppose the rate of reaction is given by r_1 [Equation (8-58)] and that for all practical purposes, $r_2/k_2 \cong 0$, $r_3/k_3 \cong 0$, which is usually written simply as

$$r_2 \cong r_3 \cong 0 \tag{8-62}$$

Thus it follows from Equations (8-59), (8-60), and (8-62) that

$$C_{AS} = \frac{C_{BS}}{K_2} \tag{8-63}$$

$$C_{BS} = \frac{p_B C_S}{K_3} \tag{8-64}$$

Elimination of C_{BS} from these two expressions yields

$$C_{AS} = \frac{p_B C_S}{K_2 K_3} \tag{8-65}$$

Equations (8-64) and (8-65) are used to eliminate C_{AS} and C_{BS} in the following expression for the total number of sites.

$$C_T = C_S + C_{AS} + C_{BS} \tag{8-66}$$

After rearrangement one obtains:

$$C_S = \frac{C_T}{1 + (p_B/K_2K_3) + p_B/K_3} \tag{8-67}$$

In view of the result given by Equation (8-65), it follows that Equation (8-58) may be restated in the form

$$r = k_1 C_S \left[p_A - \frac{p_B}{K_1K_2K_3} \right] \tag{8-68}$$

Thus by combining Equations (8-67) and (8-68),

$$r = \frac{C_T k_1 [p_A - p_B/K]}{1 + (p_B/K_2K_3) + p_B/K_3} \tag{8-69}$$

where
$$K = K_1K_2K_3$$

For the case where the surface rate r_2 is controlling, $r_1 \cong r_3 \cong 0$, and thus Equation (8-58) reduces to

$$C_{AS} = K_1 p_A C_S \tag{8-70}$$

and Equation (8-60) reduces to

$$C_{BS} = \frac{p_B C_S}{K_3} \tag{8-71}$$

Substitution of these results into Equation (8-66) followed by rearrangement yields

$$C_S = \frac{C_T}{1 + K_1 p_A + p_B/K_3} \tag{8-72}$$

Elimination of C_{AS} and C_{BS} from Equation (8-59) by use of Equations (8-70) and (8-71) followed by elimination of C_S through the use of Equation (8-72) gives

$$r = \frac{C_T k[p_A - p_B/K]}{1 + K_1 p_A + p_B/K_3} \qquad (8\text{-}73)$$

where $\qquad K = K_1 K_2 K_3 \quad \text{and} \quad k = k_2 K_1$

Finally, for the case where the rate controlling step is r_3 (the desorption of B), the resulting rate expression is given by

$$r = \frac{C_T k[p_A - p_B/K]}{1 + K_1(1 + K_2)p_A} \qquad (8\text{-}74)$$

where $\qquad k = k_3 K_1 K_2$

$$K = K_1 K_2 K_3$$

BIMOLECULAR SURFACE REACTIONS. The following mechanism proposed by Hougen and Watson [26] for the reaction $A \rightleftarrows B$ may be regarded as a bimolecular reaction because by this mechanism it is supposed that an adsorbed molecule A becomes sufficiently energized to form an activated complex with an adjacent active center, which then decomposes to form an adsorbed product molecule B. Thus instead of Equation (8-39), the surface reaction becomes

$$AS + S \underset{k_2'}{\overset{k_2}{\rightleftarrows}} BS + S \qquad (8\text{-}75)$$

Then by application of the law of mass action, the net rate at which the surface reaction proceeds is given by the difference of the forward and reverse second-order reaction rates,

$$r_2 = k_2 C_{AS} C_S - k_2' C_{BS} C_S \qquad (8\text{-}76)$$

Hougen and Watson [26] present the following elegant justification for taking the concentration of adsorbed A and adjacent empty sites as being equal to the product of the concentration C_{AS} and C_S. Consider a single adsorbed molecule A, and let s be the number of adjacent sites which are equidistant from A. If θ_S is the fraction of the sites which are empty, then an average adsorbed molecule A will have $s\theta_S$ sites adjacent to it which are empty. If each adsorbed A is so surrounded, then for C_{AS} moles of adsorbed A, it follows that

$$\left.\begin{array}{l}\text{Product of the}\\\text{concentration}\\\text{of adsorbed } A\\\text{and adjacent}\\\text{vacant sites}\end{array}\right\} = C_{AS} s \theta_S = \frac{s}{C_T} C_{AS} C_S \qquad (8\text{-}77)$$

Since s and C_T are constants, they may be incorporated into the rate constants to give the forward rate shown [see Equation (8-76)].

If it is supposed that the surface reaction is the rate controlling step of the mechanism given by Equations (8-38), (8-40), and (8-75), and whose rate expressions are given, respectively, by Equations (8-58), (8-60), and (8-76), then the rate of reaction is given by

$$r = \frac{k[p_A - p_B/K]}{[1 + K_1 p_A + p_B/K_3]^2} \tag{8-78}$$

where

$$K = K_1 K_2 K_3$$

$$k = k_1 K_1 C_T^2$$

The rate expressions corresponding to suppositions of other rate controlling steps are developed in a manner analogous to that described previously. It is of interest to note that although r_2 is second order with respect to concentrations, the numerator of the final expression is first order with respect to the partial pressures. However, for the following reaction and proposed mechanism, both the surface reaction rate and the numerator of the rate expression which is obtained by taking the surface reaction to be the rate controlling step are second order.

Consider the bimolecular reaction

$$A + B \; \rightleftharpoons \; C + D \tag{8-79}$$

which is carried out in the presence of a catalyst. One possible mechanism is:

$$A(g) + S \; \underset{k_1'}{\overset{k_1}{\rightleftharpoons}} \; AS \tag{8-80}$$

$$B(g) + S \; \underset{k_2'}{\overset{k_2}{\rightleftharpoons}} \; BS \tag{8-81}$$

$$AS + BS \; \underset{k_3'}{\overset{k_3}{\rightleftharpoons}} \; CS + DS \tag{8-82}$$

$$CS \; \underset{k_4'}{\overset{k_4}{\rightleftharpoons}} \; C(g) + S \tag{8-83}$$

$$DS \; \underset{k_5'}{\overset{k_5}{\rightleftharpoons}} \; D(g) + S \tag{8-84}$$

Equation (8-82) represents the surface mechanism wherein adjacently adsorbed molecules A and B become sufficiently energized and react forming molecules C and D which are adsorbed on the same sites originally occupied by A and B.

For the case where the surface reaction is the rate controlling step, the expression obtained for the reaction rate is as follows:

$$r = \frac{K'k_3[p_A p_B - p_C p_D / K]}{[1 + K_1 p_A + K_2 p_B + p_C / K_4 + p_D / K_5]^2} \tag{8-85}$$

where

$$K' = K_1 K_2 C_T^2$$

$$K = K_1 K_2 K_3 K_4 K_5$$

Rate expressions corresponding to the cases where one of the adsorption or desorption steps is taken to be the rate controlling step are developed in a manner analogous to that demonstrated for the set of reactions given by Equations (8-38) through (8-40) (see Problem 8-2).

An alternate mechanism for the reaction given by Equation (8-79) consists of the reaction of A and B in the gas phase with catalysts sites to produce molecules C and D in the gas phase. More precisely, suppose

$$A(g) + S_1 \underset{k_1'}{\overset{k_1}{\rightleftarrows}} C(g) + S_2 \tag{8-86}$$

$$B(g) + S_2 \underset{k_2'}{\overset{k_2}{\rightleftarrows}} D(g) + S_1$$

and that the concentrations of sites S_1 and S_2 are small. Further suppose that these sites are formed at approximately the same rate at which they react (the pseudo steady state assumption). The mechanism is seen to consist of two reactions instead of the five proposed previously. The net rate of disappearance of A is given by

$$r_A = k_1 p_A C_{S_1} - k_1' p_C C_{S_2} \tag{8-87}$$

On the basis of the pseudo steady state assumption the net rates of disappearance of sites S_1 and S_2 are approximately zero. Thus

$$r_{S_2} = -r_{S_1} = k_1 p_A C_{S_1} - k_1' p_C C_{S_2} - k_2 p_B C_{S_2} + k_2' p_D C_{S_1} \cong 0$$

and

$$C_{S_2} = C_{S_1} \left[\frac{k_1 p_A + k_2' p_D}{k_2 p_B + k_1' p_C} \right] \tag{8-88}$$

Elimination of C_{S_2} from Equation (8-88) and the expression for the conservation of sites

$$C_T = C_{S_1} + C_{S_2}$$

gives

$$C_{S_1} = \frac{C_T(k_2 p_B + k'_1 p_C)}{k_1 p_A + k_2 p_B + k'_1 p_C + k'_2 p_D} \tag{8-89}$$

Use of Equations (8-88) and (8-89) to eliminate C_{S_1} and C_{S_2} from Equation (8-87) gives the desired expression for r_A,

$$r_A = \frac{C_T k_1 k_2 (p_A p_B - p_C p_D / K)}{k_1 p_A + k_2 p_B + k'_1 p_C + k'_2 p_D} \tag{8-90}$$

where

$$K = K_1 K_2$$

C. Assumption of the Most Abundant Surface Intermediate

Boudart [29, 31, 32] introduced the assumption of the "*most abundant surface intermediate (masi)*." By this assumption, the sites occupied by all species except the most abundant surface intermediate (masi) are regarded as negligible relative to those filled by the most abundant intermediate and to those which are empty. For example, if AS is the most abundant surface intermediate in the isomerization reaction [Equation (8-37)], then Equation (8-66) reduces to

$$C_T = C_S + C_{AS} \tag{8-91}$$

Boudart [29, 31, 32] demonstrated that the same form of the rate expression for the isomerization reaction [see Equations (8-38) through (8-40)] is obtained for four different mechanisms when the assumption of the most abundant surface intermediate is utilized along with other assumptions enumerated below.

Consider first the mechanism which is based on the following assumptions:

1. All of the reaction steps are irreversible,

$$A(g) + S \xrightarrow{k_1} AS$$

$$AS \xrightarrow{k_2} BS$$

$$BS \xrightarrow{k_3} B(g) + S$$

2. The most abundant surface intermediate is BS; that is,

$$C_{AS} \cong 0 \quad \text{relative to} \quad C_S \quad \text{and} \quad C_{BS}$$

3. The concentrations of adsorbed A and B may be approximated by means of the pseudo steady state assumption; that is, $r_{AS} \cong 0$ and $r_{BS} \cong 0$.

From the first assumption, the following rates expression may be stated

$$r_A = k_1 p_A C_S$$
$$r_{AS} = k_1 p_A C_S - k_2 C_{AS} \tag{8-92}$$
$$r_{BS} = k_2 C_{AS} - k_3 C_{BS}$$

From the second assumption,

$$C_T = C_S + C_{BS} \tag{8-93}$$

From the third assumption,

$$C_{AS} = \frac{k_1}{k_2} p_A C_S \tag{8-94}$$

$$C_{BS} = \frac{k_2}{k_3} C_{AS} = \frac{k_1}{k_3} p_A C_S \tag{8-95}$$

Elimination of C_{BS} from Equations (8-92), (8-93), and (8-95) followed by rearrangement yields

$$r_A = \frac{\bar{k} p_A}{1 + \bar{K} p_A} \tag{8-96}$$

where

$$\bar{k} = k_1 C_T$$

$$\bar{K} = \frac{k_1}{k_3}$$

Three other mechanisms presented by Boudart [29] which give a rate expression of the same form as Equation (8-96) are presented in Table 8-2. The meanings of $\bar{k}$ and $\bar{K}$ are seen to be different for each mechanism and to have entirely different kinetic interpretations which give rise to the well-known ambiguities of simplified kinetic models. On the other hand, these simplified kinetic models have the advantage that they may be represented by a relatively simple rate expression such as the one given by Equation (8-96).

TABLE 8-2

SIMPLIFYING ASSUMPTIONS LEAD TO THE SAME FORM OF THE RATE EXPRESSION
FOR DIFFERENT MECHANISMS

(Taken from M. Boudart, *AIChE J.*, *18: No.3*, 465 (1972). Used with permission of the American Institute of Chemical Engineers.)

Mechanism			Assumptions*	Meaning of $\bar{k}$ in Equation (8-101)	Meaning of $\bar{K}$ in Equation (8-101)
$A + S \rightleftharpoons AS$	(1)		$r_1 \cong 0$	$k_2 K_1 C_T$	K_1
$AS \longrightarrow BS$	(2)		$r_3 \cong 0$		
$BS \rightleftharpoons B + S$	(3)				
$A + S \rightleftharpoons AS$	(1)		$r_1 \cong 0$		K_1
$AS \rightleftharpoons BS$	(2)		$r_{BS} \cong 0$	$\dfrac{C_T K_1 k_2 k_3}{(k_2' + k_3)}$	
$BS \longrightarrow B + S$	(3)				
$A + S \rightleftharpoons AS$	(1)		$r_1 \cong 0$	$k_2 K_1 C_T$	K_1
$AS \longrightarrow BS$	(2)		$r_{BS} \cong 0$		
$BS \longrightarrow B + S$	(3)				

* For each mechanism, AS is assumed to be the most abundant surface intermediate.

The next example is based on a mechanism proposed by Boudart (29) for the catalytic synthesis of ammonia. Recently, Pullman-Kellogg developed a process for the catalytic synthesis of ammonia on a large scale, producing 1000 tons per day and more. This process makes use of a horizontal reactor pictured in Figure 8-4. A flow diagram of this reactor is shown in Figure 8-5.

Figure 8-4. The M. W. Kellogg horizontal reactor for the synthesis of ammonia (Courtesy of Pullman-Kellogg).

Figure 8-5. Flow diagram of the M. W. Kellogg horizontal reactor for the synthesis of ammonia (Courtesy of Pullman-Kellogg).

Exchenbremer et al. [33] have presented additional details pertaining to this process.

During operation, the reactants are charged to the converter through the inlet nozzle, Figure 8-5, and directed toward the interchanger via the annulus formed between the cartridge and pressure shell. The reactants flow through the interchanger (shell side) and exit via the gas transfer line to the first bed and are distributed over the catalyst. The reactants flow downward through the catalyst bed, then enter the space below each bed. Quench is distributed over the length of the bed and mixes with the reactants exiting the catalyst bed. The mixture then flows up through the passage provided between adjacent beds and is charged to the next bed of catalyst. Flow is continuous in a similar manner successively through each of the catalyst beds.

The effluent from the last bed is directed toward and flows through the tube side of the interchanger, giving up heat to the reactants being charged to the first bed. The cooled product gases leave the reactor through the outlet nozzle.

EXAMPLE 8-2

For the synthesis of ammonia, $N_2 + 3H_2 \rightarrow 2NH_3$ over an iron catalyst, develop the rate expression for the following mechanism

$$H_2(g) + 2S \rightleftharpoons 2HS \tag{1}$$
$$N_2(g) + 2S \longrightarrow 2NS \tag{2}$$
$$NS + 3HS \rightleftharpoons NH_3S + 3S \tag{3}$$
$$NH_3S \rightleftharpoons NH_3(g) + S \tag{4}$$

on the basis of the following assumptions:

1. The most abundant surface intermediate is NS; that is, $C_T = C_S + C_{NS}$
2. Steps 1, 3, and 4 are in equilibrium and Step 2 is the rate determining step.
3. Suppose that the conditions at which the reaction $N_2 + 3H_2 \rightleftharpoons 2NH_3$ is carried out are such that the reverse rate is negligible.

(This mechanism and associated assumptions were proposed by Boudart [29].)

SOLUTION

By Assumption (2),

$$r = k_2 p_{N_2} C_S^2 \tag{A}$$

$$K_1 = \frac{C_{HS}^2}{p_{H_2} C_S^2} \tag{B}$$

$$K_3 = \frac{C_S^3 C_{NH_3S}}{C_{NS} C_{HS}^3} \tag{C}$$

$$K_4 = \frac{C_S p_{NH_3}}{C_{NH_3S}} \tag{D}$$

When Equations (B), (C), and (D) are solved simultaneously for C_{NS}, the following expression is obtained.

$$C_{NS} = \frac{p_{NH_3} C_S}{K p_{H_2}^{1.5}} \tag{E}$$

where

$$K = K_1^{1.5} K_3 K_4$$

Elimination of C_S from Equations (A), (E), and the expression given for C_T in the first assumption yields the final form of the rate expression

$$r = k_2 p_{N_2} \left[\frac{C_T}{1 + p_{NH_3}/K p_{H_2}^{1.5}} \right]^2 \tag{F}$$

EXAMPLE 8-3

Formaldehyde may be produced by the partial oxidation of methanol over a ferromolybdenum catalyst,

$$CH_3OH + \tfrac{1}{2}O_2 = CH_2O + H_2O$$

This reaction and compounds may be represented symbolically as follows:

$$A + \tfrac{1}{2}B \ \rightleftharpoons \ C + D$$

Develop the rate expression for the following mechanism and assumptions, which were proposed by Evmenenko et al. [34]:

$$A + S_1 \ \rightleftharpoons \ AS_1 \tag{1}$$

$$B + S_2 \ \rightleftharpoons \ BS_2 \tag{2}$$

$$AS_1 + BS_2 \ \longrightarrow \ C(g) + DS_1 + S_2 \tag{3}$$

$$DS_1 \ \rightleftharpoons \ D(g) + S_1 \tag{4}$$

where S_1 = catalyst sites occupied by water and methanol

S_2 = catalyst sites occupied by O_2

Assumptions:

1. Sites S_1 and S_2 are of a different type,

$$C_{T_1} = C_{AS_1} + C_{DS_1} + C_{S_1}$$
$$C_{T_2} = C_{BS_2} + C_{S_2}$$

2. Steps 1, 2, and 4 are in dynamic equilibrium and step 3 is the rate controlling step.

SOLUTION

Since steps 1, 2, and 4 are in dynamic equilibrium (by the second assumption), it follows that

$$C_{AS_1} = K_1 p_A C_{S_1} \qquad (A)$$

$$C_{BS_2} = K_2 p_B C_{S_2} \qquad (B)$$

$$C_{DS_1} = \frac{p_D C_{S_1}}{K_4} \qquad (C)$$

Since step 3 is the rate controlling step,

$$r = k_3 C_{AS_1} C_{BS_2} \qquad (D)$$

Equations (A) through (D) may be combined with the definitions of C_{T_1} and C_{T_2} in the first assumption, giving the final result

$$r = \frac{k_3 K_1 K_2 C_{T_1} C_{T_2} p_A p_B}{[1 + K_1 p_A + p_D/K_4][1 + K_2 p_B]}$$

D. Rate Expressions for Nonuniform Surfaces

In the above developments, the assumption of ideal surfaces or uniform surfaces was used. This assumption means that all sites are kinetically and thermodynamically equal and there is no interaction between sites. Temkin [35] and subsequently Boudart [29, 31] considered the case of noninteracting absorbed species on sites which differed kinetically and thermodynamically. For such a catalyst surface, the rate of reaction could be expected to differ for each site having a different activity.

In this case, the total rate of reaction over a unit mass of surface which contains C_T (moles of sites) is given by

$$r_A = \int_0^{C_T} r \, ds \qquad (8\text{-}97)$$

where s = moles of sites having the same activity

r = the point value of the rate of reaction, moles A reacting per unit time per mole of sites

Attempts to integrate Equation (8-97) on the basis of assumed distributions of site activities have been made by Temkin [35] and others; the resulting expressions for r_A are of the same general form as the expressions developed above on the basis of uniform site activities.

Lumpkin et al. [36] pointed out that the determination of the rate constants in the above rate expressions for catalytic reactions by use of a series of runs made under isothermal conditions at several different temperatures can lead to rate expressions which do not accurately describe the behavior of reactors which are operated adiabatically or nonisothermally. Eleven different rate expressions for the hydrogenation of a codimer which had been curve fitted by different workers on the basis of data collected from isothermally operated reactors were found to predict significantly different conversions for adiabatically operated reactors. In view of this result, the authors made the recommendation that, in addition to data collected at isothermal operation, additional data at adiabatic or nonisothermal operation should be collected and used in the determination of the rate constants.

III. DESIGN OF A FIXED-BED CATALYTIC REACTOR WHEN THE RATE-CONTROLLING STEP IS ADSORPTION, DESORPTION, OR THE SURFACE REACTION

If the rates of adsorption, reaction, and desorption are slow relative to the other steps listed at the beginning of this chapter, then the partial pressures appearing in the rate expressions developed in Part II may be set equal to the corresponding partial pressures evaluated at the bulk conditions of the reactant stream.

Consider a fixed-bed catalytic reactor of the type sketched in Figure 8-6. Suppose that the reactant stream which passes through the bed is perfectly mixed in the radial direction and that no mixing occurs in the direction of flow (plug flow). In the description of a catalytic reactor, the mass of catalyst is commonly used as a variable instead of the length or volume of the reactor.

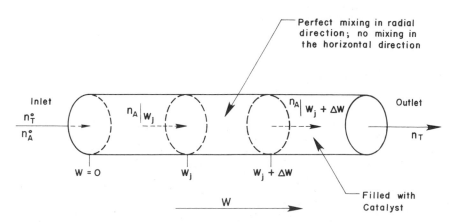

Figure 8-6. Fixed-bed catalytic reactor (W = mass of catalyst contained by the reactor from the inlet up to any point in the reactor).

The particular choice of variable to be used is arbitrary, since

$$V = Sz = \frac{W}{\rho_b} \tag{8-98}$$

where ρ_b is the bulk density of the catalyst bed (the mass of catalyst per unit volume of the reactor).

A material balance on component A over the element of bed from W_j to $W_j + \Delta W$ for the reactor shown in Figure 8-6 at steady state operation is given by

$$\left[n_A \Big|_{W_j} - n_A \Big|_{W_j + \Delta W} \right] - \int_{W_j}^{W_j + \Delta W} r_A \, dW = 0 \tag{8-99}$$

where r_A is defined in terms of the disappearance of A (moles of A disappearing per unit mass of catalyst per unit time). Application of the mean value theorems in the same manner as demonstrated for Equation (2-3) followed by the limiting process wherein ΔW is allowed to go to zero leads to the result

$$r_A = -\frac{dn_A}{dW} \tag{8-100}$$

For the case where the reactor is operated isothermally, the pressure drop is negligible, and the gas phase obeys the perfect gas law, the calculation of the mass of catalyst bed required to effect a given conversion is as follows. Suppose that the reaction to be carried out [Equation (8-37)] has a rate expression given by Equation (8-73). Let the conversion be defined in the usual way.

$$x = \frac{n_A^0 - n_A}{n_A^0} \tag{8-101}$$

Then

$$-\frac{dn_A}{dW} = n_A^0 \frac{dx}{dW} \tag{8-102}$$

Since $p_A = (1 - x)P$ and $p_B = xP$ when the feed is composed of pure $A(n_T^0 = n_A^0)$, Equations (8-73) and (8-100) may be restated in terms of the conversion x to give

$$\frac{dx}{dW} = \frac{\alpha(1 - \beta x)}{\gamma + \delta x} \tag{8-103}$$

where

$$\alpha = \frac{C_T k_1}{n_A^0}, \qquad \beta = 1 + \frac{1}{K_1}$$

$$\gamma = K_1 + \frac{1}{P} \qquad \delta = K_2 - K_1$$

For an isothermal reactor in which the pressure drop is negligible, the mass of catalyst required to achieve a specified conversion may be obtained by solving Equation (8-103). Separation of the variables in this equation followed by integration yields

$$W = \frac{\delta}{\alpha\beta}\left[\left(\frac{\gamma + \beta}{\alpha\beta}\right)\left(\log_e \frac{1}{1 - \beta x}\right) - x\right] \qquad (8\text{-}104)$$

The rate expressions for cases where adsorption, desorption, or the surface reaction is the rate controlling step of the reactions, such as the bimolecular reaction given by Equation (8-79), are integrated in a manner analogous to that demonstrated above. In order to account for the variation of the reaction temperature and the pressure throughout a flow reactor, energy balances and a modified Fanning equation are needed. The design of such reactors is analogous to that demonstrated in Chapter 7 for thermal reactors.

The design of catalytic reactors is further complicated by the sequence of mass transfer steps (listed at the beginning of this chapter) which occur in series with the catalytic reaction. The mass transfer affects are taken into account in the design of reactors as demonstrated in the next chapter.

PROBLEMS

8-1. Verify the result given by Equation (8-78).

8-2. **(a)** Obtain the rate expression where the rate of adsorption of A is the rate controlling step of the mechanism given by Equations (8-80) through (8-84).

Answer: $\quad r = \dfrac{k_1 C_T [p_A - p_C p_D / K K_1 p_B]}{1 + p_D p_C / K p_B + p_B K_2 + p_C / K_4 + p_D / K_5}$

where $K = K_2 K_3 K_4 K_5$.

(b) Repeat (a) for the case where the rate of desorption of C is the rate controlling step.

Answer: $\quad r = \dfrac{k_4 C_T\left[(K p_A p_B / p_D) - (p_C / K_4)\right]}{\left[1 + (K p_A p_B / p_D) + p_B K_2 + p_A K_1 + (p_D / K_5)\right]}$

where $K = K_1 K_2 K_3 K_5$.

8-3. Suppose that the reaction

$$A(g) + B(g) \quad \rightleftarrows \quad C(g)$$

is carried out in the presence of a catalyst, and that the surface reaction mechanism consists of the reaction of A from the gas phase with adsorbed B to produce adsorbed C; that is,

$$A(g) + S \underset{k_1'}{\overset{k_1}{\rightleftharpoons}} AS \tag{1}$$

$$B(g) + S \underset{k_2'}{\overset{k_2}{\rightleftharpoons}} BS \tag{2}$$

$$A(g) + BS \underset{k_3'}{\overset{k_3}{\rightleftharpoons}} CS \tag{3}$$

$$CS \underset{k_4'}{\overset{k_4}{\rightleftharpoons}} C(g) + S \tag{4}$$

Develop the rate expressions for r, for the cases where Steps (2), (3), and (4), respectively, are the rate controlling steps.

8-4. Butenes may be dehydrogenated with oxygen to butadiene over a bismuth molybdate catalyst [37]. The reaction is first order with respect to butene and zero order with respect to oxygen. The mechanism is

(1) $O_2(g) + 2S \rightleftharpoons 2OS$
(2) $CH_2 = CH - CH_2 - CH_3(g) + OS \longrightarrow (C_4H_7)S + OHS$
(3) $(C_4H_7)S + OS \longrightarrow CH_2 = CH - CH = CH_2(g) + OHS + S$
(4) $2OHS \longrightarrow H_2O(g) + OS + S$

Reaction (2) through (4) are assumed to be irreversible, and the second reaction is assumed to be the rate controlling step. If adsorbed oxygen is the most abundant surface intermediate and Reaction (1) is in equilibrium, show that

$$r_2 = \frac{C_T k(\sqrt{K_1 p_{O_2}}) p_B}{1 + \sqrt{K_1 p_{O_2}}}$$

which reduces to $r_2 = k C_T p_B$ if $\sqrt{K_1 p_{O_2}} \gg 1$, p_B = partial pressure of butene.

8-5. Initial rate data were used by Ahuja and Mathur [38] to study the oxidation of methane, $CH_4 + 2 O_2 = CO_2 + 2 H_2O$ over palladium at 300 to 340°C and pressures of 1.8 to 9.7 atm. The data were correlated by use of the following rate expression:

$$r = \frac{k(p_{CH_4} p_{O_2}^2 - p_{H_2O}^2 p_{CO_2}/K)}{[1 + K_{CH_4} p_{CH_4} + K_{O_2} p_{O_2} + K_{CO_2} p_{CO_2} + K_{H_2O} p_{H_2O}]^3}$$

Propose a mechanism that is in agreement with this rate expression and which makes use of the following assumptions:

1. Rate controlling step is the surface reaction

$$2 O_2 S + CH_4 S \rightleftharpoons 2 H_2 OS + CO_2 S$$

2. The remaining steps of the mechanism are in equilibrium.

8-6. The dehydrogenation of sec-butyl alcohol to methyl ethyl ketone was studied by Thaller and Thodos [39] in a differential flow reactor. The catalyst was brass stock. The temperature and pressure range were 550°F to 700°F and 0 to 14 atm.

For the temperature range of 550°F to 600°F, a dual site mechanism was proposed with the surface reaction as the rate controlling step.

$$A(g) + S \rightleftharpoons AS$$
$$AS + S \rightleftharpoons BS + CS$$
$$BS \rightleftharpoons B(g) + S$$
$$CS \rightleftharpoons C(g) + S$$

The stoichiometry is given by

$$CH_3CH_2CHOHCH_3 \rightleftharpoons CH_3COC_2H_5 + H_2$$

$$A = \text{alcohol}$$
$$B = \text{ketone}$$
$$C = \text{molecular hydrogen}$$

For temperatures equal to and greater than 600°F, the experimental results could be explained by assuming that the rate controlling step was the desorption of hydrogen.

(a) Derive the rate equation for the case where the surface reaction is the rate controlling step.

(b) Derive the rate equation for the case where the desorption of hydrogen is the rate controlling step.

8-7. In a study [40] of the vapor phase oxidation of napthalene, benzene, and anthracene over vanadium pentoxide at temperatures of 270°C to 377°C, the following rate equation was obtained:

$$r_A = \frac{C_T k_2 k_1 p_{O_2} p_A}{\beta k_1 p_A + k_2 p_{O_2}} = \frac{1}{\dfrac{1}{C_T k_1 p_A} + \dfrac{\beta}{C_T k_2 p_{O_2}}}$$

where β is equal to the stoichiometric moles of oxygen required per mole of the aromatic. (a) Use the following system of reactions plus the pseudo steady state assumption that $dC_{S_2}/dt \cong 0$ to obtain the above expression for r_A.

$$A(g) + S_1 \xrightarrow{k_1} R(g) + S_2, \qquad r_1 = k_1 p_A C_{S_1}$$
$$\beta O_2(g) + S_2 \xrightarrow{k_2} S_1, \qquad r_2 = k_2 p_{O_2} C_{S_2}$$

where $r_1 = \left(\dfrac{1}{\beta}\right) r_2$, and r_A, r_1, r_2 have the units of moles/(time)(vol)

$A = $ benzene, napthalene, or anthracene

$R = $ oxidized aromatic which obtains the oxygen from the catalyst site, S_1

$S_2 = $ reduced catalyst site

$S_1 = $ oxidized catalyst site

(a) By use of the pseudo state assumption, derive the above rate equation.

(b) For an isothermal plug-flow reactor, obtain the following expression for the V/n_T^0. (In the integration, neglect the variation of the change in the total moles with reaction.)

$$\frac{V}{n_T^0} = \frac{-1}{\bar{k}_1} \log_e \frac{p_A}{p_A^0} - \frac{1}{\bar{k}_2} \log_e \frac{p_{O_2}}{p_{O_2}^0}$$

where $\bar{k}_1 = C_T k_1$ and $\bar{k}_2 = C_T k_2$.

(c) Suggest a form for plotting the data for the purpose of estimating $\bar{k}_1$ and $\bar{k}_2$.

8-8. In the oxidation of ethylene over a silver catalyst to ethylene oxide [37], the selectivity can be approximately fitted by a triangular system of first-order reactions

$$C_2H_4 \xrightarrow{k_1} C_2H_4O \qquad \frac{k_2}{k_1} = 0.08$$

$$\searrow k_3 \qquad \swarrow k_2$$

$$CO_2 \qquad \frac{k_3}{k_1} = 0.4$$

For ethylene conversions of 20, 60, and 80 percent in an isothermal, plug-flow reactor, calculate the moles of CO_2 and the moles of ethylene oxide produced per mole of ethylene fed to a plug-flow reactor which is operated isothermally. Assume that the volumetric flow rate is constant throughout the reactor. Also, calculate the moles of ethylene oxide produced per mole of ethylene reacted.

Answer: At $x = 0.2, 0.6,$ and 0.8, moles CO_2 per mole C_2H_4 fed $= 0.393, 0.318,$ and 0.113. Moles of C_2H_4O/C_2H_4 fed $= 0.142, 0.416,$ and 0.539.

8-9. A mechanism for the dehydrogenation of butane, $C_4H_{10} \rightleftarrows C_4H_8 + H_2$ over chromia (Cr_2O_3) on alumina was postulated by Happel et al. [41] as follows:

$$C_4H_{10} + S \rightleftharpoons C_4H_{10}S \tag{1}$$

$$C_4H_{10}S + S \rightleftharpoons C_4H_9S + HS \tag{2}$$

$$C_4H_9S + S \rightleftharpoons C_4H_8S + HS \tag{3}$$

$$C_4H_8S \rightleftharpoons C_4H_8 + S \tag{4}$$

$$2\,HS \rightleftharpoons H_2 + 2S \tag{5}$$

(a) On the basis of the following assumptions, develop the corresponding rate expression. Reaction (1) is rate controlling and reactions (2) through (5) are in equilibrium. Assume adsorbed butene is the most abundant surface intermediate.

(b) Repeat Part (a) for the case where Reaction (2) is the rate controlling step, and Reactions (1), (3), (4), and (5) are in equilibrium, and butene is the most abundant surface intermediate.

(c) Examine the effect of pressure on the initial rate of reaction for the rate expressions obtained in Parts (a) and (b).

8-10. Methanol may be synthesized over a ZnO catalyst in the temperature range of 300 to 400°C at pressures of 200 to 300 atm [42]. The stoichiometry is

$$CO + 2\,H_2 \quad \rightleftharpoons \quad CH_3OH$$

Develop the rate expression for the following mechanism. Let $CO = A$, $H_2 = B$, $CH_3OH = C$, then

$$A(g) + S \quad \rightleftharpoons \quad AS \tag{1}$$

$$B(g) + S \quad \rightleftharpoons \quad BS \tag{2}$$

$$AS + 2BS \quad \rightleftharpoons \quad CS + 2S \tag{3}$$

$$CS \quad \rightleftharpoons \quad C(g) + S \tag{4}$$

Assume that Reaction (3) is the rate controlling step and that Reactions (1), (2), and (4) are in equilibrium.

NOTATION

C_{AS} = moles of A adsorbed per unit mass of catalyst.

C_T = total moles of sites per unit mass of catalyst.

E_j = heat of adsorption of layer j of adsorbed molecules [see Equation (8-17)].

p_A = partial pressure of component A in the interior of the pore of a catalyst at any given point in a reactor.

P_0 = vapor pressure of a gas being adsorbed at the temperature T of the adsorption.

r_A = rate of reaction of component A, moles of A disappearing per unit time per unit mass of catalyst.

s_j = surface area covered by j layers of adsorbed molecules [see Equation (8-16)].

v = volume (at 0°C and 1 atm) of a gas adsorbed per gram of adsorbent at the temperature T and pressure P of the adsorption experiment.

v_m = volume (at 0°C and 1 atm) per gram of adsorbent when the adsorbent is covered with a unimolecular layer.

REFERENCES

1. Frost, A. A., and R. G. Pearson, *Kinetics and Mechanisms*, John Wiley & Sons, Inc., New York (1953).

2. Holland, C. D., and P. G. Murdoch, *AIChE J.*, *3*:386 (1957). C. D. Holland, Ph. D. dissertation, Texas A & M University (May 1953).

3. Brunauer, S., *The Adsorption of Gases and Vapors*, Princeton University Press, Princeton, N.J. (1943).

4. Langmuir, I., *J. Am. Chem. Soc.*, *35*:105 (1913).

5. _____, *J. Am. Chem. Soc.*, *37*:1139 (1915).

6. _____, *J. Am. Chem. Soc.*, *40*:1361 (1918).

7. Beeck, O., *Rev. Mod. Phys.*, *17*:61 (1945).

8. Halsey, G. D., and H. S. Taylor, *J. Chem. Phys.*, *15*:624 (1947).

9. Sips, R., *J. Chem. Phys.*, *16*:490 (1948).

10. Graham, D., *AIChE Symposium Series*, *55*: *No. 24* (1927).

11. Volmer, M., *A. Phys. Chem.*, *115*:253 (1925).

12. Fowler, R. H., *Proc. Cambridge Phil. Soc.*, *31*:260 (1935).

13. Loeb, L. B., *Kinetic Theory of Gases*, McGraw-Hill Book Company, New York (1927).

14. Brunauer, S., P. H. Emmett, and E. Teller, *J. Am. Chem. Soc.*, *60*:309 (1938).

15. Livingston, H. K., *J. Colloid Sci.*, *4*:447 (1949).

16. Anderson, R. J., *Experimental Methods in Catalytic Research*, Academic Press, New York (1968).

17. Innes, W. B., *Experimental Methods in Catalytic Research*, Ch. 2. (Editor R. J. Anderson), Academic Press, New York (1968).

18. Smith, J. M., *Chemical Enginerring Kinetics*, 2d Ed., McGraw-Hill Book Company, New York (1970).

19. Gonzalez, A. J. and C. D. Holland, *AIChE J. 16*: No. 5, 718 (1970) and *17*: No. 2, 470 (1971).

20. Griffith, D. P., *The Mechanics of Contact Catalysis*, Oxford University Press, New York (1946).

21. Taylor, H. S., *Proc. Roy. Soc.*, *A108*:105 (1925).

22. _____ and S. C. Liang, *J. Am. Chem. Soc.*, *69*:1306 (1947).

23. _____, *Trans. Faraday Soc.*, *Conference*, 3 (April 1950).

24. Roberts, J. K., *Proc. Roy. Soc.*, *A152*:445 (1935).

25. Eucken, A., *Trans. Faraday Soc.*, Conference on Catalysis, 128 (April 1950).

26. Hougen, O. A., and K. M. Watson, *Chem. Proc. Princ.*, Part III, John Wiley & Sons, Inc., New York (1948).

27. Burwell, R. L., Jr., *Chemical & Eng. News*, p. 59 (August 22, 1966).

28. Walas, S. M., *Reaction Kinetics for Chemical Engineers*, McGraw-Hill Book Company, New York (1959).

29. Boudart, M., *AIChE J.*, *18*: *No. 3*, 465 (1972).

30. Krylov, Oleg V., *Catalysis by Non-Metals*, Academic Press, New York and London (1970).

31. Boudart, M., *Kinetics of Chemical Processes*, Prentice-Hall, Englewood Cliffs, N.J. (1968).

32. _____, *AIChE J.*, *2*:62 (1956).

33. Exchenbremer, G. P., and G. A. Wagner, III, *Chem. Eng. Prog.*, *68*: *No. 1*, 62 (1972).

34. Evmenenko, N. P., and Ya. B. Gorokhoustskii, *Kinetics and Catalysis*, *10*:1071 (1969). Translated from *Kinet. Katal.*, *10*: *No. 6*, 1299–1304 (1969).

35. Temkin, M. I., *Kinet. Katal.*, *3*:509 (1962).

36. Lumpkin, R. E., Jr., W. D. Smith Jr., and J. M. Doungas, *I&EC Fund.*, *8*: *No. 3*, 407 (1969).

37. Voge, Hervey H., and C. R. Adams, *Advances in Catalysis*, *17*:151 (1967).

38. Ahuja, O. P., and G. P. Mathur, *Canadian J. of Chem. Eng.*, *45*:367 (1967).

39. Thaller, L. H., and George Thodos, *AIChE J.*, *6*: *No. 3*, 369 (1960).

40. Mars, P., and D. W. Van Krevelen, Conference on Oxidation Processes, *Chem. Eng. Sci.*, Supplement *3*:41 (1954).

41. Happel, John, and R. S. Atkins, *I&EC Fund.*, *9*: *No. 1*, 11 (1970).

42. Natta, G., P. Pino, G. Mazzanti, and I. Pasquon, *Chimica e Indistria.*, *35*:705 (1953).

Mass and Heat
Transfer in the Design of
Catalytic Reactors

9

In Part I of this chapter, the effect of pore diffusion on the rate of reaction is considered, and in Part II the treatment of the rate of mass transfer from the bulk conditions of the phase outside of the catalyst to the entrance of the pores is presented. In Part III the design equations for a fixed-bed catalytic reactor are developed.

I. EFFECT OF PORE DIFFUSION ON THE RATE OF REACTION

The relatively large surface areas of commercial catalysts suggest that most of the catalytic surface is internal area rather than external area. Then one would expect to find most of the catalytic sites (the sites which promote a given reaction) in the interior of the catalyst. Thus, if the rate of a given reaction depends upon the partial pressure of A above the catalytic surface, then the rate of reaction may be affected by the net rate of diffusion into the interior of the catalyst, since the partial pressure of A in an element of pore volume depends upon the net rate at which A is supplied to the volume by diffusion and the net rate at which A disappears from the volume by reaction. A formulation of the rate expressions follows.

A. Fundamental Rate Expressions for the Rate of Reaction and the Rate of Pore Diffusion

Suppose that component A in the gas phase reacts by a single reaction in the presence of a solid catalyst with an internal pore structure. Further, suppose that the rate at which this reaction proceeds may be represented by an unidirectional nth-order rate expression. Since the number of active sites which are responsible for the activity of the catalyst is proportional to the surface area, a measurable quantity, the defining expression for the rate of reaction for a catalytic reaction is based on a unit of surface area. Then for the nth-order unidirectional reaction under consideration,

$$r_{sa}\left[\frac{\text{moles of }A\text{ reacted}}{\text{(time)(unit of surface area)}}\right] = k_{sa}p_A^n \qquad (9\text{-}1)$$

The partial pressure of a component, say A, at any point within the catalyst is denoted by p_A, and the partial pressure of A at the bulk conditions of the fluid outside of the catalyst is denoted by p_{Ab}.

In the analysis which follows, a material balance is made on component A in an element of pore volume. To make this balance, an expression for the rate of reaction which is based on a unit of pore volume is needed; that is, an expression of the form

$$r_{pore}\left[\frac{\text{moles of }A\text{ reacted}}{\text{(time)(unit of pore volume)}}\right] = k_{pore}p_A^n \qquad (9\text{-}2)$$

The rate constants k_{sa} and k_{pore} may be related through the appropriate use of the following mass densities and the surface area. Let

$$\frac{1}{\rho_p} = \text{volume of pellet per unit mass of pellet}$$

$$\frac{1}{\rho_s} = \text{volume of the solid pellet material per unit mass of the solid}$$

$$S_a = \text{surface area per unit mass of pellet}$$

$$r_{pore} = r_{sa}\left[\frac{\text{moles of }A\text{ reacted}}{\text{(time)(unit of surface area)}}\right]S_a\left(\frac{\text{surface area}}{\text{unit mass}}\right)$$

$$\cdot\left[\frac{1(\text{mass catalyst})}{(1/\rho_p - 1/\rho_s)(\text{volume of pores})}\right] = \left[\frac{S_a}{(1/\rho_p - 1/\rho_s)}\right]r_{sa}$$

Let the volume of pores per unit volume of the pellet be denoted by ε (the volume fraction of voids). Then

$$\varepsilon = \frac{1/\rho_p - 1/\rho_s}{1/\rho_p} \tag{9-3}$$

Thus

$$r_{\text{pore}} = \left(\frac{S_a \rho_p}{\varepsilon}\right) r_{sa} \tag{9-4}$$

and

$$k_{\text{pore}} = \frac{S_a \rho_p k_{sa}}{\varepsilon} \tag{9-5}$$

Next suppose that each unit of catalytic surface in the catalyst bed of a reactor is equally accessible to each reactant molecule A. Let the rate of reaction based on a unit mass of such a catalyst bed be denoted by r and the corresponding rate constant by k; that is, let the intrinsic rate be represented by

$$r\left[\frac{\text{moles of } A \text{ reacted}}{(\text{time})(\text{unit mass of catalyst bed})}\right] = kp_A^n \tag{9-6}$$

The rates r and r_{sa} and the associated rate constants are related as follows:

$$r = S_a r_{sa} \tag{9-7}$$

and

$$k = S_a k_{sa} \tag{9-8}$$

Also, Equations (9-4), (9-5), (9-7), and (9-8) may be used to show that

$$r_{\text{pore}} = \left(\frac{\rho_p}{\varepsilon}\right) r \tag{9-9}$$

$$k_{\text{pore}} = \left(\frac{\rho_p}{\varepsilon}\right) k \tag{9-10}$$

In the analysis of the effect of pore diffusion on the rate of reaction, it is customary to represent the diffusion of a mole of A through a pore by the following expression. More precisely, the moles of A diffusing in the positive direction of z per unit of cross-sectional area of pore (which is perpendicular to the direction of transfer) is given by

$$\mathcal{J}\left[\frac{\text{moles of } A \text{ transferred}}{(\text{time})(\text{area})}\right] = -\mathcal{D}\frac{dp_A}{dz} \tag{9-11}$$

where $\mathscr{D}$ = the diffusion coefficient defined by Equation (9-11) for the diffusion of A through a pore in which a catalytic reaction occurs

Procedures for estimating effective diffusion coefficients have been given by
Satterfield [1].

B. Material Balance on Reactant A in a Catalyst Pore

In 1939, Thiele [2] initiated the study of the effect of pore diffusion on the
rate at which a catalytic reaction occurs. Following Thiele, suppose that the
actual internal pore structure of a catalyst can be represented by cylindrical
pores of length $2L$ and cross-sectional area S as shown in Figure 9-1. Further
suppose that the single reaction given by Equation (9-2) occurs at steady state
operation, and that the only mechanism for the transport of A through the
pore is by the diffusion mechanism described by Equation (9-11). Again,
following Thiele, suppose that all of the pores have open ends and that A
enters each end at equal rates. For this model, the material balance on A
in the element of pore volume $S\,\Delta z$ (see Figure 9-1) is given by

$$S\mathscr{J}\Big|_{z_j} - S\mathscr{J}\Big|_{z_j+\Delta z} - \int_{z_j}^{z_j+\Delta z}\left(\frac{\rho_p}{\varepsilon}\right)rS\,dz = 0 \qquad (9\text{-}12)$$

From this integral-difference equation, the following differential equation is
obtained as described in Chapter 1.

$$\frac{-d\mathscr{J}}{dz} - \left(\frac{\rho_p}{\varepsilon}\right)r = 0 \qquad (9\text{-}13)$$

By substituting the definitions of $\mathscr{J}$ and r into Equation (9-13) and by making
a change in variables, the following equivalent form of Equation (9-13) is

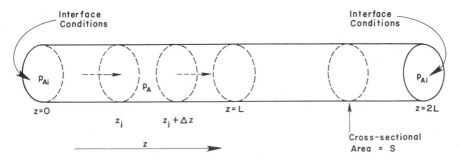

Figure 9-1. Model of an average pore of a catalyst.

obtained:

$$\frac{d^2\psi}{dZ^2} - L^2\alpha^2\psi^n = 0 \qquad (9\text{-}14)$$

where
$$\alpha = \sqrt{\frac{\rho_p k p_{Ai}^{n-1}}{\varepsilon\mathcal{D}}}, \quad \text{for an } n\text{th-order reaction}$$

$$\psi = \frac{p_A}{p_{Ai}}$$

$$Z = \frac{z}{L}$$

The product αL is commonly called the Thiele modulus. For a first-order reation ($n = 1$) and for the boundary conditions

$$\psi = 1 \quad \text{at} \quad Z = 0$$
$$\frac{d\psi}{dZ} = 0 \quad \text{at} \quad Z = 1 \qquad (9\text{-}15)$$

Figure 9-2. Partial pressure of the reactant as a function of the distance into the pore at different values of the Thiele modulus, αL.

The solution of Equation (9-14) is given by

$$\frac{p_A}{p_{Ai}} = \frac{\cosh (1 - Z)\alpha L}{\cosh \alpha L} \qquad (9\text{-}16)$$

Graphs of this function are displayed in Figure 9-2. For an actual pellet, Aris [3] suggested that the characteristic length of a pore, L, be defined as the ratio of the volume of a pellet to its external surface area. For spherical pellets, $L = R/3$. (Upon comparison of the Thiele modulus as presented above with the one presented by others (1, 2, 3, 5, 8, 9, 10), one finds the porosity of the pellet ε does not appear in their expression. This difference is a consequence of the way in which the effective diffusivities are defined. Satterfield et al. [1] bases $\mathscr{J}$ and $\mathscr{D}$ on the cross-sectional area of the porous mass; whereas, $\mathscr{J}$ and $\mathscr{D}$ in Equation (9-11) are based on the cross-sectional area of the void volume of the porous mass. Hence $\mathscr{D}$ presented by others is equal to $\varepsilon\mathscr{D}$ as used herein. The formula presented herein is preferred because it shows the effect of the void volume of the catalyst pellet on the Thiele modulus.

C. Effectiveness Factor

The effectiveness factor η is defined as follows:

$$\eta = \frac{[\text{actual moles of } A \text{ reacting in the pore per unit time}]}{\begin{bmatrix} \text{moles of } A \text{ which would have reacted in the pore if} \\ p_{Ai} \text{ were equal to } p_A \text{ for all } z \end{bmatrix}} \qquad (9\text{-}17)$$

Since the partial pressure of A is symmetrical with respect to the center L of the pore, it follows that the moles of A reacted over $2L$ is twice that reacted over the volume from $z = 0$ to $z = L$. Thus

$$\eta = \frac{2 \int_0^L \left(\dfrac{\rho_p}{\varepsilon}\right) rS \, dz}{2 \int_0^L \left(\dfrac{\rho_p}{\varepsilon}\right) r\Big|_{p_{Ai}} S \, dz} = \frac{\int_0^1 r \, dZ}{r\Big|_{p_{Ai}}} \qquad (9\text{-}18)$$

where $Z = z/L$. After the rate of reaction (for $n = 1$) has been expressed in terms of A, the integral in Equation (9-18) may be evaluated to give

$$\eta = \frac{\tanh \alpha L}{\alpha L} \qquad (9\text{-}19)$$

A graph of the effectiveness factor η as a function of αL is given in Figure 9-3.

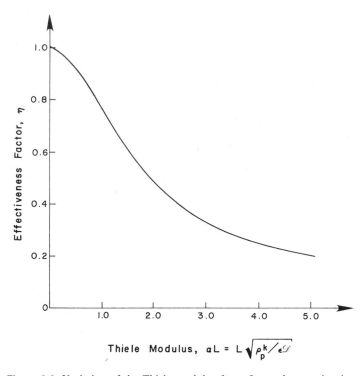

Figure 9-3. Variation of the Thiele modulus for a first-order reaction in a cylindrical pore.

This expression for η may be used to compute the mean value of the rate of reaction within the pore by use of Equation (9-21), which is developed as follows. Let the integral appearing in Equation (9-18) be replaced by its equivalent as given by the mean value theorem of integral calculus. Then

$$\eta = \frac{\int_0^1 r \, dZ}{r \Big|_{p_{Ai}}} = \frac{(r)_m}{r \Big|_{p_{Ai}}} = \frac{r_A}{r \Big|_{p_{Ai}}} \tag{9-20}$$

where r_A is used to denote the mean value of r over the length of pore L. Thus

$$r_A = \eta r \Big|_{p_{Ai}} = \left(\frac{\tanh \alpha L}{\alpha L}\right) r \Big|_{p_{Ai}} \tag{9-21}$$

If pore diffusion were the only mechanism that limited the accessibility of the catalyst surface to the reacting molecules, then the experimentally observed rate at any point in the catalyst bed would be equal to r_A.

For values of $\alpha L \geq 5$, the resistance to pore diffusion is large in the sense that pore diffusion has a pronounced effect on the rate of reaction. Since

$$\tanh \alpha L = \frac{e^{\alpha L} - e^{-\alpha L}}{e^{\alpha L} + e^{-\alpha L}} = \frac{1 - e^{-2\alpha L}}{1 + e^{-2\alpha L}}$$

it is evident that for $\alpha L \geq 5$,

$$\tanh \alpha L \cong 1$$

Thus, for $\alpha L \geq 5$, the expression for the effectiveness factor given by Equation (9-19) reduces to

$$\eta \cong \frac{1}{\alpha L} \tag{9-22}$$

For very small values of αL, the resistance to pore diffusion is said to be "small" in the sense that the rate of reaction becomes independent of pore diffusion as αL approaches zero. For, by l'Hôpital's rule,

$$\lim_{\alpha L \to 0} \eta = \lim_{\alpha L \to 0} \frac{1 - e^{-2\alpha L}}{\alpha L + \alpha L e^{-2\alpha L}} = \lim_{\alpha L \to 0} \frac{2e^{-2\alpha L}}{[1 - 2\alpha L e^{-2\alpha L} + e^{-2\alpha L}]} = 1$$

$$\tag{9-23}$$

In the region where the resistance to pore diffusion is large, the rate becomes inversely proportional to the Thiele modulus. The failure to account for pore diffusion may cause a reaction to appear to have a fractional order as illustrated by the following example.

EXAMPLE 9-1

Suppose that the Thiele model adequately describes an nth-order catalytic reaction which occurs in the presence of a catalyst surface. Thus the expression for the mean rate of reaction which would be exhibited by the reactant in the presence of a catalyst pellet is given by

$$r_A = \eta k p_{Ai}^n$$

where n is the order of the reaction when the catalytic surface is equally accessible to all molecules of A. For the case where the resistance to pore diffusion is large, what are the apparent orders of r_A for different values of n?

SOLUTION

When η in the above expression for r_A is replaced by its equivalent as given by Equation (9-22) and the expression for α given by Equation (9-14) is used, the following result is obtained:

$$r_A = \frac{1}{L} \left(\sqrt{\frac{\varepsilon \mathscr{D}}{\rho_p k p_{Ai}^{n-1}}} \right) k p_{Ai}^n = \frac{1}{L} \left(\sqrt{\frac{\varepsilon \mathscr{D} k}{\rho_p}} \right) p_{Ai}^{(n+1)/2}$$

For $n = 0$, the apparent order is $\frac{1}{2}$; for $n = 1$, the apparent order is unity; and for $n = 2$, the apparent order is $\frac{3}{2}$.

The above development was based on the assumption of constant temperature throughout a given catalyst pellet. Naturally, the question arises as to what happens when the temperature of the pellet is not uniform throughout. This is a more difficult problem in that it requires simultaneous solution of both heat and material balances. Numerical solutions have been obtained for first- and second-order reactions [4]. Exothermic reactions may have effectiveness factors η greater than unity, and endothermic reactions always have effectiveness factors less than unity [5].

D. Conversion in a Plug-Flow Reactor in which Pore Diffusion Occurs

Suppose that the rate of transfer of reactant A from the bulk phase outside of the catalyst to the entrance of the pore is exceedingly fast relative to the diffusion of A through the pores. Then the bulk partial pressure of A in the fluid flowing past a catalyst pellet is approximately equal to the partial pressure at the interface.

$$p_{Ab} \cong p_{Ai} \qquad (9\text{-}24)$$

For the first-order reaction, say,

$$A \longrightarrow R \qquad (9\text{-}25)$$

The expression given below Equation (9-14) for α reduces to

$$\alpha = \sqrt{\frac{\rho_p k}{\varepsilon \mathcal{D}}} \qquad (9\text{-}26)$$

and thus becomes independent of the partial pressure p_{Ai} which varies throughout the length of the catalyst bed. At the inlet to the pores at a given W of the reactor shown in Figure 8-6, the rate of reaction as defined by Equation (9-6) becomes

$$r \Big|_{p_{Ai}} = kp_{Ai} = kp_{Ab} \qquad (9\text{-}27)$$

Thus, by Equation (9-21), the mean rate of reaction r_A at any W becomes

$$r_A = \eta r \Big|_{p_{Ai}} = \eta k p_{Ab} = \eta k \left(\frac{n_A}{n_T}\right) P \qquad (9\text{-}28)$$

where n_A is the bulk value of the molar flow rate of A at a given W. The material-balance expression for r_A is given by Equation (8-105); namely,

$$r_A = -\frac{dn_A}{dW} \qquad (8\text{-}105)$$

Suppose that the fixed-bed catalytic reactor shown in Figure 8-6 is used to carry out the catalytic reaction given by Equation (9-25). The feed consists of pure A ($n_T^0 = n_A^0$), the reactor is operated isothermally with a negligible pressure drop, and the plug-flow assumption is valid. Thus k, n_T, and P in Equation (9-28) are independent of W, and η may likewise be regarded as essentially constant. [For any reaction for which $n \neq 1$, the effectiveness factor η depends upon composition, see Equation (9-14)]. Elimination of r_A from Equations (8-105) and (9-28) followed by integration gives the following expression for n_A at any W:

$$n_A = n_A^0 \exp\left[-\frac{\eta k P W}{n_T^0} \right] \qquad (9\text{-}29)$$

The above relationships suggest the use of experimental tests to determine if pore diffusion is significant in a given catalytic reaction. One obvious test is to determine the rates of reaction exhibited by a catalyst in two different pellet sizes. If the model constituted an exact description of the process, then by Equation (9-22), one would expect the rates to be inversely proportional to the characteristic length of the pores of the pellets in systems in which the resistance to diffusion is large. If the rates of reaction are unaffected by changing the length of the catalyst pores, then pore diffusion is fast and not a significant resistance. For nonisothermal exothermic reactions, Peterson [5] suggests the use of three different pellet sizes in order to provide meaningful results in the region where maximum values of η were predicted by the solutions of his model. Boudart [6] questioned the validity of tests of this type for pore diffusion in the zeolites. Such substances have micropores with diameters of the order of 10 Ångstrom units. For such substances, Boudart [6] suggested the use of several catalysts with differing amounts of active material. If the rate, based on the surface area of active material, is constant, then pore diffusion is fast [6]. For more advanced treatments of this topic see References [1, 5, 7, 8, 9, 10].

EXAMPLE 9-2

Suppose that the Thiele model is obeyed by an actual catalyst which is to be tested in a fixed-bed catalytic reactor. Further suppose that the first-order reaction given by Equation (9-25) is carried out at the operating conditions stated above Equation (9-29) plus the condition that the feed consists of pure A. Two tests are run at the same operating conditions and the same mass of catalyst. In the first test, pellets of length L_1 are used and in the second test the length of the pellets is doubled ($L_2 = 2L_1$).

(a) If a conversion of $x_1 = 0.3$ (moles of A converted per mole of A fed) is obtained for the first test, find the conversion x_2 to be expected from the second test for the case where resistance to pore diffusion is large ($\alpha L_1 \geq 5$).

(b) Suppose that a third test is run in which the pellets of length L_2 are used ($L_2 = 2L_1$) and the ratio W/n_A^0 is adjusted such that a conversion of $x_3 = x_1 = 0.3$ is obtained. Find the value of $(W/n_A^0)_3$ relative to $(W/n_A^0)_1$ required to achieve the same conversion obtained in the first test. Again, assume that the tests are carried out in the region in which the resistance to pore diffusion is large.

SOLUTION

(a) On the basis of the data given for the first and second tests, Equation (9-29) may be stated as follows for the first test:

$$-\log_e (1 - x_1) = \frac{\eta_1 k P W}{n_A^0}$$

and for the second test

$$-\log_e (1 - x_2) = \frac{\eta_2 k P W}{n_A^0}$$

These two equations are readily solved for x_2 to give

$$x_2 = 1 - (1 - x_1)^{\eta_2/\eta_1}$$

When resistance to pore diffusion is large,

$$\frac{\eta_2}{\eta_1} = \frac{\alpha L_1}{\alpha L_2} = \frac{L_1}{L_2} = \frac{1}{2}$$

Thus

$$x_2 = 1 - \sqrt{0.7} = 0.163$$

(b) In this case, Equation (9-29) takes the following form for the first experiment:

$$-\log_e (1 - x_1) = \eta_1 k P \left(\frac{W}{n_A^0}\right)_1$$

and for the third experiment

$$-\log_e (1 - x_1) = \eta_2 k P \left(\frac{W}{n_A^0}\right)_3$$

Since $\eta_2/\eta_1 = \frac{1}{2}$ [see Part (a)], it follows that

$$\left(\frac{W}{n_A^0}\right)_3 = 2\left(\frac{W}{n_A^0}\right)_1$$

Thus, to achieve the same conversion in the third test as the first, the mass of catalyst must be doubled, or the flow rate of the feed must be reduced by one-half.

II. MASS TRANSFER (FILM DIFFUSION) FROM BULK FLUID TO CATALYST SURFACE

The mechanism of mass transfer includes the transport of the reactant molecules from the flowing stream to the interface at the surface of the catalyst and the transport of the product molecules from the interface to the flowing stream. The mass transfer process includes Steps 1 and 7 of the catalytic process described at the beginning of Chapter 8. If mass transfer is the rate controlling step, then the interior surface of the catalyst is not being effectively used.

A. Fundamental Rate Equations

The rate of mass transfer of component A from the bulk conditions in the flowing stream to the interface is commonly represented as follows:

$$r_{mA} = k_A(p_{Ab} - p_{Ai}) \tag{9-30}$$

where $k_A = k_G a_v \phi / \rho_b$; $k_G =$ coefficient of mass transfer, moles per unit time per unit pressure per unit of surface area; $a_v =$ interfacial area for mass transfer per unit volume of the empty reactor bed; and $\rho_b =$ bulk density of the catalyst bed, mass of catalyst per unit volume of bed. The quantity ϕ is the shape factor. For spheres $\phi = 1$; for cylinders $\phi = 0.91$; and for flakes $\phi = 0.81$; for irregular granules $\phi = 0.90$ (assumed) as proposed by Yoshida et al. [11].

$r_{mA} =$ rate of mass transfer of component A from the flowing stream to the surface of the catalyst, moles of A transferred per unit time per unit mass of catalyst

The rate of mass transfer r_{mA} and the rate of reaction r_A have the same units. Furthermore, since the mass transfer step is in series with the reaction step, it follows that at steady state operation,

$$r_{mA} = r_A \tag{9-31}$$

The validity of this relationship may be shown by use of material balances [see Equations (9-72) through (9-75)].

1. EFFECT OF MASS TRANSFER AND PORE DIFFUSION ON THE RATE EXPRESSION FOR THE RATE OF REACTION. These two mechanisms of mass transfer and pore diffusion constitute two rate processes in series. To demonstrate the effect of these two rate processes on the rate of reaction in the pore of a catalyst pellet, consider the simple first-order unidirectional reaction, $A \to R$, given by Equation (9-25). The mean rate throughout the pore is given by rearranging Equation (9-20) to the form

$$r_A = \eta k p_{Ai} \tag{9-32}$$

By solving Equations (9-30) through (9-32), it is found that

$$p_{Ai} = \frac{p_{Ab}}{1 + \eta k / k_A} \tag{9-33}$$

Consequently, Equation (9-32) may be stated in terms of the bulk partial pressure p_{Ab} and the resistances to mass transfer and pore diffusion as follows:

$$r_A = \frac{p_{Ab}}{(1/k_A) + (1/\eta k)} \tag{9-34}$$

The resistance to mass transfer is $1/k_A$ and the resistance to chemical reaction as corrected for pore diffusion is represented by $1/\eta k$. If $\eta k \gg k_A$, then Equation (9-34) reduces to

$$r_A = k_A p_{Ab} \tag{9-35}$$

and mass transfer is said to be the rate controlling step. Since k_A depends upon the Reynolds number of the flowing stream, it follows that the rate of reaction is dependent upon the velocity of the flowing stream.

If $k_A \gg \eta k$, then Equation (9-34) reduces to Equation (9-28); namely,

$$r_A = \eta k p_{Ab}$$

and the rate of reaction (corrected for pore diffusion) is said to be the rate controlling step. The behavior to be expected of a reactor in which the rate of reaction (corrected for pore diffusion) is the rate controlling step has already been demonstrated by Example 9-2.

Consider now the case where the rate of mass transfer is the rate controlling step and the rate of reaction is given by Equation (9-35). Suppose that the reaction given by Equation (9-25) with the rate expression given by Equation (9-35) is carried out isothermally with a negligible pressure drop. Further suppose that the plug-flow assumption is valid. Elimination of r_A from Equations (8-105) and (9-35) followed by rearrangement and integration gives

$$n_A = n_A^0 \exp\left[-\frac{k_A P W}{n_T^0}\right] \tag{9-36}$$

The rather unusual behavior which may be exhibited by a reactor in which mass transfer is the rate controlling step results from the fact that the mass transfer rate constant k_A is also a function of the total flow rate n_T. The following equation for computing k_G is based on the correlation of Yoshida et al. [11] for $50 < N_{Re} < 1000$:

$$k_G = 0.57 \left(\frac{G}{p_f M_m}\right)(N_{Re})^{-0.41}(S_c)^{-2/3} \tag{9-37}$$

where D_{mA} = effective diffusivity of component A in a multicomponent gaseous mixture [see Equations (18) and (19) of Reference [11]]

$G = \rho v_T/S$, mass flow rate per unit of cross-sectional area

M_m = molecular weight of the mixture

$N_{Re} = \dfrac{G}{a_v \phi \mu}$, Reynolds number

$N_{Sc} = \mu/\rho D_{mA}$, Schmidt number

$p_{fA} = P - p_A \left[\dfrac{a + b - c - d}{a}\right]$, for the case where the reaction

$aA + bB = cC + dD$ occurs

ρ = mass density of the gaseous mixture

Since $k_A = k_G a_v \phi/\rho_b$ [see Equation (9-30)], it follows that

$$k_A = \left(\frac{0.57 a_v \phi}{\rho_b}\right)\left(\frac{G}{p_{fA} M_m}\right)(N_{Re})^{-0.41}(N_{Sc})^{-2/3} \tag{9-38}$$

EXAMPLE 9-3

Suppose that Equation (9-36) describes the reaction to be studied in a catalytic reactor. Suppose that two test runs are carried out at the same conditions except for the mass of the catalyst and the total flow rate. Also for convenience, suppose that the feed consists of the pure reactant $A(n_A^0 = n_T^0)$. The mass of catalyst used in the second run is twice that of the first $(W_2 = 2W_1)$. The flow rate of the second run is twice that of the first $(n_{A,2}^0 = 2n_{A,1}^0)$. If 20 percent of A is converted in the first run, calculate the conversion which may be expected in the second run. Assume that the variations of all quantities in Equation (9-38) except the total flow rate may be neglected; that is, assume

$$k_A \cong C(n_T)^{0.59} \qquad (A)$$

SOLUTION

Equation (9-36) may be rearranged and stated in the following form for each run.

$$-\log_e (1 - x_1) = k_{A,1} P \left(\frac{W_1}{n_{A,1}^0} \right) \qquad (B)$$

$$-\log_e (1 - x_2) = k_{A,2} P \left(\frac{W_2}{n_{A,2}^0} \right) \qquad (C)$$

Since $W_1/n_{A,1}^0 = W_2/n_{A,2}^0$ and since k_A is given by Equation (A), Equations (B) and (C) may be restated in the form

$$\log_e (1 - x_2) = \left(\frac{n_{A,2}^0}{n_{A,1}^0} \right)^{0.59} [\log_e (1 - x_1)] = 2^{0.59} \log_e (1 - 0.2)$$

Thus

$$x_2 = 1 - [0.8]^{1.505} = 0.2853$$

If mass transfer had been very fast relative to the rate of reaction as corrected for pore diffusion, then the same conversion would have been obtained for the second test as was obtained for the first.

Many other tests may be devised [8, 9] which make use of the same principles involved in Example 9-3. Boudart [6] urges the use of caution in the application of these tests since at low Reynolds numbers, which are often obtained in laboratory reactors, the coefficients of heat and mass transfer are fairly insensitive to changes in the velocities. The effect of mass transfer on the kinetic behavior of a reaction system is illustrated by the following experimental example.

2. ANALYSIS OF DATA FOR PROPYLENE OXIDATION. Propylene was oxidized over a copper oxide catalyst in a fixed-bed reactor by Billingsley et al. [12]. A sketch of the reactor used in this investigation is shown in Figure 9-4. It was found, as discussed below, that the stoichiometry of this oxidation

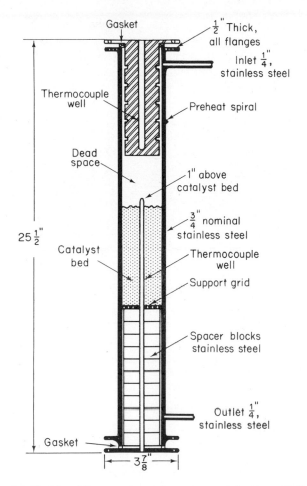

Figure 9-4. Sketch of the experimental reactor used in the oxidation of propylene by Billingsley. [Taken from D. S. Billingsley and C. D. Holland, *I&EC Fundamentals*, 2:252 (1963). Used with permission of the American Chemical Society.]

could be represented by the equations:

$$C_3H_6 + O_2 \;\rightleftharpoons\; CH_2CHCHO + H_2O \tag{9-39}$$

$$C_3H_6 + 4.5\,O_2 \;\rightleftharpoons\; 3\,CO_2 + 3\,H_2O \tag{9-40}$$

For simplicity, these compounds are denoted as follows:

$$A + B \;\rightleftharpoons\; C + D \tag{9-41}$$

$$A + 4.5B \;\rightleftharpoons\; 3E + 3D \tag{9-42}$$

These reactions may not go precisely as written; the mechanisms by which these reactions proceed may differ appreciably from these simple equations. These two equations are to be regarded as representing the stoichiometric relationships between two competing mechanisms.

For reactants A and B, the rates r_A and r_B are defined in terms of the disappearance of A and B. Similarly, for products C, D, and E, the rates r_C, r_D, and r_E are defined in terms of the appearance of C, D, and E. Furthermore, for convenience, rates r_1 and r_2 are introduced. These are the rates at which the reactions given by Equations (9-39) and (9-40) [or Equations (9-41) and and (9-42)] proceed:

$$r_1 = r_C \tag{9-43}$$

$$r_2 = \frac{r_E}{3} \tag{9-44}$$

Also, for these two stoichiometric reactions, it is readily shown that the rates are related by three independent equations:

$$r_A = r_C + \frac{r_E}{3} \tag{9-45}$$

$$r_B = r_C + \frac{4.5}{3} r_E \tag{9-46}$$

$$r_D = r_C + r_E \tag{9-47}$$

At steady state, the rate of mass transfer of each reactant from the flowing stream to the interface is equal to the rate at which it is consumed by reaction. Likewise, the rate of production of each product by reaction is equal to its rate of mass transfer from the interface to the flowing fluid. Thus, in terms of mass transfer,

$$r_A = k_A(p_{Ab} - p_{Ai}) \tag{9-48}$$

$$r_B = k_B(p_{Bb} - p_{Bi}) \tag{9-49}$$

$$r_C = k_C(p_{Ci} - p_{Cb}) \tag{9-50}$$

$$r_D = k_D(p_{Di} - p_{Db}) \tag{9-51}$$

$$r_E = k_E(p_{Ei} - p_{Eb}) \tag{9-52}$$

where, for convenience, the rates of mass transfer $r_A, r_B, \ldots, r_E$ have the same set of units as those of catalytic rates of reaction, (moles)/(time)(mass of catalyst). The mass transfer coefficients are defined in the same manner as k_A in Equation (9-30).

When the expressions given by Equations (9-48) through (9-52) are used to eliminate r_A, r_B, r_C, r_D, and r_E from Equations (9-45) through (9-47) the following set of simultaneous equations is obtained:

$$k_A(p_{Ab} - p_{Ai}) = k_C(p_{Ci} - p_{Cb}) + \frac{k_E}{3}(p_{Ei} - p_{Eb}) \tag{9-53}$$

$$k_B(p_{Bb} - p_{Bi}) = k_C(p_{Ci} - p_{Cb}) + \frac{4.5k_E}{3}(p_{Ei} - p_{Eb}) \tag{9-54}$$

$$k_D(p_{Di} - p_{Db}) = k_C(p_{Ci} - p_{Cb}) + k_E(p_{Ei} - p_{Eb}) \tag{9-55}$$

If it is supposed that the rate constants and partial pressures at the bulk conditions are known, then Equations (9-53) through (9-55) constitute three equations in the five unknown interfacial partial pressures, p_{Ai}, p_{Bi}, p_{Ci}, p_{Di}, and p_{Ei}. Thus, to solve these equations, two additional relationships are required, which could consist of two of the postulates that follow:

1. One could assume that the diffusion to and from the interior of the catalyst offers negligible resistance ($p_{Ai} \cong p_A, \ldots, p_{Ei} \cong p_E$). Then two independent rate expressions could be postulated for adsorption, desorption, and surface reactions.
2. One could again assume that the diffusion to and from the interior of the catalyst offers negligible resistance, and that all of the adsorption, desorption, and surface reactions are in dynamic equilibrium.
3. One could postulate that the mass transfer of reactants to the interface are the rate controlling steps of the entire process. This assumption gives $p_{Ai} \cong p_{Bi} \cong 0$.

On the basis of the experimental results obtained by Billingsley et al. [12], some of the above postulates were discarded and others were introduced as described below.

In the experimental investigation of Billingsley et al. [12], the reactor shown in Figure 9-4 was operated isothermally as a differential reactor. A *differential* reactor is one in which the conversion per pass is small enough so that rate of reaction may be approximated with good accuracy as a constant over the reactor. Thus Equation (8-105) may be rearranged and integrated to give

$$r_j \cong -\frac{(n_j - n_j^0)}{W} = -\frac{\Delta n_j}{W} \tag{9-56}$$

where r_j is defined in terms of disappearance. For a product component, where r_j is defined in terms of appearance.

$$r_j \cong \frac{\Delta n_j}{W} \tag{9-57}$$

In attempting to correlate the experimental results, the linear relationship shown in Figure 9-5 was discovered. The equation of the best straight line through the points is

$$\frac{r_1}{r_2} = 0.72 \frac{p_{Ab}}{p_{Bb}}$$

(9-58)

This expression was taken as an additional relationship. By use of Equations (9-43), (9-44), (9-50), and (9-52), it is possible to restate Equation (9-58) in terms of the same variables appearing in Equations (9-53) through (9-55).

$$\frac{3k_C(p_{Ci} - p_{Cb})}{k_E(p_{Ei} - p_{Eb})} = 0.72 \frac{p_{Ab}}{p_{Bb}}$$

(9-59)

Thus Equations (9-53) through (9-55) plus Equation (9-59) constitute four equations in five unknowns. The further postulate was made that the rate of mass transfer of B was rate controlling; that is,

$$p_{Bi} \cong 0$$

(9-60)

Figure 9-5. Ratio of rates of reactions producing acrolein and CO_2 varied linearly with ratio of partial pressures. [Taken from D. S. Billingsley and C. D. Holland, *I&EC Fundamentals*, 2:232 (1963). Used with permission of the American Chemical Society.]

reduces the number of unknowns to four. This postulate ($p_{Bi} = 0$) led to expressions for r_1 and r_2 that fit the experimental results better than the rate expressions based on several other postulates.

The stoichiometry was established by use of the same general approach presented by Woodham et al. [13] and described in Chapter 4. For any given feed composition, the overall mechanism was found to be independent of the residence time (or W/n_T^0) as shown in Figures 4-8 and 4-9. If secondary reactions, such as the further oxidation of acrolein to CO_2 or the polymerization of acrolein to the dimer were significant, the curves in Figures 4-8 and 4-9 would have had positive slopes. The horizontal lines shown in these figures, plus the fact that other possible products did not appear in the effluent in significant amounts, suggest the reactions are adequately described by the stoichiometric relationships given by Equations (9-39) and (9-40).

The postulates represented by Equations (9-58) and (9-60) are readily utilized to obtain expressions for r_1 and r_2 as follows. Equations (9-43), (9-44), and (9-49) may be combined to give

$$r_B = r_1 + \frac{4.5}{3}(3r_2) \tag{9-61}$$

By use of Equations (9-49), (9-58), and (9-60), it is possible to reduce Equation (9-61) to the form

$$k_B p_{Bb} = \left(0.72 \frac{p_{Ab}}{p_{Bb}} + 4.5\right) r_2 \tag{9-62}$$

Thus

$$r_2 = \frac{k_B p_{Bb}^2}{0.72 p_{Ab} + 4.5 p_{Bb}} \tag{9-63}$$

When this result is combined with Equation (9-58), the following expression is obtained:

$$r_1 = k_B \left[\frac{0.72 p_{Ab} p_{Bb}}{0.72 p_{Ab} + 4.5 p_{Bb}}\right] \tag{9-64}$$

The value of the mass transfer coefficient k_B was computed by use of Equation (9-64) and correlated as a function of the total molar flow rate. This result

$$k_B = 0.94 \times 10^{-3} (n_T^0)^{0.555} \tag{9-65}$$

was used to compute the calculated values of r_1 and r_2 shown in Figures 9-6 and 9-7. Comparison of these curves with those in Figures 4-8 and 4-9

Figure 9-6. Correlation of rate of acrolein producing reaction. [Taken from D. S. Billingsley and C. D. Holland, *I&EC Fundamentals*, *2*:232(1963). Used with permission of the American Chemical Society.]

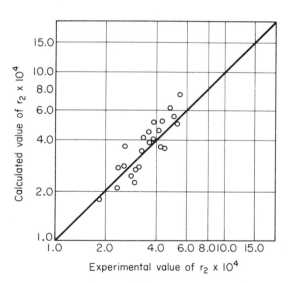

Figure 9-7. Correlation of rate of CO_2 producing reaction. [Taken from D. S. Billingsley and C. D. Holland, *I&EC Fundamentals*, *2*:232 (1963). Used with permission of the American Chemical Society.]

suggests that the accuracy of the correlation is about as good as the experimental accuracy.

The mass transfer coefficient k_B is a function of the Reynolds and Schmidt numbers. Of the quantities that appear in these numbers, only the total flow rate was varied to any appreciable extent. Because of this, k_B was correlated as a function of the single variable, total flow rate. The exponent 0.555 on the total flow rate is in general agreement with exponents given by Equation (9-38) and used in Example 9-3. This agreement lends support to the postulates represented by Equations (9-58) and (9-60).

III. DEVELOPMENT OF THE MATERIAL AND ENERGY BALANCES FOR A FIXED-BED CATALYTIC REACTOR AT STEADY STATE OPERATION

To illustrate the development of the material- and energy-balance equations required to describe catalytic reactors, a reactor having a fixed-catalyst bed such as the one shown in Figure 8-6 was selected. A heterogeneous system is considered in which a reactant in the gas phase is passed through a bed of solid catalyst particles. The development of the equations for this reactor is based on the following set of simplifying assumptions:

1. The gas phase is perfectly mixed in the radial direction and no mixing occurs in the direction of flow of the gas; that is, plug flow is assumed.
2. The rate of reaction can be represented by a mean rate for a catalyst particle.
3. The catalyst particles and the enclosed gas phase are at the same temperature throughout the interior of each particle.
4. The rate of heat transfer along the walls of the reactor in the direction of flow of the gas is negligible.
5. The rate of heat transfer by mixing or eddy diffusion in the direction of flow of the gas is negligible.

The above assumptions are the ones commonly made and are usually valid. If the diameter and length of a reactor are of the same order of magnitude, however, the flow pattern may be more nearly approximated by the assumption of a perfectly mixed flow reactor rather than the plug-flow assumption stated above. Even though the ratio of the diameter to the length of a reactor is small, the temperature gradients in the radial direction may not be negligible for reactors having relatively large diameters.

The second assumption listed above may be approximated by use of the mean value of the rate of reaction within the interior of the catalyst as discussed in the previous section or if the resistance to pore diffusion is negligible relative to the resistances for all other steps, then the rate of reaction is the same at all interior points. The equations are developed for the general case of a reaction whose stoichiometry is represented by

$$aA + bB = cC + dD$$

A. Material Balances

In all of the material and energy balances which follow, a fixed-catalytic bed in a single tube is considered. The rates of mass transfer of the reactants from the bulk phase to the interior of the catalyst are defined as follows:

$$r_{mA} = k_A(p_{Ab} - p_{Ai})$$
$$r_{mB} = k_B(p_{Bb} - p_{Bi})$$

$$(9\text{-}66)$$

and, for the products, the rate of mass transfer from the interior of the catalyst to the bulk phase are defined as follows:

$$r_{mC} = k_C(p_{Ci} - p_{Cb})$$
$$r_{mD} = k_D(p_{Di} - p_{Db})$$

$$(9\text{-}67)$$

For the reactants, the rates of reaction are defined in terms of disappearance, and for the products the rates of reaction are defined in terms of appearance.

1. MATERIAL BALANCES ON THE REACTANTS AND PRODUCTS IN THE GAS PHASE OUTSIDE OF THE CATALYST. A schematic diagram of the streams involved is shown in Figure 9-8. A material balance on component A over the element of volume ΔV is given by

$$n_A \Big|_V - n_A \Big|_{V+\Delta V} - \int_V^{V+\Delta V} r_{mA}\rho_b \, dV = 0 \qquad (9\text{-}68)$$

For product C, the balance is given by

$$n_C \Big|_V - n_C \Big|_{V+\Delta V} + \int_V^{V+\Delta V} r_{mB}\rho_b \, dV = 0 \qquad (9\text{-}69)$$

The corresponding differential equations listed below are obtained in the usual way by use of the mean value theorems followed by the limiting

Figure 9-8. Sketch of the reactor used in making the material balances.

process wherein ΔV is allowed to go to zero; namely,

$$\frac{dn_A}{dV} + r_{mA}\rho_b = 0$$

$$\frac{dn_B}{dV} + r_{mB}\rho_b = 0$$

$$\frac{dn_C}{dV} - r_{mC}\rho_b = 0 \tag{9-70}$$

$$\frac{dn_D}{dV} - r_{mD}\rho_b = 0$$

Note also, that since the mass of catalyst in the bed is related to the volume of the bed, namely, $W = \rho_b V$, the above equations may be restated in terms of the variable W rather than V in a manner analogous to that which follows for component A.

$$\frac{dn_A}{dW} + r_{mA} = 0 \tag{9-71}$$

2. MATERIAL BALANCE ON THE GAS PHASE IN THE INTERIOR OF THE CATALYST PELLETS. The equality of the rate of mass transfer and the rate of

reaction as given by Equation (9-31) for component A is shown to be true by making the following material balance. Consider component A which is being transferred from the bulk gas phase to the gas phase in the interior of the catalyst at the rate r_{mA}. In the interior of the catalyst, component A is being consumed by reaction at the mean rate r_A. Then over the element of volume ΔV (see Figure 9-8), the material balance on A is given by

$$\int_V^{V+\Delta V} r_{mA}\rho_b \, dV - \int_V^{V+\Delta V} r_A\rho_b \, dV = 0 \tag{9-72}$$

Since r_{mA} and r_A are regarded as continuous functions, Equation (9-72) may be restated in the form

$$\int_V^{V+\Delta V} [r_{mA}\rho_b - r_A\rho_b] \, dV = 0 \tag{9-73}$$

Since Equation (9-73) applies for all values of V greater than zero and all values of $V + \Delta V$ less than the total volume of the reactor, it follows that the integrand must be equal to zero for values of V in the interval $(0 < V < V_{total})$. Thus

$$r_{mA} - r_A = 0 \tag{9-74}$$

When the remaining equations are treated in a similar manner, the following relationships are obtained:

$$r_{mB} = r_B, \qquad r_{mC} = r_C, \qquad r_{mD} = r_D \tag{9-75}$$

Also the stoichiometry of the reaction requires that the rates of reaction be related by

$$r_A = \frac{a}{b}r_B = \frac{a}{c}r_C = \frac{a}{d}r_D \tag{9-76}$$

B. Energy Balances

A schematic diagram of the stream flows involved in these balances is shown in Figure 9-9. The rate of heat transfer through the wall to the gas phase outside of the catalyst is denoted by q_c, and the rate of heat transfer from the gas phase to the catalyst is denoted by q_g. The flow rate of gas into the element of volume ΔV is denoted by n_T, and the total heat content of this gas stream is denoted by H. The rate of mass transfer of each component to (or from) the catalyst phase from (or to) the gas phase outside of the catalyst is shown in Figure 9-9.

Figure 9-9. Sketch used in making the energy balances on the gas and the catalyst phases.

For definiteness, suppose that heat is being transferred across the wall and the gas film to the gas phase in the catalyst bed at the rate q_c (Btu per unit time per unit length) at all points along the boundary. If a heat-transfer medium is used, then q_c at any V (that is, at any point along the boundary) is given by

$$q_c = U_c a_c (T_c - T) \tag{9-77}$$

where T_c is the temperature of the heat-transfer medium and T is the temperature of the gas phase. The heat-transfer area per unit length of reactor is denoted by a_c. (The overall heat-transfer coefficient U_c and a_c are consistent in that if U_c is based on the interior surface area of the tube then a_c is the interior surface area.)

The rate of heat transfer from the gas phase to the catalyst phase is given by

$$q_g = U_g a_g (T - T_s) \tag{9-78}$$

where a_g is the exterior surface area of the catalyst particles per unit length of the reactor bed which is effective in heat transfer, and T_s is the temperature of the catalyst particle and the enclosed gas.

1. ENERGY BALANCE ON THE GAS PHASE OUTSIDE OF THE CATALYST PARTICLES. On the basis of the assumptions stated at the beginning of this section and by use of the schematic diagram presented in Figure 9-9, an energy balance on the gas phase on the outside of the catalyst pellets in the

element of volume from V to $V + \Delta V$ is given by

$$
n_T H \Big|_V - n_T H \Big|_{V+\Delta V} + \int_V^{V+\Delta V} \left(\frac{q_c - q_g}{S} \right) dV
$$

$$
- \int_V^{V+\Delta V} \rho_b [r_{mA} \bar{H}_A + r_{mB} \bar{H}_B - r_{mC} \bar{H}_C - r_{mD} \bar{H}_D] \, dV = 0 \quad (9\text{-}79)
$$

where all of the enthalpies are evaluated at the temperature T of the gas phase at the composition at a particular V. The differential equation corresponding to Equation (9-79) is given by

$$
-\frac{d(n_T H)}{dV} + \frac{q_c - q_g}{S} + \rho_b r_A \left[\frac{c}{a} \bar{H}_C + \frac{d}{a} \bar{H}_D - \bar{H}_A - \frac{b}{a} \bar{H}_B \right] = 0 \quad (9\text{-}80)
$$

where r_{mA}, r_{mB}, r_{mC}, and r_{mD} have been replaced by their equivalents as given by Equations (9-75) and (9-76).

In order to evaluate $d(n_T H)/dV$ and the partial molar enthalpies which appear in Equation (9-80), a generalized expression for the enthalpy of a nonideal solution is needed. Such an expression is obtained by introducing an additive function Ω to the expression for $n_T H$, (as discussed in Chapter 11) to give

$$
n_T H = \sum_{i=1}^{c} n_i H^{\circ}_{fi} + n_T \Omega \quad (9\text{-}81)
$$

For any given equation of state for either the vapor or liquid phase, a formula for the evaluation of Ω may be obtained as demonstrated in Chapter 11. In the above summation, let the component A be denoted by the number 1, component B by 2, component C by 3, and component D by 4, which is equal to the total number of components c. For convenience, let the right-hand side of Equation (9-81) be denoted by $f(P, T, n_A, n_B, n_C, n_D)$ or simply f. Then

$$
\frac{d(n_T H)}{dV} = \frac{\partial f}{\partial T} \frac{dT}{dV} + \frac{\partial f}{\partial n_A} \frac{dn_A}{dV} + \frac{\partial f}{\partial n_B} \frac{dn_B}{dV} + \frac{\partial f}{\partial n_C} \frac{dn_C}{dV} + \frac{\partial f}{\partial n_D} \frac{dn_D}{dV} \quad (9\text{-}82)
$$

From the definition of f, it is evident that

$$
\frac{\partial f}{\partial T} = n_T \left[\sum_{i=1}^{c} \frac{n_i}{n_T} \frac{\partial H^{\circ}_{fi}}{\partial T} + \frac{\partial \Omega}{\partial T} \right] = n_T C_p \quad (9\text{-}83)
$$

By use of the relationships given by Equations (9-70), (9-75), (9-76), and (9-83), it is possible to restate Equation (9-82) in the following form:

$$
\frac{d(n_T H)}{dV} = n_T C_p \frac{dT}{dV} + \rho_b r_A \left[\frac{c}{a} \frac{\partial f}{\partial n_C} + \frac{d}{a} \frac{\partial f}{\partial n_D} - \frac{\partial f}{\partial n_A} - \frac{b}{a} \frac{\partial f}{\partial n_B} \right] \quad (9\text{-}84)
$$

The partial molar enthalpy of component i of a mixture is defined as follows:

$$\bar{H}_i = \left(\frac{\partial f}{\partial n_i}\right)_{P,T,n_j} = \frac{\partial f}{\partial n_i} \tag{9-85}$$

Thus the third term on the left-hand side of Equation (9-80) may be expressed in terms of the enthalpy function f

$$\rho_b r_A \left[\frac{c}{a}\bar{H}_C + \frac{d}{a}\bar{H}_D - \bar{H}_A - \frac{b}{a}\bar{H}_B\right]$$

$$= \rho_b r_A \left[\frac{c}{a}\frac{\partial f}{\partial n_C} + \frac{d}{a}\frac{\partial f}{\partial n_D} - \frac{\partial f}{\partial n_A} - \frac{b}{a}\frac{\partial f}{\partial n_B}\right] \tag{9-86}$$

Comparison of the second term on the right-hand side of Equation (9-84) with the right-hand side of Equation (9-86) shows them to be identical. Because of a difference in sign, these two terms cancel when the expressions given by Equations (9-84) and (9-86) are substituted into Equation (9-80). The resulting equation for an enthalpy balance on an element of volume of the gas phase outside of the catalyst pellets is given by

$$-n_T C_p \frac{dT}{dV} + \frac{q_c - q_g}{S} = 0 \tag{9-87}$$

2. ENERGY BALANCE ENCLOSING THE CATALYST PHASE, THE PELLETS, AND THE GAS PHASE WITHIN THE PELLETS. This energy balance is the complement of the one considered above in that it encloses the remainder of the system. The energy balance on the catalyst phase over the element of volume ΔV in Figure 9-9 is given by

$$\int_V^{V+\Delta V} \rho_b[r_{mA}\bar{H}_A + r_{mB}\bar{H}_B + r_{mC}\bar{H}_C - r_{mD}\bar{H}_D]\, dV + \int_V^{V+\Delta V} \frac{q_g}{S}\, dV = 0 \tag{9-88}$$

Since Equation (9-88) is valid for all choices of V and $V + \Delta V$ $(0 < V < V + \Delta V < V_T$, where V_T is the total volume of the reactor filled by catalyst pellets), it follows that

$$\rho_b[r_{mA}\bar{H}_A + r_{mB}\bar{H}_B - r_{mC}\bar{H}_C - r_{mD}\bar{H}_D] + \frac{q_g}{S} = 0 \tag{9-89}$$

By use of the relationships given by Equations (9-75) and (9-76), it is possible to restate Equation (9-89) in the form

$$-\rho_b r_A \left[\frac{c}{a}\bar{H}_C + \frac{d}{a}\bar{H}_D - \bar{H}_A - \frac{b}{a}\bar{H}_B\right] + \frac{q_g}{S} = 0 \tag{9-90}$$

In order to evaluate the first term on the left-hand side of Equation (9-90) in terms of the nonideal expression for the enthalpy, it is necessary to carry the differentiation out one step further on the right-hand side of Equation (9-86). After the partial derivatives of the function f have been taken with respect to each n_i, the following result is obtained:

$$\rho_b r_A \left[\frac{c}{a}\bar{H}_C + \frac{d}{a}\bar{H}_D - \bar{H}_A - \frac{b}{a}\bar{H}_B \right] = \rho_b r_A \, \Delta H_r \qquad (9\text{-}91)$$

where $\Delta H_r = \Delta H_r^{\circ} + \dfrac{c}{a}\dfrac{\partial(n_T\Omega)}{\partial n_C} + \dfrac{d}{a}\dfrac{\partial(n_T\Omega)}{\partial n_D} - \dfrac{\partial(n_T\Omega)}{\partial n_A} - \dfrac{b}{a}\dfrac{\partial(n_T\Omega)}{\partial n_B}$

$\Delta H_r^{\circ} = \dfrac{c}{a}H_{fC}^{\circ} + \dfrac{d}{a}H_{fD}^{\circ} - H_{fA}^{\circ} - \dfrac{b}{a}H_{fB}^{\circ}$, the heat of reaction of the

perfect gas mixture at the temperature T of the reacting mixture

Thus Equation (9-90) may be stated in the form

$$-\rho_b r_A \, \Delta H_r + \frac{q_g}{S} = 0 \qquad (9\text{-}92)$$

where ΔH_r is to be evaluated at the bulk condition of the reacting mixture.

3. ENERGY BALANCE ON THE HEAT-TRANSFER MEDIUM. As in the above formulation of the energy balance on the gas phase outside of the catalyst phase, suppose that heat is transferred through the walls of the reactor at the rate q_c from the heat-transfer medium as depicted in Figure 9-10. This heat-transfer process gives rise to an additional relationship; namely, an energy

Figure 9-10. Sketch used in making the energy balance on the heat-transfer medium.

balance on the heat-transfer medium. Suppose that the heat-transfer medium is passed through the jacket of the reactor in the same direction as the reacting stream and that the outside of the jacket is perfectly insulated. An energy balance on an element of fluid in the jacket is given by

$$wH_c \Big|_V - wH_c \Big|_{V+\Delta V} - \int_V^{V+\Delta V} \frac{q_c}{S} dV = 0 \qquad (9\text{-}93)$$

The corresponding differential equation is

$$wC_{pc} \frac{dT_c}{dV} + \frac{q_c}{S} = 0 \qquad (9\text{-}94)$$

4. PRESSURE DROP IN FIXED-BED CATALYTIC REACTORS. Equations for describing the flow of fluids through a fixed-catalyst bed are to be found in the literature on the flow of fluids through porous media. The correlation presented is based on the one proposed by Ergun [14]

$$-\frac{dP}{dV} = \frac{150\mu v_T(1 - \varepsilon_T)^2}{S^2 D_p^2 \varepsilon_T^3} + \frac{1.75\rho v_T^2(1 - \varepsilon_T)}{S^3 D_p \varepsilon_T^3} \qquad (9\text{-}95)$$

where $a_v = \dfrac{\text{surface area of a catalyst particle}}{\text{volume of the catalyst particle}}$

$D_p = \dfrac{6}{a_v}$

P = pressure in consistent units

S = cross-sectional area of the bed

v_T = volumetric flow rate of the fluid

V = volume of the bed

ε_T = total volume fraction of voids in the catalyst bed

μ = viscosity of the fluid in consistent units

ρ = mass density of the fluid

5. SUMMARY OF THE EQUATIONS DESCRIBING THE FIXED-BED CATALYTIC REACTOR SHOWN IN FIGURES 9-8 THROUGH 9-10. The equations presented above for the description of the steady state behavior of the reactor shown in Figure 9-10 are perhaps best summarized by demonstrating how they might be applied to a design problem.

EXAMPLE 9-4

Suppose that the reaction having the stoichiometry

$$aA + bB \longrightarrow cC + dD$$

has been carried out in an experimental reactor. The experimental reactor was filled with the commercial catalyst of interest. A series of tests demonstrated that the rate of reaction was first order with respect to A.

$$r_A = k_{exp}p_{Ab}$$

For a given set of design conditions for a commercial reactor, it is desired to determine the reactor volume required to achieve a specified conversion of the reactant A. It may be supposed that all of the diameters and wall thicknesses of the reactor have been fixed as well as the feed rate n_T^0 and the flow rate w of the heat-transfer medium. The feed composition is fixed as well as its inlet temperature. Likewise the composition of the nonreactive heat-transfer medium and its inlet temperature are fixed. All of the physical properties of the streams and the catalyst bed are known as well as the overall heat-transfer coefficients. The problem thus reduces to finding the values of n_A, n_B, n_C, n_D, T, T_s, T_c, and P for each choice of the volume V.

Formulate a set of functional expressions which may be used to solve this design problem numerically.

SOLUTION

For a given choice of n_A at any $V > 0$, the corresponding values of n_B, n_C, and n_D may be found by use of the stoichiometry of the reaction as demonstrated by Equation (6-21). Of the set of flow rates, the flow rate n_A will be regarded as an independent variable and the remaining flow rates will be regarded as dependent variables. For each independently selected element of volume ΔV, there exist five independent equations which must be satisfied over this element of volume; namely, Equations (9-87), (9-92), (9-94), and (9-95) plus the differential equation for the rate of reaction. The last equation is obtained by eliminating r_A from Equations (9-71), (9-74), and from the rate expression given in the statement of the problem.

$$-\frac{1}{\rho_b}\frac{dn_A}{dV} = k_{exp}p_{Ab} \tag{B}$$

In the numerical solution of these five equations over each element of volume, the problem to be solved consists of finding the values of five variables, n_A, T, T_c, T_s, and P at the end of each element of volume. Of the many numerical methods which could be used to solve this set of equations [15], the method demonstrated in Chapter 7 will be employed in the formulation of the problem. The implicit method is used to transform the set of differential equations into a corresponding set of algebraic equations.

414

The algebraic equations as obtained are stated in functional notation and solved for the values of n_A, T, T_c, T_s, and P at the end of each element of volume by use of the Newton-Raphson method. The functions to be solved are as follows:

$$F_1 = n_A - n_A \Big|_{①} + \left\{ \mu \rho_b k_{\exp} \left(\frac{n_A}{n_T} \right) P + (1 - \mu) \left[\rho_b k_{\exp} \left(\frac{n_A}{n_T} \right) P \right] \Big|_{①} \right\} \Delta V$$

$$F_2 = -\left\{ \mu n_T C_p + (1 - \mu)[n_T C_p] \Big|_{①} \right\} (T - T_{①})$$

$$+ \left\{ \mu(q_c - q_g) + (1 - \mu)[q_c - q_g] \Big|_{①} \right\} \frac{\Delta V}{S}$$

$$F_3 = -\rho_b k_{\exp} \left(\frac{n_A}{n_T} \right) P \, \Delta H_r + \frac{q_g}{S}$$

$$F_4 = w \left\{ \mu C_{pc} + (1 - \mu) C_{pc} \Big|_{①} \right\} \left(T - T_c \Big|_{①} \right)$$

$$+ \left\{ \mu q_c + (1 - \mu) q_c \Big|_{①} \right\} \frac{\Delta V}{S}$$

$$F_5 = (P - P_1) + \left\{ \mu f + (1 - \mu) f \Big|_{①} \right\} \frac{\Delta V}{S}$$

where f is used to denote the right-hand side of Equation (9-95) and μ is the weight factor which may be assigned any arbitrary value lying between zero and one. [For $\mu = 0$, the implicit method reduces to Euler's one point predictor, and for $\mu = 1/2$, the implicit method reduces to the trapezoidal rule. Equations such as those stated above are likely to be stiff, and a value of μ lying between 1/2 and 1 should be used.] The symbol ① is used to denote the fact that the values of the variables so denoted are to be evaluated at the beginning of the increment of volume. The absence of ① denotes the fact that the variables are to be evaluated at the end of the increment of volume.

For a given increment of volume ΔV, the correct set of values of the variables, n_A, T, T_c, T_s, and P at the end of the increment of volume ΔV are found by successive application of the Newton-Raphson equations until the set of values of the variables has been found that makes $F_1 = F_2 = F_3 = F_4 = F_5 = 0$, simultaneously. For the system under consideration, the Newton-Raphson equations may be represented as follows:

$$\begin{bmatrix} \dfrac{\partial F_1}{\partial n_A} & \dfrac{\partial F_1}{\partial T} & \dfrac{\partial F_1}{\partial T_c} & \dfrac{\partial F_1}{\partial T_s} & \dfrac{\partial F_1}{\partial P} \\ \vdots & \vdots & \vdots & \vdots & \vdots \\ \dfrac{\partial F_5}{\partial n_A} & \dfrac{\partial F_5}{\partial T} & \dfrac{\partial F_5}{\partial T_c} & \dfrac{\partial F_5}{\partial T_s} & \dfrac{\partial F_5}{\partial P} \end{bmatrix} \begin{bmatrix} \Delta n_A \\ \Delta T \\ \Delta T_c \\ \Delta T_s \\ \Delta P \end{bmatrix} = - \begin{bmatrix} F_1 \\ F_2 \\ F_3 \\ F_4 \\ F_5 \end{bmatrix}$$

PROBLEMS

9-1. Show that the following general solution to the differential equation given by Equation (9-14)

$$Z = \int \frac{d\psi}{\sqrt{(2\alpha^2 L^2/n + 1)\psi^{n+1} + C_1}} + C_2$$

may be obtained by use of the following relationship:

$$\frac{d^2\psi}{dZ^2} = \frac{d[d\psi/dZ]}{dZ} = \frac{d[d\psi/dZ]}{d\psi}\frac{d\psi}{dZ} = \frac{1}{2}\frac{d(d\psi/dZ)^2}{d\psi}$$

Hint: Use this relationship and the differential equation [Equation (9-14)] to show that

$$\left(\frac{d\psi}{dZ}\right)^2 = \frac{2\alpha^2 L^2}{n+1}\psi^{n+1} + C_1$$

9-2. (a) By use of the boundary condition that at $z = L$, $dp_A/dz = 0$, and the differential equation given by Equation (9-13), show that the moles of A reacting per unit time in the pore volume is equal to rate of transfer of A by diffusion at the entrance to pore $z = 0$; that is, show that

$$\mathscr{I}\Big|_{z=0} = -\mathscr{D}\left(\frac{dp_A}{dz}\right)\Big|_{z=0} = \int_0^L \left(\frac{\rho_p r}{\varepsilon}\right) dz$$

(b) For the case of an nth-order reaction, show that when the result given in Part (a) is used to evaluate the effectiveness factor defined by Equation (9-17), the following result is obtained:

$$\eta = \frac{-1}{(\alpha L)^2}\left(\frac{d\psi}{dZ}\right)\Big|_{Z=0}$$

(c) On the basis of the boundary condition stated in Part (a) and the additional boundary condition that $\psi = 0$ at $Z = 1$ and the result of Problem 9-1, show that

$$\frac{d\psi}{dZ} = -\sqrt{\frac{2\alpha^2 L^2\psi^{n+1}}{n+1}}$$

Then use this result to evaluate the expression given in Part (b) for η when the reaction is zero, first, or second order.

(d) Show that the additional boundary condition introduced in Part (c) implies that αL is large.

9-3. In a manner analogous to that shown for Equation (9-29), obtain the corresponding integral expression for the general case of the reaction $A \rightarrow R$ which has a rate

416

of order n ($n \neq 1$) when carried out in the presence of a catalytic surface which is not equally accessible to all reactant molecules.

$$Answer: \quad \frac{1}{n_A^{(n-1)/2}} - \frac{1}{(n_A^0)^{(n-1)/2}} = \frac{1}{L}\left(\sqrt{\frac{\varepsilon \mathscr{D} k}{\rho_p}}\right)\left(\frac{P}{n_T^0}\right)^{(n+1)/2}\left[\frac{(n-1)}{2}\right]\left[\frac{2}{n+1}\right]^{1/2} W$$

9-4. Suppose that the experimental evidence for the reaction $A \rightarrow B + 2C$ shows that the rate of mass transfer from the bulk conditions of the gas phase to the catalyst is the rate controlling step. The rate of reaction is given by $r_A = k_A p_{Ab}$ where $k_A = (k_G a_v \phi)/\rho_b = 0.048$ g moles per hour per atmosphere per gram of catalyst bed. It is desired to produce 100 g moles of B per minute. Calculate the mass of catalyst required to obtain 90% conversion of A in a plug-flow reactor. The feed contains 50% A and 50% inerts (on a mole basis). Also, calculate the molar flow rate of A in the feed which would be required to achieve the specified production rate of B. The reactor is to be operated isothermally at a pressure of 5 atm.
Answer: 206 kg

NOTATION

a_c = heat-transfer area per unit length of the reactor; based on the diameter consistent with the overall heat-transfer coefficient U_c.

a_g = heat-transfer area per unit length of the reactor; based on the diameter consistent with the overall heat-transfer coefficient U_g.

a_v = surface area of a catalyst particle per unit volume of the catalyst particle.

D_p = $6/a_v$, mean particle diameter.

$\mathscr{D}$ = diffusion coefficient; defined by Equation (9-11).

$\mathscr{J}$ = moles of a component transferred in the positive direction of z per unit time per unit of area which is available for diffusion and which is perpendicular to the direction of transfer [see Equation (9-11)].

k = a reaction rate constant; defined by Equation (9-6).

k_A = mass transfer coefficient; defined by Equation (9-30).

k_{pore} = reaction rate constant; defined by Equation (9-2).

k_{sa} = reaction rate constant; defined by Equation (9-1).

L = one-half of the length of a cylindrical pore.

p_A = partial pressure of component A at any given location in a cylindrical pore.

p_{Ai} = partial pressure of component A at the inlet of a pore.

p_{Ab} = partial pressure of component A at the bulk conditions of the flowing stream.

P = total pressure.

q_c = rate of heat transfer [see Equation (9-77)].

q_g = rate of heat transfer [see Equation (9-78)].

r = rate of reaction; defined by Equation (9-6).

r_A = a mean rate of reaction over the length of pore L; defined by Equation (9-21).

r_{pore} = a rate of reaction; defined by Equation (9-2).

r_{sa} = a rate of reaction; defined by Equation (9-1).

r_{mA} = rate of mass transfer of component A from the gas phase to the interface at the entrance of the pore [see Equation (9-30)].

S = cross-sectional area of the fixed-catalyst bed.

S_a = surface area of a catalyst per unit mass.

T = temperature of the gas phase.

T_c = temperature of the heat-transfer medium.

T_s = temperature of the catalyst phase.

U_c = overall heat-transfer coefficient; defined by Equation (9-77).

U_g = overall heat-transfer coefficient; defined by Equation (9-78).

W = mass of catalyst.

z = length of pore; $z = 0$ at the inlet, $z = L$, at the center, and $z = 2L$ at the opposite end.

Z = z/L, a dimensionless length.

Greek Letters

α = a parameter; defined below Equation (9-14). The product αL is called the Thiele modulus.

ε = volume of pore per unit volume of a pellet.

ε_T = fraction of voids [see Equation (9-95)].

η = effectiveness factor; defined by Equation (9-17).

μ = viscosity [see Equation (9-95)]; also used as a weight factor in Example 9-4.

ρ = mass density of the gas phase [see Equation (9-95)].

ρ_b = bulk density of the catalyst bed.

ρ_p = mass density of a pellet.

ρ_s = mass density of the solid catalyst material.

ψ = ratio of partial pressure, p_A/p_{Ai}.

REFERENCES

1. Satterfield, C. N., and T. K. Sherwood, *The Role of Diffusion in Catalysts*, Addison-Wesley Publishing Company, Reading, Mass. (1963); *Mass Transfer in Catalysis*, MIT Press, Cambridge, Mass. (1970).

2. Thiele, E. W., *Ind. Eng. Chem.*, *31*:916 (1939).

3. Aris, R., *Chem. Eng. Sci.*, *6*:262 (1957).

4. Tinkler, J. D., and A. B. Metzner, *IE&C*, *53*:663 (1961).

5. Peterson, E. E., *Chemical Reaction Analysis*, Prentice-Hall, Inc., Englewood Cliffs, N.J. (1965).

6. Boudart, M., *AIChE J.*, *18*: *No. 3*, 465 (1972).

7. Wheeler, A., in *Catalysis*, Vol. 2, P. H. Emmett, Editor, Reinhold Publishing Corporation, New York (1955).

8. Levenspiel, O., *Chemical Reaction Engineering*, John Wiley & Sons, Inc., New York (1972).

9. Hougen, O. A., and K. M. Watson, *Chem. Proc. Prin.*, Part III, John Wiley & Sons, Inc., New York (1948).

10. Carberry, J. J., *AIChE J.*, *7*:350 (1961).

11. Yoshida, F., D. Ramajwami, and O. A. Hougen, *AIChE J.*, *8*:5–11 (1962).

12. Billingsley, D. S., and C. D. Holland, *I&EC Fund.*, *2*:252 (1963).

13. Woodham, J. F., and C. D. Holland, *I&EC Fund.*, *52*:985 (1960).

14. Ergun, S., *Chem. Eng. Prog.*, *48*:89 (1952).

15. Carnahan, B., H. A. Luther, and J. O. Wilkes, *Applied Numerical Methods*, John Wiley & Sons, Inc., New York (1969).

Section III :

Advanced Topics

Polymerization Reactions 10

Polymerization reactions are a combination of series and simultaneous reactions. These reactions are involved in the production of plastics, synthetic rubber, paint resins, and waxes. The reactions by which these macromolecules are produced are called *addition* and *condensation* reactions [1].

Addition reactions are further classified according to two types: *free radical addition* and *stepwise addition*. In the free radical addition, the long chain polymers are produced almost instantaneously at low conversions; whereas, in stepwise addition long chain polymers are only produced at high conversions. Monomers such as ethylene, propylene, vinyl chloride, styrene, butadiene, isoprene, and methylmethacrylate polymerize by addition reactions. Cationic, anionic, and coordination polymerizations are also examples of addition polymerizations. Examples of products formed by condensation reactions are the polyurethanes, polyureas, polyphenylesters, polycarbonates, and phenolic resins.

In Part I of this chapter, addition reactions which are initiated by free radicals are treated. Although only the one class of polymerizations is treated, a number of other polymerizations such as ionic, cationic, and coordination polymerizations may be treated in an analogous manner. All of these polymerizations have in common the fact that the pseudo steady state assumption may be used in the analysis of their corresponding mechanisms. In Part II, stepwise addition and condensation polymerizations and copolymerizations are treated.

Figure 10-1. Continuously stirred reactor used for the batch production of polystyrene (Courtesy of Cosden Oil & Chemical Company).

In the design of polymerization reactors, appropriate provisions must be made for mixing and removing the heat of reaction from the reacting mixture. Heats of polymerizations commonly range from 13 to 21 kcal/g mole [2]. An industrial reactor used in the production of polystyrene is shown in Figure 10-1.

I. POLYMERIZATIONS BY FREE-RADICAL ADDITION REACTIONS

The common addition monomers such as ethylene ($CH_2{=}CH_2$), vinylchloride ($CH_2{=}CHCl$), vinyl acetate ($CH_3COOCH{=}CH_2$), and styrene ($CH_2{=}CHC_6H_5$) may be represented by the vinyl group $CH_2{=}CHX$, where X represents any one of the above attached groups. The monomer methyl methacrylate [$CH_2{=}C(CH_3)COOCH_3$] may be represented as $CH_2{=}C(CH_3)X$.

Most of the commercially significant addition polymerizations are carried out in the presence of a catalyst. The two types of catalysts commonly employed may be classified as (1) free-radical type catalysts and (2) ionic type catalysts. These catalysts are also called initiators. For free radical type catalysts, the role of the initiator is to produce molecules with unpaired electrons or free radicals.

Typical initiators are benzoyl peroxide and azobisisobutyronitrile (AIBN). For benzoyl peroxide, the decomposition reactions are as follows:

where the dot · represents a free electron, two dots : or — represents a pair of shared electrons or a single bond. A double bond or two pairs of shared electrons is represented by $=$ or : :. Also, the aromatic ring which is com-

monly symbolized by is represented herein by the symbol ,

which has been suggested by several recent authors.

The decomposition of azobisisobutyronitrile is commonly represented by

The decomposition of the initiator I to produce the free radicals ϕ is commonly represented as follows:

$$I \longrightarrow 2\phi$$

The free radical ϕ then reacts with a monomer to produce another free radical. For example, the benzoyl free radical may react with the monomer $CH_2=CHX$ to produce another free radical

This reaction is called the "initiation reaction." In the above reaction, the free radical is seen to add to the monomer through the formation of a single bond with the monomer, which is made possible by the redistribution of electrons. This initiation of free radicals is represented by

$$\phi + M \longrightarrow R_1$$

where R_1 is the free radical formed and M is the monomer. A monomer may now add to the free radical R_1. For example,

This reaction is called the *propagation* reaction, and it is represented symbolically by

$$R_1 + M \longrightarrow R_2$$

Thus, in general,

$$R_j + M \longrightarrow R_{j+1}$$

where R_j consists of the free radical ϕ with j attached monomer units. For example,

The propagation reactions continue until a termination reaction occurs.

The combination of any two free radicals, say R_j and R_i (where j and i represent any two arbitrary number of monomer units), serves to terminate the propagation step. For example,

Symbolically,

$$R_j + R_i \longrightarrow P_{j+i}$$

where the dead polymer is represented by the symbol P. The propagation reactions may also be terminated by a disproportionation reaction in which a hydrogen atom is transferred from one radical to another. A terminal double bond is formed in one radical and a saturated single bond in the other. For example,

$$\langle\bigcirc\rangle\text{---}(CH_2CHX)_{j-1}\text{---}CH_2CHX\cdot \; + \; \langle\bigcirc\rangle\text{---}(CH_2CHX)_{i-1}\text{---}CH_2CHX\cdot$$

$$\longrightarrow \; \langle\bigcirc\rangle\text{---}(CH_2CHX)_{j-1}CH\text{==}CHX \; + \; \langle\bigcirc\rangle\text{---}(CH_2CHX)_{i-1}\text{---}CH_2CH_2X$$

or symbolically

$$R_j + R_i \longrightarrow P_j + P_i$$

Normally, the monomer M adds to the free radical R_j. However, the monomer may terminate the polymerization by reacting as follows:

$$\langle\bigcirc\rangle\text{---}(CH_2CHX)_{j-1}\text{---}CH_2CHX\cdot \; + \; CH_2\text{==}CHX$$

$$\longrightarrow \; \langle\bigcirc\rangle\text{---}(CH_2CHX)_{j-1}\text{---}CH\text{==}CHX \; + \; CH_3CHX\cdot$$

The reactivity of $CH_3CHX\cdot$ is customarily assumed to be the same as that of the free radical $\langle\bigcirc\rangle\text{---}CH_2CH_2\cdot$ (called R_1). Symbolically, this termination reaction is represented as follows:

$$R_j + M \longrightarrow P_j + R_1$$

The propagation reactions may also be terminated by the reaction of the free radical R_j with the solvent S. For example, suppose that the polymerization considered above is carried out in the solvent toluene. In this case, the following termination reaction may occur:

$$\langle\bigcirc\rangle\text{---}(CH_2CHX)_{j-1}\text{---}CH_2CHX\cdot \; + \; \langle\bigcirc\rangle\text{---}CH_3$$

$$\longrightarrow \; \langle\bigcirc\rangle\text{---}(CH_2CHX)_{j-1}\text{---}CH_2CHXH \; + \; \langle\bigcirc\rangle\text{---}CH_2\cdot$$

Again, it is customary to assume that the free-radical form of toluene has the same reactivity as that of R_1 for the above polymerization. This reaction may then be represented by

$$R_j + S \longrightarrow P_j + R_1$$

Termination of the propagation step may be promoted by the addition of a chain transfer agent. For the above polymerization, carbon tetrachloride acts as a chain transfer agent as follows:

$$\langle O \rangle\text{—}(CH_2CHX)_{j-1}\text{—}CH_2CHX\cdot + CCl_4$$

$$\longrightarrow \langle O \rangle\text{—}(CH_2CHX)_{j-1}\text{—}CH_2CHXCl + CCl_3\cdot$$

Again, it is customary to assume that the free radical $CCl_3\cdot$ has the same reactivity as R_1 for the above polymerization. Symbolic representation of the termination of the propagation step by use of a chain transfer agent C is

$$R_j + C \longrightarrow P_j + R_1$$

In the above example, "head-to-tail" addition of the monomer was assumed, which produces a chain of the form

$$\begin{array}{cccc} H & H & H & H \\ | & | & | & | \\ \cdots\text{—}C\text{—}C\text{—}C\text{—}C\text{—}\cdots & & & \\ | & | & | & | \\ H & X & H & X \end{array} \qquad \text{(head-to-tail)}$$

"Head-to-head" addition is also possible, and it produces a chain of the form

$$\begin{array}{cccc} H & H & H & H \\ | & | & | & | \\ \cdots\text{—}C\text{—}C\text{—}C\text{—}C\text{—}\cdots & & & \\ | & | & | & | \\ H & X & X & H \end{array} \qquad \text{(head-to-head)}$$

"Head-to-tail" addition is generally the most probable one [3, 4].

A. Characterization of Mixtures of Polymer Molecules

The word "polymer" is used herein to refer to a single, long chain molecule as well as a collection of molecules having any arbitrary distribution of chain lengths. Definitions of the quantities commonly used in the characterization of these polymers follow.

1. WEIGHT FRACTION. The weight fraction W_j of polymer molecules having chains composed of j monomer units in a mixture of polymer molecules having all possible chain lengths is defined by

$$W_j = \frac{\text{mass of molecules composed of } j \text{ monomer units}}{\text{total mass of polymer}}$$

The weight fraction is calculated as follows:

$$W_j = \frac{M_j P_j}{\sum M_j P_j} \tag{10-1}$$

where P_j = concentration of polymer P_j in moles per unit volume

M_j = molecular weight of the polymer P_j

$\sum M_j P_j$ = sum of the products $M_j P_j$ over all possible chain lengths, j
$(j = 1, 2, \ldots)$

A molecule composed of j monomer units has a molecular weight equal to j times the molecular weight of the monomer,

$$M_j = jM_M \tag{10-2}$$

where M_M = molecular weight of the monomer

[Note: Equation (10-2) neglects the contribution of the free radical $R \cdot$ to the molecular weight of the polymer. Instead of Equation (10-2), the correct molecular weight of the polymer is given by $M_j = jM_M + M_R$, where M_R is the molecular weight of the free radical $R \cdot$.]

When M_j in Equation (10-1) is replaced by its equivalent as given by Equation (10-2) the following expression is obtained:

$$W_j = \frac{jP_j}{\sum jP_j} = \frac{jP_j}{\Gamma_1(P_j)} \tag{10-3}$$

where $\Gamma_1(P_j) = \sum_{j=1}^{\infty} jP_j$,   the first moment of the P_j's

Since the mass of the monomer which has reacted at any time must be in the form of polymer, it follows that

$$M_M(M^0 - M) = \sum M_j P_j = M_M \sum jP_j \tag{10-4}$$

and that $M^0 - M = \Gamma_1(P_j) \tag{10-5}$

where M^0 and M represent the initial and final concentrations of the monomer.

2. MOLECULAR WEIGHT DISTRIBUTION. As polymerization reactions proceed, polymer molecules of different lengths are produced. The plot of the weight fraction of molecules of the same length versus the length is called a "molecular weight distribution" (see Figure 10-2). The plot of the mole fraction of molecules of the same length versus the length is called the "molecular number" or the "number fraction distribution" (see Figure 10-3).

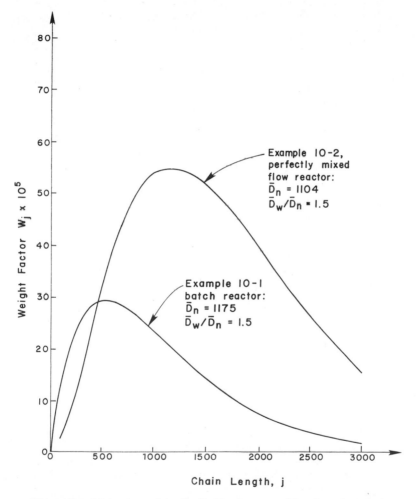

Figure 10-2. Molecular weight distributions computed for the polymerizations of styrene in a batch reactor (Example 10-1) and in a perfectly mixed reactor (Example 10-2).

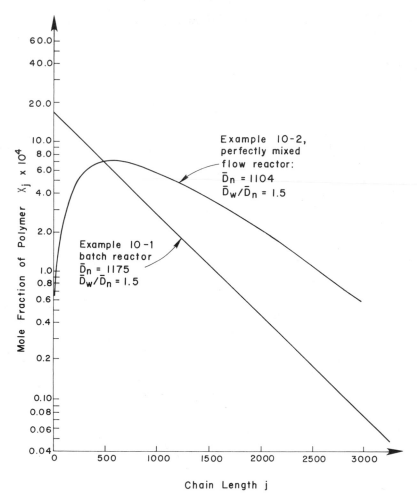

Figure 10-3. Mole fraction distributions for the polymerization of styrene in a batch and in a perfectly mixed reactor.

The mole fraction x_j is defined in the usual way; namely,

$$x_j = \frac{P_j}{\sum P_j} \tag{10-6}$$

3. NUMBER AVERAGE MOLECULAR WEIGHT. The number average molecular weight $\bar{M}_n$ is defined by

$$\bar{M}_n = \frac{\sum P_j M_j}{\sum P_j} \tag{10-7}$$

Since $M_j = jM_M$ [Equation (10-2)], $\bar{M}_n$ may be stated in the form

$$\bar{M}_n = M_M \frac{\sum jP_j}{\sum P_j} = M_M \frac{\Gamma_1(P_j)}{\Gamma_0(P_j)} \tag{10-8}$$

where $\Gamma_0(P_j) = \displaystyle\sum_{j=1}^{\infty} P_j$,   the total concentration of all polymers

4. WEIGHT AVERAGE MOLECULAR WEIGHT. This average molecular weight is defined by

$$\bar{M}_W = \frac{\sum W_j M_j}{\sum W_j} \tag{10-9}$$

Elimination of M_j and W_j from Equation (10-9) by use of Equations (10-2) and (10-3), respectively, gives

$$\bar{M}_W = M_M \frac{\sum j^2 P_j}{\sum jP_j} = M_M \frac{\Gamma_2(P_j)}{\Gamma_1(P_j)} \tag{10-10}$$

where $\Gamma_2(P_j)$ is the second moment of the P_j's.

5. THE NUMBER AVERAGE DEGREE OF POLYMERIZATION. This quantity is denoted by the symbol $\bar{D}_n$ and defined by

$$\bar{D}_n = \frac{\sum jP_j}{\sum P_j} = \frac{\Gamma_1(P_j)}{\Gamma_0(P_j)} \tag{10-11}$$

A comparison of Equations (10-8) and (10-11) shows that

$$\bar{D}_n = \frac{\bar{M}_n}{M_M} \tag{10-12}$$

6. THE WEIGHT AVERAGE DEGREE OF POLYMERIZATION. This measure of the extent of the polymerization is defined by

$$\bar{D}_W = \frac{\sum j^2 P_j}{\sum jP_j} = \frac{\Gamma_2(P_j)}{\Gamma_1(P_j)} \tag{10-13}$$

From the definition of $\bar{M}_W$ [Equation (10-10)], it is seen that

$$\bar{D}_W = \frac{\bar{M}_W}{M_M} \tag{10-14}$$

7. THE DISPERSION INDEX. This quantity, also called the *heterogeneity index* by some authors, is defined as the ratio of $\bar{D}_W/\bar{D}_n$. By use of the above relationships, the dispersion index may be stated in the form

$$\frac{\bar{D}_W}{\bar{D}_n} = \frac{\bar{M}_W}{\bar{M}_n} = \frac{(\sum j^2 P_j)(\sum P_j)}{(\sum j P_j)^2} \tag{10.15}$$

When Equation (10-15) is restated in terms of the mole fractions [Equation (10-6)], the following expression is obtained for the dispersion index:

$$\frac{\bar{D}_W}{\bar{D}_n} = \frac{\sum j^2 x_j}{(\sum j x_j)^2} \tag{10-16}$$

The significance of the dispersion index is perhaps best demonstrated by the consideration of some numerical examples which present limiting cases. First, if all of the polymer molecules are of the same length, then Equation (10-16) reduces to

$$\frac{\bar{D}_W}{\bar{D}_n} = \frac{j^2(\sum x_j)}{j^2(\sum x_j)^2} = 1 \tag{10-17}$$

Next, suppose that a mixture is composed of 1 molecule of 1000 monomer lengths and 19 molecules of 1 monomer length. [Note: A polymer of one monomer unit consists of one monomer and one initiator molecule.] For this case, Equation (10-16) becomes

$$\frac{\bar{D}_W}{\bar{D}_n} = \frac{(1000)^2(\frac{1}{20}) + (1)^2(\frac{19}{20})}{[(1000)(\frac{1}{20}) + (1)(\frac{19}{20})]^2}$$

$$= 20\left[\frac{(1000)^2 + 19}{(1000 + 19)^2}\right] = 19.26$$

or

$$\frac{\bar{D}_W}{\bar{D}_n} \cong \frac{1}{x_{1000}} = 20$$

Thus the dispersion index varies from unity for polymers composed of molecules of equal lengths and increases to numbers greater than unity as the range of molecular weights of the constituents is increased and the relative number of molecules having the higher molecular weights is decreased. The precise distribution of molecular weights is lost in the value given by the dispersion index because, for any value of the dispersion index greater than unity, there are infinitely many distributions that have the same index. Thus, to characterize a mixture of polymers, several different types of experimental determinations are needed.

In particular, the weight average molecular weight may be measured by light scattering techniques [3, 4]; the number average molecular weight may be found by use of vapor phase osmometry [3, 4] or by membrane osmometry [3, 4]. The molecular weight distribution of a polymer such as the ones which are plotted in Figures 10-1 and 10-2 may be found by use of gel permeation chromatography [4]. The distribution so obtained may be used to compute the number and weight average molecular weights of the polymer. The monomer concentration, temperature, and pressure are other variables which are commonly measured in experimental investigations.

B. A Mechanism for Free-Radical Polymerization

Polymerization reactions are normally composed of initiation, propagation, termination, transfer, and branching reactions. The following general mechanism is applicable to the polymerization of styrene, vinyl chloride, methylmethacrylate, and acrylamides [3, 4, 5, 6]. The important termination and transfer reactions for each monomer are shown in Table 10-1.

Decomposition: $\qquad I \xrightarrow{k_0} 2\phi$ $\qquad$ (10-18)

Initiation: $\qquad \phi + M \xrightarrow{k_i} R_1$ $\qquad$ (10-19)

Propagation: $\qquad R_j + M \xrightarrow{k_p} R_{j+1}$ $\qquad$ (10-20)

Termination by addition
(or combination): $\qquad R_j + R_i \xrightarrow{k_a} P_{j+i}$ $\qquad$ (10-21)

Termination by
disproportionation: $\qquad R_j + R_i \xrightarrow{k_d} P_j + P_i$ $\qquad$ (10-22)

Termination by
monomer transfer: $\qquad R_j + M \xrightarrow{k_M} P_j + R_1$ $\qquad$ (10-23)

Termination by
solvent transfer: $\qquad R_j + S \xrightarrow{k_S} P_j + R_1$ $\qquad$ (10-24)

Termination by
chain transfer: $\qquad R_j + C \xrightarrow{k_C} P_j + R_1$ $\qquad$ (10-25)

where $j = 1, 2, \ldots$, and $i = 1, 2, \ldots$. The solvent is denoted by S and the chain transfer agent by C.

TABLE 10-1
TERMINATION AND TRANSFER REACTIONS IN FREE RADICAL POLYMERIZATION
OF VINYL MONOMERS*

Monomer	Termination	Transfer Reaction	Heats of Polymerization kcal/g mole
Styrene	Combination	Solvent and monomer transfer	16.7
Vinyl chloride	Disproportionation	Monomer transfer	22.7
Methylmethacrylate	Disproportionation	None of major importance	13.2
Acrylamide	Disproportionation	Monomer transfer	19.8

* Prepared from information presented in [2] and [6].

The first step in the analysis of the mechanism given by Equations (10-18) through (10-25) is the formulation of the rate expressions. The decomposition of the initiator I to form free radicals ϕ is represented by Equation (10-18). The rate of decomposition of the initiator r_0 is generally first order,

$$r_0 = k_0 I \tag{10-26}$$

where I denotes the concentration of the initiator. A rate constant k_0 may be determined independently of the given polymerization for which it is to be used. For most initiators in common use, the rate constants k_0 have been determined [3, 4, 5].

The rate of initiation r_i is defined as the rate of disappearance of free radicals ϕ or the rate of formation of free radicals R_1, and

$$r_i = k_i \phi M \tag{10-27}$$

where ϕ and M denote the concentrations of the free radicals and the monomers, respectively. It is customary to let f denote the efficiency of the utilization of the free radicals ϕ. The value of f for many polymer initiator systems has been determined by analyzing the polymer to determine the number of initiator fragments associated with the polymer molecules. The net rate of disappearance of free radicals ϕ is given by

$$r_\phi = k_i \phi M - 2 f k_0 I \tag{10-28}$$

Consider next the propagation reactions represented by Equation (10-20). In order to produce polymers having high molecular weights, it is necessary that the rate for the propagation reactions be greater than those for all other reactions of the mechanism. An assumption commonly made is that the rate constant k_p is independent of the chain length. The rate of disappearance of free radicals R_j by propagation is given by

$$(r_p)_{R_j} = k_p M R_j - k_p M R_{j-1}$$

or
$$(r_p)_{R_j} = k_p M (R_j - R_{j-1}), \qquad (j = 2, 3, \ldots) \qquad (10\text{-}29)$$

The "rate of propagation" is a term which is in common usage, and it means the rate of disappearance of the monomer by all possible propagation reactions,

$$(r_p)_M = k_p M \sum_{j=1}^{\infty} R_j \qquad (10\text{-}30)$$

All termination reactions of a given type, such as termination by combination [Equation (10-21)], are assumed to have the same rate constants. For example, consider the case where the dead polymer P_6 is formed by combination. The distinguishable reactions by which P_6 may be formed are as follows:

$$R_1 + R_5 \longrightarrow P_6, \qquad r_5 = r_1 = k_a R_1 R_5$$
$$R_2 + R_4 \longrightarrow P_6, \qquad r_4 = r_2 = k_a R_2 R_4$$
$$R_3 + R_3 \longrightarrow P_6, \qquad r_3 = k_a R_3 R_3$$

where r_1, r_2, r_3, r_4, and r_5 are the rates of disappearance of the free radicals $R_1, R_2, \ldots$, and R_5. The net rate of appearance of P_6 by the combination mechanism is given by

$$(r_a)_{P_6} = r_1 + r_2 + \tfrac{1}{2} r_3$$

The factor of $\tfrac{1}{2}$ appears in the above expression because the rate constant k_a is defined with respect to the disappearance of the free radicals (two molecules of R_3 disappear by the third reaction for each molecule of P_6 formed). Since the reactions $R_5 + R_1 \rightarrow P_6$ and $R_4 + R_2 \rightarrow P_6$ are indistinguishable from the first two, it follows that the rate of appearance of the polymer P_6 by combination may be represented as follows:

$$(r_a)_{P_6} = \frac{k_a}{2} R_1 R_5 + \frac{k_a}{2} R_5 R_1 + \frac{k_a}{2} R_2 R_4 + \frac{k_a}{2} R_4 R_2 + \frac{k_a}{2} R_3 R_3$$

or
$$(r_a)_{P_6} = \frac{k_a}{2} \sum_{i=1}^{5} R_{6-i} R_i$$

Then for the rate of appearance of any polymer P_j,

$$(r_a)_{P_j} = \frac{k_a}{2} \sum_{i=1}^{j-1} R_{j-i} R_i \qquad (10\text{-}31)$$

The rate of disappearance of the free radical R_j by all possible termination reactions by the combination mechanism is given by

$$(r_a)_{R_j} = k_a R_j \sum_{i=1}^{\infty} R_i \qquad (10\text{-}32)$$

The rate of production of the polymer P_j by the disproportionation mechanism [Equation (10-22)] is given by

$$(r_d)_{P_j} = k_d R_j \sum_{i=1}^{\infty} R_i \qquad (10\text{-}33)$$

For the disproportionation reaction, the rate of appearance of polymers P_j is equal to the rate of disappearance of free radicals R_j; that is,

$$(r_d)_{P_j} = (r_d)_{R_j}$$

The rate of disappearance of free radicals R_j by each type of transfer reaction is represented as follows. For monomer transfer [Equation (10-23)],

$$(r_M)_{R_j} = k_M M R_j \qquad (10\text{-}34)$$

For solvent transfer [Equation (10-24)],

$$(r_S)_{R_j} = k_S S R_j \qquad (10\text{-}35)$$

For chain transfer [Equation (10-25)],

$$(r_C)_{R_j} = k_C C R_j \qquad (10\text{-}36)$$

The rates of appearance of polymers P_j by each of the above transfer reactions are equal to the rates of disappearance of the free radicals R_j by each of these reactions; that is,

$$(r_M)_{P_j} = (r_M)_{R_j}, \qquad (r_S)_{P_j} = (r_S)_{R_j}, \qquad (r_C)_{P_j} = (r_C)_{R_j} \qquad (10\text{-}37)$$

The monomer M disappears by the initiation reaction, the propagation reactions, and the termination reaction by monomer transfer. Thus the total rate of disappearance of the monomer M is given by

$$r_M = r_i + (r_p)_M + \sum_{j=1}^{\infty} (r_M)_{R_j} \tag{10-38}$$

and by use of Equations (10-30) and (10-34) it follows that

$$r_M = r_i + (k_p + k_M)M \sum_{j=1}^{\infty} R_j \tag{10-39}$$

C. Analysis of the Proposed Mechanism
for Free Radical Polymerization

Because the concentrations of the free radicals R_j ($j = 1, 2, \dots$) present at any time during a polymerization process are generally too small to be conveniently measured, it is desirable to solve for the R_j's in terms of other variables which may be followed experimentally.

1. STATEMENT OF THE INITIATION RATE r_i IN TERMS OF THE CONCENTRATION OF THE INITIATOR I. The concentration ϕ of free radicals is generally small because they are consumed by the initiation reaction almost as fast as they are formed by the decomposition of the initiator I. Thus, if the pseudo steady state assumption is applied to the free radicals ϕ, then $r_\phi = 0$, and Equation (10-28) may be solved for ϕ to give

$$\phi = \frac{2f k_0 I}{k_i M} \tag{10-40}$$

Elimination of ϕ from Equations (10-27) and (10-40) gives

$$r_i = 2f k_0 I \tag{10-41}$$

Since k_0 is generally known for most initiators and f is known for a given initiator and polymerization [4], Equation (10-41) may be used to evaluate r_i for any known concentration of the initiator.

2. STATEMENT OF THE TOTAL CONCENTRATION OF THE FREE RADICALS R_j IN TERMS OF r_i. The total concentration, $\Gamma_0(R_j)$, of the R_j's is defined as follows:

$$\Gamma_0(R_j) = \sum_{j=1}^{\infty} R_j \tag{10-42}$$

Since the concentrations of the R_j's are not easily determined and r_i can be evaluated, it is fortunate that the total concentration of the R_j's may be expressed in terms of r_i. The desired result may be obtained by making use of the fact that the free radicals R_j are consumed by reaction at approximately the same rate at which they are formed (the pseudo steady state assumption); that is,

$$\sum_{j=1}^{\infty} r_{R_j} = 0 \qquad (10\text{-}43)$$

where r_{R_j} is the net rate of disappearance of free radicals R_j by all steps of the mechanism given by Equations (10-18) through (10-25). The net rate of disappearance of R_1 is given by

$$r_{R_1} = k_p R_1 M + k_a R_1 \Gamma_0 + k_d R_1 \Gamma_0 - r_i$$
$$- k_M M \sum_{j=2}^{\infty} R_j - k_C C \sum_{j=2}^{\infty} R_j - k_S S \sum_{j=2}^{\infty} R_j \qquad (10\text{-}44)$$

(In the above equation and in the remainder of the development the argument R_j of the functions Γ_0, Γ_1, and Γ_2 is omitted whenever possible.) For $j \geq 2$, the net rate of disappearance of R_j is given by

$$r_{R_j} = k_p M(R_j - R_{j-1}) + (k_a + k_d)R_j \Gamma_0$$
$$+ k_M M R_j + k_C S R_j + k_S C R_j, \quad (j \geq 2) \qquad (10\text{-}45)$$

After Equation (10-45) has been summed over all $j \geq 2$ and the result so obtained has been added to Equation (10-44), the following result is obtained.

$$\sum_{j=1}^{\infty} r_{R_j} = (k_a + k_d)\Gamma_0^2 - r_i \qquad (10\text{-}46)$$

When the pseudo steady state assumption [Equation (10-43)] is imposed upon Equation (10-46), the resulting expression may be solved for Γ_0 to give

$$\Gamma_0(R_j) = \left(\frac{r_i}{k_a + k_d}\right)^{1/2} \qquad (10\text{-}47)$$

Since r_i may be evaluated by use of Equation (10-41), Equation (10-47) may be used to evaluate the total concentration of the R_j's.

3. STATEMENT OF r_M IN TERMS OF r_i AND M. When the expression given by Equation (10-47) for Γ_0 is substituted into Equation (10-39), the following expression is obtained for r_M.

$$r_M = r_i + (k_p + k_M)M \left(\frac{r_i}{k_a + k_d}\right)^{1/2} \qquad (10\text{-}48)$$

In order for a high molecular weight polymer to be formed, the rate of free radical initiation [Equation (10-19)] and the rate of monomer transfer [Equation (10-23)] must be small relative to the rate of propagation [Equation (10-20)]. These conditions imply that $k_M \ll k_p$, and that r_i is very small, relative to the second term. Thus, the expression given by Equation (10-48) reduces to

$$r_M = k_p M \left(\frac{r_i}{k_a + k_d} \right)^{1/2} \tag{10-49}$$

When $[r_i/(k_a + k_d)]^{1/2}$ is replaced by its equivalent as given by Equation (10-47), the following expression for r_M is obtained:

$$r_M = k_p M \Gamma_0(R_j) = k_p M \sum_{j=1}^{\infty} R_j \tag{10-50}$$

In the developments which follow, the expression given by Equation (10-50) is a more convenient form to use than the one given by Equation (10-49).

   In addition to the concentrations of I and M, the concentrations of dead polymers P_j ($j = 1, 2, \ldots$), the solvent S, and the chain transfer agent C may be followed experimentally. Also, on the basis of the proposed mechanism, the concentrations of the solvent S and the chain transfer agent C may be expressed relative to the concentration of the monomer M. Let r_S denote the rate of disappearance of the solvent S by the solvent transfer reaction. Then by Equation (10-35)

$$r_S = \sum_{j=1}^{\infty} (r_S)_{R_j} = k_S S \sum_{j=1}^{\infty} R_j \tag{10-51}$$

Similarly, let r_C denote the rate of disappearance of the chain transfer agent C by the chain transfer reaction. Then by Equation (10-36)

$$r_C = \sum_{j=1}^{\infty} (r_C)_{R_j} = k_C C \sum_{j=1}^{\infty} R_j \tag{10-52}$$

Thus by use of the expression given by Equation (10-50) for r_M, it follows that

$$\frac{r_S}{r_M} = \frac{k_S S}{k_p M} \tag{10-53}$$

and

$$\frac{r_C}{r_M} = \frac{k_C C}{k_p M} \tag{10-54}$$

For a given type of reactor, the concentrations of S and C may be expressed in terms of M as shown in the following section on reactor design.

Unfortunately, most of the rate expressions contain the concentrations of the free radicals R_j. Since these concentrations are generally very small, they are not customarily measured. Thus the major effort in the analysis of the mechanism consists of expressing the R_j's in terms of r_i, I, M, C, and S. The first step in the analysis of the reaction mechanism is the development of expressions for the polymer selectivities. These expressions, which are valid for any type of reactor, may be used with the material-balance equations in the analysis of various types of reactors.

4. THE NUMBER DEGREE OF POLYMER SELECTIVITY. This new variable is denoted by $\bar{d}_n$ and is defined as the total moles of polymer produced per mole of monomer reacted at any instant at any position in any given type of reactor. Thus

$$\bar{d}_n = \frac{\sum\limits_{j=1}^{\infty} r_{P_j}}{r_M} \tag{10-55}$$

where r_{P_j} is the rate of appearance of dead polymer P_j by the termination and transfer steps of the mechanism [Equations (10-21) through (10-25)]. (The reciprocal of the function $\bar{d}_n$ is sometimes called the "instantaneous number degree of polymerization" because it may be used to compute $\bar{D}_n$ for a given type of reactor.)

5. ELIMINATION OF THE FREE-RADICAL CONCENTRATIONS R_j FROM THE EXPRESSION FOR $\bar{d}_n$. The rate of appearance of polymers P_1 by all possible reactions is given by

$$r_{P_1} = k_d R_1 \Gamma_0(R_j) + k_M R_1 M + k_S R_1 S + k_C R_1 C \tag{10-56}$$

and for $j \geq 2$, the rate of appearance of polymer P_j by all possible reactions is given by

$$r_{P_j} = \frac{k_a}{2} \sum_{i=1}^{j-1} R_{j-i} R_i + k_d R_j \Gamma_0(R_j) + k_M R_j M + k_S R_j S + k_C R_j C \tag{10-57}$$

When the expression given by Equation (10-57) is summed over all j ($j = 2, 3, \ldots$) and added to the expression given by Equation (10-56) for r_{P1}, the following result is obtained upon rearrangement:

$$\sum_{j=1}^{\infty} r_{P_j} = \frac{k_a}{2} \sum_{j=2}^{\infty} \sum_{i=1}^{j-1} R_{j-i} R_i + k_d [\Gamma_0(R_j)]^2 + [k_M M + k_S S + k_C C] \Gamma_0(R_j)$$

$$\tag{10-58}$$

The double summation in Equation (10-58) may be expressed as follows [7]:

$$\sum_{j=2}^{\infty} \sum_{i=1}^{j-1} R_{j-i} R_i = \left(\sum_{j=1}^{\infty} R_j\right)^2 = [\Gamma_0(R_j)]^2 \qquad (10\text{-}59)$$

Thus

$$\sum_{j=1}^{\infty} r_{P_j} = \left(\frac{k_a}{2} + k_d\right) [\Gamma_0(R_j)]^2 + [k_M M + k_S S + k_C C]\Gamma_0(R_j) \qquad (10\text{-}60)$$

By use of this expression for the sum of the r_{P_j}'s and the expression given by Equation (10-50) for r_M, the following expression is obtained for $\overline{d}_n$ for the formation of high molecular weight polymers.

$$\overline{d}_n = \left[\frac{(k_a/2) + k_d}{k_p}\right]\left[\frac{\Gamma_0(R_j)}{M}\right] + T \qquad (10\text{-}61)$$

where
$$T = \frac{k_M}{k_p} + \frac{k_C}{k_p}\left(\frac{C}{M}\right) + \frac{k_S}{k_p}\left(\frac{S}{M}\right)$$

The first term on the right-hand side of Equation (10-61) represents the contribution of the terminations by addition and disproportionation, and the second term represents the contributions of terminations by monomer, solvent, and chain transfer to $\overline{d}_n$.

6. WEIGHT SELECTIVITY. The "weight selectivity" w_j for polymer P_j is defined as the weight of polymer P_j produced per unit weight of monomer M reacted at any instant in any given type of reactor,

$$w_j = \frac{M_j r_{P_j}}{M_M r_M} \qquad (10\text{-}62)$$

Since $M_j = j M_M$ [Equation (10-2)], the above definition may be stated in the alternate form

$$w_j = \frac{j r_{P_j}}{r_M} \qquad (10\text{-}63)$$

(The weight selectivity is also called the "instantaneous weight fraction" because it may be used to compute the weight fraction in any given type of reactor.)

7. THE WEIGHT DEGREE OF POLYMER SELECTIVITY. The "weight degree of polymer selectivity" $\overline{d}_W$ is defined as follows:

$$\overline{d}_W = \sum j w_j \qquad (10\text{-}64)$$

Elimination of w_j from this expression by use of Equation (10-62) gives

$$\bar{d}_W = \frac{\sum\limits_{j=1}^{\infty} j^2 r_{P_j}}{r_M} \tag{10-65}$$

The function $\bar{d}_W$ is useful for computing the weight average degree of poly-merization, $\bar{D}_W$, for any given type of reactor as demonstrated in a subsequent section.

8. ELIMINATION OF THE FREE-RADICAL CONCENTRATIONS R_j FROM THE EXPRESSION FOR $\bar{d}_w$. The summation in Equation (10-65) may be evaluated by multiplying the expression given by Equation (10-57) for r_{P_j} by j^2. After this expression has been summed over all $j \geq 2$, the result so obtained may be added to the expression given by Equation (10-56) for r_{P_1} to give

$$\sum\limits_{j=1}^{\infty} j^2 r_{P_j} = \frac{k_a}{2} \sum\limits_{j=2}^{\infty} j^2 \sum\limits_{i=1}^{j-1} R_{j-i} R_i + [k_d \Gamma_0(R_j) + k_M M + k_S S + k_C C] \Gamma_2(R_j) \tag{10-66}$$

The double summation may be expressed [7] as

$$\sum\limits_{j=2}^{\infty} j^2 \sum\limits_{i=1}^{j-1} R_{j-i} R_i = 2 \left(\sum\limits_{j=1}^{\infty} j R_j \right)^2 + 2 \left(\sum\limits_{j=1}^{\infty} R_j \right) \left(\sum\limits_{j=1}^{\infty} j^2 R_j \right) \tag{10-67}$$

and thus Equation (10-66) may be stated in the form

$$\sum\limits_{j=1}^{\infty} j^2 r_{P_j} = k_a [\Gamma_1(R_j)]^2 + [(k_a + k_d)\Gamma_0(R_j) + k_M M$$
$$+ k_S S + k_C C] \Gamma_2(R_j) \tag{10-68}$$

For the proposed mechanism the first and second moments, $\Gamma_1(R_j)$ and $\Gamma_2(R_j)$, may be expressed in terms of $\Gamma_0(R_j)$ or r_i, M, C, S, and the rate constants. The first step in the evaluation of $\Gamma_1(R_j)$ and $\Gamma_2(R_j)$ is to obtain an expression for R_j. On the basis of the pseudo steady state assumption, $r_{R_j} = 0$, Equations (10-44) and (10-45) may be solved for R_1 and R_j ($j \geq 2$), respectively. After r_{R1} has been set equal to zero, Equation (10-44) may be solved for R_1 to give

$$R_1 = \gamma \psi \tag{10-69}$$

where

$$\gamma = \frac{r_i}{k_p M} + T \Gamma_0(R_j)$$

$$\psi = \left[1 + T + \left(\frac{k_a + k_d}{k_p M} \right) \Gamma_0(R_j) \right]^{-1}$$

On the basis of the assumption that $r_{R_j} = 0$ for $j \geq 2$, Equation (10-45) may be solved for R_j to give

$$R_j = \psi R_{j-1}, \qquad (j \geq 2) \tag{10-70}$$

Then

$$R_j = \psi^{j-1} R_1 = \gamma \psi^j \tag{10-71}$$

Thus

$$\Gamma_1(R_j) = \sum_{j=1}^{\infty} j R_j = \gamma \sum_{j=1}^{\infty} j \psi^j = \gamma \psi \sum_{j=1}^{\infty} j \psi^{j-1}$$

and since $\psi < 1$, it follows [7] that

$$\Gamma_1(R_j) = \frac{\gamma \psi}{(1 - \psi)^2} \tag{10-72}$$

Similarly,

$$\Gamma_2(R_j) = \sum_{j=1}^{\infty} j^2 R_j = \frac{(1 + \psi)\gamma \psi}{(1 - \psi)^3} \tag{10-73}$$

Now observe that Equation (10-68) may be restated in terms of ψ as follows:

$$\sum_{j=1}^{\infty} j^2 r_{P_j} = k_a [\Gamma_1(R_j)]^2 + k_p M \left(\frac{1 - \psi}{\psi} \right) \Gamma_2(R_j) \tag{10-74}$$

The desired expression for $\bar{d}_W$ may now be obtained bv use of Equations (10-50) and (10-72) through (10-74); namely,

$$\bar{d}_W = \frac{\sum\limits_{j=1}^{\infty} j^2 r_{P_j}}{r_M} = \frac{\gamma}{(1 - \psi)^2 \Gamma_0(R_j)} \left[1 + \psi + \left(\frac{\psi}{1 - \psi} \right)^2 \frac{\gamma k_a}{k_p M} \right] \tag{10-75}$$

9. Elimination of the Free-Radical Concentrations from the Expression for the Weight Selectivity. The expression given by Equation (10-57) for r_{P_j} ($j \geq 2$) may be restated in terms of the termination function T [see Equation (10-61)] as follows:

$$r_{P_j} = \frac{k_a}{2} \sum_{i=1}^{j-1} R_{j-i} R_i + k_d R_j \Gamma_0(R_j) + k_p M T R_j \tag{10-76}$$

The summation may be expanded to give

$$\sum_{i=1}^{j-1} R_{j-i} R_i = R_{j-1} R_1 + R_{j-2} R_2 + \cdots + R_1 R_{j-1} \tag{10-77}$$

When each R_j appearing in this series is replaced by its equivalent as given by Equation (10-71), the following result is obtained:

$$\sum_{i=1}^{j-1} R_{j-i}R_i = \gamma^2[\psi^{j-1}\psi^1 + \psi^{j-2}\psi^2 + \cdots + \psi^1\psi^{j-1}] = \gamma^2(j-1)\psi^j \quad (10\text{-}78)$$

When R_j in the second term of Equation (10-76) is replaced by its equivalent $\gamma\psi^j$ [Equation (10-71)] and the summation is replaced by the result given by Equation (10-78), the following expression is obtained for r_{P_j} $(j \geq 2)$

$$r_{P_j} = \gamma\psi^j \left[\frac{k_a\gamma(j-1)}{2} + k_d\Gamma_0(R_j) + k_pMT \right] \quad (10\text{-}79)$$

Thus, for $j \geq 2$, the expression for the weight selectivity becomes

$$w_j = \frac{jr_{P_j}}{r_M} = j\gamma\psi^j \left[\frac{k_a\gamma(j-1)}{2k_pM\Gamma_0(R_j)} + \frac{k_d}{k_pM} + \frac{T}{\Gamma_0(R_j)} \right] \quad (10\text{-}80)$$

where r_M is given by Equation (10-50).

When $j = 1$, Equation (10-80) gives the correct formula for w_1. This statement is readily confirmed by commencing with the expressions for r_M and r_{P_1} and eliminating R_1 by use of its equivalent given by Equation (10-69).

D. Design of Reactors for Carrying Out Free-Radical Polymerizations

The design of reactors for carrying out polymerizations follows an approach similar to that demonstrated for thermal and catalytic reactors. The reaction time for a batch reactor or the volume of a flow reactor must be selected such that the specified number average or weight average degree of polymerization [$\bar{D}_n$ and $\bar{D}_W$, see Equations (10-12) and (10-14)] is satisfied. These quantities as well as the molecular weight distributions [see Equations (10-1) and (10-6)] may be used in the quality control of polymers. All of these functions may be found by use of the results of the various types of chemical and physical analyses described at the end of the introduction. From such analyses, the total concentration and the moments of the concentrations of the dead polymers [$\Gamma_0(P_j)$, $\Gamma_1(P_j)$, and $\Gamma_2(P_j)$] may be evaluated as well as other functions such as $\bar{D}_n$, $\bar{D}_W$, $\bar{M}_n$, $\bar{M}_W$, and W_j.

On the basis of the proposed mechanism, the selectivities defined above, and the material-balance equation for a given type of reactor, the monomer and initiator conversion, molecular weights, and molecular weight distribution may be predicted as demonstrated below for the three types of reactors: batch, plug-flow, and perfectly mixed flow reactors. Because of the similarity of the design of polymerization reactors to the design of thermal and catalytic reactors, an abbreviated treatment of the design of polymerization reactors is presented. In particular, it is supposed that the reactors are operated isothermally and that the mass density of the reacting mixture is independent of the extent of polymerization.

1. BATCH REACTORS. The design equations for a perfectly mixed batch reactor are developed as follows. As shown in Chapter 1, the limit of a material balance on the monomer in the reactor as the time period over which the balance is made is allowed to go to zero is given by

$$r_M = -\frac{dM}{dt} \tag{10-81}$$

where it has been supposed that the volume of the reacting mixture remains constant throughout the course of the polymerization. Elimination of r_M from Equations (10-50) and (10-81) gives

$$-\frac{dM}{dt} = k_p M \left(\frac{r_i}{k_a + k_d}\right)^{1/2} \tag{10-82}$$

By continuously feeding a small amount of initiator I to the reactor and by operating the reactor isothermally, the rate r_i [see Equation (10-41)] may be held constant throughout the polymerization. For the case where r_i is held fixed and the reactor is operated isothermally, Equation (10-82) may be integrated and rearranged to give

$$M = M^0 \exp\left[-k_p \left(\frac{r_i}{k_a + k_d}\right)^{1/2} t\right] \tag{10-83}$$

Since r_i may be evaluated by use of Equation (10-41), the concentration of the monomer M at any time t may be computed by use of Equation (10-83). After the concentration M at time t has been computed, the corresponding concentrations of the solvent S and the chain transfer agent C may be computed by relationships which are developed as follows. First observe that Equation (10-53) for r_S/r_M may be restated as follows:

$$\frac{dS}{dM} = \frac{k_S S}{k_p M} \tag{10-84}$$

Separation of the variables in this equation followed by integration and rearrangement gives

$$S = S^0 \left(\frac{M}{M^0}\right)^{k_S/k_p} \tag{10-85}$$

where S^0 is the concentration of the solvent at time $t = 0$. Similarly, by restating Equation (10-54) for r_C/r_M in the form,

$$\frac{dC}{dM} = \frac{k_C}{k_p} \frac{C}{M}$$

(10-86)

and integrating, it is found that

$$C = C^0 \left(\frac{M}{M^0}\right)^{k_C/k_p}$$

(10-87)

where C^0 is the concentration of the chain transfer agent at time $t = 0$.

On the basis of the proposed mechanism and the resulting expression given by Equation (10-61) for the number degree of selectivity, an expression for computing the number average degree of polymerization [defined by Equation (10-11)] may be developed as follows. First observe that the definition of the number degree of polymer selectivity [Equation (10-55)] may be restated as follows for a batch reactor operated at constant volume

$$\bar{d}_n = \frac{\displaystyle\sum_{j=1}^{\infty} r_{P_j}}{r_M} = \frac{\displaystyle\sum_{j=1}^{\infty} (dP_j/dt)}{-(dM/dt)}$$

(10-88)

Separation of the variables followed by integration gives

$$\int_0^t \sum_{j=1}^{\infty} \frac{dP_j}{dt} \, dt = -\int_0^t \bar{d}_n \frac{dM}{dt} \, dt$$

(10-89)

For $P_j = 0$ for all j at $t = 0$, this equation may be integrated to give

$$\sum_{j=1}^{\infty} P_j = -\int_{M^0}^{M} \bar{d}_n \, dM$$

(10-90)

By use of this result, Equations (10-5) and (10-11), the following expression, which may be used to compute $\bar{D}_n$, is obtained:

$$\bar{D}_n = -\frac{M^0 - M}{\displaystyle\int_{M^0}^{M} \bar{d}_n \, dM}$$

(10-91)

where $\bar{d}_n$ and M are given by Equations (10-61) and (10-83), respectively. [Note that when the proper set of rate constants has been selected, the value of $\bar{D}_n$ computed by use of Equation (10-91) must be equal to the value found by use of the experimentally determined moments; namely, $\bar{D}_n = \Gamma_1(P_j)/\Gamma_0(P_j)$.]

Similarly, the weight average degree of polymerization may be computed on the basis of the proposed mechanism by use of an expression which is developed as follows. By commencing with the following form of the defining equation for the weight degree of polymer selectivity for a batch reactor,

$$\bar{d}_W = \frac{\sum\limits_{j=1}^{\infty} j^2(dP_j/dt)}{-(dM/dt)} \tag{10-92}$$

and integrating as before, it is found that

$$\sum_{j=1}^{\infty} j^2 P_j = -\int_{M^0}^{M} \bar{d}_W \, dM \tag{10-93}$$

By use of the definition of the weight degree of polymerization $\bar{D}_W$ [Equations (10-13)], Equations (10-5), and (10-93), the following expression for computing $\bar{D}_W$ on the basis of the proposed mechanism is obtained:

$$\bar{D}_W = -\frac{\int_{M^0}^{M} \bar{d}_W \, dM}{M^0 - M} \tag{10-94}$$

where M is given by Equation (10-83).

Similarly, an expression for the weight fraction [defined by Equation (10-3)] may be obtained by commencing with the weight selectivity [Equation (10-63)] and following a procedure similar to that shown above for $\bar{d}_n$. The final result is

$$W_j = -\frac{\int_{M^0}^{M} w_j \, dM}{M^0 - M} \tag{10-95}$$

where the expression for w_j is given by Equation (10-80) and the expression for M is given by Equation (10-83).

EXAMPLE 10-1

Styrene is to be polymerized at 60°C with the free-radical initiator, benzoyl peroxide in a batch reactor. The initial concentration of the styrene is 8.35 g moles per liter, and the concentration of the initiator is to be maintained constant at 0.04 g mole per liter throughout the polymerization. (To achieve this condition, the initiator is fed continuously to the reactor throughout the course of the reaction.) In this example, it is supposed that the significant reactions of the mechanism proposed above are initiation, propagation, and termination by addition (or combination). The rate constants at the temperature of the polymerization, 60°C, are as follows [3]:

$$k_0 = 3.2 \times 10^{-6} \text{ sec}^{-1}$$

$$f = 0.6$$

$$k_p = 176 \text{ liters/g mole sec}$$

$$k_a = 3.6 \times 10^7 \text{ liters/g mole sec}$$

(a) Calculate the rate at which the initiator must be fed to the reactor in order for the concentration of the initiator to remain constant throughout the polymerization. The volume of the reactor filled by the reacting mixture is 3760 liters, and the variation of the volume of the reacting mixture with time may be neglected.
(b) For a reaction time of 180 min, compute the following: (1) the percentage of the styrene polymerized, (2) the number average molecular weight, (3) the weight molecular weight, (4) the molecular weight distribution, and (5) the mole fraction and molar distributions.

SOLUTION

(a) As illustrated in Chapter 2, the limit of a material balance on the initiator entering the perfectly mixed reactor as the time period over which the balance is made is allowed to go to zero is given by

$$n_I^0 - k_0 IV = \frac{d(IV)}{dt}$$

where n_I^0 is the feed rate of the initiator to the reactor at any time t. Since the concentration I of the initiator and the volume V are constant, $d(VI)/dt = 0$, and thus

$$n_I^0 = k_0 IV$$

$$n_I^0 = (3.2 \times 10^{-6})(0.04)(3760) = 4.813 \times 10^{-4} \text{ g moles/sec}$$

(b) (1) The styrene conversion is calculated by use of Equations (10-41) and (10-83). By Equation (10-41),

$$r_i = 2f k_0 I = (2)(0.6)(3.2)(10^{-6})(0.04) = 1.536 \times 10^{-7} \text{ g moles/sec}$$

From Equation (10-83),

$$M = M^0 \exp\left[-k_p(\sqrt{r_i/k_a})t\right]$$

$$= 8.35 \exp\left[-176(\sqrt{(1.536 \times 10^{-7})/(3.6 \times 10^7)})10,800\right]$$

$$= 7.375 \text{ g moles/liter}$$

And the percentage of the styrene converted is

$$\frac{8.35 - 7.375}{8.35} \times 100 = 11.68\%$$

(2) The number average molecular weight is computed by use of Equations (10-47), (10-61), and (10-91). The total concentration of polymers is given by Equation (10-47)

$$\Gamma_0(R_j) = \left(\frac{r_i}{k_a}\right)^{1/2} = \left(\frac{1.536 \times 10^{-7}}{3.6 \times 10^7}\right)^{1/2} = 6.532 \times 10^{-8} \text{ g moles/liter}$$

By Equation (10-61),

$$\bar{d}_n = \frac{k_a \Gamma_0}{2k_p M} = \frac{(3.6 \times 10^7)(6.532 \times 10^{-8})}{(2)(176)M}$$

$$\bar{d}_n = \frac{6.68 \times 10^{-3}}{M}$$

After this expression for $\bar{d}_n$ has been substituted into Equation (10-91), the number average degree of polymerization may be computed as follows:

$$\bar{D}_n = -\frac{M^0 - M}{\int_{M^0}^M \bar{d}_n \, dM} = -\frac{M^0 - M}{\int_{M^0}^M 6.68 \times 10^{-3} \frac{dM}{M}}$$

Thus

$$\bar{D}_n = -\left(\frac{8.35 - 7.375}{6.68 \times 10^{-3} \log_e (7.375)/(8.35)}\right)$$

$$\bar{D}_n = 1175.5$$

The number average molecular weight of the polystyrene may now be computed by use of Equation (10-12). Since the molecular weight of styrene $M_M = 104$,

$$\bar{M}_n = \bar{D}_n M_M = (1175.5)(104) = 122,252$$

(3) To compute the weight average molecular weight, the weight average degree of polymerization is first computed by use of Equation (10-94). In order to evaluate $\bar{D}_W$ by this equation, it is necessary to obtain an expression for $\bar{d}_W$ by use of Equation (10-75). On the basis of the assumptions given in the statement of the problem, the expression for ψ given below Equation (10-69) reduces to

$$\psi = \frac{1}{1 + (k_a \Gamma_0/k_p M)} = \frac{1}{1 + 2\bar{d}_n}$$

$$= \frac{1}{1 + 0.01336/M}$$

The expression for γ, given below Equation (10-69), reduces to

$$\gamma = \frac{r_i}{k_p M} = \frac{1.536 \times 10^{-7}}{176M} = \frac{8.727 \times 10^{-10}}{M}$$

By use of these values for ψ and γ, the given values of k_a and k_p, and the computed value of Γ_0, the weight degree of polymer selectivity $\bar{d}_w$ by Equation (10-75) may be expressed in terms of M. The following approximations are valid in the evaluation of $\bar{d}_w$ because M has values that lie between 7.375 and 8.35. First

$$1 - \psi = \frac{0.01336}{M + 0.01336} \cong \frac{0.01336}{M}$$

and

$$\psi = \frac{M}{M + 0.01336} \cong 1$$

Then, by use of Equation (10-75),

$$\bar{d}_w = \frac{(8.727 \times 10^{-10})M}{(1.336 \times 10^{-2})^2(6.532 \times 10^{-8})}\left[2 + \frac{(8.727 \times 10^{-10})(3.6 \times 10^7)}{(1.336 \times 10^{-2})^2(1.76 \times 10^2)}\right]$$

$$= 224.56M$$

This result may now be used to compute the weight average degree of polymerization by use of Equation (10-94)

$$\bar{D}_W = -\frac{\int_{M^0}^{M} \bar{d}_w \, dM}{M^0 - M} = \frac{224.56 \int_{M}^{M_0} M \, dM}{M^0 - M}$$

$$\bar{D}_W = (224.56)\left(\frac{M^0 + M}{2}\right) = (224.56)\left(\frac{8.35 + 7.375}{2}\right)$$

$$\bar{D}_W = 1765.6$$

By use of this value of $\bar{D}_W$, the weight average molecular weight may be computed by use of Equation (10-14); namely,

$$\bar{M}_W = \bar{D}_W M_M = (1765.6)(104) = 183{,}622$$

(4) For the polymerization under consideration, the expression given by Equation (10-80) for the weight selectivity reduces to

$$w_j = \frac{\gamma^2 \psi^j}{M}\left[\frac{j(j-1)k_a}{2k_p \Gamma_0(R_j)}\right]$$

For convenience, let the expressions obtained previously for ψ and γ be restated as follows:

$$\psi = \frac{1}{1 + a/M}, \qquad \gamma = \frac{b}{M}$$

Then

$$w_j = \frac{1}{M^3(1 + a/M)^j}\left[\frac{j(j - 1)b^2k_a}{2k_p\Gamma_0(R_j)}\right]$$

Substitution of this expression for $\bar{d}_W$ into Equation (10-95) followed by the change in variable

$$u = \frac{1}{M}$$

gives

$$W_j = \frac{j(j - 1)b^2k_a}{a[(1/u^0) - (1/u)]k_p\Gamma_0(R_j)}\left[\int_{u^0}^u \frac{au\,du}{(1 + au)^j}\right]$$

For $j = 1$, $W_j = 0$. Since the integral in the above expression may be stated in the form

$$\int_{u^0}^u \frac{au\,du}{(1 + au)^j} = \int_{u^0}^u \frac{du}{(1 + au)^{j-1}} - \int_{u^0}^u \frac{du}{(1 + au)^j}$$

it is readily shown that for $j = 2$,

$$\int_{u^0}^u \frac{au\,du}{(1 + au)^2} = \frac{1}{a}\left\{\left[\log_e(1 + au) + \frac{1}{(1 + au)}\right]\Big|_{u^0}^u\right\}$$

and for $j > 2$,

$$\int_{u^0}^u \frac{au\,du}{(1 + au)^j} = \frac{1}{a}\left\{\left[\frac{1}{(j - 1)(1 + au)^{j-1}} - \frac{1}{(j - 2)(1 + au)^{j-2}}\right]\Big|_{u^0}^u\right\}$$

A graph of the values of W_j versus j, which were computed by use of the above expression, is presented in Figure 10-2 on page 429.

(5) After W_j has been computed, the corresponding mole fractions x_j may be found as follows:

$$x_j = W_j\left(\frac{\bar{D}_n}{j}\right)$$

This expression is shown to reduce to the definition of x_j given by Equation (10-6) by use of Equations (10-3) and (10-11). A graph of x_j versus chain length j is shown in Figure 10-3 on page 430.

Similarly, after W_j has been computed, the corresponding molar concentrations of polymers P_j of chain length j are given by

$$P_j = \frac{W_j(M^0 - M)}{j}$$

A plot of the results so obtained are shown in Figure 10-4. A variety of other mechanisms and corresponding molecular weight distributions have been presented by Peebles [7].

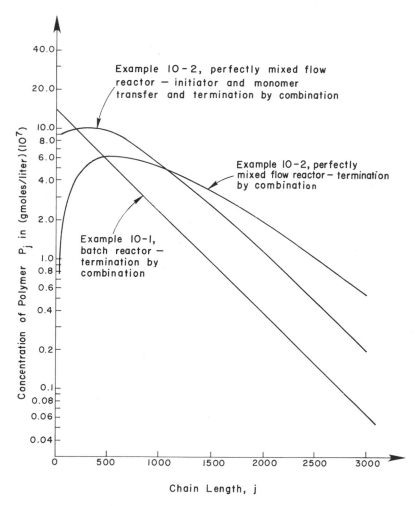

Figure 10-4. Molar distributions for the polymerization of styrene in batch and perfectly mixed flow reactors.

2. Plug-Flow Reactors. As demonstrated in Chapter 2, the design equations for plug-flow reactors may be obtained from those for isothermally operated batch reactors provided that the following conditions are satisfied: (1) the plug-flow reactor is operated isothermally at steady state, (2) the flow rate through the reactor satisfies the condition for plug-flow (see Chapter 2), and (3) the density or volumetric flow rate of the reacting mixture remains constant throughout the reactor. To obtain the design equations for plug-flow reactors from those stated above, concentrations and time in the equations for the batch reactors are replaced by their equivalents, molar

flow rates divided by the total volumetric flow rate and plug-flow reactor volume divided by the total volumetric flow rate, respectively.

$$M = \frac{n_M}{v_T}, \qquad t = \frac{V}{v_T} \qquad (10\text{-}96)$$

where n_M = flow rate of the monomer in moles of monomer per unit time

$\quad v_T$ = total volumetric flow rate of the reacting mixture in volume units per unit time

$\quad V$ = volume of the plug-flow reactor

3. PERFECTLY MIXED FLOW REACTORS. For a perfectly mixed flow reactor at steady state operation, a component-material balance on the monomer yields

$$r_M = \frac{n_M^0 - n_M}{V} \qquad (10\text{-}97)$$

When the density of the reacting mixture is constant, Equation (10-97) may be expressed as follows:

$$r_M = \frac{n_M^0/v_T - n_M/v_T}{V/v_T} = \frac{M^0 - M}{\theta} \qquad (10\text{-}98)$$

where M^0 is the concentration of the monomer entering the reactor, M is the concentration of the monomer in the stream leaving the reactor, and θ is the residence time. By eliminating r_M from Equations (10-48) and (10-98) and solving the expression so obtained for M, the following result for computing M is obtained:

$$M = \frac{M^0}{1 + k_p[r_i/(k_a + k_d)]^{1/2}\theta} \qquad (10\text{-}99)$$

By beginning with Equations (10-53) and (10-54), the following expressions for the concentrations of the solvent S and the chain transfer agent C are obtained in a manner analogous to that demonstrated for M; namely,

$$S = \frac{S^0}{1 + (k_S/k_p)[(M^0/M) - 1]} \qquad (10\text{-}100)$$

and

$$C = \frac{C^0}{1 + (k_C/k_p)[(M^0/M) - 1]} \qquad (10\text{-}101)$$

By use of the component-material balances for a perfectly mixed flow reactor, it is possible to restate the defining equation for the number degree of polymer selectivity in the following form:

$$\bar{d}_n = \frac{\displaystyle\sum_{j=1}^{\infty} P_j}{M^0 - M} \tag{10-102}$$

By use of this result as well as the one given by Equation (10-5), the definition of $\bar{D}_n$ given by Equation (10-11) may be restated as follows:

$$\bar{D}_n = \frac{\displaystyle\sum_{j=1}^{\infty} jP_j}{\displaystyle\sum_{j=1}^{\infty} P_j} = \frac{M^0 - M}{(M^0 - M)\bar{d}_n} = \bar{d}_n^{-1} \tag{10-103}$$

By use of an approach analogous to that demonstrated for $\bar{d}_n$ and $\bar{D}_n$, the following expressions are obtained for the weight selectivity and weight degree of polymer selectivity:

$$\bar{d}_W = \frac{\displaystyle\sum_{j=1}^{\infty} j^2 r_{P_j}}{r_M} = \frac{\displaystyle\sum_{j=1}^{\infty} j^2 P_j}{M^0 - M} \tag{10-104}$$

and

$$\bar{D}_W = \frac{\displaystyle\sum_{j=1}^{\infty} j^2 P_j}{\displaystyle\sum_{j=1}^{\infty} jP_j} = \frac{(M^0 - M)\,\bar{d}_W}{(M^0 - M)} = \bar{d}_W \tag{10-105}$$

Similarly, it can be shown that the weight fraction and the weight selectivity are equal when the reaction is carried out in a perfectly mixed flow reactor at steady state; that is,

$$W_j = w_j \tag{10-106}$$

EXAMPLE 10-2

Styrene is to be polymerized at 60°C in a perfectly mixed flow reactor. The styrene concentration in the feed is 8.35 g moles per liter. The concentration of benzoyl peroxide in the effluent is to be maintained at 0.04 g mole per liter. The volume of the reactor filled by the reacting mixture at any time is 3760 liters. The rate constants and mechanism of Example 10-1 are applicable in Parts (a), (b), and (c).

(a) Calculate the residence time required to obtain 11.67% conversion of the styrene.
(b) Calculate the volumetric flow rate of the feed and the concentration of initiator, benzoyl peroxide, in the feed.
(c) Calculate the following: (1) the number average molecular weight, (2) the weight average molecular weight, (3) the molecular weight distribution, and (4) the mole fraction and molar distributions.
(d) Calculate the molar distribution of the styrene polymer for the case where termination by monomer transfer and termination by chain transfer with the initiator are also considered. The rate constants for these two transfer mechanisms are as follows:

$$k_M = 105.6 \times 10^{-4} \text{ liter/g mole sec}$$

$$k_C = 9.68 \text{ liters/g mole sec}$$

SOLUTION

(a) The residence time θ may be found by solving Equation (10-99) for θ.

$$\theta = \frac{M^0 - M}{k_p M [r_i/k_a]^{1/2}}$$

The value of r_i was computed in Example 10-1(b), and the values for the remaining variables appearing in this expression were given in the statement of the example. Thus

$$\theta = \frac{8.35 - 7.375}{(176)(7.375)[(1.536 \times 10^{-7})/(3.6 \times 10^7)]^{1/2}}$$

$$\theta = 1.15 \times 10^4 \text{ sec} = 3.19 \text{ hr}$$

(b) $v_T = V/\theta = 3760/(1.15 \times 10^4) = 0.327 \text{ liter/sec}$
Since

$$r_0 = \frac{I^0 - I}{\theta}, \qquad I^0 = I + r_0 \theta$$

and thus
$$I^0 = 0.04 + (1.28 \times 10^{-7})(1.15 \times 10^4)$$

$$I^0 = 0.0415 \text{ g mole/liter}$$

(c) (1) The number average degree of polymerization may be found by use of Equation (10-103),

$$\bar{D}_n = \bar{d}_n^{-1}$$

As demonstrated in Example 10-1, the expression given by Equation (10-61) for $\bar{d}_n$ may be used to compute $\bar{D}_n$ as follows:

$$\bar{D}_n = \bar{d}_n^{-1} = \left(\frac{6.68 \times 10^{-3}}{7.375} \right)^{-1} = 1.104 \times 10^3$$

The number average molecular weight follows from Equation (10-12),

$$\bar{M}_n = \bar{D}_n M_M = (1.104 \times 10^3)(104) = 114,816$$

(2) The weight average degree of polymerization is given by, Equation (10-105),

$$\bar{D}_W = \bar{d}_W$$

and by use of Equation (10-75) as demonstrated in Example 10-1,

$$\bar{D}_W = \bar{d}_W = 224.56M = 1.656 \times 10^3$$

Then, by Equation (10-14),

$$\bar{M}_W = \bar{D}_W M_M = (1.652 \times 10^3)(104) = 1.718 \times 10^5$$

(3) By Equation (10-106),
$$W_j = w_j$$

The expression for w_j given in Part (b4) of Example 10-1 is applicable. In this case $M = 7.375$ and the mass fraction W_j of polymers of length j may be computed as follows:

$$W_j = w_j = \frac{j(j-1)b^2 k_a}{M^3(1 + a/M)^j[2k_p\Gamma_0(R_j)]}$$

$$W_j = w_j = \frac{j(j-1)[8.727 \times 10^{-10}]^2(3.6 \times 10^7)}{(7.375)^3\left[1 + \dfrac{0.01336}{7.375}\right]^j (2)(176)(6.532 \times 10^{-8})}$$

A graph of the results given by this expression are presented in Figure 10-2.

After the weight fraction W_j has been computed, the corresponding values of x_j and P_j are computed as described in Problem 10-1. These results are plotted in Figures 10-2 and 10-3 see pages 429 and 430, respectively.

(d) The two additional reactions to be considered are as follows:

$$R_j + M \xrightarrow{k_M} P_j + R_1$$

$$R_j + I \xrightarrow{k_C} P_j + R_1$$

Since some additional initiator is required for the termination reactions, and since it has been specified that the outlet concentration of I is to be 0.04 g mole/liter, it is necessary to recompute the concentration of the initiator in the feed. In this case,

$$\frac{I^0 - I}{\theta} = r_0 + k_C I \Gamma_0(R_j)$$

Then, from the results of Parts (b) and (c) of Example 10-1,

$$I^0 = I + \theta[r_0 + k_C I \Gamma_0(R_j)]$$

$$= 0.04 + 1.15 \times 10^4[1.28 \times 10^{-7} + (9.68)(0.04)(6.532 \times 10^{-8})]$$

$$= 0.04 + 0.00176 = 0.04176$$

Thus, the initiator transfer reaction has only a small effect on the feed concentration of the initiator.

In the calculation of the number average degree of polymerization, the expression for $\bar{d}_n$ now becomes

$$\bar{d}_n = \frac{k_a \Gamma_0}{2k_p M} + T$$

where $T = \dfrac{k_M}{k_p} + \dfrac{k_C}{k_p}\left(\dfrac{I}{M}\right) = \dfrac{105.6 \times 10^{-4}}{176} + \left(\dfrac{9.68}{176}\right)\left(\dfrac{0.04}{7.375}\right) = 0.358 \times 10^{-3}$

By use of the expression obtained in Part (b2) of Example 10-1,

$$\bar{d}_n = \frac{6.68 \times 10^{-3}}{7.375} + 0.358 \times 10^{-3} = 1.264 \times 10^{-3}$$

Then

$$\bar{D}_n = \bar{d}_n^{-1} = \frac{1}{1.264 \times 10^{-3}} = 791$$

and

$$\bar{M}_n = \bar{D}_n M_M = (791)(104) = 8.23 \times 10^4$$

Note, the effect of the two transfer reactions is to reduce the number average molecular weight by 28.3%.

In the weight average degree of polymerization, the term $T\Gamma_0(R_j)$ must be added to the value of γ found in Part (c3) of Example 10-1. That is, in this case,

$$\gamma = \frac{r_i}{k_p M} + T\Gamma_0(R_j)$$

$$= \frac{8.727 \times 10^{-10}}{7.375} + (0.358 \times 10^{-3})(6.532 \times 10^{-8})$$

$$= 1.417 \times 10^{-10}$$

In this case the expression for ψ becomes

$$\psi = \frac{1}{1 + T + \dfrac{k_a \Gamma_0}{k_p M}} = \frac{1}{1.000358 + \dfrac{0.01336}{7.375}}$$

$$= 0.99783$$

By use of these values for γ and ψ as well as other computed results, the expression given by Equation (10-75) for $\bar{d}_W$ may be evaluated to give

$$\bar{d}_W = 1303$$

From Equation (10-105),

$$\bar{d}_W = \bar{D}_W = 1303$$

and by Equation (10-14),

$$\bar{M}_W = \bar{D}_W M_M = (1311)(104) = 1.355 \times 10^5$$

Note, the transfer reactions have reduced the weight average molecular weight found in Part (c2) by 20.7%.

The distribution curve of weight fraction may be computed by use of the following expression, which is obtained by use of Equations (10-80) and (10-106).

$$W_j = w_j = \frac{j\gamma\psi^j}{\Gamma_0(R_j)}\left[\frac{k_a\gamma(j-1)}{2k_pM} + T\right]$$

The values for γ, ψ, and T are those computed above for the case where the additional termination reactions are considered. The resulting distribution computed by this expression for W_j is presented in Figure 10-2.

After the weight fraction W_j has been computed, the corresponding values of P_j are computed as described in Problem 10-1. These results are plotted in Figure 10-4.

4. THE GEL OR TROMSDOFF EFFECT. The names "gel" or "Trommsdorff effect" [5, 8, 9] are used to describe the tendency of reactions in which high molecular weight polymers are formed to become "diffusion controlled." Because of the size of the relatively large polymer molecules, their kinetic velocities are far less than those of the monomers. Thus the chance of collision between two large polymer molecules followed by a termination reaction [Equations (10-21) and (10-22)] is much less than the chance of collision between a monomer and a polymer followed by propagation reaction [Equation (10-20)]. The net result of this effect on the rate of reaction of the monomer may be seen by examining the expression obtained by elimination of r_i from Equations (10-41) and (10-49).

$$r_M = \left(\frac{k_p\sqrt{2k_0f}}{\sqrt{k_a + k_d}}\right) MI^{1/2} = k_{ob}MI^{1/2} \qquad (10\text{-}107)$$

where k_{ob} is the observed rate constant. When the polymerization becomes diffusion controlled, the rate constants for termination, k_a and k_d, decrease, and consequently the observed rate constant k_{ob} increases. Consequently, the tendency to produce higher molecular weight polymers by the propagation reaction rather than termination of the polymerization [Equations (10-21) and (10-22)] is increased.

Hamielec [6] observed that the onset of diffusion control begins with a viscosity of 10 centipoise in the polymerization of styrene. Hui and Hamielec [9] and Biesenberger et al. [8] have treated the diffusion effect in more detail.

Sacks et al. [10, 11], Beckman [12], and Lynn and Huff [13] have considered the cases of optimal temperature profiles for batch reactors, problems of designing large-scale reactor vessels, and deviations from plug flow, respectively.

II. STEPWISE ADDITION AND CONDENSATION POLYMERIZATIONS AND COPOLYMERIZATIONS

First the chemistry of the above types of polymerizations is presented and then stepwise addition polymerizations are treated quantitatively.

A. The Chemistry of Selected Polymerizations

The chemistry of selected polymerizations is presented in the order in which they appear in the above title.

1. STEPWISE ADDITION POLYMERIZATIONS. Stepwise addition polymerizations are characteristic of the *living polymers* as coined by Szwarc [14]. Two basic reactions occur, which are

$$I + M \xrightarrow{\ k_i\ } R_1 \qquad \text{(initiation)} \qquad\qquad (10\text{-}108)$$

$$R_j + M \xrightarrow{\ k_p\ } R_{j+1} \qquad \text{(propagation)} \qquad\qquad (10\text{-}109)$$

For this simple case no transfer or termination reactions occur. The polymer species R_j has a long lifetime, and the reaction must be terminated by an outside agent such as water.

Cationic, anionic, and coordinated polymerizations are examples of stepwise addition polymerizations. An example of the use of an ionic type of catalyst is the stepwise polymerization of styrene in a solvent by use of butyllithium. The initiation step is where the abbreviated form

$$\left[\begin{array}{c} H \quad H \\ | \quad\quad | \\ Bu\text{—}C\text{—}C: \\ | \\ H \end{array} \right]^{-}$$

denotes

$$\left[\begin{array}{c} H \quad H \quad H \quad H \quad H \quad H \\ | \quad | \quad | \quad | \quad | \quad | \\ H\text{—}C\text{—}C\text{—}C\text{—}C\text{—}C\text{—}C: \\ | \quad | \quad | \quad | \quad | \\ H \quad H \quad H \quad H \quad H \end{array} \right]^{-}$$

This initiation reaction may be represented symbolically by Equation (10-108).

The propagation step then begins by the reaction of R_1 with M to give R_2; that is,

$$\left[\begin{array}{c} H \quad H \\ | \quad\quad | \\ Bu\text{—}C\text{—}C: \\ | \\ H \end{array} \right]^{-} \left[Li \right]^{+} + \begin{array}{c} H \quad H \\ | \quad\quad | \\ C: :C \\ | \\ H \end{array} \longrightarrow \left[Bu(CH_2CH)_2 \right]^{-} \left[Li \right]^{+}$$

This reaction is represented symbolically by Equation (10-109). Stepwise-addition polymerizations do not have a termination step, and water or some other impurity must be injected into the reacting mass in order to stop the polymerization reaction [14]. In ionic polymerizations, the length of the polymer molecules is dependent upon the initiator concentration and the monomer conversion. In order to produce long chain polymers, low initiator concentrations of the order of 10^{-6} moles per liter and high monomer conversions are required.

2. CONDENSATION POLYMERIZATIONS. Examples of products formed by condensation reactions are the polyurethanes, polyureas, polyphenylesters, polycarbonates, and phenolic resins. An example of condensation polymerizations is the formation of nylon by the reaction of diamino-hexane and adipic acid [3]. The first step is

$$\begin{array}{c} H \quad H \quad H \quad H \quad H \quad H \quad H \quad H \\ | \quad | \quad | \quad | \quad | \quad | \quad | \quad | \\ N\text{—}C\text{—}C\text{—}C\text{—}C\text{—}C\text{—}C\text{—}N \\ | \quad | \quad | \quad | \quad | \quad | \quad | \quad | \\ H \quad H \quad H \quad H \quad H \quad H \quad H \quad H \end{array} + \begin{array}{c} O \quad H \quad H \quad H \quad H \quad O \\ || \quad | \quad | \quad | \quad | \quad || \\ C\text{—}C\text{—}C\text{—}C\text{—}C\text{—}C \\ | \quad | \quad | \quad | \\ OH \quad H \quad H \quad H \quad H \quad OH \end{array}$$

Diaminohexane   Adipic acid

$$\longrightarrow \begin{array}{c} H \\ | \\ N\text{—}(CH_2)_6\text{—}N\text{—}C(CH_2)_4\text{—}C \\ | \quad\quad\quad\quad | \\ H \quad\quad\quad\quad OH \end{array} + H_2O$$

Additional reactions occur at both ends of this polymer molecule to form long chain polymers. A characteristic of condensation reactions is the production of small molecules such as H_2O, NH_3, HCHO, and NaCl. Usually the small molecules must be removed during the polymerization in order to produce high molecular weight polymer molecules.

3. COPOLYMERIZATION. A copolymer is a polymer chain composed of two monomers which may be represented as monomers A and B. Possible copolymer chains are [15] as follows:

A—B—A—B—A—B   (alternating copolymer)

$$\left.\begin{array}{l} \text{A—A—B—A—B—B—A—B—A—B—A—A} \\ \text{A—A—A—B—A—B—B—B—A} \end{array}\right\} \quad \text{(random copolymers)}$$

A—A—A—A—A—A—A—A—B—B—B—B—B—B   (block copolymer)

Examples of commercially important copolymers are styrene-butadiene, vinylidene chloride-vinyl chloride, ethylene-vinyl acetate, and butadiene-acrylonitrile.

B. Analysis of Stepwise Addition Polymerizations

The reaction mechanism considered consists of the initiation reaction [Equation (10-108)] and the propagation reactions [Equation (10-109)]. The rate of disappearance of the initiator I is represented by

$$r_i = k_i IM \tag{10-110}$$

Again the assumption made in the analysis of the propagation reactions in Part I is employed; namely, the rate constant k_p, is independent of the chain length. Let the rate of appearance of the active species R_j be denoted by r_{R_j}. Then for $j = 1$,

$$r_{R_1} = k_i IM - k_p MR_1 \tag{10-111}$$

and for $j \geq 2$,

$$r_{R_j} = k_p M(R_{j-1} - R_j), \qquad (j = 2, 3, \ldots) \tag{10-112}$$

The rate of propagation or the rate of disappearance of the monomer M by all propagation reactions is given by

$$(r_p)_M = k_p M \sum_{j=1}^{\infty} R_j \tag{10-113}$$

Let the total rate of disappearance of the monomer be denoted by r_M. Then

$$r_M = r_i + (r_p)_M \tag{10-114}$$

The summation of the r_{R_j}'s over all j ($j = 1, 2, \ldots$) is given by

$$\sum_{j=1}^{\infty} r_{R_j} = k_i IM - k_p MR_1 + k_p M \left[\sum_{j=2}^{\infty} R_{j-1} - \sum_{j=2}^{\infty} R_j \right]$$

$$= k_i IM + k_p M \left[\sum_{j=2}^{\infty} R_{j-1} - \sum_{j=1}^{\infty} R_j \right]$$

$$= k_i IM + k_p M \left[\sum_{k=1}^{\infty} R_k - \sum_{j=1}^{\infty} R_j \right]$$

$$= k_i IM = r_i \tag{10-115}$$

The total polymer concentration, $\sum_{j=1}^{\infty} R_j$, which appears in Equation (10-113), may be evaluated by making a material balance on the initiator. In particular, since each polymer molecule R_j has associated with it one molecule of initiator I, it follows that

$$I^0 - I = \sum_{j=1}^{\infty} R_j = \Gamma_0(R_j) \tag{10-116}$$

Similarly, by making a mass balance on the monomer, the first moment of the R_j's may be evaluated. That is, since the monomer M must be in either the monomer form or in the polymer form, it follows that

$$M_M(M^0 - M) = \sum_{j=1}^{\infty} M_j R_j = M_M \sum_{j=1}^{\infty} j R_j$$

and thus

$$M^0 - M = \sum_{j=1}^{\infty} j R_j = \Gamma_1(R_j) \tag{10-117}$$

1. DEFINITIONS OF THE NUMBER AND WEIGHT DEGREE OF POLYMER SELECTIVITY. For stepwise addition polymerizations, the number degree of polymer selectivity, $\bar{d}_n$, is defined by

$$\bar{d}_n = \frac{\sum\limits_{j=1}^{\infty} r_{R_j}}{r_M} \tag{10-118}$$

Then

$$\bar{d}_n = \frac{r_i}{r_i + (r_p)_M} = \frac{1}{1 + (k_p/k_i)(I^0/I - 1)} \tag{10-119}$$

The weight degree of polymer selectivity is defined by

$$\bar{d}_W = \frac{\sum\limits_{j=1}^{\infty} j^2 r_{R_j}}{r_M} \tag{10-120}$$

In this case,

$$\sum_{j=1}^{\infty} j^2 r_{R_j} = k_i IM + k_p M \sum_{j=1}^{\infty} [(j+1)^2 - j^2] R_j$$

$$= k_i IM + k_p M \sum_{j=1}^{\infty} (2j+1) R_j$$

$$= k_1 IM + 2k_p M(M^0 - M) + k_p M(I^0 - I) \tag{10-121}$$

Since $r_M = r_i + (r_p)_M$, it follows that

$$\bar{d}_W = 1 + \frac{2k_p(M^0 - M)}{k_i I + k_p(I^0 + I)} \tag{10-122}$$

C. Polymerization in Batch Reactors

Throughout the following developments, it is supposed that the batch reactor operates isothermally and that the volume of the reacting mixture remains constant with respect to time.

1. NUMBER AND WEIGHT AVERAGE DEGREES OF POLYMERIZATION. Although the selectivities $\bar{d}_n$ and $\bar{d}_W$ found above may be used to obtain expressions for the number average degree of polymerizations, $\bar{D}_n$, and the weight average degree of polymerization, $\bar{D}_W$, the following approach is simpler for the treatment of batch reactors. The first step of this approach is to obtain expressions for the amounts of the initiator I and monomer M as functions of a new variable τ which is related to time. The second step consists of the development of an expression for computing the time t corresponding to each value of τ.

Elimination of r_i from the component-material balance

$$r_i = -\frac{dI}{dt}$$

and Equation (10-110) gives,

$$\frac{-dI}{dt} = k_i IM \tag{10-123}$$

Let the new variable τ be defined as follows:

$$\tau = \int_0^t M \, dt$$

or
$$d\tau = M \, dt \tag{10-124}$$

After this change in variable has been made, Equation (10-123) reduces to

$$\frac{-dI}{d\tau} = k_i I \tag{10-125}$$

Separation of variables followed by integration and rearrangement yields

$$I = I^0 \exp\left(-k_i \tau\right) \tag{10-126}$$

The expression obtained for I as a function of τ may now be used to express the amount of monomer as a function of τ. Equations (10-81), (10-110), (10-113), and (10-114) may be combined to give

$$\frac{-dM}{dt} = k_i I M + k_p M \sum_{j=1}^{\infty} R_j \tag{10-127}$$

After each member of this equation has been divided by M and the sum of the R_j's has been eliminated by use of Equation (10-116), one obtains

$$\frac{-dM}{d\tau} = k_i I + k_p (I^0 - I) \tag{10-128}$$

Elimination of I by use of Equation (10-126) gives

$$\frac{-dM}{d\tau} = k_i I^0 e^{-k_i \tau} + k_p I^0 (1 - e^{-k_i \tau}) \tag{10-129}$$

Multiplication of each term of this equation by $d\tau$ followed by termwise integration and rearrangement yields

$$(M^0 - M) = I^0 (1 - e^{-k_i \tau})\left(1 - \frac{k_p}{k_i}\right) + k_p I^0 \tau \tag{10-130}$$

A one-to-one correspondence between τ and t may now be obtained by first eliminating M from Equations (10-124) and (10-130). The resulting expression may be integrated to give

$$t = \int_0^\tau \frac{d\tau}{M^0 - I^0[(1 - k_p/k_i)(1 - e^{-k_i\tau}) + k_p\tau]} \tag{10-131}$$

By use of this equation to obtain the t for any given τ, the corresponding values of I and M at time t may be found by use of Equations (10-126) and (10-130), respectively.

Since the number average degree of polymerization as given by Equation (10-11) is equal to $\Gamma_1(R_j)$ divided by $\Gamma_0(R_j)$, and since these moments are given by Equations (10-116) and (10-117), respectively, it follows that

$$\bar{D}_n = \frac{\Gamma_1(R_j)}{\Gamma_0(R_j)} = \frac{M^0 - M}{I^0 - I} \tag{10-132}$$

It should be remarked that this expression is valid for any type of reactor. For the case of a batch reactor, I and M in Equation (10-132) may be stated in terms of τ by use of Equations (10-126) and (10-130), respectively, to give

$$\bar{D}_n = \left(1 - \frac{k_p}{k_i}\right) + \frac{k_p\tau}{(1 - e^{-k_i\tau})} \tag{10-133}$$

and, for any τ, the corresponding value of t is given by Equation (10-131).

To express the weight average degree of polymerization $\bar{D}_W [\bar{D}_W = \Gamma_2(R_j)/\Gamma_1(R_j)]$ in terms of τ requires the development of an expression for the second moment of the R_js in terms of τ. Such an expression may be obtained by commencing with Equation (10-121), and the material balances

$$r_{R_j} = \frac{dR_j}{dt} \qquad (j = 1, 2, \ldots) \tag{10-134}$$

Elimination of the r_{R_j}s in Equation (10-121) by use of Equation (10-134) gives

$$\sum_{j=2}^{\infty} j^2 \frac{dR_j}{dt} = [k_i IM + 2k_p M(M^0 - M) + k_p M(I^0 - I)] \tag{10-135}$$

After each member of this equation has been divided by M, and then I and $(M^0 - M)$ are replaced by their equivalents as given by Equations (10-126) and (10-130), the resulting expression may be integrated to give the desired result

$$\sum_{j=1}^{\infty} j^2 R_j = I^0 \left\{ \left(1 - \frac{k_p}{k_i}\right)\left(1 - \frac{2k_p}{k_i}\right)\left(1 - e^{-k_i\tau}\right) \right.$$

$$\left. + k_p\tau\left[(1 + k_p\tau) + 2\left(1 - \frac{k_p}{k_i}\right)\right]\right\} \qquad (10\text{-}136)$$

Then, by use of this result and the results given by Equations (10-117) and (10-130), the following expression is obtained for $\bar{D}_W$:

$$\bar{D}_W = \frac{\left(1 - \frac{k_p}{k_i}\right)\left(1 - \frac{2k_p}{k_i}\right)(1 - e^{-k_i\tau}) + k_p\tau\left[1 + k_p\tau + 2\left(1 - \frac{k_p}{k_i}\right)\right]}{\left(1 - \frac{k_p}{k_i}\right)(1 - e^{-k_i\tau}) + k_p\tau}$$

$$(10\text{-}137)$$

where the time t corresponding to a given τ is found by use of Equation (10-131).

2. DISTRIBUTION OF THE POLYMERS R_j. In order to compute the weight fraction or mole fraction of R_j in the mixture, expressions are needed for computing the R_j's ($j = 1, 2, \ldots$). The desired expressions for the R_j's may be obtained by the following procedure.

Elimination of r_{R_j} from Equations (10-111) and (10-112) by use of the corresponding material balances,

$$r_{R_j} = \frac{dR_j}{dt} \qquad (j = 1, 2, \ldots)$$

gives

$$\frac{dR_1}{d\tau} = k_i I - k_p R_1 \qquad (10\text{-}138)$$

and

$$\frac{dR_j}{d\tau} = k_p(R_{j-1} - R_j) \qquad (10\text{-}139)$$

after the change of variable $d\tau = M\,dt$ has been made. Since I is known as a function of τ [Equation (10-126)], Equation (10-138) may be rearranged to the form

$$\frac{dR_1}{dt} + k_p R_1 = k_i I^0 e^{-k_i\tau} \qquad (10\text{-}140)$$

The solution to this differential equation is well known [see Equations (3-57) and (3-58)]. For the boundary condition $R_1 = 0$ at $\tau = 0$, the solution of Equation (10-140) is given by

$$R_1 = \left[\frac{k_i I^0}{k_p - k_i}\right][e^{-k_i \tau} - e^{-k_p \tau}] \tag{10-141}$$

where $k_p \neq k_i$. By use of this expression and Equation (10-112) for $j = 2$, the following equation in R_2 and τ is obtained:

$$\frac{dR_2}{d\tau} + k_p R_2 = k_p \left(\frac{k_i I^0}{k_p - k_i}\right)[e^{-k_i \tau} - e^{-k_p \tau}] \tag{10-142}$$

The solution of Equation (10-142) is of the same general form as the one for Equation (10-140), and for $R_2 = 0$ at $\tau = 0$,

$$R_2 = \frac{k_i I^0 k_p}{(k_p - k_i)^2}[e^{-k_i \tau} - e^{-k_p \tau}] - \frac{k_p k_i I^0 \tau e^{-k_p \tau}}{k_p - k_i} \tag{10-143}$$

By continuation of this procedure, the following expression is obtained:

$$R_j = \frac{(k_i I^0)k_p^{j-1} e^{-k_i \tau}}{(k_p - k_i)^j}\left[1 - e^{-z}\left(\sum_{n=0}^{j-1}\frac{z^n}{n!}\right)\right] \tag{10-144}$$

where

$$z = (k_p - k_i)\tau$$

The incomplete gamma function

$$\Gamma(z, n) = \int_0^z \frac{x^n e^{-x}\,dx}{n!} \tag{10-145}$$

has been tabulated. By successive integration of the right-hand side of Equation (10-145) by parts, the following equivalent form of the incomplete gamma function is obtained:

$$\Gamma(z, n) = 1 - e^{-z}\left(\sum_{k=0}^{n}\frac{z^k}{k!}\right) \tag{10-146}$$

Thus Equation (10-144) reduces to

$$R_j = \frac{k_i I^0 k_p^{j-1} e^{-k_i \tau}}{(k_p - k_i)^j}[\Gamma(z, j - 1)] \tag{10-147}$$

where the time t corresponding to a given τ is found by use of Equation (10-131). [Zeman et al. [15] proposed numerical procedures for the calculation of the R_j's for more complex mechanisms and more general operating conditions than those used to obtain Equation (10-147).]

After the set of R_j's has been computed, the weight fractions and other distribution functions may be computed. For example, the weight fraction W_j of polymer R_j may be computed by use of the following formula:

$$W_j = \frac{jR_j}{M^0 - M} \tag{10-148}$$

where $M^0 - M$ is given by Equation (10-130) and the time t corresponding to each τ is given by Equation (10-131). The relationship given by Equation (10-148) follows immediately from Equations (10-3) and (10-117).

EXAMPLE 10-3

Suppose that for the reactions given by Equations (10-108) and (10-109), $k_i = 0.032$ (liter/g mole min) and $k_p = 1.2$ (liters/g mole min). (a) For the initial concentrations of $M^0 = 1$ (g mole/liter) and $I^0 = 0.01$ (g mole/liter), calculate the times required to achieve 50% and 85% conversion of the monomer. (b) At 50% and 85% conversion of the monomer, calculate the corresponding initiator conversions. (c) At 50% and 85% conversions of the monomer, calculate the corresponding values for the number average degree of polymerization, the weight average degree of polymerization, and the dispersion index. Also plot the corresponding distributions on a molar and a weight fraction basis.

SOLUTION

(a) To find the time t required to achieve a given conversion of the monomer requires a graphical integration of Equation (10-131). Computed values of the integrand of Equation (10-131) for different choices of τ are listed below and plotted in Figure 10-5.

τ	$\dfrac{1}{M}$	τ	$\dfrac{1}{M}$
5	1.006	30	1.156
10	1.020	40	1.276
15	1.043	50	1.446
20	1.072	60	1.691
25	1.110	70	2.057
80	2.654	105	10.83
90	3.780	110	29.24
100	6.661		

That $1/M$ is equal to the integrand of Equation (10-131) follows immediately from Equations (10-124) and (10-130).

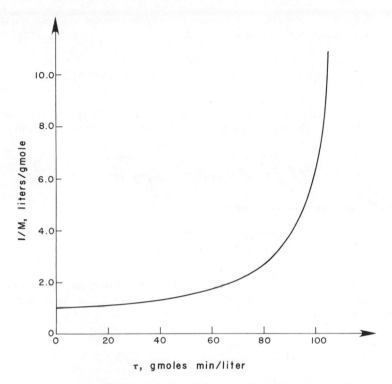

Figure 10-5. Graphical integration of Equation (10-131) at the conditions stated in Example 10-3.

At 50% conversion, $M = M^0 - 0.5M^0$, and $1/M = 2.0$. From Figure 10-5, $\tau = 67.5$ at $1/M = 2.0$. At 85% conversion, $1/M = 6.67$, and $\tau = 100$. Then at 50% conversion of the monomer, the value of t is found by graphical evaluation of the following integral through the use of Figure 10-5; that is, at 50% conversion,

$$t = \int_{\tau=0}^{\tau=67.5} \frac{d\tau}{M} \cong 87 \text{ min}$$

Similarly, at 85% conversion of the monomer,

$$t = \int_{\tau=0}^{\tau=100} \frac{d\tau}{M} = 200 \text{ min}$$

(b) At 50% conversion of the monomer, the corresponding conversion of the initiator may be computed by rearranging Equation (10-126) to the form

$$\frac{I^0 - I}{I^0} = 1 - \exp(-k_i\tau) = 1 - \exp(-0.032 \times 67.5)$$

$$= 0.885 \text{ or } 88.5\%$$

Similarly, at 85% conversion of the monomer, the corresponding conversion of the initiator is computed as follows:

$$\frac{I^0 - I}{I^0} = 1 - \exp(-0.032 \times 100) = 0.959 \text{ or } 95.9\%$$

The number average degree of polymerization at each of the two conversions may now be computed by use of Equation (10-132). At 50% conversion of the monomer,

$$\bar{D}_n = \frac{M^0[(M^0 - M)/M^0]}{I^0[(I^0 - I)/I^0]} = \frac{(1)(0.5)}{(0.01)(0.885)} = 56.5$$

At 85% conversion of the monomer,

$$\bar{D}_n = \frac{M^0[(M^0 - M)/M^0]}{I^0[(I^0 - I)/I^0]} = \frac{(1)(0.85)}{(0.01)(0.959)} = 88.6$$

The weight average degree of polymerization at each of the conversions may be computed by use of Equation (10-137). At 50% conversion of the monomer, the factors in Equation (10-137) take on the following values:

$$\left(1 - \frac{k_p}{k_i}\right)\left(1 - \frac{2k_p}{k_i}\right)[1 - \exp(-k_i\tau)]$$

$$= \left(1 - \frac{1.2}{0.032}\right)\left(1 - \frac{2 \times 1.2}{0.032}\right)[1 - \exp(-0.032 \times 67.5)] = 2389.5$$

$$k_p\tau\left[1 + k_p\tau + 2\left(1 - \frac{k_p}{k_i}\right)\right]$$

$$= 1.2 \times 67.5\left[1 + 1.2 \times 67.5 + 2\left(1 - \frac{1.2}{0.032}\right)\right] = 729$$

$$\text{and } \left(1 - \frac{k_p}{k_i}\right)[1 - \exp(-k_i\tau)] + k_p\tau = \left(1 - \frac{1.2}{0.032}\right)[1 - \exp(-0.032 \times 67.5)]$$

$$+ 1.2 \times 67.5 = 48.71$$

After these values have been substituted into Equation (10-137), it is found that the weight average degree of polymerization has the following value:

$$\bar{D}_W = 64.02$$

At 50% conversion, the dispersion index may now be calculated; namely,

$$\frac{\bar{D}_W}{\bar{D}_n} = \frac{64.02}{56.5} = 1.134$$

At 85% conversion of the monomer, the value $\bar{D}_W$ is computed in a manner analogous to that demonstrated above for 50% conversion. The result so obtained is $\bar{D}_W = 98.2$. Thus the dispersion index at 85% conversion is given by

$$\frac{\bar{D}_W}{\bar{D}_n} = \frac{98.2}{88.6} = 1.11$$

(c) By use of the above results and Equation (10-144) [or Equation (10-147)], the distributions shown in Figure 10-6 are obtained. (Alternately, the procedure proposed by Zeman et al. [15] may be used.) After each R_j has been computed, the corresponding W_j is found by use of Equation (10-148). The results so obtained are shown in Figure 10-7.

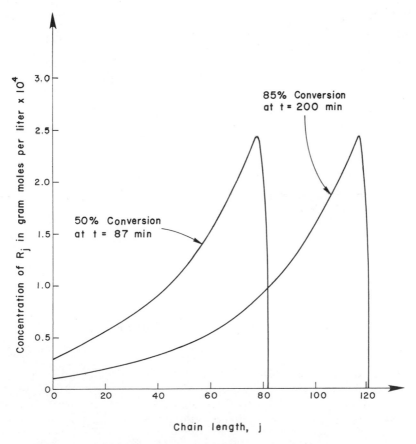

Figure 10-6. Molar concentrations of polymers R_j for Example 10-3 at 50% and 85% conversion of the monomer.

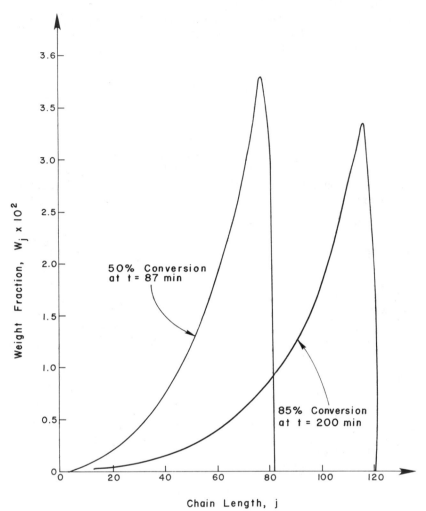

Figure 10-7. Molecular weight distributions for Example 10-3 at 50% and 85% conversion of the monomer.

D. Polymerization in Plug-Flow and Perfectly Mixed Flow Reactors

1. PLUG-FLOW REACTORS. The equations describing plug-flow reactors at isothermal operation and constant volumetric flow rate v_T throughout the reactor are of the same form as those stated above for batch reactors and may be obtained from them by making the following substitutions:

$$t = \frac{V}{v_T}, \qquad M = \frac{n_M}{v_T},$$

$$I = \frac{n_I}{v_T}, \qquad R_j = \frac{n_{R_j}}{v_T}$$

2. PERFECTLY MIXED FLOW REACTORS. In the following development, the reactor is assumed to be operated at steady state, and it is further supposed that the volumetric flow rate v_T is independent of the amount of polymerization which has taken place. Material balances on the initiator and monomer are as follows:

$$r_i = \frac{n_I^0/v_T - n_I/v_T}{V/v_T} = \frac{I^0 - I}{\theta} \tag{10-149}$$

$$r_M = \frac{n_M^0/v_T - n_M/v_T}{V/v_T} = \frac{M^0 - M}{\theta} \tag{10-150}$$

Elimination of r_i from Equations (10-110) and (10-149) gives

$$I^0 - I = k_i I M \theta \tag{10-151}$$

Similarly, elimination of r_M from Equations (10-150) and (10-114) gives

$$M^0 - M = k_i I M \theta + k_p M (I^0 - I) \theta \tag{10-152}$$

where $(r_p)_M$ has been replaced by its equivalent as given by Equations (10-113) and (10-116).

Equations (10-151) and (10-152) are seen to involve the three variables I, M, and θ. To obtain the value of M for a given value of I, the following expression, which was obtained by eliminating θ from Equations (10-151) and (10-152), may be used.

$$M = M^0 - (I^0 - I)\left[1 + \frac{k_p(I^0 - I)}{k_i I}\right] \tag{10-153}$$

After M has been computed for a given I by use of this equation, then the corresponding value of θ may be found by use of these values of M and I and Equation (10-151). Alternately, Equation (10-153) may be used to eliminate M from either Equation (10-151) or Equation (10-152) to give an explicit expression for I as a function of θ.

3. NUMBER AVERAGE DEGREE AND WEIGHT AVERAGE DEGREE OF POLYMERIZATION. The number average degree of polymerization is given by Equation (10-132). Replacing $M^0 - M$ in this expression for $\bar{D}_n$ gives

$$\bar{D}_n = \frac{M^0 - M}{I^0 - I} = \frac{k_i I M \theta + k_p M (I^0 - I)\theta}{k_i I M} = 1 + \frac{k_p}{k_i}\left(\frac{I^0 - I}{I}\right) \tag{10-154}$$

By comparison of Equations (10-154) and (10-119), it is seen that

$$\bar{D}_n = \frac{1}{\bar{d}_n} \tag{10-155}$$

For a perfectly mixed flow reactor in which the volumetric flow rate is constant, the r_{R_j}'s and r_M may be eliminated from the defining equation for $\bar{d}_W$ by use of the component-material balances

$$r_M = \frac{M^0 - M}{\theta} \tag{10-156}$$

$$r_{R_j} = \frac{R_j}{\theta} \qquad (j = 1, 2, \ldots) \tag{10-157}$$

to give

$$\bar{d}_W = \frac{\sum\limits_{j=1}^{\infty} j^2 r_{R_j}}{r_M} = \frac{\sum\limits_{j=1}^{\infty} j^2 R_j}{M^0 - M}$$

Since $\bar{D}_W = \Gamma_2(R_j)/\Gamma_1(R_j)$ and since $\Gamma_1(R_j) = M^0 - M$, it follows from Equation (10-122) that

$$\bar{D}_W = \bar{d}_W = 1 + \frac{2k_p(M^0 - M)/k_i I}{1 + k_p(I^0 - I)/k_i I} \tag{10-158}$$

Elimination of $k_p(I^0 - I)/k_i I$ and $(M^0 - M)$ by use of the relationship given by Equation (10-153) gives

$$\bar{D}_W = 2\bar{D}_n - 1 \tag{10-159}$$

For large values of $\bar{D}_n$, Equation (10-159) reduces approximately to

$$\frac{\bar{D}_W}{\bar{D}_n} \cong 2 \tag{10-160}$$

4. DISTRIBUTION OF THE POLYMERS R_j. On the basis of the assumptions of steady state operation and constant density of the reacting mixture, the material balances on the polymers $R_1, R_2, \ldots,$ may be represented by Equation (10-157), where it has been supposed that the feed to the perfectly mixed reactor contains no polymers. Elimination of r_{R_j} $(j = 1, 2, \ldots)$ from Equations (10-111), (10-112), and (10-157) gives

$$\frac{R_1}{\theta} = k_i I M - k_p R_1 M \tag{10-161}$$

$$\frac{R_j}{\theta} = k_p M(R_{j-1} - R_j), \qquad (j = 2, 3, \ldots) \tag{10-162}$$

Equation (10-161) may be solved for R_1 and Equation (10-162) for R_j to give

$$R_1 = \frac{k_i I M \theta}{1 + k_p \theta M} \tag{10-163}$$

and

$$R_j = \frac{k_p \theta M R_{j-1}}{1 + k_p \theta M} \tag{10-164}$$

For $j = 2$, Equation (10-164) contains R_1, which may be eliminated by use of Equation (10-163) to give

$$R_2 = \frac{(k_i I M \theta)(k_p \theta M)}{(1 + k_p \theta M)^2} \tag{10-165}$$

Continuation of this procedure leads to

$$R_j = (k_i I M \theta) \frac{(k_p \theta M)^{j-1}}{(1 + k_p \theta M)^j} \tag{10-166}$$

or

$$R_j = R_1 \left[\frac{k_p \theta M}{1 + k_p \theta M} \right]^{j-1} \tag{10-167}$$

For a given polymerization, θ is fixed. The concentrations of M and I in the effluent from the reactor may be computed by use of Equations (10-151) through (10-153). Then R_1 and R_j ($j = 2, 3, \ldots$) may be computed by use of Equations (10-163) and (10-167), respectively. The weight fraction of polymer R_j may then be computed by use of the equation

$$W_j = \frac{j R_j}{M^0 - M} \tag{10-168}$$

Procedures for calculating molecular weight distributions for living polymer systems with reversible termination and complex initiation rate expressions have been presented by Edgar *et al.* [16], Landon and Anthony [17], Porter *et al.* [18], Maggott *et al.* [19], and Ahmad *et al.* [20].

EXAMPLE 10-4

The reactions given by Equations (10-108) and (10-109) with the rate constants given in Example 10-3 are to be carried out in a perfectly mixed flow reactor. The initial concentrations of the monomer and initiator are: $M^0 = 1.0$ g mole per liter, and I^0 is equal to 0.01 mole per liter. (a) For a 75% conversion of the initiator, compute the corresponding conversion of the monomer. (b) Calculate the residence time $\theta = V/v_T$ required to obtain a 75% conversion of the initiator. (c) At a conversion of 75% of the initiator, compute the number and weight average degrees of polymerization. Also plot the corresponding distributions on a molar and a weight fraction basis.

SOLUTION

(a) Since it is given that $I = 0.25I^0$, the fraction of monomer converted may be found by use of Equation (10-153) after it has been rearranged to the following form:

$$\frac{M^0 - M}{M^0} = \frac{(I^0 - I)}{M^0}\left[1 + \frac{k_p(I^0 - I)}{k_i I}\right]$$

$$= \left[\frac{(0.01)(0.75)}{1.0}\right]\left[1 + \frac{(1.2)(0.01)(0.75)}{(0.032)(0.25)(0.01)}\right]$$

Thus

$$\frac{M^0 - M}{M^0} = 0.8512$$

and

$$M = 0.1488 \text{ g mole/liter}$$

(b) The residence time required to achieve a 75% conversion of the initiator is found by use of the result of Part (a) and Equation (10-151); namely,

$$\theta = \frac{I^0 - I}{k_i I M} = \frac{(0.01)(0.75)}{(0.032)(0.25)(0.01)(0.1488)}$$

$$= 630.04 \text{ min} = 10.5 \text{ hr}$$

(c) The number average degree of polymerization may be found by use of Equation (10-132),

$$\bar{D}_n = \frac{M^0 - M}{I^0 - I} = \frac{(0.8512)}{(0.75)(0.01)} = 113.5$$

The weight average degree of polymerization may be computed by use of Equation (10-159),

$$\bar{D}_W = 2\bar{D}_n - 1 = 226$$

Then the dispersion index is given by

$$\frac{\bar{D}_W}{\bar{D}_n} = \frac{226}{113.5} = 1.991$$

The distribution of polymers may now be computed by use of Equations (10-163) and (10-167). By use of Equation (10-163),

$$R_1 = \frac{k_i I M \theta}{1 + k_p \theta M} = \frac{(0.032)(0.25)(0.01)(0.1488)(630.04)}{1 + (1.2)(630.04)(0.1488)}$$

$$= 6.608(10^{-5}) \text{ g mole/liter}$$

For each chain length j, the corresponding polymer concentration R_j is found by use of Equation (10-167) as follows:

$$R_j = R_1 \left[\frac{k_p \theta M}{1 + k_p \theta M} \right]^{j-1} = (6.608)(10^{-5}) \left[\frac{(1.2)(630.04)(0.1488)}{1 + (1.2)(630.04)(0.1488)} \right]^{j-1}$$

Thus

$$R_j = (6.608)(10^{-5})[0.99189]^{j-1}$$

and

$$W_j = \frac{jR_j}{M^0 - M} = \frac{jR_j}{0.8512}$$

Plots of the results obtained by use of these equations for R_j and W_j are shown in Figures 10-8 and 10-9, respectively.

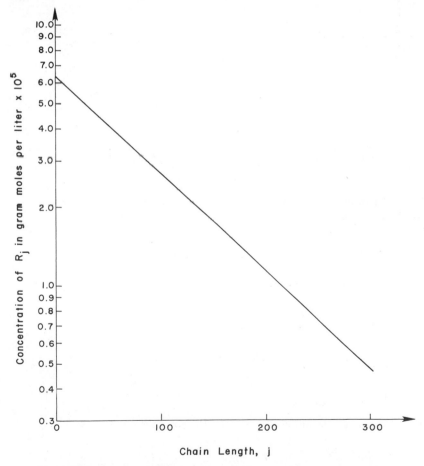

Figure 10-8. Molar concentrations of polymers R_j for Example 10-4 at 75% conversion of the initiator.

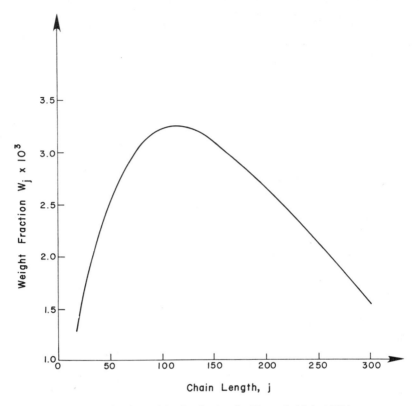

Figure 10-9. Molecular weight distribution for Example 10-4 at 75% conversion of the initiator.

PROBLEMS

10-1. By use of the relationships given in the text, show that

    (a) $\bar{M}_n = M_M \Gamma_1(x_j)$

    (b) $\bar{M}_W = M_M \dfrac{\Gamma_2(x_j)}{\Gamma_1(x_j)}$

    (c) $\bar{D}_n = \Gamma_1(x_j)$

    (d) $\bar{D}_W = \dfrac{\Gamma_2(x_j)}{\Gamma_1(x_j)}$

10-2. By use of the definition of x_j, W_j, and $\bar{D}_n$ show that

    (a) $x_j = \dfrac{W_j \bar{D}_n}{j}$

    (b) $P_j = \dfrac{W_j[M^0 - M]}{j}$

10-3. Begin with Equation (10-145) and produce the result given by Equation (10-146).

10-4. Begin with the expression given by Equation (10-158) for $\bar{D}_W$ and obtain the expression given by Equation (10-159) for $\bar{D}_W$ in terms for $\bar{D}_n$.

NOTATION

C = chain transfer agent; also used to denote the concentration of the chain transfer agent; C^0 is the initial concentration of the chain transfer agent.

$\bar{d}_n$ = number degree of polymer selectivity; total moles of polymer produced per mole of monomer reacted at any instant at any position in any given type of reactor; defined by Equation (10-55).

$\bar{D}_n$ = number average degree of polymerization; defined by Equation (10-11).

$\bar{d}_W$ = weight degree of polymer selectivity; defined by Equation (10-64).

$\bar{D}_W$ = weight average degree of polymerization; defined by Equation (10-13).

I = initiator; also used to denote the concentration of the initiator.

j = number of monomer molecules in a given polymer P_j.

M = monomer; also used to denote the concentration of the monomers, moles per unit volume. M^0 is the initial concentration of monomers.

M_j = molecular weight of a polymer composed of j monomer molecules.

$\bar{M}_n$ = number average molecular weight; defined by Equation (10-11).

$\bar{M}_W$ = weight average molecular weight, defined by Equation (10-10).

P_j = a polymer composed of j monomer molecules; also used to denote the concentration of such polymers.

$(r_a)_{P_j}$ = rate of appearance of polymer P_j by addition (or combination).

$(r_a)_{R_j}$ = rate of disappearance of free radicals or active species R_j by addition (or combination).

r_C = rate of disappearance of the chain transfer agent C by the chain transfer reaction.

$(r_C)_{R_j}$ = rate of disappearance of free radicals or active species R_j by chain transfer.

$(r_d)_{P_j}$ = rate of appearance of polymer P_j by the disporportionation reaction.

$(r_d)_{R_j}$ = rate of disappearance of free radicals or active species R_j by the disproportionation reaction.

r_i = rate of disappearance of free radicals ϕ, moles/(unit time) (unit volume) [see Equation (10-27)].

R_j = a free radical or active species of j monomer molecules; also used to denote the concentration of these free radicals, moles/unit volumes.

$(r_M)_{R_j}$ = rate of disappearance of free radicals or active species R_j by monomer transfer.

r_{P_j} = net rate of appearance of polymers P_j.

$(r_p)_M$ = rate of disappearance of the monomer M by propogation [see Equation (10-30)].

$(r_p)_{R_j}$ = rate of disappearance of free radicals or active species R_j by propogation [see Equation (10-29)].

r_{R_j} = net rate of disappearance of free radicals R_j by all steps of the mechanism.

r_S = rate of disappearance of the solvent S by the solvent transfer reaction.

$(r_S)_{R_j}$ = rate of disappearance of free radicals R_j by solvent transfer.

r_ϕ = net rate of disappearance of free radicals.

S = solvent; also used to denote the concentration of the solvent.

W_j = weight fraction of polymer molecules having chains composed of j monomer units in a mixture of polymer molecules having all possible chain lengths.

w_j = weight selectivity for polymer P_j; defined by Equation (10-62).

x_j = mole fraction of polymer P_j.

Greek Letters

$\Gamma_0(P_j)$ = total concentration of all polymers of all possible chain lengths.

$\Gamma_1(P_j)$ = first moment of the P_j; defined below Equation (10-3).

$\Gamma_2(P_j)$ = second moment of the P_j's [see Equation (10-10)].

ϕ = free radical produced by the initiator I; also used to denote the concentration of these free radicals, moles/unit volume.

REFERENCES

1. Carothers, W. H., *J. Am. Chem. Soc.*, *51*:2548 (1929).

2. Platzer, N., IUPAC International Symposium on Macromolecular Chemistry, pp. 155–184, Budapest, Hungary (1969).

3. Flory, P. J., *Principles of Polymer Chemistry*, Cornell University Press, Ithaca, NY (1953).

4. Rodriquez, F., *Principles of Polymer Systems*, McGraw-Hill Book Company, New York (1970).

5. Bamford, C. H., W. G. Barb, A. D. Jenkins, and P. F. Onyon, *The Kinetics of Vinyl Polymerization by Radical Mechanisms*. Butterworth & Co. Publishers Limited, London (1958).

6. Hamielec, A. E., Symposium on Polymer Reaction Engineering, Laval University, Quebec City, Quebec, Canada (June 4–7, 1972).

7. Peebles, L. H., Jr., *Molecular Weight Distributions in Polymers*, Wiley/Interscience Publisher, New York (1971).

8. Biesenberger, J. A., M. Sacks, and I. Dubdevani, *Proceedings of the Symposium on Polymer Reaction Engineering*, Laval University, Quebec City, Quebec, Canada (June 5–7, 1972).

9. Hui, A. W., and A. E. Hamielec, *J. Applied Polymer Sci.*, Part C., *No. 25*, 167 (1968).

10. Sacks, M. E., Soo-il Lee, and J. A. Biesenberger, *Chem. Eng. Sci.*, *28*:2281–2289 (1972).

11. Sacks, M. E., Soo-il Lee, and J. A. Biesenberger, *Chem. Eng. Sci.*, *28*:241–257 (1973).

12. Beckman, G., *Chem. Tech.*, p. 304 (May 1973).

13. Lynn, S., and J. E. Huff, *AIChE J.*, *17*: *No. 2*, 475 (1971).

14. Szwarc, M., *Carbanions, Living Polymers, and Electron Transfer Processes*, Wiley/Interscience Publishers, New York (1968).

15. Zeman, R. J., and N. R. Amundson, *AIChE J.*, *9*:297 (1968).

16. Edgar, T. D., S. Hasan, and R. G. Anthony, *Chem. Eng. Sci. 25*, 1463–1423 (1970)

17. Landon, T. R., and R. G. Anthony, *AIChJ 18*, 843 (1972)

18. Porter, R. E., A. Ahmad, and R. G. Anthony, *J. Applied Polymer Sci. 18*, 1805–1819, (1974)

19. Maggott, R. J., A. Ahmad, and R. G. Anthony, *J. Applied Polymer Sci. 19*, 165 (1975)

20. Ahmad A., and R. G. Anthony, *J. Applied Polymer Sci. 21*, 1401–1408 (1977)

Thermodynamics and Energy Balances for Highly Nonideal Solutions

11

The effects of pressure and heats of mixing on the enthalpies of the components in the reacting mixture which were neglected in Chapters 5 and 6 are included in the energy balances in this chapter. In Part I, a generalized method for representing and calculating the enthalpies of nonideal solutions is developed. The result so obtained is used in Part II to modify the energy balances presented in Chapter 6 to include the effects of pressure and heats of mixing on the enthalpies of the components present in the reacting mixture.

I. EFFECT OF HEATS OF MIXING AND PRESSURE ON THE ENTHALPY OF A MIXTURE

In all of the enthalpy changes represented in Chapter 5 by various paths, the participating components are shown in separate containers at given values of temperature and pressure. In order to represent the actual reacting mixture at any point in a reactor, these components must be mixed (or placed in solution). Methods for computing the change of enthalpy that accompanies mixing are developed and demonstrated below.

A. Deviation of the Enthalpy of a Mixture of Gases at a Given Pressure and Temperature from the Enthalpy of a Mixture of the Same Gases in the Perfect Gas State at the Same Temperature

The path shown in Figure 11-1 may be used to compute the change in enthalpy when n_1, n_2, ..., n_c (moles or molar flow rates) of components 1, 2, ..., c in the state of perfect gases at $P = 1$ atm and the temperature T are mixed at P and T to form the solution as it exists in a reactor. In the first step shown in Figure 11-1 the perfect gas is expanded isothermally from $P = 1$ atm to $P = P_0$. In the limit as P_0 goes to zero, State 2 becomes a converter in the sense that a perfect gas enters and an actual gas leaves State 2. Thus, in the limit as P_0 approaches zero,

$$\Delta H_1 = \sum_{i=1}^{c} n_i[H_i(0, T) - H_i^\circ(1, T)]$$

where n_T is equal to the sum of $n_1, n_2, \ldots, n_c$ moles of components 1 through c. Next the actual gas is compressed isothermally to the pressure P, and for this step,

$$\Delta H_2 = \sum_{i=1}^{c} n_i[H_i(P, T) - H_i(0, T)]$$

In the third step, $n_1, n_2, \ldots, n_c$ moles of components 1, 2, ..., c are mixed at constant temperature and pressure, and for this step,

$$\Delta H_3 = \sum_{i=1}^{c} n_i[\bar{H}_i(P, T) - H_i(P, T)]$$

where $\bar{H}_i(P, T)$ is the partial molar enthalpy of component i at the temperature, pressure, and composition of the final state shown in Figure 11-1. [In the interest of simplicity, the complete functional representation of the partial molar enthalpy, $\bar{H}_i(P, T, n_1, n_2, \ldots, n_c)$ is abbreviated as $\bar{H}_i(P, T)$ or simply $\bar{H}_i$.] Thus the total change in enthalpy ΔH between the final and initial states for the path shown in Figure 11-1 is given by

$$\Delta H = \Delta H_1 + \Delta H_2 + \Delta H_3 = \sum_{i=1}^{c} [\bar{H}_i(P, T) - H_i^\circ(1, T)]n_i = n_T H - n_T H^\circ$$

$$(11\text{-}1)$$

where
$$n_T H = \sum_{i=1}^{c} n_i \bar{H}_i(P, T)$$

$$n_T H^\circ = \sum_{i=1}^{c} n_i H_i^\circ(1, T)$$

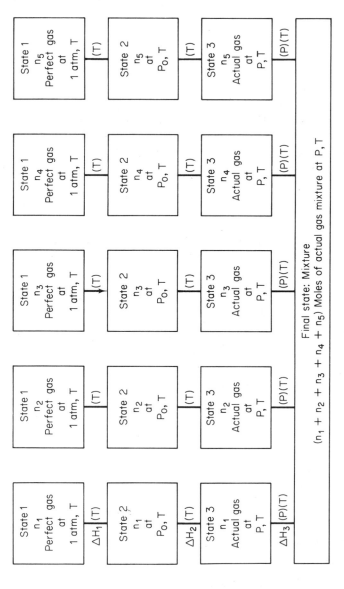

Figure 11-1. Path for calculating the effects of pressure and heats of mixing on the enthalpy of a mixture. [Taken from C. D. Holland, *I&EC Fundamentals*, *16*: No. 1, 143 (1977). Used with permission of the American Chemical Society.]

Let the deviation of the enthalpy of the total moles of a mixture from the enthalpy of the perfect gas mixture be denoted by Ω. Then the enthalpy H per mole of mixture is equal to the enthalpy of the perfect gas mixture plus the deviation per mole; that is,

$$H = H° + \Omega \tag{11-2}$$

Generally, the direct calculation of the partial molar enthalpies from an equation of state is far more difficult than is the calculation of Ω from an equation of state. Fortunately, there exists a set of functions $\{\hat{H}_i\}$ called the "virtual values" of the partial molar enthalpies which are a simple function of Ω and which give the correct enthalpy of the mixture. These functions were introduced by Holland et al. [1]. The virtual value of the partial molar enthalpy is related to Ω as follows:

$$\hat{H}_i = H_i° + \Omega \tag{11-3}$$

where $H_i° = H_i°(1, T), \quad \Omega = \Omega(P, T, n_1, n_2, \ldots, n_c),$

and $\hat{H}_i = \hat{H}_i(P, T, n_1, n_2, \ldots, n_c).$

The quantities $\{\hat{H}_i\}$ are called the virtual values of the partial molar enthalpies because they may be used to compute the correct enthalpy of a mixture, but they may differ individually from the true values of the partial molar enthalpies. A proof of this statement follows the development of expressions for the partial molar enthalpies.

B. Partial Molar Enthalpies

The ideal solution relationship for the enthalpy of a mixture

$$n_T H = \sum_{i=1}^{c} n_i H_i(P, T) \tag{11-4}$$

is not adequate for computing the enthalpy of highly nonideal solutions. The enthalpy of a nonideal solution may be expressed in terms of the partial molar enthalpies of the individual components. The origin of these enthalpies is a consequence of the characteristics of homogeneous functions. A function $f(x_1, x_2, \ldots, x_c)$ is said to be homogeneous of order m if

$$f(\lambda x_1, \lambda x_2, \ldots, \lambda x_c) = \lambda^m f(x_1, x_2, \ldots, x_c) \tag{11-5}$$

where λ is any arbitrary, real number. By this definition, the total enthalpy of a mixture $\mathcal{H}$ (which is equal to $n_T H$) is homogeneous of degree one because the enthalpy of two moles of a given mixture is twice that of one mole of the same mixture at a fixed temperature and pressure; that is,

$$\mathscr{H}(\lambda n_1, \lambda n_2, \ldots, \lambda n_c) = \lambda \mathscr{H}(n_1, n_2, \ldots, n_c) \tag{11-6}$$

If the function $f(x_1, x_2, \ldots, x_c)$ is homogeneous of degree m in the x_i's and has continuous first partial derivatives, then by Euler's theorem,

$$x_1 \frac{\partial f}{\partial x_1} + x_2 \frac{\partial f}{\partial x_2} + \cdots + x_c \frac{\partial f}{\partial x_c} = mf(x_1, x_2, \ldots, x_c) \tag{11-7}$$

Since the total enthalpy of a mixture is homogeneous of degree one in the n_i's at a fixed temperature and pressure, Euler's theorem gives

$$n_1 \left(\frac{\partial(n_T H)}{\partial n_1} \right)_{P,T,n_j} + n_2 \left(\frac{\partial(n_T H)}{\partial n_2} \right)_{P,T,n_j} + \cdots + n_c \left(\frac{\partial(n_T H)}{\partial n_c} \right)_{P,T,n_j} = n_T H \tag{11-8}$$

The subscript n_j is used to denote the fact that the moles of all components are to be held fixed, except the particular one with which the partial derivative is to be taken. The partial derivatives appearing in Equation (11-8) were given the name "partial molar enthalpies" by Gibbs. They are commonly identified by the symbol $\bar{H}_i$; that is,

$$\bar{H}_i = \left(\frac{\partial(n_T H)}{\partial n_i} \right)_{P,T,n_j} \tag{11-9}$$

Equation (11-9) may be used to state Equation (11-8) in this more compact form:

$$n_T H = \sum_{i=1}^{c} n_i \bar{H}_i \tag{11-10}$$

C. Relationship between the Virtual Values of Partial Molar Enthalpies and the Partial Molar Enthalpies

The virtual value of the partial molar enthalpy [defined by Equation (11-3)] and the partial molar enthalpy [defined by Equation (11-9)] may be related in the following manner. First let each member of Equation (11-2) be multiplied by the total number of moles to give

$$n_T H = n_T H^\circ + n_T \Omega \tag{11-11}$$

Then at constant temperature and pressure, partial differentiation of each member of Equation (11-11) with respect to n_i with T, P, and the moles of each component except i held fixed gives

$$\bar{H}_i = \sum_{k=1}^{c} H_k^{\circ} \left(\frac{\partial n_k}{\partial n_i} \right)_{P,T,n_j} + \Omega \left(\frac{\partial n_T}{\partial n_i} \right)_{P,T,n_j} + n_T \left(\frac{\partial \Omega}{\partial n_i} \right)_{P,T,n_j}$$

or

$$\bar{H}_i = H_i^{\circ} + \Omega + n_T \left(\frac{\partial \Omega}{\partial n_i} \right)_{P,T,n_j} \qquad (11\text{-}12)$$

The difficulty of computing the partial molar enthalpies lies in the relatively large number of terms required to evaluate the derivative $(\partial \Omega / \partial n_i)_{P,T,n_j}$. For example, one entire page (page 478) of Reference [2] is required to present the formula obtained by Papadopoulos et al. [3] for the partial molar enthalpy when it is based on the Benedict-Webb-Rubin equation of state [4].

Fortunately, it can be shown as follows that the derivative $(\partial \Omega / \partial n_i)_{P,T,n_j}$ may be neglected in the calculation of the enthalpy of a mixture. Multiplication of each term of Equation (11-12) by n_i followed by the summation over all components yields

$$\sum_{i=1}^{c} \bar{H}_i n_i = \sum_{i=1}^{c} H_i^{\circ} n_i + \Omega n_T + n_T \sum_{i=1}^{c} n_i \left(\frac{\partial \Omega}{\partial n_i} \right)_{P,T,n_j} \qquad (11\text{-}13)$$

By Equation (11-8) the left-hand side of Equation (11-13) is equal to $n_T H$, and by Euler's theorem [Equation (11-7)] it follows that

$$\sum_{i=1}^{c} n_i \left(\frac{\partial \Omega}{\partial n_i} \right)_{P,T,n_j} = 0 \qquad (11\text{-}14)$$

since Ω is homogeneous of degree zero. Thus Equation (11-13) reduces to Equation (11-11) and division of each term of this expression by n_T gives Equation (11-2). Since the last term of Equation (11-12) disappears in the calculation of the enthalpy of a mixture, it follows that this derivative may be omitted in the expression for $\bar{H}_i$ to give the expression for $\hat{H}_i$, Equation (11-3). Proof of this statement follows. Multiplication of each term of Equation (11-3) by n_i followed by the summation over all components i gives

$$\sum_{i=1}^{c} \hat{H}_i n_i = n_T H^{\circ} + n_T \Omega \qquad (11\text{-}15)$$

Comparison of Equations (11-10), (11-11), and (11-15) shows that

$$n_T H = \sum_{i=1}^{c} \hat{H}_i n_i = \sum_{i=1}^{c} \bar{H}_i n_i \qquad (11\text{-}16)$$

Although the virtual values of the partial molar enthalpies give the correct enthalpy of a mixture as shown by Equation (11-16), they do differ individually from the partial molar enthalpies. They are related by use of Equations (11-3) and (11-12) as follows:

$$\bar{H}_i = \hat{H}_i + n_T \left(\frac{\partial \Omega}{\partial n_i} \right)_{P,T,n_j} \tag{11-17}$$

D. Calculation of the Virtual Values of the Partial Molar Enthalpies from an Equation of State

For illustrative purposes, consider the Benedict-Webb-Rubin equation of state [4].

$$P = RT\rho + \left(B_0 RT - A_0 - \frac{C_0}{T^2} \right) \rho^2 + (bRT - a)\rho^3$$

$$+ a\alpha\rho^6 + \frac{c\rho^3}{T^2} (1 + \gamma\rho^2)e^{-\gamma\rho^2} \tag{11-18}$$

The usual mixing rules for this equation of state are

$$B_0 = \sum_{i=1}^{c} X_i B_{0i} \qquad\qquad a = \left[\sum_{i=1}^{c} X_i a_i^{1/3} \right]^3$$

$$A_0 = \left[\sum_{i=1}^{c} X_i A_{0i}^{1/2} \right]^2 \qquad c = \left[\sum_{i=1}^{c} X_i c_i^{1/3} \right]^3$$

$$C_0 = \left[\sum_{i=1}^{c} X_i C_{0i}^{1/2} \right]^2 \qquad \alpha = \left[\sum_{i=1}^{c} X_i \alpha_i^{1/3} \right]^3$$

$$b = \left[\sum_{i=1}^{c} X_i b_i^{1/3} \right]^3 \qquad \gamma = \left[\sum_{i=1}^{c} X_i \gamma_i^{1/2} \right]^2$$

where X_i is the mole fraction of component i in either phase. The Lorentz rule or a quadratic form of B_0 of the mixture is sometimes used.

$$B_0 = \sum_{ij} X_i X_j [(B_{0i})^{1/3} + (B_{0j})^{1/3}]/8 \qquad \text{(Lorentz)}$$

$$B_0 = \left[\sum_{i=1}^{c} X_i B_{0i}^{1/2} \right]^{1/2} \qquad \text{(quadratic)}$$

Following others, Orye [5] suggested that the following mixing rule for A_0 be used instead of the one listed above:

$$A_0 = \sum_{i=1}^{c} X_i^2 A_{0i} + \sum_i \sum_{\substack{j \\ j \neq i \\ j > i}} M_{ij} X_i X_j A_{0i}^{1/2} A_{0j}^{1/2}$$

An examination of all of the above expressions for the evaluation of the constants A_0, B_0, C_0, a, c, α, and γ shows that they are all homogeneous of degree zero.

An abbreviated development of the expressions needed to compute the value of the deviation function for a given mixture at a specified temperature and pressure follows. The enthalpy $H_i(P, T)$ of pure component i is related to its fugacity by the well-known relationship

$$H_i(P, T) - H_i^\circ(1, T) = -RT^2 \left(\frac{\partial \log_e f_i}{\partial T} \right)_P \qquad (11\text{-}19)$$

where $H_i^\circ(1, T) =$ the enthalpy of pure component i in the perfect gas state at 1 atm pressure and at the temperature T

Fugacity may be expressed in terms of pressure P by eliminating dG from Equations (5-29) and (5-31) to give

$$RT d \log_e f = \frac{1}{\rho} dP \qquad (11\text{-}20)$$

Since P is given by the equation of state [Equation (11-18)], Equation (11-20) may be integrated at constant temperature to give

$$RT \log_e f = RT \log_e \rho RT + 2\rho \left(B_0 RT - A_0 - \frac{C_0}{T^2} \right) + \frac{3\rho^2(bRT - a)}{2}$$
$$+ \frac{6a\alpha\rho^5}{5} + \frac{c\rho^2}{T^2} \left[\frac{1 - e^{-\gamma\rho^2}}{\gamma\rho^2} + \frac{e^{-\gamma\rho^2}}{2} + \gamma\rho^2 e^{-\gamma\rho^2} \right] \qquad (11\text{-}21)$$

The fugacity in the vapor phase is obtained by using vapor density, and the fugacity in the liquid phase is obtained by using liquid density.

An expression for the enthalpy of a mixture is obtained by first carrying out the differentiation implied by Equation (11-19) with the aid of Equations (11-18) and (11-21). Then the constants for the pure component in the expression so obtained are replaced by the constants for the mixture. The result so obtained may be represented as follows:

$$H - H^\circ = -RT^2 \left(\frac{\partial \log_e f}{\partial T} \right)_{P,M}$$ (11-22)

The subscript M has been added in order to emphasize that after the differentiation has been performed, the constants for the pure component have been replaced by the constants for the mixture; for example, see Orye [5]. Comparison of Equations (11-2) and (11-22) shows that

$$\Omega = -RT^2 \left(\frac{\partial \log_e f}{\partial T} \right)_{P,M}$$ (11-23)

The expression Ω for the Benedict-Webb-Rubin equation is

$$\Omega = \left(B_0 RT - 2A_0 - \frac{4C_0}{T^2} \right) \rho + (2bRT - 3a)\frac{\rho^2}{2} + \frac{6a\alpha\rho^5}{5}$$
$$+ \frac{c\rho^2}{T^2} \left[3 \frac{(1 - \exp(-\gamma\rho^2))}{\gamma\rho^2} - \frac{\exp(-\gamma\rho^2)}{2} + \gamma\rho^2 \exp(-\gamma\rho^2) \right]$$ (11-24)

For the case where A_0, C_0, b, and γ are taken to be functions of temperature, a formula for $H - H^\circ$ or Ω has been given by Orye [5].

When other equations of state are used to represent a mixture, the deviation Ω of the enthalpy of the actual mixture from that of a perfect gas mixture at the same temperature is computed in a manner analogous to that shown above for the Benedict-Webb-Rubin equation of state. After Ω has been obtained, the corresponding set of the virtual values of the partial molar enthalpies is computed by use of the defining equation, Equation (11-3).

Equations or correlations based on the law of corresponding states for the enthalpies may be used to compute Ω and the $\hat{H}_i$'s of a mixture as outlined in the next section.

E. Calculation of the Virtual Values of the Partial Molar Enthalpies from Correlations Based on the Law of Corresponding States

At a given value of the critical compressibility factor Z_c for the mixture, Lydersen et al. [6, 7, 8] were able to correlate the enthalpies of mixtures as functions of the reduced temperatures and pressures. These correlations were of the general form

$$\frac{H - H^\circ}{RT_c} = \frac{f_1(T_r, P_r)}{f_2(T_r, P_r)} \qquad \text{(at a given } Z_c) \qquad (11\text{-}25)$$

where H = enthalpy of one mole of mixture at a given temperature and pressure

$\qquad P_c = \displaystyle\sum_{i=1}^{c} P_{ci}X_i$, pseudo critical pressure of the mixture;

$\qquad\qquad P_{ci}$ = the critical pressure of pure component i

$\qquad T_c = \displaystyle\sum_{i=1}^{c} T_{ci}X_i$, pseudo critical temperature of the mixture:

$\qquad\qquad T_{ci}$ = the critical temperature of pure component i

$\qquad Z_c = \displaystyle\sum_{i=1}^{c} Z_{ci}X_i$, pseudo critical compressibility factor for the mixture

$\qquad\qquad Z_{ci}$ = the critical compressibility factor for pure component i

$\qquad P_r = P/P_c$, reduced pressure

$\qquad T_r = T/T_c$, reduced temperature

The simplified formulas for calculating the enthalpy result from the fact that the reduced temperature and reduced pressure are homogeneous functions of degree zero in the n_i's, which is shown as follows. Since

$$T_r(n_1, n_2, \ldots, n_c) = \frac{T}{T_c} = \frac{n_T T}{\displaystyle\sum_{i=1}^{c} T_{ci}n_i} \qquad (11\text{-}26)$$

then $\qquad T_r(\lambda n_1, \lambda n_2, \ldots, \lambda n_c) = \dfrac{\lambda n_T T}{\displaystyle\sum_{i=1}^{c} T_{ci}\lambda n_i} = T_r(n_1, n_2, \ldots, n_c) \qquad (11\text{-}27)$

Since T_r and P_r are homogeneous of degree zero, any function of these variables which has continuous first derivatives with respect to the n_is at a fixed temperature and pressure is also homogeneous of degree zero. Also, it can be shown that any combinations of a set of homogeneous functions is also homogeneous.

Since T_c, f_1, and f_2 are all homogeneous of degree zero, then $T_c f_1/f_2$ is homogeneous of degree zero, and consequently Equation (11-25) may be stated in the form given by Equation (11-2) by setting

$$\Omega = \frac{RT_c f_1}{f_2} \tag{11-28}$$

Expressions for Ω for other equations of state and correlations such as those proposed by others [9, 10, 11] are developed in a manner analogous to that demonstrated above.

EXAMPLE 11-1

For an equimolar mixture of ethane and ethylene, calculate the virtual value of the enthalpy of each component and the enthalpy of the mixture at 292.5 atm. and 588.12°K. The critical temperatures and pressures are as follows:

Component	T (°C)	P_c (atm)
ethane	32.1	48.8
ethylene	9.7	50.5

Use the plot of $(H° − H)/T_c$ versus T_r at parameters of P_r in Figure 4-36, page 4-52 of the *Chemical Engineer's Handbook* [6]. This figure is based on data originally published by Lydersen et al. [7]. Use the data in Table 5-3 to compute $H_i°$ for each component at $T = 588.12°K$.

SOLUTION

The reduced temperature and the reduced pressure of the mixture are computed as follows:

$$T_r = \frac{T}{T_c} = \frac{588.12}{0.5(305.26) + 0.5(282.86)} = \frac{588.12}{294.06} = 2.0$$

$$P_r = \frac{P}{P_c} = \frac{292.5}{0.5(48.8) + 0.5(50.5)} = \frac{292.5}{49.65} = 5.89$$

By use of Figure 4-36 on page 4-52 of Reference [6],

$$\frac{H° − H}{T_c} = 2.25$$

Thus

$$\Omega = H − H° = (−2.25)(294.06) = −661.6 \text{ cal}$$

The following data at $T = 588.12°K$ were found by interpolation from those stated in Table 5-3. The virtual values of the partial molar enthalpies for ethane and ethylene in 1 g mole of the equal molar mixture at 588.12°K and 292.5 atm are found by use of

Equation (11-3) as follows:

Component	$H_i^\circ = H_T^\circ - H_0^\circ$ (cal/g mole) at $T = 588.12°K$	$\hat{H}_i = H_i^\circ + \Omega$ (cal/g mole)
ethane	7769	7107.4
ethylene	6538	5876.4

Then the enthalpy of one mole of the mixture is computed by use of the virtual values of the partial molar enthalpies as follows:

Component	$X_i \hat{H}_i$ (cal/g mole)
ethane	3553.7
ethylene	2938.2
	$H = 6491.9$

F. Virtual Values of the Partial Molar Heat Capacities

The partial molar heat capacity is defined by

$$\bar{C}_{pi} = \left(\frac{\partial \bar{H}_i}{\partial T}\right)_{P,n_i} \tag{11-29}$$

where the subscript n_i means that the moles of all components are held fixed in the differentiation process. Termwise differentiation of Equation (11-12) with respect to T and with P and the moles of all components held fixed yields

$$\bar{C}_{pi} = C_{pi}^\circ + \left(\frac{\partial \Omega}{\partial T}\right)_{P,n_i} + n_T \frac{\partial}{\partial T}\left[\left(\frac{\partial \Omega}{\partial n_i}\right)_{P,T,n_j}\right]_{P,n_i} \tag{11-30}$$

Since the last term on the right-hand side of Equation (11-30) is homogeneous of degree zero, it will vanish in the calculation of the molar heat capacity of the mixture, and, consequently, this term is omitted in the definition of the virtual value of the partial molar heat capacity,

$$\hat{C}_{pi} = C_{pi}^\circ + \left(\frac{\partial \Omega}{\partial T}\right)_{P,n_i} \tag{11-31}$$

By multiplication of each member of Equations (11-30) and (11-31) by n_i followed by the summation over all components, it is evident that

$$\sum_{i=1}^{c} \bar{C}_{pi} n_i = \sum_{i=1}^{c} \hat{C}_{pi} n_i \tag{11-32}$$

Thus the virtual values of the partial molar heat capacities lead to the correct heat capacity of a mixture. As shown below, these virtual values of the partial molar heat capacities arise in the formulation of the enthalpy balance on chemical reactors.

The heat capacity C_p is often calculated in terms of second derivatives of PVT data and the perfect gas value C_p°. Except for a very simple equation of state, the final equation for $C_p - C_p^\circ$ is complex for a pure component [12], and the prospect of the calculation of C_p for a mixture by the usual route of the partial molar values, $\bar{C}_{pi}$, is so complex as to discourage most workers. By use of the virtual values of the partial molar heat capacities, however, the evaluation of the heat capacity for a mixture is reduced to the use of the equation for a pure component with the parameters and density for the pure component replaced by those for the mixture.

G. Enthalpy Function for the Nonideal Liquid Phase

It will now be demonstrated that Equation (11-2) also applies for a mixture in the liquid phase; provided, that the symbol H in Equation (11-2) represents the enthalpy of 1 mole of the liquid mixture and Ω denotes the deviation of the enthalpy of 1 mole of the liquid mixture from the enthalpy of 1 mole of the mixture in the perfect gas state at 1 atm and the temperature T of the mixture.

A path in which each component is taken from its standard state of a perfect gas at 1 atm and the temperature T to the final state of a liquid mixture is shown in Figure 11-2. When the changes in enthalpy for this process are summed over all steps and components, the following result is obtained in the limit as P_0 is allowed to go to zero.

$$\Delta H_1 + \Delta H_2 + \Delta H_3 + \Delta H_4 + \Delta H_5 = \sum_{i=1}^{c} [\bar{h}_i(P, T) - H_i^\circ(1, T)]n_i$$

$$= n_T H - n_T H^\circ \qquad (11\text{-}33)$$

where $\bar{h}_i$ is the partial molar enthalpy of component i in the liquid mixture at P and T, and it is defined by

$$\bar{h}_i = \left(\frac{\partial (n_T H)}{\partial n_i} \right)_{P,T,n_j} \qquad (11\text{-}34)$$

and H denotes the enthalpy per mole of the liquid mixture. The lower case letter h is used to emphasize that the partial molar enthalpy is for the liquid state. Thus, when the deviation of the enthalpy of 1 mole of the mixture at P and T from the enthalpy of 1 mole of a perfect gas mixture is set equal to Ω, one again obtains Equation (11-2).

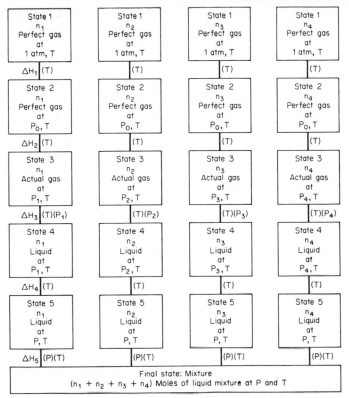

Figure 11-2. Path for computing the effects of pressure and heats of mixing on the enthalpy of a liquid mixture.

For a liquid mixture, Equation (11-22) takes the following form:

$$H - H^\circ = -RT^2 \left(\frac{\partial \log_e f^L}{\partial T} \right)_{P,M} \tag{11-35}$$

where f^L is the fugacity of the pure component in the liquid phase. Thus

$$\Omega = -RT^2 \left(\frac{\partial \log_e f^L}{\partial T} \right)_{P,M} \tag{11-36}$$

For the special case of an ideal solution which also has the property that its liquid enthalpy is independent of pressure and its vapor behaves as a perfect gas, the enthalpy of the liquid mixture may be computed by setting Ω equal to the negative of the average latent heat of vaporization of the mixture; that is,

$$n_T \Omega = -\sum_{i=1}^{c} n_i \lambda_i(T) \tag{11-37}$$

where $\lambda_i(T)$ is the latent heat of pure component i at the temperature T. Then the enthalpy of such liquid mixtures may be computed as follows.

$$n_T H = \sum_{i=1}^{c} [H_i^{\circ}(1, T) - \lambda_i(T)]n_i \tag{11-38}$$

The result given by Equation (11-38) is readily verified as follows. For the case of an ideal solution, the partial molar enthalpy, $\bar{h}_i(P, T)$ is equal to the enthalpy of pure component i, $h_i(P, T)$, in the liquid phase. Thus

$$n_T H = \sum_{i=1}^{c} n_i \bar{h}_i = \sum_{i=1}^{c} n_i h_i$$

and Equation (11-11) may be solved for $n_T \Omega$ to give

$$n_T \Omega = n_T H - n_T H^{\circ} = \sum_{i=1}^{c} [h_i(P, T) - H_i^{\circ}(1, T)]n_i \tag{11-39}$$

Since the effect of pressure on the liquid is negligible, it follows that

$$h_i(P, T) \cong h_i(P_i, T) \tag{11-40}$$

where P_i is the vapor pressure of pure component i. If the vapors behave as perfect gases, then

$$H_i(P_i, T) = H_i^{\circ}(P_i, T) = H_i^{\circ}(1, T) \tag{11-41}$$

and since the latent heat of vaporization of pure component i is defined by

$$\lambda_i(P_i, T) = H_i(P_i, T) - h_i(P_i, T) \tag{11-42}$$

Equation (11-33) reduces to Equation (11-37).

$$n_T \Omega = -\sum_{i=1}^{c} [H_i(P_i, T) - h_i(P_i, T)]n_i = -\sum_{i=1}^{c} n_i \lambda_i(T)$$

In many instances, data on the behavior of liquid mixtures are meager, and Equation (11-37) will be found useful because many compilations of heats of formation and latent heats are available; for example, see Reference [13].

In conclusion, Equation (11-2) is applicable for both the gas and liquid phases, provided that an appropriate equation of state is used in the evaluation of Ω according to Equations (11-23) and (11-35).

II. ENERGY-BALANCE EQUATIONS FOR REACTORS IN WHICH THE REACTING MIXTURES HAVE ENTHALPIES WHICH DEPEND UPON TEMPERATURE, PRESSURE, AND COMPOSITION

In the enthalpy balances developed in Chapter 6, the effects of pressure and heats of mixing on the enthalpies of the components in the reacting mixture were neglected. The enthalpy $n_T H$ of the mixture flowing past any plane in a flow reactor may be stated for the general case of a nonideal solution by use of Equation (11-3) as follows:

$$n_T H = \sum_{i=1}^{c} n_i H_{fi}^{\circ} + n_T \Omega \tag{11-43}$$

This expression for $n_T H$ differs from the one used in Chapter 6 by the term $n_T \Omega$ [see Equation (6-32)], which accounts for the deviation of an actual solution from a perfect gas mixture. In particular this term accounts for the deviation resulting from the effects of pressure and heats of mixing on the enthalpy of the reacting mixture. Thus to correct the energy-balance equations developed in Chapter 6 for the effect of pressure and heats of mixing amounts to including the contribution $n_T \Omega$.

A. Plug-Flow Reactors at Steady State Operation

When the expression given by Equation (11-43) is substituted into the energy balance given by Equation (6-18), one obtains

$$\frac{-d\left[\sum_{i=1}^{c} n_i H_{fi}^{\circ}\right]}{dz} - \frac{d(n_T \Omega)}{dz} + q = 0 \tag{11-44}$$

Since the H_{fi}°'s are independent of pressure, the first term on the left-hand side of Equation (11-44) is evaluated as demonstrated by Equations (6-36) through (6-40). The second term of Equation (11-44) is evaluated as follows:

$$\frac{d(n_T \Omega)}{dz} = \sum_{i=1}^{c} \frac{\partial(n_T \Omega)}{\partial n_i} \frac{dn_i}{dz} + n_T \frac{\partial \Omega}{\partial P} \frac{dP}{dz} + n_T \frac{\partial \Omega}{\partial T} \frac{dT}{dz} \tag{11-45}$$

Elimination of dn_i/dz from the summation in Equation (11-45) by use of the component-material balances [Equation (6-42)] and substitution of the result so obtained into Equation (11-44) gives

$$-n_T C_p \frac{dT}{dz} - n_T \frac{\partial \Omega}{\partial P} \frac{dP}{dz} + S \sum_{i=1}^{c} \left[H_{fi}^\circ r_i + \frac{\partial(n_T \Omega)}{\partial n_i} r_i \right] + q = 0 \quad (11\text{-}46)$$

where

$$C_p = \sum_{i=1}^{c} \left(\frac{n_i}{n_T} \right) \frac{\partial H_{fi}^\circ}{\partial T} + \frac{\partial \Omega}{\partial T} = C_p^\circ + \frac{\partial \Omega}{\partial T}$$

For the case where the single reaction given by Equation (6-19) occurs, the first term in the summation in Equation (11-46) may be restated in terms of r_A and the heat of reaction ΔH_r° as indicated by Equations (6-44) and (6-45). Evaluation of the second term of the summation provides a formula for computing ΔH_r,

$$\sum_{i=1}^{c} \left[H_{fi}^\circ + \frac{\partial(n_T \Omega)}{\partial n_i} \right] r_i = -r_A \left[\Delta H_r^\circ + \frac{c}{a} \frac{\partial(n_T \Omega)}{\partial n_C} + \frac{d}{a} \frac{\partial(n_T \Omega)}{\partial n_D} \right.$$
$$\left. - \frac{\partial(n_T \Omega)}{\partial n_A} - \frac{b}{a} \frac{\partial(n_T \Omega)}{\partial n_B} \right] = -r_A \, \Delta H_r \quad (11\text{-}47)$$

The enthalpy balances for plug-flow reactors at unsteady state operation for the case where the effects of pressure and heats of mixing on the enthalpies are taken into account are developed in a manner analogous to that demonstrated above for steady state operation.

B. Perfectly Mixed Flow Reactors at Steady State Operation

For the general case where any number of reactions occur and the enthalpy terms appearing in Equation (6-55) are evaluated by use of Equation (11-39), the following result is obtained:

$$\sum_{i=1}^{c} n_i^0 [H_{fi}^\circ(T_0) + \Omega_0] - \sum_{i=1}^{c} n_i [H_{fi}^\circ(T) + \Omega] + \int_0^{z_T} q \, dz = 0 \quad (11\text{-}48)$$

where the function Ω_0 is evaluated at the feed conditions at the inlet to the reacting mixture and Ω is evaluated at the conditions of the reacting mixture. Use of the component-material balance expression, given by Equation (6-57) to eliminate the n_i's from Equation (11-48) gives

$$\sum_{i=1}^{c} n_i^0 \{[H_{fi}^\circ(T_0) + \Omega_0] - [H_{fi}^\circ(T) + \Omega]\}$$
$$+ V \sum_{i=1}^{c} [H_{fi}^\circ(T) + \Omega] r_i + \int_0^{z_T} q \, dz = 0 \quad (11\text{-}49)$$

C. Batch Reactors

Equations (6-68) through (6-73) in the development of the energy balance for a batch reactor are applicable. For a batch system, the enthalpy of a nonideal solution is expressed as follows:

$$N_T H = \sum_{i=1}^{c} N_i H_{fi}^{\circ} + N_T \Omega \qquad (11\text{-}50)$$

Differentiation of this expression with respect to time gives

$$\frac{d(N_T H)}{dt} = \frac{d\left[\sum\limits_{i=1}^{c} N_i H_{fi}^{\circ}\right]}{dt} + \frac{d(N_T \Omega)}{dt} \qquad (11\text{-}51)$$

The derivative of the summation in Equation (11-51) has the value given by the right-hand side of Equation (6-75).

If N_i, the moles of each component, is regarded as an independent variable in the evaluation of $d(N_T\Omega)/dt$, then

$$\frac{d(N_T \Omega)}{dt} = \sum_{i=1}^{c} \frac{\partial(N_T \Omega)}{\partial N_i} \frac{dN_i}{dt} + N_T \frac{\partial \Omega}{\partial P} \frac{dP}{dt} + N_T \frac{\partial \Omega}{\partial T} \frac{dT}{dt} \qquad (11\text{-}52)$$

After dN_i/dt in Equation (11-52) has been eliminated by use of Equation (6-77) and after the expression so obtained has been substituted into Equation (6-73), the following result is obtained upon rearrangement:

$$N_T C_p \frac{dT}{dt} + N_T \frac{\partial \Omega}{\partial P} \frac{dP}{dt} - \frac{d(PV)}{dt} - V \sum_{i=1}^{c} \left[H_{fi}^{\circ} + \frac{\partial(N_T \Omega)}{\partial N_i} \right] r_i - Q = 0$$

$$(11\text{-}53)$$

where C_p is defined beneath Equation (11-46).

For the case where the single reaction given by Equation (6-19) occurs, Equation (11-53) reduces to

$$N_T C_p \frac{dT}{dt} + N_T \frac{\partial \Omega}{\partial P} \frac{dP}{dt} - \frac{d(PV)}{dt} + V \Delta H_r r_A - Q = 0 \qquad (11\text{-}54)$$

where $\quad \Delta H_r = \Delta H_r^{\circ} + \dfrac{c}{a} \dfrac{\partial(N_T \Omega)}{\partial N_C} + \dfrac{d}{a} \dfrac{\partial(N_T \Omega)}{\partial N_D} - \dfrac{\partial(N_T \Omega)}{\partial N_A} - \dfrac{b}{a} \dfrac{\partial(N_T \Omega)}{\partial N_A}$

For other choices of the standard state, expressions for the energy balances may be developed by use of the same general approach demonstrated above, and the expressions obtained will be of the same general form as those presented. The thermodynamic relationship given by Equation (11-23) for Ω depends, however, upon the particular standard state selected.

The techniques demonstrated above for the formulation of the energy balances for reactive and nonreactive systems containing nonideal solutions requires little more effort than that required for systems containing ideal solutions. Use of the virtual values of the partial molar quantities leads to equations in which the nonideal solution contributions are separated from the ideal solution contributions. Also, use of the virtual values of the partial molar enthalpies and the partial molar heat capacities instead of the corresponding partial molar quantities reduces the calculations for mixtures by several orders of magnitude. With the present availability of computers and the resulting demands to obtain more exact answers to chemical engineering problems, the techniques suggested herein should prove useful to the practicing engineer.

PROBLEMS

11-1. For the case of a plug-flow reactor at unsteady state operation, show that when the enthalpy $n_T H$ in Equation (6-47) is evaluated by use of Equation (11-11), the following result is obtained:

$$-n_T C_p \frac{\partial T}{\partial z} - n_T \frac{\partial \Omega}{\partial P}\frac{\partial P}{\partial z} + S \sum_{i=1}^{c}\left[H^{\circ}_{fi} + \frac{\partial(n_T\Omega)}{\partial n_i}\right]r_i + q - \mathscr{W}$$

$$= S\left[\frac{n_T C_p}{v_T}\frac{\partial T}{\partial t} + \left(\frac{n_T}{v_T}\frac{\partial \Omega}{\partial P} - 1\right)\frac{\partial P}{\partial t}\right]$$

11-2. Show that the constants in the Benedict-Webb-Rubin equation of state [Equation (11-18)] are homogeneous of degree zero.

NOTATION

(Also see Chapters 5 and 6)

C°_p = heat capacity (at constant pressure) of a perfect gas or perfect gas mixture; defined by Equation (6-39).

C_p = heat capacity (at constant pressure) of the actual substance or mixture; defined below Equation (11-46).

$\mathscr{H}$ = total enthalpy of a mixture; $\mathscr{H} = n_T H$, where H is the enthalpy per mole of mixture.

n_i = molar flow rate of component i.

n_T = total molar flow rate.

N_i = moles of component i.

N_T = total moles of mixture.

Q = total rate of heat transfer, energy per unit time [see Equation (6-68)].

q = point value of the rate of heat transfer; energy transferred per unit time per unit length [see Equation (6-7)].

r_i = rate of disappearance of component i by reaction, moles per unit time per unit volume of the reacting mixture.

S = cross-sectional area.

t = time.

U = internal energy; also used to denote the overall heat-transfer coefficient.

v_T = total volumetric flow rate.

v = molar volume of the reacting mixture, volume per mole.

V = volume of the reactor filled by the reacting mixture.

z = length.

REFERENCES

1. Holland, C. D., and P. T. Eubank, *Hydrocarbon Processing*, *53*: *No. 11*, 176 (1974).

2. Holland, C. D., *Multicomponent Distillation*, Prentice-Hall, Inc., Englewood Cliffs, N.J. (1963).

3. Papadopoulos, A., R.L. Pigford, and L. Friend, *Chem. Eng. Prog.* Symposium Series, *49*: *No. 7*, 119 (1953).

4. Benedict, M., G. B. Webb, and L. C. Rubin, *J. Chem. Phys.*, *8* (1940), *334*: *No. 10*, 747 (1942).

5. Orye, R. V. *I&EC Proc. Design and Develop.*, *8*: 579 (1969).

6. Perry, John H., Cecil H. Chilton, and Sidney D. Kirkpatrick, *Chemical Engineers' Handbook*, 4th Ed. McGraw-Hill Book Company, New York (1963).

7. Lydersen, A. L., R. A. Greenkorn, and O. A. Hougen, Wisc. Univ. Eng. Exp. Sta. Rept., *4* (October 1955).

8. Hougen, O. A., K. M. Watson, and R. A. Ragatz, *Chem. Proc. Princ.*, *Part II, Thermodynamics*, 2d Ed. John Wiley & Sons, New York (1959).

9. Redlich, O., and J. N. S. Kwong, *Chem. Rev.*, *44*:233 (1949).

10. Yen, L. C., and R. E. Alexander. *AIChE J.*, *11*:334 (1965).

11. Wagman, D. D., *Tables of Selected Values of Chemical Properties*, National Bureau of Standards (July 1, 1953).

12. Dowling, D. W., and P. T. Eubank, API Project 44, Report on Investigation on the Calculation of the Compressibility Factor and Thermodynamic Properties of Methane, API Project 44, Thermodynamics Research Center, College Station, Texas (1966).

13. "Selected Values of Physical and Thermodynamic Properties of Hydrocarbons and Related Compounds," API Research Project 44, Thermodynamics Research Center, Texas A&M University, (Loose-leaf data sheets).

Theory of Reaction Rates

12

The concept of first-order reaction rates was proposed by Wilhelmy in 1850 to explain the experimental observation of the inversion of cane sugar. In the presence of an aqueous solution of a dilute acid, the concentration of the sucrose was found to decrease exponentially with time to form glucose and fructose.

During the 15-year period from 1864 to 1879, Guldberg and Waage proposed and applied the *principal of mass action* to reaction rates and chemical equilibria. If a reaction goes precisely as written, then the law of mass action asserts that the rate is proportional to the product of the concentration of the reactants raised to powers equal to their respective stoichiometric numbers. For example, at high pressures, the reaction

$$2NO + O_2 \rightleftharpoons 2NO_2$$

goes as written. By the principal of mass action the forward rate of reaction of NO is given by

$$r_f = k_c C_{NO}^2 C_{O_2} \tag{12-1}$$

and the rate of appearance of NO by reverse reaction is

$$r_r = k_c' C_{NO_2}^2 \tag{12-2}$$

Then the net rate of disappearance of NO is given by

$$r_{NO} = r_f - r_r \tag{12-3}$$

At equilibrium, $r_{NO} = 0$, and

$$K_c = \frac{k_c}{k'_c} = \frac{C^2_{NO_2}}{C^2_{NO}\,C_{O_2}} \qquad (12\text{-}4)$$

In 1889, Arrhenius proposed that molecules must become activated before they react. To relate the energy of activation to the rate constant, Arrhenius commenced with the Van't Hoff equation.

$$\frac{d\log_e K_c}{dt} = \frac{\Delta E}{RT^2} \quad \text{(at constant volume)} \qquad (12\text{-}5)$$

where ΔE = change in internal energy when the reaction goes one time;
$\quad\quad\ \Delta E = E'\,(\text{products}) - E\,(\text{reactants})$

The relationship between the internal energies of the products and reactants is displayed in Figure 12-1. The term "reaction coordinate" is loosely used to mean the energy levels between reactants and products and to demonstrate the relationship

$$E + E_A = E' + E'_A \qquad (12\text{-}6)$$

$$\Delta E = E' - E = E_A - E'_A \qquad (12\text{-}7)$$

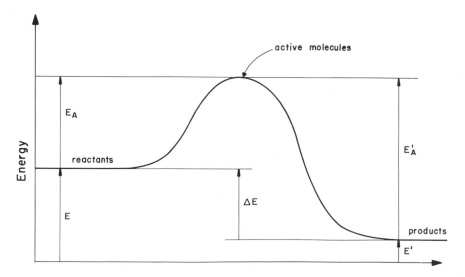

Figure 12-1. Relationship between the heat of reaction at constant volume ΔE, and the energies of activation E_A and E'_A.

The internal energy E of the reactants may be regarded as the average energy of all reactant molecules, and E_A the average energy of the "active molecules." The same interpretations are applicable for E' and E'_A. The active molecules are those that possess enough energy to undergo reaction. As a further interpretation of the reaction process, Arrhenius proposed that in a reacting system, an equilibrium exists between the reactant molecules and the active molecules.

Since $K_c = k_c/k'_c$, Equations (12-5) and (12-7) may be combined to give

$$\frac{d \log_e k_c}{dT} - \frac{d \log_e k'_c}{dT} = \frac{E_A}{RT^2} - \frac{E'_A}{RT^2} \tag{12-8}$$

Then, in general,

$$\frac{d \log_e k_c}{dT} = \frac{E_A}{RT^2} + f(T) \tag{12-9}$$

and

$$\frac{d \log_e k'_c}{dT} = \frac{E'_A}{RT^2} + f(T) \tag{12-10}$$

Note that the same function $f(T)$ is required for each equation in order to satisfy the thermodynamic relationship, Equation (12-8), or more precisely Equation (12-5). Integration of Equation (12-9) yields

$$\log_e k_c = \frac{-E_A}{RT} + \int f(T)\, dT + \log_e A \tag{12-11}$$

where $\log_e A$ is the constant of integration. In many cases experimental results may be described by taking

$$\int f(T)\, dT = 0 \tag{12-12}$$

On the basis of this assumption, Equation (12-11) reduces to the relationship commonly called the Arrhenius equation; namely,

$$k_c = A e^{-E_A/RT} \tag{12-13}$$

The concept of the activated state carries over both into the *collision theory* for bimolecular reactions and into the *transitions state theory*. These are the two principal theories that have been advanced to explain the rates at which reactions proceed.

The collision theory for bimolecular reactions makes use of relationships belonging to the body of knowledge known as the *kinetic theory*.

I. KINETIC THEORY

Since concepts of the kinetic theory of gases are useful not only in the interpretation of reaction rates but also in the development of rate expressions for adsorption, the development of the Maxwellian distribution of velocities as presented follows closely the proof first advanced by Maxwell around 1860. A more general derivation based on the study of equilibrium states existing among the molecules making elastic impacts was presented by Boltzmann toward the end of the 19th century.

The formulas employed in the kinetic theory to calculate the probability of the occurrence of a given event can perhaps be better understood by considering the axial (or longitudinal) mixing which occurs when a fluid flows through a horizontal tube. Consider a horizontal tube as shown in Figure 2-14 through which a pure solvent is flowing. Further suppose that mixing is perfect in the radial direction and that some mixing occurs in the axial direction. Now suppose that between times $t = 0$ and $t = \beta$, a pulse of a moles of solute A is introduced uniformly over the time period β; that is,

$$n_A^0 = 0, \qquad (t < 0)$$

$$n_A^0 = \frac{a}{\beta}, \qquad (0 < t < \beta) \tag{12-14}$$

$$n_A^0 = 0, \qquad (t > \beta)$$

In the interest of simplicity, it may be supposed that the total volumetric flow rate is not altered by the introduction of the solute. This condition may be realized approximately by either decreasing the volumetric flow rate of the solvent by an amount equal to the volumetric flow rate of the solute or by employing a pulse such that the inlet flow rate of the solute over the time period β is negligible relatively to the flow rate of the solvent. (Mixing problems have also been considered by Denbigh [1].)

In any event suppose that the residence time V/v_T is θ. When no axial mixing occurs in the tube, the conditions at the outlet at time θ become

$$n_A = 0, \qquad (t < \theta)$$

$$n_A = \frac{a}{\beta}, \qquad (\theta \le t \le \theta + \beta) \tag{12-15}$$

$$n_A = 0, \qquad (t > \theta + \beta)$$

as shown in Figure 12-2.

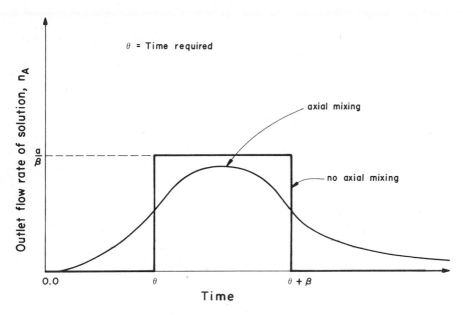

Figure 12-2. Outlet flow rate of the solute A.

When the mixing is perfect in the radial direction and some mixing occurs along the axis of the tube, component A begins to appear in the effluent at some time $t < \theta$. All of A will have been swept out of the tube as the time elapsed is allowed to increase without bound; that is,

$$\int_0^\infty n_A \, dt = a \tag{12-16}$$

The plot of n_A versus time represents the distribution of residence times. As pointed out by A. S. Foss [2], the use of residence time distributions dates back to Stewart [3], who in 1894 determined flows through small blood vessels by measuring the time necessary for an injected salt tracer to flow from one point to another.

To emphasize that n_A depends on t, the notation $n_A(t)$ is employed. The area $n_A(t_k) \cdot \Delta t_k$ of the rectangle shown in Figure 12-3 is approximately equal to the moles of solute A that remain in the tube a period of time lying between $t_k - \Delta t_k/2$ and $t_k + \Delta t_k/2$, or on the average the moles of solute $n_A(t_k) \cdot \Delta t_k$ remain in the tube a period of time t_k. The language used in these statements may be placed in correspondence with that employed in the classical kinetic theory of gases in the following manner. Since the elements of area with base Δt_k will be involved eventually in a limit, the construction of the rectangles is arbitrary and that shown in Figure 12-4

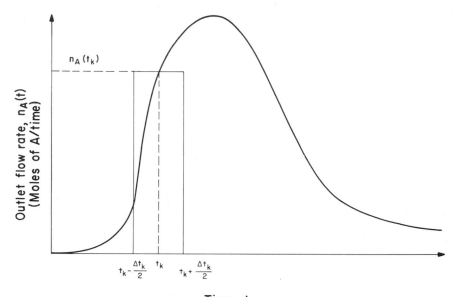

Figure 12-3. Distribution of residence times.

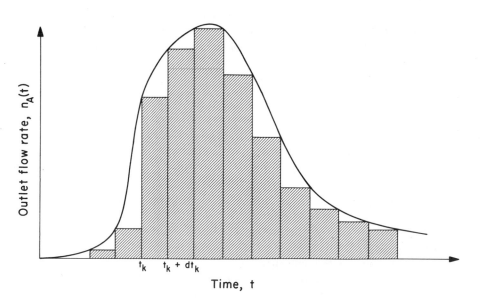

Figure 12-4. The molecules represented by the approximate area $n_A(t_k)dt_k$ have residence times between t_k and $t_k + dt_k$.

508

may be used. In this case, the moles of A represented by the area $n_A(t_k)\,dt_k$ are those having a residence time between t_k and $t_k + dt_k$. Also, since t is an independent variable, the substitution of $\Delta t_k = dt_k$ is permissible.

Then, of the total moles of A that leave, the fraction having a residence time between t_k and $t_k + dt_k$ is given by

$$\frac{n_A(t_k)\,dt_k}{a} \tag{12-17}$$

Note that a also represents the number of successes plus the number of failures for molecules leaving to have the residence time t_k; that is,

$$a \cong \underbrace{n_A(t_k)\,\Delta t_k}_{} + \underbrace{\sum_{i=1,i\neq k}^{i=n} n_A(t_i)\,\Delta t_i}_{} \tag{12-18}$$

Moles of A	Moles of A (or the
(or number of	number of failures;
successes; moles	moles of A that do
of A that have	not have residence
residence time t_k)	time t_k)

Then in the limit as Δt_k and Δt_i go to zero, and as n increases without bound, Equation (12-18) reduces to Equation (12-16). Consequently, Equation (12-17) or its equivalent

$$P_{t_k} = \bar{n}_A(t_k)\,dt_k \tag{12-19}$$

where $\bar{n}_A(t_k) = n_A(t_k)/a$, represents the probability that a molecule leaving the system will have a residence time between t_k and $t_k + dt_k$. Note that the normalized function $\bar{n}_A(t)$ has the property

$$\int_0^\infty \bar{n}_A(t)\,dt = 1 \tag{12-20}$$

Since the probability that t lies between t_k and $t_k + dt_k$ is represented by Equation (12-19), then Equation (12-20) represents the probability that t lies between 0 and ∞. Since the latter probability is unity, then the probability that t lies between 0 and ∞ is said to be a certainty.

A. Maxwell's Deduction of the Distribution of Velocities

If one measured the speed of each automobile passing a given reference line on a highway, it would be found that the speeds would range from some small value to speeds greater than the maximum speed limit. The average

Reaction Rates   Chap. 12

of all observed speeds would probably lie somewhere in the near neighborhood of the maximum speed limit.

A similar though more random behavior is exhibited by a collection of gas molecules in a closed vessel. The distribution of velocities of such a collection of molecules was deduced by Maxwell on the basis of the following postulates.

1. It is postulated that the system is at steady state, the velocity distribution is independent of time, the observed temperature of the mixture is constant, the total pressure is fixed, the mixture is not subject to any type of force field which would promote one direction of motion over another, and the mixture consists of monatomic gas molecules of the same type.

2. Let the scalar value of the velocity vector of a molecule in three-dimensional space be denoted by c. Let the velocity components along the x, y, z axes of a rectangular coordinate system be denoted by u, v, and w, respectively. It is postulated that u, v, and w are mutually independent, and that all directions of the component velocities are equally likely. The velocity c is related to the component velocities as follows:

$$c^2 = u^2 + v^2 + w^2 \tag{12-21}$$

3. It is postulated that the probability that a molecule have a velocity u in the x-direction is a function of u alone, that it have a velocity v in the y-direction is a function of v alone, and that it have a velocity w in the z-direction is a function of w alone. Thus, the probability that the velocity, u, lies between u and $u + du$ is given by

$$P_u = f(u)\,du \tag{12-22}$$

Similarly the probability that v lies between v and $v + dv$, and that w lies between w and $w + dw$ is given, respectively, by

$$P_v = f(v)\,dv \tag{12-23}$$

$$P_w = f(w)\,dw \tag{12-24}$$

Since there is no preferred direction in space, the functions $f(u)$, $f(v)$, and $f(w)$ are necessarily of the same form. Furthermore, just as $\bar{n}_A(t)$ was a normalized function, so are the functions $f(u)$, $f(v)$, and $f(w)$. Consequently,

$$\int_{-\infty}^{\infty} f(\zeta)\,d\zeta = 1 \tag{12-25}$$

where ζ may be set equal to u, v, or w. That is, the probability that a given component velocity has some value between $-\infty$ and $+\infty$ is a certainty.

Since the probabilities P_u, P_v, and P_w are mutually independent, the probability W that a molecule has velocity components simultaneously between u and $u + du$, v and $v + dv$, and w and $w + dw$ is equal to the product $P_u P_v P_w$, or

$$W(u, v, w) = f(u)f(v)f(w)\,du\,dv\,dw \qquad (12\text{-}26)$$

This equation also represents the probability that a particular velocity vector (whose components are u, v, and w) will terminate in the volume $du\,dv\,dw$.

It follows from the basic postulates that all velocity directions are equally probable. Then the probability that a molecule has a velocity c, regardless of direction, is a function of c alone; namely, $F(c)$, and the probability W that c terminates in the volume $du\,dv\,dw$ is given by

$$W = F(c)\,du\,dv\,dw \qquad (12\text{-}27)$$

Comparison of Equations (12-26) and (12-27) shows that

$$f(u)f(v)f(w) = F(c) = F(\sqrt{u^2 + v^2 + w^2}) \qquad (12\text{-}28)$$

Then

$$\log_e f(u) + \log_e f(v) + \log_e f(w) = \log_e F(c) \qquad (12\text{-}29)$$

Since u, v, and w are independent, differentiation of Equation (12-29) with respect to u gives

$$\frac{d \log_e f(u)}{du} = \left[\frac{d \log_e F(c)}{dc}\right]\frac{dc}{du} = \left[\frac{d \log_e F(c)}{dc}\right]\frac{u}{c} \qquad (12\text{-}30)$$

where dc/du was evaluated by use of Equation (12-21). Differentiation of Equation (12-29) with respect to v and w yields expressions of the same form as Equation (12-30). Thus

$$\frac{1}{u}\frac{d \log_e f(u)}{du} = \frac{1}{v}\frac{d \log_e f(v)}{dv} = \frac{1}{w}\frac{d \log_e f(w)}{dw} = \frac{1}{c}\frac{d \log_e F(c)}{dc} \qquad (12\text{-}31)$$

Since u, v, and w are independent, the only way that the equality given by Equation (12-31) can hold is for each term to be equal to a constant, say $-2/\alpha^2$. The negative sign is selected in order that Equation (12-25) be satisfied. Then

$$\int \frac{d\log_e f(u)}{du}\, du = -\frac{2}{\alpha^2}\int u\, du + \log_e A \qquad (12\text{-}32)$$

where $\log_e A$ is the constant of integration. Integration of this expression as well as the corresponding ones for v and w yields

$$f(u) = Ae^{-u^2/\alpha^2}$$
$$f(v) = Ae^{-v^2/\alpha^2} \qquad (12\text{-}33)$$
$$f(w) = Ae^{-w^2/\alpha^2}$$

Since functions $f(v)$, $f(u)$, and $f(w)$ are of the same form, it follows that the constant of integration $\log_e A$ is the same for each function. Also, in view of Equations (12-21), (12-28), and (12-33), it follows that

$$F(c) = A^3 e^{-c^2/\alpha^2} \qquad (12\text{-}34)$$

The constant A is evaluated by use of Equations (12-25) and (12-33); that is,

$$\int_{-\infty}^{\infty} Ae^{-u^2/\alpha^2}\, du = 1 \qquad (12\text{-}35)$$

Integration of this expression gives

$$A = \frac{1}{\alpha\sqrt{\pi}} \qquad (12\text{-}36)$$

and, consequently, $f(u)$, $f(v)$, and $f(w)$ are of the form

$$f(u) = \left(\frac{1}{\alpha\sqrt{\pi}}\right) e^{-u^2/\alpha^2} \qquad (12\text{-}37)$$

and

$$F(c) = \frac{1}{\alpha^3 \pi^{3/2}} e^{-c^2/\alpha^2} \qquad (12\text{-}38)$$

EVALUATION OF α. By use of the result given by Equation (12-38) for the probability that a molecule has a velocity c regardless of direction, it is possible to compute the distribution of velocities in a gaseous mixture containing N_T molecules. That is, all of the molecules that have velocity vectors between c and $c + dc$ terminate in a spherical shell described about the origin by the radii c and $c + dc$. Since the volume of this shell is $4\pi c^2 \, dc$, the fraction of the molecules having a velocity between c and $c + dc$ is given by

$$\frac{dN_c}{N_T} = F(c)[4\pi c^2 \, dc] \qquad (12\text{-}39a)$$

or

$$W = \frac{dN_c}{N_T} = \left[\frac{1}{\alpha^3 \pi^{3/2}}\right] e^{-c^2/\alpha^2} 4\pi c^2 \, dc \qquad (12\text{-}39b)$$

where dN_c = molecules having a velocity between c and $c + dc$

To evaluate α that appears in Equation (12-38), the translational or kinetic energy of a mixture of molecules with the distribution of velocities given by Equation (12-39) is computed as follows. Let $\bar{E}_{tr}$ denote the total kinetic energy per molecule in the mixture. Then

$$N_T \bar{E}_{tr} = \int_0^{N_T} \frac{mc^2}{2} \, dN_c \qquad (12\text{-}40)$$

where m = mass per molecule

By the *mean value theorem of integral calculus*, it follows that

$$\int_0^{N_T} \frac{mc^2}{2} \, dN_c = \frac{\overline{mc^2}}{2} N_T \qquad (12\text{-}41)$$

where $\overline{c^2}$ = mean square velocity

$\sqrt{\overline{c^2}}$ = root mean square velocity

By rearranging Equation (12-41), the following expression is obtained for $\overline{c^2}$,

$$\overline{c^2} = \int_0^{N_T} c^2 \frac{dN_c}{N_T}$$

Elimination of dN_c/N_T from this expression by use of Equation (12-39) yields

$$\overline{c^2} = \frac{4}{\alpha^3 \sqrt{\pi}} \int_0^{\infty} e^{-c^2/\alpha^2} c^4 \, dc \qquad (12\text{-}42)$$

After the integration indicated has been carried out, the following result is obtained:

$$\overline{c^2} = \frac{3\alpha^2}{2} \qquad (12\text{-}43)$$

In a similar manner, the kinetic energy in each direction is computed. For example, in the x-direction

$$\overline{u^2} = \frac{1}{\alpha\sqrt{\pi}} \int_{-\infty}^{\infty} u^2 e^{-u^2/\alpha^2} \, du \tag{12-44}$$

Thus

$$\overline{u^2} = \frac{\alpha^2}{2}, \qquad \overline{v^2} = \frac{\alpha^2}{2}, \qquad \overline{w^2} = \frac{\alpha^2}{2} \tag{12-45}$$

It should be noted at this point that Equations (12-43) and (12-45) imply equipartition of kinetic energy; that is, one-third of the kinetic energy of the mixture is distributed along each axis.

$$\frac{N_T m \overline{u^2}}{2} + \frac{N_T m \overline{v^2}}{2} + \frac{N_T m \overline{w^2}}{2} = \frac{N_T m}{2}(\overline{u^2} + \overline{v^2} + \overline{w^2}) = \frac{N_T m}{2}\overline{c^2} \tag{12-46}$$

where the final equality follows from Equations (12-43) and (12-45).

Thus the translational energy (the kinetic energy) may be divided equally among the three directions of motion or freedom. Therefore,

$$\overline{E}_{tr} = 3\varepsilon_{tr} \tag{12-47}$$

where $\varepsilon_{tr} =$ translational energy per molecule per degree of freedom

From a kinetic interpretation of gas pressure, Joule first showed in 1851 that

$$PV = \tfrac{1}{3} N_T m \overline{c^2} \tag{12-48}$$

Since experiments show that $PV = N_T kT$, it follows from Equations (12-40), (12-41), and (12-48), that

$$PV = \frac{2}{3}\left(\frac{N_T m \overline{c^2}}{2}\right) = \frac{2}{3}(N_T \overline{E}_{tr}) = N_T kT \tag{12-49}$$

where $k =$ Boltzmann constant $= 1.3805 \times 10^{-16}$ ergs/($^\circ$K molecule)

Thus

$$\frac{2}{3}(N_T 3\varepsilon_{tr}) = N_T kT$$

or

$$\varepsilon_{tr} = \frac{kT}{2} \tag{12-50}$$

or the translational energy (kinetic energy per degree of freedom) is $kT/2$. Thus

$$\frac{m\overline{c^2}}{2} = \frac{3kT}{2} \tag{12-51}$$

Elimination of $\overline{c^2}$ from Equations (12-43) and (12-51) gives

$$\alpha^2 = \frac{2kT}{m} \tag{12-52}$$

for a system with three degrees of freedom. Thus Equations (12-37) and (12-39) may be stated in the form

$$f(u) = \left(\frac{m}{2\pi kT}\right)^{1/2} e^{-mu^2/2kT} \tag{12-53}$$

and

$$\frac{dN_c}{N_T} = \left(\frac{m}{2\pi kT}\right)^{3/2} e^{-mc^2/2kT} 4\pi c^2 \, dc \tag{12-54}$$

B. The Average and Most Probable Velocities

The *average velocity*, c_{av}, is defined by

$$c_{av}N_T = \int_0^{N_T} c \, dN_c \tag{12-55}$$

This equality is seen to follow immediately from the *mean value theorem of integral calculus*. Then

$$c_{av} = \int_0^{N_T} c \, \frac{dN_c}{N_T} = 4\pi \left(\frac{m}{2\pi kT}\right)^{3/2} \int_0^{\infty} e^{-mc^2/2kT} c^3 \, dc \tag{12-56}$$

Integration yields

$$c_{av} = \sqrt{\frac{8kT}{\pi m}} \tag{12-57}$$

The root mean square velocity, $\sqrt{\overline{c^2}}$, the average velocity, c_{av}, and the most probable velocity, c_w, are compared in the graph shown in Figure 12-5. The most probable velocity is obtained as follows. Let

$$\frac{dN_c}{N_T \, dc} = \phi(c) = \left(\frac{m}{2\pi kT}\right)^{3/2} e^{-mc^2/2kT} 4\pi c^2 \tag{12-58}$$

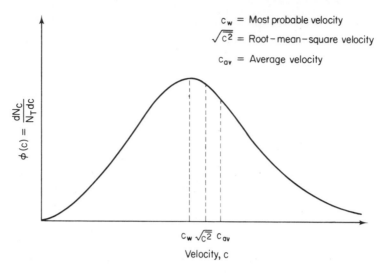

Figure 12-5. Maxwellian distribution velocities c for motion in three dimensions.

The *most probable velocity* is that value of c possessed by the greatest number of the molecules of a given mixture. At this value of c,

$$\frac{d\phi(c)}{dc} = 0 \qquad (12\text{-}59)$$

When this differentiation is carried out, it is found that the most probable velocity, c_w, is given by

$$c_w = \sqrt{\frac{2kT}{m}} \qquad (12\text{-}60)$$

The *mean relative velocity* $\bar{r}$ for two different types of molecules A and B takes into account the complete distribution of velocities of these molecules in space as well as their difference in mass. The somewhat lengthy derivation of $\bar{r}$ is not presented, but it is generally available [4, 5]. The result is

$$\bar{r} = \sqrt{\frac{8kT}{\pi\mu}} \qquad (12\text{-}61)$$

where $\qquad\qquad \mu = \dfrac{m_A m_B}{m_A + m_B}$

m_A, m_B = mass per molecule of A and B, respectively

For two like molecules, $\mu = m/2$ and Equation (12-61) reduces to

$$\bar{r} = \sqrt{2}c_{av} \tag{12-62}$$

C. Postulates of the Kinetic Theory of Bimolecular Reactions

The postulates for the kinetic theory of bimolecular reactions are as follows:

1. A collision between the two reacting molecules A and B must occur before they can react.
2. Of the total number of collisions, only those molecules react that have a kinetic energy equal to or greater than ε along the line of centers at the moment of contact, provided that the molecules are properly orientated.

The number of collisions of molecules A and B per second per cubic centimeter with a kinetic energy equal to or greater than ε along the line of centers at the time of collision may be calculated directly by use of the distribution laws as shown by Frost et al. [4]. Alternately, the number of two-body collisions may be computed and then the fraction f of the molecules having an energy equal to or greater than ε may be computed. The latter procedure is used. The rate of reaction of A or B is then given by

$$r_A \left(\frac{\text{molecules of } A \text{ reacting}}{\text{sec cm}^3} \right) = r_B = p Z_{AB} f \tag{12-63}$$

where Z_{AB} = number of two-body collisions between two unlike molecules A and B per sec per cm^3

p = fraction of the molecules that collide that have the proper orientation

D. Number of Two-Body Collisions per Second per Cubic Centimeter

Consider first two unlike molecules A and B with diameters σ_A and σ_B, respectively. A collision is said to have occurred when there is contact between the surface of molecule A and the surface of molecule B. Consider a molecule of type A moving in an arbitrary direction with a mean relative velocity $\bar{r}$ with respect to a molecule of type B. If the centers of the two molecules come within a distance

$$\sigma_{AB} = \left(\frac{\sigma_A + \sigma_B}{2} \right) \tag{12-64}$$

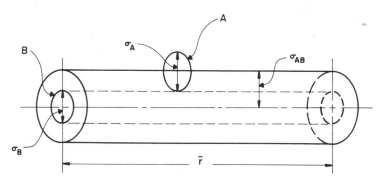

Figure 12-6. Cylinder containing the centers of the molecules that will collide per second.

of one another, a collision will occur. During a period of 1 sec, molecule A will travel a distance $\bar{r}$ relative to molecule B. Then the total number of collisions of 1 molecule of A per second is approximated by the volume swept out by the sphere of influence of radius, σ_{AB}, times the number of molecules of B per cubic centimeter. The volume swept out by the sphere of influence is represented graphically in Figure 12-6. Then

$$\begin{matrix} \text{Number of collisions which one molecule of} \\ A \text{ experiences per second per cubic centimeter} \end{matrix} = \pi\sigma_{AB}^2\bar{r}C_B \qquad (12\text{-}65)$$

where C_B = concentration of B, molecules/cm^3

Since each molecule of A experiences the same number of collisions given by Equation (12-65), then the total number of two-body collisions of unlike molecules A and B per second per cubic centimeter is given by

$$Z_{AB} = \pi\sigma_{AB}^2\bar{r}C_AC_B \qquad (12\text{-}66)$$

The number of collisions of like molecules, say A and A, is equal to one-half the number of two-body collisions given by setting $A = B$ in Equation (12-66). Thus, for this case, the number of collisions suffered by molecule A per second per cubic centimeter is given by

$$Z_{2A} = \frac{\pi\sigma_A^2\sqrt{2}c_{av}C_A^2}{2} \qquad (12\text{-}67)$$

However, for every collision that results in a reaction, it is evident that two molecules of A react. Then for bimolecular reactions of like molecules,

$$r_A = 2pfZ_{2A} \qquad (12\text{-}68)$$

E. Fraction of the Colliding Molecules that have an Energy Equal to or Greater than the Activation Energy

Let this minimum activation energy be denoted by ε (erges per molecule) or E (calories per g mole). The fraction of colliding molecules that have an energy equal to or greater than ε may be approximated by considering the kinetic energy in the plane of reaction as being available for reaction. This calculation is carried out for like molecules. Let u and v be the velocities of the two molecules in the plane of collision. Then

$$\overline{c^2} = \overline{u^2} + \overline{v^2} \tag{12-69}$$

and for two-dimensional space, Equation (12-43) reduces to

$$\overline{c^2} = \alpha^2 \tag{12-70}$$

For two degrees of freedom,

$$\frac{m\overline{c^2}}{2} = 2\left(\frac{kT}{2}\right) \tag{12-71}$$

Thus

$$\alpha = \sqrt{\frac{2kT}{m}} \tag{12-72}$$

and for two degrees of freedom the function $F(c)$ is given by

$$F(c) = \left(\frac{m}{2\pi kT}\right) e^{-mc^2/2kT} \tag{12-73}$$

Furthermore, all velocity vectors between c and $c + dc$ terminate in the annulus described about an origin by circles of radii c and $c + dc$. Since the area of this annulus is $2\pi c\, dc$, the fraction of molecules having a velocity between c and $c + dc$ is given by

$$\frac{dN_c}{N_T} = \left(\frac{m}{2\pi kT}\right) e^{-mc^2/2kT} 2\pi c\, dc \tag{12-74}$$

Since the kinetic energy ε_{tr} per molecule is given by

$$\varepsilon_{tr} = \frac{mc^2}{2} \tag{12-75}$$

it follows that $\qquad\qquad d\varepsilon_{tr} = mc\, dc \tag{12-76}$

519

Equation (12-74) may be restated in terms of the fraction of molecules having an energy lying between ε_{tr} and $\varepsilon_{tr} + d\varepsilon_{tr}$ by substituting Equations (12-75) and (12-76) into Equation (12-74) to obtain

$$\frac{dN_c}{N_T} = \frac{1}{kT} e^{-\varepsilon_{tr}/kT} \, d\varepsilon_{tr} \tag{12-77}$$

Thus the fraction f of the total molecules that have an energy equal to or greater than ε is given by

$$f = \int_{\varepsilon}^{\infty} e^{-\varepsilon_{tr}/kT} \left(\frac{d\varepsilon_{tr}}{kT}\right) = e^{-\varepsilon/kT} \tag{12-78}$$

If the value of f for unlike molecules is approximated by taking it equal to the value computed for like molecules, then for the reaction

$$A + B \longrightarrow \text{products}$$

$$r_A = r_B = pf Z_{AB} = pe^{-\varepsilon/kT} \pi \sigma_{AB}^2 \bar{F} C_A C_B$$

$$= p\sigma_{AB}^2 \sqrt{\frac{8\pi kT}{\mu}} \, e^{-\varepsilon/kT} C_A C_B \tag{12-79}$$

For the reaction,

$$2A \longrightarrow \text{products}$$

$$r_A = 2pf Z_{2A} = 4p\sigma_A^2 \sqrt{\frac{\pi kT}{m}} \, e^{-\varepsilon/kT} C_A^2 \tag{12-80}$$

Instead of expressing the rate expressions in the units of molecules, cm^3, $°K$, and ergs, the system of units of g moles, cm^3, $°K$, and cal is used. For this case, Equation (12-80) becomes,

$$r_A \left(\frac{\text{g moles}}{\text{sec } cm^3}\right) = 4p\sigma_A^2 \sqrt{\frac{\pi RT}{M}} \, e^{-E/RT} C_A^2 \tag{12-81}$$

where
$$C_A = \text{concentration of } A, \text{ g moles/cm}^3$$
$$E = \text{energy of activation, cal/g mole}$$
$$R = \text{gas constant, cal/(g mole)(°K)}$$
$$M = \text{molecular weight of } A, \text{ g/g mole}$$

Then the rate constant, k_c, as predicted by the kinetic theory for the reaction $2A \rightarrow$ products, with the rate $r_A = k_c C_A^2$, is given by

$$k_c = \left(4p\sigma_A^2 \sqrt{\frac{\pi R T}{M}} \right) e^{-E/RT} \tag{12-82}$$

In general, the number of collisions far exceeds the number of molecules reacting. For example, Z_{2A} as given by Equation (12-67) is approximately equal to 10^{28} collisions per second per cubic centimeter for a typical gas at standard conditions. Although the fractions p and f do reduce the number of collisions, the predicted rate constants are inaccurate, unreliable, and must be, therefore, determined experimentally. Equation (12-82) predicts that the variation of k_c with temperature is given by

$$k_c \propto \sqrt{T} e^{-E/RT} \tag{12-83}$$

The most significant term of this expression is the exponential $e^{-E/RT}$, which is in agreement with many experimental observations of the variation of k_c with temperature.

Also, the kinetic theory predicts the correct form of the rate expression; that is, for $2A \rightarrow$ products,

$$r_A \propto C_A^2 \tag{12-84}$$

The collision theory can be extended to account for third-order reactions on the basis of trimolecular collisions as demonstrated by Frost and Pearson [4]. However, it remained for Lindermann [6] to explain unimolecular reactions on the basis of the collision theory. The theory developed by Lindermann [6] and Hinshelwood [7] also accounts for the observation that certain reactions exhibit a second-order rate at low pressures and a first-order rate at high pressures. The Lindermann-Hinshelwood theory is demonstrated by an example in Chapter 4.

II. TRANSITION-STATE THEORY

More modern than the kinetic theory of reaction rates is the transition-state theory, also called the activated complex theory as well as the theory of absolute reaction rates. Laidler [8] credits Mercelin [9] with the original formulation of this theory. The theory was first applied to a specific reaction by Pelzer and Wigner [10] and further developed to its present general form by Eyring et al. [11, 12].

The transition-state theory takes into account the internal energy distribution within the molecules as well as the translational energy possessed by the molecules. According to this theory, there is some configuration through which the reacting molecules must pass in going from reactants to products. This particular configuration in space is called the *transition state*, and the molecules in this state are called the *activated complex*.

The postulates of the transition-state theory are as follows:

1. In order for a chemical reaction to occur, it is necessary for the atoms or molecules to come together and form an activated complex.
2. The activated complexes are in dynamic equilibrium with the reactant molecules.
3. The rate of reaction is equal to the concentration of activated complexes that pass from reactants to products (from left to right) divided by the time required for an activated complex to traverse the distance across the energy barrier in the direction from left to right.

The energies of the reactants, the activated complex, and the products under different conditions are commonly represented by potential energy surfaces. Dynamic equilibrium between reactants and activated complexes is treated by statistical mechanics. Before further consideration of the transition-state theory, the concepts of potential energy surfaces and statistical mechanics are reviewed briefly.

A. Potential Energy Surfaces

The concept of potential energy surfaces is introduced herein by consideration of the case where the atoms X, Y, and Z are involved in the reaction

$$XY + Z = X + YZ \qquad (12\text{-}85)$$

The potential energy of the system may be represented in three-dimensional space by plotting the potential energy of X, Y, and Z as a function of the $X - Y$ and $Y - Z$ distances. The lowest energy states correspond to the stable molecules XY and YZ. The potential energy corresponding to different $X - Y$ and $Y - Z$ distances may be presented as a contour map of the same form as that which might be used to represent a mountain range. Lines of equal elevation would correspond to lines of equal energy. The two stable states XY and YZ (the reactant and product molecules) have the lowest potential energies of any configuration and may be placed in correspondence with two valleys separated by mountains. All the ancient roads and most of the modern ones cross mountain ranges through passes, gaps, or saddle points. Similarly, most of the reacting molecules follow an energy path from reactants to products that has a minimum potential energy barrier, which corresponds to a "pass," "gap," or "saddle point" in the potential energy

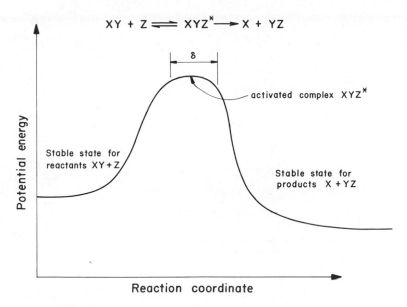

Figure 12-7. Potential energy along the reaction coordinate. [Taken from Kenneth Denbigh, *The Principles of the Chemical Equilibrium*, 3rd ed. (1971). Used with permission of the Cambridge University Press.]

surface. This energy path followed by most of the molecules is called the reaction coordinate. The potential energy along this path is depicted in Figure 12-7.

In the stable states, the molecule XY is far removed from the center of the atom Z, and YZ is far removed from X. As molecule XY and atom Z approach each other, higher energies are required to overcome van der Waals repulsive force. As XY and Z approach the transition state, the atom Y takes a position about half way between X and Z. This configuration is called the activated complex and denoted by $XYZ^{\dagger}$. The descent into the YZ valley is marked by a breaking away of X from YZ, which is reflected by a decrease in energy.

The concept presented of potential energy surfaces has been simplified considerably. In principle the potential energy surface can be obtained by quantum mechanical calculations [13]. However, because of computational difficulties, the potential energy surface of even the simplest of systems, H_2, is obtained by means of a semiempirical method such as the one devised by Eyring and Polanyi [11].

B. Relationships from Statistical Mechanics

The development of this subject from first principles has been presented by others [14, 15, 16, 17, 18, 19, 20], and certain results of this theory are taken as the starting point in the present analysis. Maxwell-Boltzmann statistics are based on the suppositions that the molecules of a gas are independent (the gas obeys the perfect gas law) and that every molecule is in a discrete energy state. These postulates lead to the partition function Q for a gas mixture containing N molecules of the same type.

$$Q = \frac{1}{N!} f^N$$

$$f = \sum_{i=1}^{n} \omega_i e^{-\varepsilon_i/kT} \tag{12-86}$$

where n = number of energy levels

ω_i = number of times a given energy state ε_i occurs, and

ε_i = molecular energy levels

For a mixture containing N_1 molecules of Type 1, N_2 of Type 2, and N_3 of Type 3, the expression for the partition function is given by

$$Q = \frac{1}{N_1!\, N_2!\, N_3!} f_1^{N_1} f_2^{N_2} f_3^{N_3} \tag{12-87}$$

In order to evaluate the molecular partition function f, it is necessary to postulate that Schrödinger's wave equation describes the mechanical behavior of matter on the atomic scale. Only the one solution of this equation that corresponds to 1 degree of freedom of translation (one coordinate) is needed in the subsequent analysis. For a molecule of mass m, which is permitted to move a distance δ in the x-direction, the partition function f_x is given by

$$f_x = \frac{\delta}{h} (2\pi mkT)^{1/2} \tag{12-88}$$

where h = Planck's constant = 6.624×10^{-27} (erg sec)/molecule

A given molecular energy level, ε_i, is made up of the sum of the translational (ε_t), rotational (ε_r), vibrational (ε_v), and electronic (ε_e) energies; that is,

$$\varepsilon_i = \varepsilon_t + \varepsilon_r + \varepsilon_v + \varepsilon_e \tag{12-89}$$

Then as shown by Denbigh [14], the molecular partition function f can be stated in terms of the corresponding partition functions

$$f = f_t f_r f_v f_e \tag{12-90}$$

where the individual partition functions are of the same form as that which follows for f_t.

$$f_t = \sum_j \omega_{tj} e^{-\varepsilon_{tj}/kT} \tag{12-91}$$

where ω_{tj} is the number of times the energy state ε_{tj} occurs.

The partition function Q for a gaseous mixture containing N molecules is related to the Helmholtz free energy function A [$A \equiv U$ (internal energy) $-$ TS (entropy)] as follows:

$$A = -kT \log_e Q \tag{12-92}$$

From classical thermodynamics [1], the following condition must be satisfied at equilibrium:

$$\sum_i \alpha_i \mu_i = 0 \tag{12-93}$$

The α_i's are the stoichiometric coefficients. For example, for the reaction

$$aA + bB \rightleftharpoons cC + dD \tag{12-94}$$

$$\alpha_A = -a, \qquad \alpha_B = -b, \qquad \alpha_C = c, \quad \text{and} \quad \alpha_D = d$$

The μ_i's are the partial molar quantities, which may be stated in terms of the Helmholtz free energy A of a mixture as follows:

$$\mu_i = \left(\frac{\partial A}{\partial N_i}\right)_{T,V,N_j} \tag{12-95}$$

The subscript N_j means that in carrying out the partial differentiation, the moles of all components except component i are held fixed. For the general reaction given by Equation (12-94),

$$A = -kT \log_e \frac{f_A^{N_A} f_B^{N_B} f_C^{N_C} f_D^{N_D}}{N_A! \, N_B! \, N_C! \, N_D!} \tag{12-96}$$

From Equations (12-92) through (12-95) it follows that

$$c\left(\frac{\partial A}{\partial N_C}\right) + d\left(\frac{\partial A}{\partial N_D}\right) - a\left(\frac{\partial A}{\partial N_A}\right) - b\left(\frac{\partial A}{\partial N_B}\right) = 0 \tag{12-97}$$

Since the number of molecules is relatively large, Stirling's approximation for $N!$ is used,

$$N! \cong N^N e^{-N} \sqrt{2\pi N} \tag{12-98}$$

which may be further simplified to

$$N! \cong N^N e^{-N} \tag{12-99}$$

Use of this approximation to restate Equation (12-96) yields

$$A = -kT \left[-\sum_{A,B,C,D} N_i \log_e N_i + \sum_{A,B,C,D} N_i + \sum_{A,B,C,D} N_i \log_e f_i \right] \tag{12-100}$$

Then

$$\left(\frac{\partial A}{\partial N_i} \right)_{T,V,N_j} = -kT[-\log_e N_i + \log_e f_i]$$

$$= -kT \left[-\log_e \frac{N_i}{V} + \log_e \frac{f_i}{V} \right], \quad (i = A, B, C, D) \tag{12-101}$$

where V is the total volume of the reacting mixture. Substitution of the result given by Equation (12-101) for $i = A$, B, C, and D into Equation (12-97) gives the following result for a perfect gas mixture:

$$K_c = \frac{(f_C/V)^c (f_D/V)^d}{(f_A/V)^a (f_B/V)^b} \tag{12-102}$$

where

$$K_c = \frac{C_C^c C_D^d}{C_A^a C_B^b}$$

Equation (12-102) requires that each partition function be computed relative to the same zero datum. However, it is customary to compute the partition function of each molecule relative to its own lowest energy level. Relative to any arbitrary zero energy level, let the lowest energy levels of molecules A, B, C, and D be denoted by ε_A, ε_B, ε_C, and ε_D, respectively. Then Equation (12-102) becomes

$$K_c = \frac{\phi_C^c \phi_D^d}{\phi_A^a \phi_B^b} e^{-[c\varepsilon_C + d\varepsilon_D - a\varepsilon_A - b\varepsilon_B]/kT} \tag{12-103}$$

where the partition functions f are related to the partition functions ϕ in the same manner as that which follows for component C:

$$\phi_C = \frac{f_C}{V} e^{-\varepsilon_C/kT} \tag{12-104}$$

Instead of stating the energies on a molecule basis, a mole basis may be employed; that is, let

$$\frac{\Delta E_0}{RT} = \frac{[c\varepsilon_C + d\varepsilon_D - a\varepsilon_A - b\varepsilon_B]}{kT} \qquad (12\text{-}105)$$

Then the general result follows immediately from Equation (12-103):

$$K_c = \frac{\phi_C^c \phi_D^d}{\phi_A^a \phi_B^b} e^{-\Delta E_0/RT} \qquad (12\text{-}106)$$

C. Derivation of the Rate Equation

On the basis of the postulates of the transition-state theory, the forward rate of the reaction given by Equation (12-94) is formulated in the following manner. Since existence of an activated complex is given by the first postulate, Equation (12-94) may be restated as follows:

$$aA + bB \;\rightleftharpoons\; M \;\rightleftharpoons\; cC + dD \qquad (12\text{-}107)$$

In view of the second postulate (the reactants and the activated complex are in equilibrium), it follows from Equations (12-102) and (12-106) that

$$K_c = \frac{C_M}{C_A^a C_B^b} = \frac{\phi_M}{\phi_A^a \phi_B^b} e^{-\Delta E_0/RT} \qquad (12\text{-}108)$$

The activated complex M has only one degree of translational freedom as it travels the distance δ along the reaction coordinate. Then by use of Equations (12-88) and (12-90) it follows that

$$\phi_M = \phi_M^\dagger \left(\frac{\delta}{h}\right)(2\pi m_M kT)^{1/2} \qquad (12\text{-}109)$$

where $\phi_M^\dagger$ denotes the remainder of the partition function ϕ_M after the translational partition function over δ has been factored out. Thus Equation (12-108) may be restated as follows:

$$K_c = \frac{C_M}{C_A^a C_B^b} = \left[\frac{\phi_M^\dagger}{\phi_A^a \phi_B^b}\right]\left(\frac{\delta}{h}\right)(2\pi m_M kT)^{1/2} e^{-\Delta E_0/RT} \qquad (12\text{-}110)$$

Let

$$K^\dagger = \frac{\phi_M^\dagger e^{-\Delta E_0/RT}}{\phi_A^a \phi_B^b} \qquad (12\text{-}111)$$

Then

$$K_c = \frac{C_M}{C_A^a C_B^b} = K^\dagger \left(\frac{\delta}{h}\right)(2\pi m_M kT)^{1/2} \qquad (12\text{-}112)$$

To compute the mean velocity at which activated complexes move to the right along the reaction coordinate and through the distance δ, the velocity distribution for one-dimensional motion [Equation (12-53)] may be employed. Since one-half of the activated complex molecules are free to move to the left and one-half are free to move to the right, it follows that for those moving to the right,

$$\bar{v}\frac{N_M}{2} = \int_0^{N_M/2} v \, dN_M, \qquad \bar{v} = 2 \int_0^{N_M/2} v \frac{dN_M}{N_M} \tag{12-113}$$

Then from Equation (12-53), it follows that

$$\bar{v} = 2 \left(\frac{m_M}{2\pi kT}\right)^{1/2} \int_0^\infty e^{-m_M v^2/2kT} v \, dv \tag{12-114}$$

where m_M = mass per molecule of the activated complex M

The limits of 0 to ∞ results from the fact that only those velocities having a direction to the right are to be included in the average. Integration of Equation (12-114) yields

$$\bar{v} = \left(\frac{2kT}{\pi m_M}\right)^{1/2} \tag{12-115}$$

The average time required for an activated complex to move to the right through the transition state is given by

$$\frac{\delta}{\bar{v}} = \delta \left(\frac{\pi m_M}{2kT}\right)^{1/2}$$

Then the rate of reaction r in terms of the number of complexes crossing per unit time per unit volume is given by

$$r = \left(\frac{C_M}{2}\right)\left(\frac{\bar{v}}{\delta}\right) = \left(\frac{C_M}{\delta}\right)\left(\frac{kT}{2\pi m_M}\right)^{1/2} \tag{12-116}$$

When C_M is replaced by its equivalent as given by Equation (12-112), the result

$$r = \left(\frac{kT}{h}\right) K^\dagger C_A^a C_B^b \tag{12-117}$$

is obtained. Thus the transition-state theory predicts the correct molecularity $(a + b)$ of the forward reaction. It also accounts for a unimolecular reaction. The quantity $K_c^\dagger$ is not actually an equilibrium constant, but differs from the equilibrium constant K_c by the translational partition function for the activated complex [see Equations (12-108) and (12-111)].

To allow for the probability that not every activated complex reaching the top of the potential energy barrier is converted into a reaction product, Laidler [8] and Eyring et al [13]   employ a transmission coefficient κ in Equation (12-117) to give

$$r = \kappa \frac{kT}{h} K^\dagger C_A^a C_B^b \qquad (12\text{-}118)$$

As suggested by Denbigh [14], the effect of temperature on the rate of reaction may be accounted for by regarding $K^\dagger$ as an equilibrium constant and relating it to a "standard" free energy change $\Delta G^\dagger$.

$$\Delta G^\dagger = -RT \log_e K^\dagger \qquad (12\text{-}119)$$

Then for $\kappa = 1$, the rate constant in the expression $r_A = k_c C_A^a C_B^b$ is given by

$$k_c = \left(\frac{kT}{h}\right) e^{-\Delta G\dagger/RT} = \left[\frac{kT}{h} e^{\Delta S\dagger/R}\right] e^{-\Delta H\dagger/RT} \qquad (12\text{-}120)$$

A similar approach for the treatment of the effect of temperature on k_c is suggested by Laidler [8] and Glasstone et al. [17].

PROBLEMS

12-1. Use the fact that

$$\int_0^\infty e^{-a^2 x^2}\, dx = \frac{\sqrt{\pi}}{2a}$$

to show that Equation (12-35) may be integrated to give Equation (12-36).

12-2. Use the fact that

$$\int_0^\infty x^4 e^{-ax^2}\, dx = \frac{3}{8a^2}\sqrt{\frac{\pi}{a}}$$

to obtain Equation (12-43) from Equation (12-42).

12-3. (a) Use the fact that

$$\int_0^\infty x^2 e^{-ax^2}\, dx = \frac{1}{4a}\sqrt{\frac{\pi}{a}}$$

to obtain the result given by Equation (12-45) from Equation (12-44).

(b) Show that the result given by Equation (12-57) may be obtained by evaluating the integral appearing in Equation (12-56).

12-4. Begin with Equation (12-58), the expression for $\phi(c)$, and make use of Equation (12-59) to show that the most probable velocity is given by Equation (12-60).

12-5. Perform the integration indicated in Equation (12-78) and obtain the result shown.

12-6. (a) Begin with Equation (12-96) and make use of Equation (12-99) to obtain the expression given by Equation (12-100).

      (b) Use the result of (a) and the relationship given by Equation (12-97) to obtain the expression given by Equation (12-102).

REFERENCES

1. Denbigh, Kenneth, *Chemical Reactor Theory*, Cambridge University Press, New York (1965).

2. Foss, A. S., "Liquid Mixing on Bubble Trays and its Effects upon Plate Efficiency," Ph.D. dissertation, University of Delaware, Newark, Del. (1957).

3. Stewart, G. N., *J. Physiology*, *15*:1 (1894).

4. Frost, A. A., and R. G. Pearson, *Kinetics and Mechanisms*, John Wiley & Sons, Inc., New York (1953).

5. Loeb, L. B., *Kinetic Theory of Gases*, McGraw-Hill Book Company, New York (1927).

6. Lindermann, F. A., *Trans. Faraday Soc.*, *17*:598 (1922).

7. Hinshelwood, C. N., *Proc. Roy. Soc.*, *A113*:230 (1927).

8. Laidler, K. J., *Chemical Kinetics*, McGraw-Hill Book Company, New York (1950).

9. Mercelin, A., *Ann. Phys.*, *3*:158 (1915).

10. Pelzer, H., and E. Wigner, *Z. Physikal Chem.*, *B15*:123 (1932).

11. Eyring, H., and M. Polanyi, *Z. Physikal Chem.*, *12B*:279 (1931).

12. Eyring, H., *J. Chem. Phys.*, *3*:107 (1935).

13. Eyring, H., and E. M. Eyring, *Modern Chem. Kin.*, Reinhold Publishing Corporation, New York (1965).

14. Denbigh, Kenneth, *The Principles of Chemical Equilibrium with Applications in Chemistry and Chemical Engineering*, Cambridge University Press, New York (1955).

15. Fowler, R. H., *Statistical Mechanics*, Cambridge University Press, New York (1938).

16. Mayer, J. E., and M. G. Mayer, *Statistical Mechanics*, John Wiley & Sons, Inc., New York (1940).

17. Glasstone, S., K. J. Laidler, and H. Eyring, *Theory of Rate Processes*, McGraw-Hill Book Company, New York (1941).

18. Rushbrook, G. S., *Introduction to Statistical Mechanics*, Oxford University Press, New York (1949).

19. Sommerfeld, Arnold, *Thermodynamics and Statistical Mechanics*, Academic Press, New York (1964).

20. Tolman, R. C., *Principles of Statistical Mechanics*, Oxford University Press, New York (1938).

Index

534   Index